Geography of the USSR

Geography of the

USSR

A REGIONAL SURVEY

Theodore Shabad

COLUMBIA UNIVERSITY PRESS

NEW YORK

to

LESLIE and STEVEN

Preface

THE AIM of the author in presenting this book is to make available to students, research workers, and others interested in the USSR an up-to-date treatment of the geography of that country. In preparing discussions, seminars, and reports on the Soviet Union there is generally felt a distinct lack of factual knowledge regarding such matters as the localization of industry, the status of the political-administrative divisions, the sites of current construction projects, and even the present names of important cities. This lack of factual background on the part of many interested observers of the USSR probably results from two main considerations: the scarcity of published materials in the English language and the dynamic nature of Soviet geography. While it is incorrect to assume that no geographical information on the USSR leaks through what has come to be known as the "iron curtain," the fact nevertheless remains that this information is generally not complete and not available to the non-Russian-reading student. In order to obtain a complete picture of the current geography of the USSR, innumerable notes and articles appearing in Soviet geographical literature, books, and periodicals have to be examined, analyzed, compared. This is clearly beyond the resources of students interested in research on a specific aspect of the USSR. To add to this difficulty, the geography of the USSR lends itself probably less than that of any other country to any definitive treatment because of its very nature. The rapid progress in industrialization, the creation of new cities and renaming of others, the altering of the physical landscape of the country by vast reservoirs, these and many other factors tend to make any geographic survey of the Soviet Union out of date within a short time. One can hope to do no more than to explain this characteristic feature of Soviet geography and to anticipate probable changes within the near future.

These are some of the considerations which prompted the author to prepare the present volume. It was not intended to give any definitive treatment to the geography of the USSR, nor would that have been possible within the scope of this book. For this reason, it will be noted, current problems have been emphasized throughout the study, and among these questions, those of a political and economic nature have received the most detailed attention. Other sources would have to be consulted by any reader interested in the broad background of Russian geography.

The first part of the book is a general survey and is intended to describe some of the general principles, trends, and policies which guide Soviet geography. Here factual material is restricted to a minimum, and a general perspective of the entire field can be gained. Some attention has been devoted to every aspect of the geography of the USSR (again, with emphasis on political and economic problems), even to the point of including a section on the geologic history, with special reference to mineral deposits. Readers can easily pass over this section without losing the benefit of other sections of the book.

The regional plan adopted for the second part of the volume is novel in American presentation, but one which has been used in Soviet publications. It is based primarily on the political division of the country into sixteen constituent union republics. Of these, the Russian SFSR, by far the largest division, has been subdivided into a number of physico-economic regions. Smaller republics, such as the four Central Asian units, have been treated together under a common regional heading. The regional division by political units, rather than by natural geographic regions (for instance, the soil and vegetation zones), has been adopted because it seemed more in accordance with the emphasis in treatment. Certainly, the political-administrative divisions of the USSR are much more plausible as study units, because of their economic and national autonomous undertones, than would be, for example, the departments of France. Although the great number of study units tends to break the continuity of the volume and make it rather encyclopedic in nature, it was felt that this presentation was the only possible means of covering the entire country systematically and in great detail from the political and economic points of view. Each regional study is prefaced by an over-all survey of the area, in which special attention is devoted to the physical pattern, before the detailed description of the individual political divisions is attempted. Here the emphasis lies in the political and economic field, particularly such problems as toponymy, changes in the political-administrative framework, localization of industry, details of construction projects, as well as thumbnail sketches of the principal cities. This interest in individual urban centers is also prompted by the rapid pattern of urbanization, a distinctive feature of Soviet geography. The grouping of lesser political divisions into the regional study units was dictated by physico-economic considerations. Some groupings, such as the units making up the Urals, are rather universally recognized in Soviet literature, while others may be more arbitrary. Thus, it appears that Murmansk Oblast is sometimes also included within the European Northwest because of its transportation links with the Leningrad region. For the purpose of this book, it is discussed as part of the European North. Similarly, Gor'kiy Oblast may fall within the Central Industrial Region rather than within the Volga Region as it has been classed. These questions, however, hardly affect the treatment of the particular area, but may touch only on the emphasis in its economic links with adjacent regions.

Because the material for this book was collected largely during the period of the postwar Five-Year Plan of the USSR, construction projects scheduled by the Plan are emphasized throughout the text. Officially entitled the Five-Year Plan of Reconstruction and Development of the National Economy of the USSR for 1946–50, it is usually referred to here as the current Plan or postwar Plan.

To facilitate and complement the use of the text, the author has prepared a number of maps, some of a topical nature, others merely for locational purposes. Notes on methodology and on the transliteration of Russian names, some statistical tables, a bibliography, and a place-name index complete the work.

The human factor, insofar as it applies to the labor force, has not been discussed in this book, which is principally concerned with the localization of the economy. Particularly has no mention been made of the "corrective labor camps," which are known to exist in the USSR, but on which reliable data regarding localization, extent, and type of production are not sufficiently available.

The area of the USSR discussed in this book is contained within the *de facto* limits of the country as of the end of 1950. This area includes Southern Sakhalin and the Kurile Islands, where final disposition awaits the Japanese peace treaty, Kaliningrad Oblast (northern East Prussia), which is to be definitely adjudged by the German peace treaty, and the three Baltic republics of Lithuania, Latvia, and Estonia, of which the incorporation into the USSR has not been recognized by the United States Government.

The author has drawn upon many sources for his material and is particularly indebted to the staff members of the American Russian Institute, Inc., New York, for making available their facilities and to Martin A. Bacheller, of C. S. Hammond & Co., for the use of an extensive reference file. Of exceptional importance within the framework of the book were the 1947 election district data supplied by John V. Grauman, of the American University, to whom the author wishes to extend his sincere appreciation. Thanks are expressed also to Professor Stephen B. Jones, of Yale University, whose advice on problems of organization and treatment proved invaluable, and to Dr. William Bridgwater, Editor of the Columbia University Press, for his suggestions and encouragement during the preparation of the manuscript.

THEODORE SHABAD

New York
January, 1951

Methodology

RECOGNIZING the inherent importance of the political-administrative pattern with respect to the economic development of the USSR, the author has based his work largely on the evolution of the administrative setting, particularly in the preparation of the regional survey.

The basic working material has been an extensive card file of the political-administrative divisions of the USSR, in which are recorded all territorial units from the republic to the rayon, the respective administrative headquarters, the area and population figures of major territorial units. The file also contains, within their respective units of jurisdiction, all urban centers of the USSR (cities of varying ranks, workers' settlements, and city-type settlements) with their date of formation or promotion in rank. The information contained in this file of more than 10,000 names has been culled over a number of years and is being maintained currently, on the basis of various editions of the territorial-administrative guides of the USSR and the Russian SFSR and on the basis of notices of administrative changes appearing in the official Soviet periodical *Vedomosti Verkhovnogo Soveta SSSR*, which carries the texts of laws and decrees passed by the higher governmental bodies of the USSR.

The author has proceeded on the assumption, which has been largely confirmed in the course of the work, that the changes in the territorial-administrative pattern reflect accurately the development of the economy of the USSR. Thus, the stepping up of production in an industrial region will manifest itself in the creation of a separate oblast for that region, as was the case during the Second World War, when the Kuznetsk Basin, for example, was constituted the separate Kemerovo Oblast. Also, the development of a new mine or the construction of a new industrial plant, is evident in the creation of a new workers' settlement or city-type settlement. Further growth and expansion of the new urban nucleus is revealed when it is declared a city, which may come progressively under the jurisdiction of a rayon, an oblast, or a republic. This type of development is illustrated, for example, by the construction of the new steel-milling center of Rustavi in the Georgian SSR. Rustavi, where construction was begun in 1943, first appeared on the administrative map of the USSR in 1946, when it became a city-type settlement within one of the rayons of the Georgian SSR. As the project proceeded, its population grew and the construction site expanded. These changes were again reflected in the administrative pattern in 1948, when Rustavi was removed from the jurisdiction of the rayon and became a city of republic rank, subordinated directly to the government of the Georgian SSR. Thus, in basing the work on the administrative pattern and in examining carefully each creation of a new urban center, it became unlikely that any significant industrial development within the USSR would be overlooked. Such a possibility might exist only in cases of industrial development of a classified nature, where the formation of new urban centers is not made public. It should be remarked, however, that any such classified development of all but the smallest scope could not but have some repercussion in such a closely-knit economy as that of the USSR, and would manifest itself indirectly through the creation of new urban centers. For this reason, statements to the effect that large unnamed cities engaged in secret production abound in the USSR should be submitted to a very critical examination. Any classified activity requiring a great industrial potential, such as atomic research, is probably taking place in the very midst of one of the existing industrial complexes, rather than in some remote corner of the Siberian taiga.

Once the administrative pattern was known, the problem consisted in relating it to isolated notices of economic changes (construction projects, discovery of new mineral deposits, introduction of new industrial crops, and so forth) which appear in the Soviet press and periodicals. These incomplete and widely scattered bits of information, supplementing the prewar material available through the Great Soviet World Atlas, Volumes I and II, were collated with the administrative changes and pointed the way to many trends and developments in the Soviet economy. It became evident that while many cases of formation of smaller urban centers (workers' settlements and city-type settlements) could not be identified with a specific local economic development, the procedure was eminently successful in the case of all larger urban centers. The probable industry leading to the creation of a new urban center could frequently be identified without specific reference to the new town concerned. This was the case with sawmilling towns established in a forested area at the typical location of a river and railroad crossing and with fish-processing establishments formed in the midst of a previously established fisheries area. Similarly, the formation of a workers' settlement on the site of a previously reported mineral deposit was a probable indication of mining activity.

The specific economic information thus obtained was interwoven into the regional plan, adapted from Soviet geographical works, principally the economic geography of Baranskiy. It should be noted, incidentally, that Soviet textbooks and other publications on the economic geography of the USSR suffer as much from the dynamic nature of the subject as do non-Soviet works. This fact illustrates again the great sensitivity of the administrative pattern in pointing out very early the presence of economic changes which are not discussed in Soviet geographical (as opposed to current periodical) publications until a considerably later date.

No great difficulty was encountered in presenting area figures for the administrative units under discussion. These figures appear regularly in the above-mentioned administrative-territorial guides of the USSR. The situation was totally different, however, with respect to population data.

The results of the last census of the USSR, held in 1939, have appeared only in preliminary and incomplete form for the then-existing union republics, the political divisions of the Russian SFSR, the cities with a population of more than 50,000, and the numbers for each major ethnic group with more than 20,000 people, excluding some nationalities of Siberia for which no figures were available. The results also included demographic data by ages, literacy, education, and social classes. Confronted with the lack of population figures for the present political-administrative divisions of the USSR and the major cities, the author made a series of estimates based on the elections to the Soviets of greater and lesser administrative units in 1946, 1947, 1948, and 1950.

Each election was preceded by the publication of a list of election districts for the area covered by the given election. Each election district is defined in terms of the administrative units which it comprises, or, in the case of local city elections, the sections of the particular city. By law each election district is established in such a manner as to include a uniform number of people, depending on the type of election and the consequent size of the election district. Each election district sends one representative (deputy) to the particular elective body concerned. It will be readily seen that the election district will vary tremendously in area and population. In the case of the election to the Soviet of the Union (one of the two chambers of the Supreme Soviet of the USSR), an election district is intended to include about 300,000 people, a figure which may vary according to local conditions between 150,000 and 450,000. In northern Siberia such a district may cover 500,000 or more square miles. At the other extreme, one may consider the elections to the local Soviet of an urban center, say, a city of about 50,000 in the Russian SFSR. Here the law provides for the creation of an election district for every 350 inhabitants, an area calculated in city blocks.

It becomes clear that the number of election districts established in a particular area will give an approximate indication of the total population of the given area, and that the precision of the estimate increases inversely with the number of inhabitants assigned to each election district. The population within a few hundred people, for example, would be indicated in the case of the city of about 50,000. Assuming that 121 election districts had been established for the election of a 121-man city Soviet, the population of the given city would be 42,350 within the margin of ±175. Conversely, the population within the margin ±150,000 is obtained on the basis of the election districts to the Soviet of the Union.

Lists of election districts to local or regional elections, are published in local or regional newspapers, which are not available in the United States. This lack of material precluded the precise calculation of population figures for all urban centers and administrative units of the USSR. The author had available the election district lists for the election to the Supreme Soviet of the USSR in 1946, most of the lists for the Republic elections of 1947, and the list for the Union election of 1950 (the detailed source materials are listed on p. 520). The 1947 districts have been used throughout the book to impute the population of politico-administrative divisions and large cities. The population per district varies from 150,000 for the Russian SFSR to 5,000 for the Armenian SSR; consequently the precision of the imputed figures varies accordingly (see Table 1, p. 499, for detailed comments on the quality of the imputed population figures).

Although the 1950 election district list became available while the book was still in preparation, it was considered advisable to keep the

1947 figures, because of their greater precision, rather than substitute the more recent, though less accurate (unit of 300,000) 1950 figures.

For comparison with the 1946 figures, the 1950 estimates are given below.

Republic	1946	1950
Russian SFSR in Europe	93,000,000	94,800,000
Russian SFSR in Asia	19,800,000	21,600,000
Russian SFSR (total)	112,800,000	116,400,000
Ukrainian SSR	40,800,000	40,800,000
Belorussian SSR	9,300,000	9,300,000
Azerbaijan SSR	3,300,000	3,300,000
Georgian SSR	3,600,000	3,600,000
Armenian SSR	1,200,000	1,500,000
Karelo-Finnish SSR	600,000	600,000
Moldavian SSR	2,700,000	2,700,000
Lithuanian SSR	3,000,000	3,000,000
Latvian SSR	2,100,000	2,100,000
Estonian SSR	1,200,000	1,200,000
Turkmen SSR	1,200,000	1,200,000
Uzbek SSR	6,000,000	6,000,000
Kazakh SSR	6,000,000	6,600,000
Kirghiz SSR	1,500,000	1,500,000
Tadzhik SSR	1,500,000	1,500,000
USSR in Europe	160,800,000	162,900,000
USSR in Asia	36,000,000	38,400,000
USSR (total)	196,800,000	201,300,000

It will be seen that the only district revisions during the period 1946–50 occurred in the Armenian SSR, the Kazakh SSR, and the Russian SFSR.

The 300,000 increase in the Armenian SSR is the result of the post-war immigration from abroad. In Kazakhstan, the increases took place in Akmolinsk Oblast, where the new South Siberian Railroad is attracting settlement, and in South Kazakhstan Oblast, where additional areas of the Golodnaya Steppe were placed under irrigation.

In the Russian SFSR increases were recorded mainly in the Moscow area, where three new districts (representing a population of 900,000) were created, including two in Moscow city. Two new electoral districts each were set up in Kaliningrad Oblast (northern East Prussia) and in Sakhalin, recently annexed areas that have received a large population influx from other parts of the USSR. Other areas that showed gains in population were Murmansk Oblast, Molotov Oblast, where the Kizel coal basin experienced considerable urbanization in recent years, Keme-rovo Oblast (Kuznetsk Basin), and the Far East.

Notes on Transliteration

THE TRANSLITERATION of Russian names used in the text, maps, and tables follows (with a few exceptions) the recommendations * of the Permanent Committee on Geographical Names of the Royal Geographical Society, 1942, with minor modifications recommended by the United States Board on Geographic Names, 1944.

The modifications recommended by the United States Board on Geographic Names are as follows:

In the case of the alternatives *e, ye,* the latter should be used only at the beginning of a word, or following a vowel, soft sign, or hard sign.

The half-vowel, or short *i* in Russian (used only in conjunction with another vowel), should always be rendered as *y,* even when it follows or precedes (as in names of non-Russian origin) the full vowel which is also rendered as *y.*

In the case of the alternatives *dzh, j,* the latter should not be used.

The soft sign (which modifies the preceding consonant) should always be rendered as an apostrophe; the hard sign (which appears only in the middle of names) should be rendered as a double apostrophe.

The exceptions to the original recommendations are as follows:

The vowel *ë, yë* is rendered here as *e, ye,* principally because the diaeresis is usually omitted from the original Russian names; for example, Orel, Mogilev, Artemovsk should properly be written Orël, Mogilëv, Artëmovsk.

For those who wish to use a simplified system that would be satisfactory for all general purposes, it is suggested that the following changes be made from the system adopted here:

The apostrophe and the rare double apostrophe, representing the Russian soft and hard signs, may be omitted entirely. The half-vowel *i,* which is here rendered as *y,* may be omitted following *i* and *y* and is

---

* These recommendations were embodied in Permanent Committee on Geographical Names, *Glossaries, 2: Russian,* London, Royal Geographical Society, 1942.

rendered as *i* following *a, e, o, u*. According to this simplification, Gor'kiy would become Gorki, Altay would become Altai, and Baykal would become Baikal.

The place-name policy of the United States Board on Geographic Names has been followed to the extent, that conventional English forms have been adopted for features common to more than one language area. Thus, we use Amu Darya, common to the USSR and Afghanistan, rather than the Russian transliterated form Amu-Dar'ya. For the sake of consistency the spelling Darya has been adopted wherever the term occurs.

It should be noted that the soft vowels rendered here as *ya, ye, yu* appear in some transliterations, notably that of the Library of Congress, as *ia, ie, iu*. Similarly, the half-vowel rendered here as *y* is omitted and/or rendered as *i* in some transliterations, such as the simplified system recommended above.

A number of departures have also been made from strict letter-for-letter transliteration in rendering the Russian names of administrative-territorial divisions. These names usually include the generic designation of the political unit, such as constituent union republic (SSR), autonomous republic (Autonomous SSR), kray, oblast, autonomous oblast, and national okrug, preceded by the specific designation of the particular unit, as an adjective, inflected to agree in gender and case with the noun that it modifies. The exact transliteration of these adjectival forms (e.g., Moskovskaya Oblast' for Moscow Oblast; Chukotskiy Natsional'nyy Okrug for Chukchi National Okrug) is unduly cumbersome. Therefore, except where adjectival names are well established in English usage, for example, Ukrainian, Belorussian, Armenian, the nominative or root form is used here as an adjective, as Turkmen SSR, rather than Turkmenian SSR; Chukchi National Okrug, rather than Chukotsk National Okrug. Familiar English conventional forms are used for a few well-known places: Moscow rather than Moskva, Kiev rather than Kiyev, Georgia rather than Gruziya, and Kirghiz rather than Kirgiz.

A special problem was encountered in the transliteration of names of non-Russian origin, particularly where the Russian form is itself a phonetic transcription from a language using the Latin alphabet, for example, Lithuanian, Latvian, Estonian. Because consistency in transliteration was desired, and since the name obtained through this double transliteration was sometimes obscure, the retransliterated form is always followed in parentheses by the original spelling in the Latin alphabet, for example, Vil'nyus (Vilnius), Liepaya (Liepāja), Yykhvi (Jõhvi).

In accordance with the principles adopted for the writing of Russian political divisions, the generics of physical features have usually been translated into the most suitable English form, while nominative or root forms have been used wherever possible as adjectival specific designations. Specific designations which have familiar English equivalents have been translated in whole or in part, as New Siberian Islands rather than Novo-Sibirskiye Ostrova; South Kazakhstan Oblast rather than Yuzhno-Kazakhstan Oblast.

In order to avoid confusion, some generic designations of types of administrative units, such as oblast, kray, okrug, and rayon, have not been translated, but have been used as English terms. It happens that these units have been translated variously and indiscriminately as province, region, territory, area, district, and county.

The newly adopted names of non-Russian origin of several minor ethnic groups have been used in preference to the conventional older Russian forms. However, the modern official designation is usually followed by the more familiar older form, for example, Komi (Zyryan), Udmurt (Votyak), Nentsy (Samoyed), and Evenki (Tungus).

Contents

METHODOLOGY   xi

NOTES ON TRANSLITERATION   xvii

PART ONE · GENERAL SURVEY

1. THE PHYSICAL SETTING   3

Location and Boundaries, *p. 3*

Seas and Coasts, *p. 5*

Geologic History, *p. 10*

Structure and Relief, *p. 15*

Hydrography, *p. 21*

Climate, *p. 24*

Soils and Vegetation, *p. 27*

Mineral Resources, *p. 33*

2. THE POLITICAL FRAMEWORK   39

Population, *p. 39*

Administrative-territorial Divisions, *p. 41*

Toponymy, *p. 49*

3. THE ECONOMIC PATTERN   54

Agriculture, *p. 54*

Industry, *p. 68*

Transportation and Commerce, *p. 82*

PART TWO · REGIONAL SURVEY

4. RUSSIAN SOVIET FEDERATED SOCIALIST REPUBLIC (RUSSIA)   95

5. CENTRAL INDUSTRIAL REGION   104

     MOSCOW OBLAST, *p. 110*

     YAROSLAVL' OBLAST, *p. 116*

KOSTROMA OBLAST, *p.* 118

IVANOVO OBLAST, *p.* 119

VLADIMIR OBLAST, *p.* 121

RYAZAN' OBLAST, *p.* 122

TULA OBLAST, *p.* 123

6. CENTRAL BLACK-EARTH REGION   125

OREL OBLAST, *p.* 129

TAMBOV OBLAST, *p.* 130

VORONEZH OBLAST, *p.* 131

KURSK OBLAST, *p.* 132

7. THE EUROPEAN WEST   134

BRYANSK OBLAST, *p.* 137

KALUGA OBLAST, *p.* 138

SMOLENSK OBLAST, *p.* 139

VELIKIYE LUKI OBLAST, *p.* 140

KALININ OBLAST, *p.* 140

8. THE EUROPEAN NORTHWEST   143

NOVGOROD OBLAST, *p.* 146

PSKOV OBLAST, *p.* 147

LENINGRAD OBLAST, *p.* 148

9. THE EUROPEAN NORTH   154

MURMANSK OBLAST, *p.* 160

KOMI AUTONOMOUS SOVIET SOCIALIST REPUBLIC, *p.* 163

VOLOGDA OBLAST, *p.* 165

ARKHANGEL'SK OBLAST, *p.* 167

10. VOLGA REGION   170

Upper Volga Region (Forest Section), p. 174

KIROV OBLAST, *p.* 176

GOR'KIY OBLAST, *p.* 178

MARI AUTONOMOUS SOVIET SOCIALIST REPUBLIC, *p.* 180

Middle Volga Region (Wooded Steppe Section), p. 181

CHUVASH AUTONOMOUS SOVIET SOCIALIST REPUBLIC, *p.* 185

MORDVINIAN AUTONOMOUS
SOVIET SOCIALIST REPUBLIC, *p.* 186

TATAR AUTONOMOUS SOVIET SOCIALIST REPUBLIC, *p.* 187

PENZA OBLAST, *p.* 189

UL'YANOVSK OBLAST, *p.* 190

KUYBYSHEV OBLAST, *p.* 191

Lower Volga Region (Steppe Section), p. 193

SARATOV OBLAST, *p.* 196

STALINGRAD OBLAST, *p.* 199

ASTRAKHAN' OBLAST, *p.* 201

11. THE EUROPEAN SOUTH 204

CRIMEAN OBLAST, *p.* 204

Lower Don and Northern Caucasus, p. 209

ROSTOV OBLAST, *p.* 214

KRASNODAR KRAY, *p.* 217

STAVROPOL' KRAY, *p.* 221

KABARDINIAN AUTONOMOUS
SOVIET SOCIALIST REPUBLIC, *p.* 224

NORTH OSSETIAN AUTONOMOUS
SOVIET SOCIALIST REPUBLIC, *p.* 226

GROZNYY OBLAST, *p.* 228

DAGESTAN AUTONOMOUS
SOVIET SOCIALIST REPUBLIC, *p.* 230

12. URALS 233

SVERDLOVSK OBLAST, *p.* 238

MOLOTOV OBLAST, *p.* 243

CHELYABINSK OBLAST, *p.* 248

UDMURT AUTONOMOUS SOVIET SOCIALIST REPUBLIC, *p.* 251

BASHKIR AUTONOMOUS SOVIET SOCIALIST REPUBLIC, *p.* 253

CHKALOV OBLAST, *p.* 256

13. WESTERN SIBERIA 260

KURGAN OBLAST, *p.* 266

TYUMEN' OBLAST, *p.* 268

OMSK OBLAST, *p.* 270

NOVOSIBIRSK OBLAST, *p.* 272

TOMSK OBLAST, *p.* 273

ALTAY KRAY, *p.* 274

KEMEROVO OBLAST, *p.* 276

14. EASTERN SIBERIA   281

KRASNOYARSK KRAY, *p.* 289

TUVA AUTONOMOUS OBLAST, *p.* 294

IRKUTSK OBLAST, *p.* 295

BURYAT-MONGOL AUTONOMOUS
    SOVIET SOCIALIST REPUBLIC, *p.* 300

CHITA OBLAST, *p.* 302

YAKUT AUTONOMOUS SOVIET SOCIALIST REPUBLIC, *p.* 304

15. SOVIET FAR EAST   308

AMUR OBLAST, *p.* 315

KHABAROVSK KRAY, *p.* 318

MARITIME KRAY, *p.* 326

SAKHALIN OBLAST, *p.* 329

16. KAZAKH SOVIET SOCIALIST REPUBLIC (KAZAKHSTAN)   334

General Survey, *p.* 334

Oblast Survey, *p.* 350

Western Kazakhstan, p. 350

WEST-KAZAKHSTAN OBLAST, *p.* 350

GUR'YEV OBLAST, *p.* 351

AKTYUBINSK OBLAST, *p.* 352

Northern Kazakhstan, p. 352

KUSTANAY OBLAST, *p.* 353

NORTH-KAZAKHSTAN OBLAST, *p.* 353

KOKCHETAV OBLAST, *p.* 353

Central Kazakhstan, p. 354

AKMOLINSK OBLAST, *p.* 354

KARAGANDA OBLAST, *p.* 355

Eastern Kazakhstan, p. 356

PAVLODAR OBLAST, *p.* 357

SEMIPALATINSK OBLAST, *p.* 357

EAST-KAZAKHSTAN OBLAST, *p.* 358

Southern Kazakhstan, p. 358

    TALDY-KURGAN OBLAST, *p.* 360

    ALMA-ATA OBLAST, *p.* 360

    DZHAMBUL OBLAST, *p.* 361

    SOUTH-KAZAKHSTAN OBLAST, *p.* 362

    KZYL-ORDA OBLAST, *p.* 362

17. CENTRAL ASIA   364

18. KIRGHIZ SOVIET SOCIALIST REPUBLIC   371

General Survey, *p.* 371

Oblast Survey, *p.* 375

    FRUNZE OBLAST, *p.* 375

    ISSYK-KUL' OBLAST, *p.* 376

    TYAN'-SHAN' OBLAST, *p.* 377

    OSH OBLAST, *p.* 378

    DZHALAL-ABAD OBLAST, *p.* 379

    TALAS OBLAST, *p.* 379

19. TADZHIK SOVIET SOCIALIST REPUBLIC   380

General Survey, *p.* 380

Oblast Survey, *p.* 385

    LENINABAD OBLAST, *p.* 385

    STALINABAD OBLAST, *p.* 385

    KULYAB OBLAST, *p.* 386

    GARM OBLAST, *p.* 387

    GORNO-BADAKHSHAN AUTONOMOUS OBLAST, *p.* 387

20. UZBEK SOVIET SOCIALIST REPUBLIC   888

General Survey, *p.* 388

Oblast Survey, *p.* 393

    ANDIZHAN OBLAST, *p.* 393

    FERGANA OBLAST, *p.* 393

    NAMANGAN OBLAST, *p.* 394

    TASHKENT OBLAST, *p.* 394

    SAMARKAND OBLAST, *p.* 396

    SURKHAN-DARYA OBLAST, *p.* 397

    KASHKA-DARYA OBLAST, *p.* 397

BUKHARA OBLAST, *p.* 397

KHOREZM OBLAST, *p.* 398

KARA-KALPAK AUTONOMOUS
SOVIET SOCIALIST REPUBLIC, *p.* 398

21. TURKMEN SOVIET SOCIALIST REPUBLIC   400

General Survey, *p.* 400

Oblast Survey, *p.* 404

ASHKHABAD OBLAST, *p.* 404

MARY OBLAST, *p.* 406

CHARDZHOU OBLAST, *p.* 407

TASHAUZ OBLAST, *p.* 408

22. TRANSCAUCASIA   409

AZERBAIJAN SOVIET SOCIALIST REPUBLIC, *p.* 413

ARMENIAN SOVIET SOCIALIST REPUBLIC, *p.* 420

GEORGIAN SOVIET SOCIALIST REPUBLIC, *p.* 424

23. UKRAINIAN SOVIET SOCIALIST REPUBLIC   434

General Survey, *p.* 434

Oblast Survey, *p.* 445

The Right-Bank Wooded Steppe, *p.* 445

KIEV OBLAST, *p.* 446

VINNITSA OBLAST, *p.* 447

KAMENETS-PODOL'SKIY OBLAST, *p.* 447

The Left-Bank Wooded Steppe, *p.* 447

KHAR'KOV OBLAST, *p.* 448

POLTAVA OBLAST, *p.* 448

SUMY OBLAST, *p.* 449

Donets Basin, *p.* 449

STALINO OBLAST, *p.* 450

VOROSHILOVGRAD OBLAST, *p.* 452

Dnieper Bend, *p.* 452

DNEPROPETROVSK OBLAST, *p.* 453

ZAPOROZH'YE OBLAST, *p.* 453

The Black Sea Lowland, *p.* 454

KHERSON OBLAST, *p.* 455

NIKOLAYEV OBLAST, *p.* 455

ODESSA OBLAST, *p.* 455

KIROVOGRAD OBLAST, *p.* 456

IZMAIL OBLAST, *p.* 456

Poles'ye, p. 457

ZHITOMIR OBLAST, *p.* 458

CHERNIGOV OBLAST, *p.* 458

Western Ukraine, p. 459

CHERNOVTSY OBLAST, *p.* 459

STANISLAV OBLAST, *p.* 460

DROGOBYCH OBLAST, *p.* 460

ROVNO OBLAST, *p.* 461

VOLYN' OBLAST, *p.* 461

TERNOPOL' OBLAST, *p.* 462

L'VOV OBLAST, *p.* 462

TRANSCARPATHIAN OBLAST, *p.* 463

24. MOLDAVIAN SOVIET SOCIALIST REPUBLIC   464

25. BELORUSSIAN SOVIET SOCIALIST REPUBLIC   469

General Survey, *p.* 469

Oblast Survey, *p.* 474

MINSK OBLAST, *p.* 474

POLOTSK OBLAST, *p.* 475

VITEBSK OBLAST, *p.* 475

MOGILEV OBLAST, *p.* 475

GOMEL' OBLAST, *p.* 476

BOBRUYSK OBLAST, *p.* 476

POLES'YE OBLAST, *p.* 476

PINSK OBLAST, *p.* 477

BREST OBLAST, *p.* 477

GRODNO OBLAST, *p.* 477

BARANOVICHI OBLAST, *p.* 477

MOLODECHNO OBLAST, *p.* 478

26. BALTIC REGION   479

LITHUANIAN SOVIET SOCIALIST REPUBLIC, *p.* 482

CONTENTS

LATVIAN SOVIET SOCIALIST REPUBLIC, *p.* 485

ESTONIAN SOVIET SOCIALIST REPUBLIC, *p.* 487

KALININGRAD OBLAST (RUSSIAN SFSR), *p.* 490

27. KARELO-FINNISH SOVIET SOCIALIST REPUBLIC   493

APPENDIX: TABLES   499

SELECTED BIBLIOGRAPHY   515

INDEX   523

Tables

1. Population of the Union Republics of the USSR — 499
2. Administrative-Territorial Divisions of the USSR — 500
3. Population of Cities with Over 50,000 Inhabitants — 506
4. Major Ethnic Groups of the USSR
   and Their Autonomous Political Divisions — 512

Maps

MAIN PHYSICAL FEATURES OF THE EUROPEAN USSR   16

MAIN PHYSICAL FEATURES OF THE ASIATIC USSR   17

VEGETATION ZONES OF THE EUROPEAN USSR   28

VEGETATION ZONES OF THE ASIATIC USSR   29

MINERAL RESOURCES OF THE EUROPEAN USSR   34

MINERAL RESOURCES OF THE ASIATIC USSR   35

DISTRIBUTION OF CITIES OF THE EUROPEAN USSR   42

DISTRIBUTION OF CITIES OF THE ASIATIC USSR   43

CHIEF AGRICULTURAL AREAS OF THE EUROPEAN USSR   56

CHIEF AGRICULTURAL AREAS OF THE ASIATIC USSR   57

CHIEF INDUSTRIAL AREAS OF THE EUROPEAN USSR   70

CHIEF INDUSTRIAL AREAS OF THE ASIATIC USSR   71

RAILROADS OF THE EUROPEAN USSR   86

RAILROADS OF THE ASIATIC USSR   87

CENTRAL INDUSTRIAL REGION   105

MOSCOW AREA   115

CENTRAL BLACK-EARTH REGION   127

EUROPEAN WEST   135

EUROPEAN NORTHWEST   145

LENINGRAD AREA   153

EUROPEAN NORTH   155

MURMANSK OBLAST   161

UPPER VOLGA REGION   173

MIDDLE VOLGA REGION   183

LOWER VOLGA REGION   195

LOWER DON (ROSTOV OBLAST)   205

CRIMEA   205

Northern Caucasus 211
Urals 235
Central Urals 241
Western Siberia 261
Novosibirsk and Kuznetsk Basin 279
Eastern Siberia 283
Eastern Siberia (Southern Portion) 297
Soviet Far East 311
Amur Oblast 317
Maritime Kray and Khabarovsk 321
Vladivostok Area 327
Sakhalin 331
Kazakh Soviet Socialist Republic 338–339
Altay Region 359
Kirghiz Soviet Socialist Republic 373
Tadzhik Soviet Socialist Republic 381
Uzbek Soviet Socialist Republic 389
Fergana Valley 395
Turkmen Soviet Socialist Republic 401
Azerbaijan Soviet Socialist Republic 415
Baku Area 415
Armenian Soviet Socialist Republic 421
Georgian Soviet Socialist Republic 427
Ukrainian Soviet Socialist Republic 436–437
Donets Basin 451
Moldavian Soviet Socialist Republic 465
Belorussian Soviet Socialist Republic 471
Baltic Region (Estonian, Latvian, Lithuanian SSRs) 481
Kaliningrad Oblast 491
Karelo-Finnish Soviet Socialist Republic 495

PART ONE

General Survey

CHAPTER 1

The Physical Setting

THE UNION OF SOVIET SOCIALIST REPUBLICS (USSR), also known as the Soviet Union, includes the eastern half of Europe and about one-third of the continent of Asia, with its entire northern portion (Siberia), the western section of Central Asia, and part of the Middle East in the region of the Caucasus. In addition to this continuous land area, the segment of the Arctic Ocean between the meridians of Murmansk and the Bering Strait and reaching north to the North Pole is claimed by the USSR, which also controls the leased naval base districts of Porkkala, west of Helsinki (Finland), and of Port Arthur, on the Liaotung Peninsula in South Manchuria.

LOCATION AND BOUNDARIES

From north to south, the territory of the USSR proper extends from Cape Chelyuskin (77° 44′ N) nearly 3,000 miles south to Kushka (35° N) on the Afghanistan frontier. From the extreme western point of the USSR, at 20° E, near Kaliningrad, it is nearly 7,000 miles to Cape Dezhnev (170° W), on Bering Strait, almost halfway around the world. The total area of the USSR is about 8½ million square miles, representing nearly one-sixth of the inhabited land area of the world (not counting Antarctica). It is the largest continuous political unit and is exceeded in area only by the British Commonwealth of Nations. The Soviet Union is nearly three times as vast as the continental United States.

The major portion of the country lies in the temperate zone, 16 percent of the area extending into the cold zone and only about 4 percent, in the extreme south, into the subtropical zone. The well-known continentality, which serves to explain many geographic peculiarities of the USSR, is due mainly to its location in latitudes where the Eurasian continent reaches its greatest east-west dimensions. In particular, this circumstance places the major part of the Soviet Union far to the east of the influence of the prevailing westerly winds.

The total length of the boundaries of the USSR reaches more than 35,000 miles, of which over two-thirds are coast lines (chiefly in the north and the east) and less than one-third, land frontiers in the west and the south. Since the Finnish armistice of 1944, which adjudged to the USSR the district of Pechenga (Petsamo), the Soviet Union borders on Norway in the extreme northwest, on the coast of the Barents Sea. The frontier then proceeds south to the Gulf of Finland, separating the USSR from Finland along a line dating partly from the Treaty of Moscow (1940). After passing through the Baltic Sea, the frontier reaches land north of Braniewo (Poland) and runs east to the former meeting point of Germany, Lithuania, and Poland. This line, separating the northern (Soviet) half from the southern (Polish) part of former East Prussia, was provisionally defined at the Potsdam Conference (1945). Continuing south to the Carpathians, the Soviet-Polish frontier is based roughly on the Curzon line and was fixed by mutual agreement in August, 1945. The cession of the Carpatho-Ukraine (Ruthenia) by Czechoslovakia in 1945 placed the USSR frontier on the southern slopes of the Carpathian Mountains, where it borders on Hungary and Rumania along the Tisza valley. Cutting back across the Carpathians, the boundary with Rumania (dating from 1940) follows the Prut River to its mouth in the Danube and along the northern branch of the Danube delta to the Black Sea. Passing through the Black Sea, the frontier continues through the Armenian upland and along the Aras River to the Caspian Sea, separating the USSR from Turkey and Iran. East of the Caspian Sea, the USSR borders on Iran as far as the Tedzhen River. At this point begins the border of Afghanistan, passing across the desert to the Amu Darya, which it follows to the source of the upper Panj River, near the Chinese frontier. In this region, south of the Pamir-Alay mountain system, a narrow tongue of Afghan territory separates the USSR from Pakistan. Leaving the Pamir highlands, the subject of a Chinese territorial claim, the USSR-China frontier passes across the Tien Shan system and its branches to the Altay Mountains. The boundary with Mongolia then continues along the Tannu-Ula, eastern Sayan, and Transbaykal ranges to the Argun' River. The frontier with Manchuria runs along the Argun' River to its confluence with the Shilka, along the Amur and the Ussuri to Lake Khanka, from which a short overland section brings the boundary to Pos'yet Bay, an inlet of the Sea

of Japan. In the neighborhood of Pos'yet Bay, the USSR briefly borders
on Korea along the lower Tumen River.

SEAS AND COASTS

Although the USSR has the longest coast line of any country, it
borders a littoral that is largely rendered worthless by frozen seas and
low, marshy shores. The greater portion of the coasts lies in sparsely
settled or uninhabited regions along the Arctic Ocean. Where the coasts
show a more concentrated population, closed seas often make access difficult, as in the case of the Black and the Caspian seas. Only a few rocky
shores provide the country with good natural ports, and year-around
access to the open sea is offered only by the temperate Murman coast,
in the extreme northwest.

The northern coast line of the USSR borders the Arctic Ocean, a vast
body of water extending to the North Pole, two-thirds of which are always
covered with floating ice driven by the winds and the marine currents.
Within the confines of the continental platform, which extends far to
the north from the Eurasian shores, the Arctic Ocean forms a number
of shallow seas separated from each other by island groups. The Barents
Sea, the westernmost of these subsidiaries of the Arctic Ocean, connects
to the west with the Norwegian Sea, between the Scandinavian peninsula
and Spitsbergen. Its coast bears a rocky character in the west, where
it is deeply indented by fiords, and becomes low in the east, where its
principal inlets are the White Sea, curving around the large Kola Peninsula, Chesha Bay, on the east side of the Kanin Peninsula, and Pechora
Bay, at the mouth of the Pechora River. Kolguyev (northeast of the
Kanin Peninsula) is the largest island in the Barents Sea. The warm Gulf
Stream penetrates into the southwestern section of the sea along the
Murman coast and renders it ice-free throughout the year. Fish and
seal herds abound along the coasts. The White Sea, which connects with
the Barents Sea through a mouth only thirty miles wide, in turn forms
several long bays, including those of Kandalaksha, Onega, and Dvina.
It is a shallow body of water, which has rocky, indented coasts in the
west and low, marshy shores in the east ; it is usually frozen from November until May.

The Barents Sea is bordered in the north by Franz-Josef Land, an
archipelago of about sixty islands which constitute the northernmost
land area of the USSR within this Arctic sector. Rudolf Island
(81° 50′ N) is the site of a polar station. The islands are generally rocky

with heights rising to 2,500 feet; their glaciers feed icebergs into the sea. In the east the Barents Sea is bounded by Novaya Zemlya and Vaygach Island, which separate it from the Kara Sea. Novaya Zemlya consists of two islands separated by the strait of Matochkin Shar. The northern island, largely glaciated, is deeply indented by fiord-like gulfs. The range rising in the center of the islands is a northward extension of the Ural Mountains. Vaygach Island, to the south, is separated from Novaya Zemlya and the mainland by the straits of Karskiye Vorota and Yugorskiy Shar, leading into the Kara Sea. Much colder than the Barents Sea and encumbered by ice nearly all the year, the Kara Sea sends long inlets deep into the low Siberian shores. These long bays, among which those of the Ob', Taz, and Yenisey are to be noted, describe in turn the Yamal and Gyda peninsulas. Here the summer is shorter and animal life is less developed than in the seas to the west.

The Kara Sea connects with the Laptev Sea via Boris Vil'kitskiy Strait lying between Cape Chelyuskin on the large Taymyr Peninsula and Severnaya Zemlya (North Land). This archipelago, largely explored only since the Bolshevik Revolution, includes the four large islands of Bol'shevik, Oktyabr'skaya Revolyutsiya (October Revolution), Pioner, and Komsomolets. The Laptev Sea coast is featured by the long Khatanga Gulf and the delta of the Lena River. To the east lie the New Siberian, Lyakhov, and De Long islands. This archipelago, sometimes known by the common name New Siberian (Novo-Sibirskiye) Islands, is characterized by the presence of huge layers of fossilized ice, dating from the Ice Age and intermixed with sand, clay, and peat strata. Due to the observed progressive warming of the Arctic, a few of the smaller islands are gradually melting and decreasing in size through the action of the sea. The East Siberian Sea, similar in its shallowness and severe ice conditions to the Laptev Sea, is bordered on the east by Vrangel' (Wrangel) Island, lying nearly one hundred miles off the coast. It is one hundred miles long and over thirty miles wide and is equipped with a polar station. Since 1926 it has had a permanent Luoravetlan (Chukchi) and Eskimo population. The easternmost Chukchi Sea, noted for its concentration of ice-bearing currents, lies north of the Chukchi Peninsula and connects, through the Bering Strait, with the Bering Sea. It is in Bering Strait that United States territory lies within three miles of the USSR. Despite their proximity, Little Diomede Island (part of the Second Judicial District of Alaska) and Big Diomede Island (part of the Chukchi National Okrug in Kamchatka Oblast of Khabarovsk Kray) are twenty-four hours apart in time, due to the presence of the intervening International Date Line.

The Pacific Ocean proper touches the shores of the USSR only in the southeastern Kamchatka Peninsula, the site of the naval base of Petropavlovsk, and along the festooned Kurile Islands. The remainder of the Soviet coasts are washed by the Bering Sea, the Sea of Okhotsk, and the Sea of Japan. Although the cold waters of the Arctic Ocean do not penetrate to any great extent into the Bering Sea, its conditions hardly differ from those of the seas along the Arctic coast of the USSR. It is separated from the Pacific by the chain of the Aleutians and the Commander (Komandorskiye) Islands, the latter forming part of the USSR.

The Sea of Okhotsk, with an area of nearly 600,000 square miles, is enclosed by the Kamchatka Peninsula in the east, the Kurile Islands in the southeast, and by Sakhalin and the continent in the west. It is connected with the Pacific Ocean by a number of deep straits (to 6,500 feet) between the islands of the Kurile chain and with the Sea of Japan by the shallow Tatar and La Pérouse straits, west and south of Sakhalin. The sea, which shows an average depth of 2,500 feet, produces the highest tides of the USSR in northeastern Penzhina Bay (35 feet). The shores are frozen in from November until May or June. Frequent storms prevent the formation of pack ice in the central reaches. Fish (especially salmon), seal, walrus, and whale herds abound. The major port is Magadan, a new city which developed in the 1930's at Nagayevo Bay as a supply point for the Kolyma mining region. Since 1945, following the acquisition of southern Sakhalin and the Kurile Islands, the Sea of Okhotsk has become virtually an internal sea of the USSR.

The Sea of Japan, which washes the extreme southeastern coast of the USSR, is characterized by high, rocky shores along a marine basin with depths reaching 10,000 feet. While the coast of Japan is influenced by the warm Japan Current, an opposite cold current from the north parallels the Asiatic continent. Due to the extreme climatic conditions stemming from the winter high-pressure area in Eastern Siberia, ice forms in the extreme northern section of the sea, roughly north of a line from Vladivostok to the southern tip of Sakhalin. The port of Vladivostok is threatened by ice during 3½ months, but is kept clear by means of icebreakers. Sovetskaya Gavan' is an important naval base in the Tatar Strait.

In great contrast to the extensive, but largely useless, coasts in the north and the east of the USSR are the lesser, but vastly more important, shores in the western and southwestern parts of the country. Of primary importance is the Baltic Sea, which in its eastern part describes the large gulfs of Finland and Riga within the territory of the USSR. This sea, which serves as the shortest route to the Atlantic Ocean and the overseas countries, is the site of the principal ports of the Soviet Union, most of which were acquired as a result of territorial gains (1940–45). They are Leningrad and its outer naval base of Kronshtadt, Vyborg, Tallin (Tallinn), Paldiski, Riga, Ventspils, Liepaya (Liepāja) Klaypeda (Klaipéda), and Kaliningrad. The basin of the Baltic Sea, formed as a result of geologic faulting, was filled with ice during the glacial period. The glacial remains, such as boulders, reefs, and sand-banks, now constitute considerable navigational hazards. Large stretches of the Baltic coast are covered with dunes, 65–200 feet high, which often form narrow sand-banks, closing off the so-called "haffs" (lagoons). The Baltic Sea is considerably poorer in fisheries than the other seas of the USSR. From the point of view of transportation, it should be noted that the Baltic is not an open sea and that, except for Kaliningrad and occasionally Liepaya (Liepāja) and Ventspils, its ports are blocked by ice during the winter.

The Black Sea is a residual sea, once connected with the Mediterranean Sea, then isolated, and later reconnected with the Mediterranean through the Bosporus. It includes a shallow section north of the line Varna-Yevpatoriya, where the depth is less than 600 feet, and a deep basin between the Crimea and Asia Minor, where the depth exceeds 7,000 feet. The northern coast is low and characterized by the so-called "limans," flooded river mouths which now constitute shallow lagoons nearly closed off by sand bars. Along the coast of the Caucasus the shores are rocky, and the shallow zone above the continental shelf remains comparatively narrow. One peculiar aspect of the Black Sea is its stratification into an aerated fresh-water layer (to a depth of 600 feet), constituting the habitat of nearly all the animal and plant life, and a deeper salt-water stratum of 6,000 feet, which receives no oxygen and is extensively polluted by the decay of micro-organisms and the ensuing production of hydrogen sulphide. The principal fish species are herring and sturgeon. Dolphins are also caught along the southeast coast, and iodine is processed from marine plants. The major importance of the Black Sea lies in the fact that, except for a short period along the northern shores, it is open to navigation throughout the year and offers an excellent route to the lands of the Mediterranean and the Atlantic Ocean. However, control of the straits by Turkey does reduce the usefulness of the Black Sea from the Russian standpoint. The principal ports include the naval base of Sevastopol', Odessa, Nikolayev, Zhdanov, Novorossiysk, Poti, and Batumi. The Sea of Azov is a shallow inlet of the Black Sea reached through the four-mile-wide Kerch' Strait. Its depth, about fifty feet, is gradually decreasing, due to the deposit of sediments by the Don River. Prevailing northeasterly winds have caused the formation of character- istic sandspits along the north coast. The Arabat spit, seventy miles long, closes off the shallow Sivash or Putrid Sea along the eastern and the northern shores of the Crimea. Thanks to its shallowness, the abundance of fresh water carried by its inlets, and the presence of exten- sive plankton fields, the Sea of Azov offers excellent fishing grounds. Its catch exceeds by four times that of the Black Sea.

The Caspian Sea is the largest inland sea of the world with an area of 163,825 square miles. The basin of the Caspian has undergone several transformations in recent geologic periods; it was once joined to the Black Sea in the west and the Aral Sea in the east. At another stage its area was reduced to that of its present section south of the latitude of Baku. During the past one hundred years the level of the sea has been oscillating within the range of about four feet. In recent years, however, a steady fall has been noted, its present surface being ninety-two feet below sea level. With respect to depth, the Caspian forms three sections. The northernmost and shallowest is being gradually filled by the sedi- ments of the Volga River. Its average depth is 16 feet; nowhere does it exceed 165 feet. The middle and southern sections are two deep basins separated by a submarine range which forms the link between the Cau- casus and the Balkhan and Kopet Dagh ranges in Central Asia. The mid- dle portion reaches a depth of 2,590 feet, and the southernmost, 3,200 feet. The salinity of the sea is relatively weak, an average 13 percent. This is due largely to the action of the gulf of Kara-Bogaz-Gol, which acts as a natural evaporating basin drawing off the water of the Caspian and depositing salt along its shores. A number of circumstances, includ- ing the especially low salinity in the northern portion of the sea, its shallowness, and the abundance of micro-organisms (discharged by the Volga) and ensuing plankton formation, have turned that section of the Caspian into the richest fishing grounds of the USSR, furnishing 35 percent of the total catch. About one-half of the eighty species are food types. These include sturgeon, salmon, about twenty types of herring, carp, and many other varieties. The Caspian seal is extensively hunted. The use of the sea for navigation is limited, due to the lack of outlet; however, it serves as the main transportation route for the littoral areas of the Caucasus, Central Asia, Kazakhstan, and the lower Volga. Trade with Iran is also being maintained via the Caspian Sea. Its principal ports are Astrakhan', Krasnovodsk, Baku, and Makhachkala. Similarly to the Black Sea, the deeper reaches of the sea are also polluted by hydrogen sulphide emanations, which do not, however, extend above the level of 1,300 feet.

GEOLOGIC HISTORY

Underlying the territory of the USSR are ancient crystalline rocks which date from the dawn of geologic history. These Pre-Cambrian formations constitute rigid blocks in the earth's crust and form vast continental platforms hidden by younger sedimentary deposits. In some sections of the country, however, the ancient rock formations (granite, gneiss, mica schist, phyllite, marble, and quartzite) are exposed, either in the form of shields or as the core of profoundly eroded mountain ranges. The crystalline shields are the Fenno-Scandian, or Baltic, shield in the northwest, the Azov-Podolian shield in the Ukraine, and in Eastern Siberia the Aldan and Anabar shields. In addition, Pre-Cambrian rocks appear in the eroded core of the Caucasus, the Urals, and the mountains of the Asiatic USSR. Throughout the extensive lowlands these rocks are covered by later deposits of varying thickness; in the Moscow region they have not been reached by the deepest borings, while they lie sometimes as little as three hundred feet below the surface in the area of Kursk. The minerals, which have been formed in the Pre-Cambrian deposits as a result of magmatic intrusion, metamorphism, or lode deposition, include the iron ore of Krivoy Rog and of the Kursk magnetic anomaly, the iron deposits of the Fenno-Scandian shield, and the Khibiny apatite. The gold lode deposits of Siberia and the Far East, as well as the Siberian sites of manganese, bismuth, copper, mica, and graphite, also belong to this period. The crystalline bedrock itself furnishes excellent building stone.

At the opening of the Paleozoic era the Cambrian period saw the formation of the Caledonian geosyncline roughly parallel to the western margin of the Russian platform. In the Asiatic USSR the Ural-Tien Shan trough swung around south of the Siberian platform and joined the East Siberian geosyncline. South of the continental platforms lay the vast Tethys sea, of which the Mediterranean, Black, and Caspian seas are the residual basins. In the southern hemisphere was the continent of Gondwana, which united the present land areas of Brazil, Africa, Madagascar, India, and Australia. Cambrian formations appear near Leningrad in the shape of blue clays, used extensively in the making of pottery, and, to a lesser extent, in the mountains of the European USSR, Central Asia, and Eastern Siberia. The following Silurian period was a time of intensive mountain formation culminating in the Caledonian revolution and affecting to a lesser extent the other geosynclines. As a result of these disturbances, marine transgressions flooded the continental platforms. Silurian deposits are widespread within the territory of the USSR and appear at the surface in the area of Leningrad, the western Ukraine, the Urals, Central Asia, and between the Yenisey and the Lena rivers in the form of sandstone, gray shale, and, mainly, limestone. Land appeared in the Silurian period over the greater portion of the European USSR as a wedge pointing southeast to the region south of the Aral Sea and as a number of islands in the present Ob'-Irtysh basin. Among the main economic deposits dating from this period are the oil shales of the Baltic littoral, the phosphorites of the western Ukraine, the lead, zinc, and copper ores of the northern Urals, Pay-Khoy, Vaygach Island, and Novaya Zemlya, the rock salt and gypsum of the Siberian platform, slate and construction limestone.

The beginning of the Devonian time witnessed the presence of the vast northern Atlantic continent (Atlantida) formed as a result of the late Caledonian upheaval, while in the Tethys sea, to the south, the new Hercynian geosyncline was gradually accumulating marine sediments. East of the Russian platform, where Old Red sandstone (a continental sediment) had a wide distribution, partly covered by shallow-water marine deposits of the Later Devonian, the Ural-Tien Shan geosyncline continued to exist and was characterized by strong volcanic activity. The period is represented by thick limestone beds on the western slopes of the Urals, while on the eastern side, volcanic rocks and tuff are in evidence. During the Devonian age, the sea apparently covered Western Siberia and Central Asia and was bordered in the east by the Siberian and the Chinese platforms, which in turn were separated by the Central Asian geosyncline. The decomposition of animal and vegetable remains in the Devonian seas led to the formation of petroleum deposits, of which those of the Pechora (Ukhta) basin are typical. Also related to this period are the iron and manganese ores of the Urals, and iron and copper deposits of contact-metamorphic origin in areas visited by volcanism.

The Hercynian revolution, a gigantic mountain-building process, took place during the Middle Carboniferous period. This orogeny, which was located principally in western Europe and created the well-known mountains of Brittany, the Ardennes, the Vosges, the Harz, and other mountain ranges, also extended to the USSR where the Ural Mountains began to arise out of the Ural-Tien Shan geosyncline. These crustal movements caused considerable marine shifts and left lake-covered lowlands, swamps, and shallow gulfs over a large segment of the European USSR. The tropical humid climate and the luxuriant swamp vegetation of the period served to produce the major coal deposits of the USSR, including the Moscow, Donets, Karaganda, and Kuznetsk basins. Bauxite, refractory clays, and intrusive formations of iron and manganese ores are also found in Carboniferous strata.

The powerful mountain-building processes continued into the Permian period and culminated in the complete filling of the Hercynian geosyncline and the formation of several mountain systems along its course. At the southern foot of these Hercynian ranges a new Alpine geosyncline was assuming shape. The Permian period was thus characterized chiefly by the creation of a vast continent in the Northern Hemisphere, which rivaled the southern land mass of Gondwana in its east-west extent. The Permian sea occupied only a narrow belt on the Russian platform and became quite shallow in the Late Permian, depositing large layers of gypsum, salt (at Sol'-Iletsk and Sol'vychegodsk), and of potash (at Solikamsk). Dry desert conditions west of the Urals also resulted in the formation of copper-bearing sandstone from the desiccation of older ores. East of the Urals, however, tropical climate similar to that of the Carboniferous period continued to favor the production of coal. The Pechora deposits and the upper strata of the Kuznetsk Basin date from this time, as do also the coal formations of the Tunguska Basin, where some coal was metamorphosed into graphite by lava flows.

The grandiose dislocations of the Carboniferous and Permian periods were followed in the Mesozoic era by a comparative quiescence. Whatever changes in the configuration of continents and seas took place were caused by epeirogenic crustal movements. Only toward the very end of the Mesozoic era do renewed orogenic processes presage the stormy mountain-building period of the following Cenozoic era.

The opening Triassic period of the Mesozoic was marked by continuing marine regression and dry conditions. Except for some border areas of Siberia, the entire territory of the USSR remained above water and is lacking in marine sediments. Only in the south, where shallow gulfs of the Tethys sea penetrated into the Crimea, the Caucasus, and the Mangyshlak Peninsula (on the Caspian Sea), do we encounter typical Triassic marine deposits of marl, clay, sandstone, and limestone. As for continental sediments, large regions of the northern land mass were covered during the Triassic period with red sand and clays of desert origin. Sodium chloride and gypsum remain the chief economic minerals from this period.

The beginning of the Jurassic period marked renewed marine transgressions, which split up the large continents into smaller land masses and islands. The warm humid climate continued to prevail. In the USSR, the Jurassic sea invaded the Russian platform between the young Ural Mountains and the Pre-Cambrian shield in the northwest and the southwest. Most of the sediments are of the shallow-water marine type and include marl and clay, colored in dark shades by the presence of microorganisms. They occur in the northern and middle sections of the European USSR, in the Caucasus, where the first orogeny is becoming noticeable, in the Crimea, and northeast of the Caspian Sea. Continental deposits occur in Siberia and Central Asia. Jurassic coal fields of low caloric content lie near Chelyabinsk, in the Far East, the Caucasus, and Central Asia. Also related to this period are oil shales in the Volga Region, phosphorites, lithographic slate, refractory clays, and sandstone.

The second half of the Cretaceous period witnessed a radical rearrangement of land and water masses, which manifested itself in a broad marine invasion of the Russian platform. This sea deposited thick layers of chalk, which are found today in the area of Belgorod and along the middle Volga River. Toward the Late Cretaceous a regression set in. At the same time, mountain-building processes accelerated in the Alpine geosyncline, and were particularly strong in northeastern Siberia along the shores of the Pacific Ocean. The most common economic minerals are, in addition to the chalk, lignite in Siberia and the Far East, petroleum (Emba), phosphorites, limonites, and construction sandstone.

Only at the end of the Mesozoic era did the vast continents of the northern and the southern hemispheres split up into sections approaching the present configurations. Gondwana formed the modern land areas of Africa, Madagascar, Arabia, India, South America, and Australia, while the northern continent divided into North America, Greenland, and Eurasia. During the Cenozoic era, which is continuing to the present time, the seas and continents gradually took on the forms with which we are familiar today. The orogeny, heralded by the tectonic movements of the Jurassic and the Cretaceous periods, culminated during the Cenozoic era in the widespread Alpine revolution.

Tertiary deposits are located principally in the southern part of the USSR. Conglomerates, unconsolidated sands, clays, and marls are found in the Ukraine, the Crimea, the Volga Region, the Caucasus, and Turkmenistan. They also cover vast areas on the eastern slopes of the Urals, in Siberia, and in northern and western Kazakhstan. The first thrusting of the Alpine orogeny came in the Eocene; however, it was not until the Oligocene that the Carpathians, the Crimean mountains, the Caucasus, and the ranges of the Pamir-Alay system came into existence. Further compression from the south and regional uplifts lifted the mountains to their present height in the late Cenozoic. As a result of the disappearance of the Alpine geosyncline, the Tethys sea found itself reduced to a series of residual basins, the present Mediterranean, Black, and Caspian seas. A few portions of the Tertiary sea became isolated from the main body of water, and the stagnant waters began to secrete hydrogen sulphide. This phenomenon occurred in the Early Tertiary in the Fergana basin, and in the Late Tertiary along the northern and the southeastern slopes of the Caucasus, resulting in the formation of petroliferous strata. During the same period the Black and Caspian seas, which originally formed a single basin, became separated, and the Black Sea was joined to the Mediterranean after subsidence in the area of the Bosporus. Volcanic activity in the Tertiary ranges is shown by the now extinct volcanoes of mounts El'brus and Kazbek in the Caucasus, and the remains of lava flows in Armenia. The richest petroleum deposits of the USSR are found in Tertiary rocks on the Apsheron Peninsula at Baku, in the Northern Caucasus, in Central Asia, Sakhalin, and Kamchatka. The rich iron and manganese deposits of the Caucasus and the Ukraine were formed in the littoral portions of the Tertiary sea; lake and lagoon sediments furnish lignite and salt, while Tertiary sand, sandstone, and limestone provide construction materials. Amber, which represents a hardened resin of Tertiary conifers, occurs along the Baltic littoral of Kaliningrad Oblast.

In the Pleistocene epoch glacier ice spread over vast areas of the land surface of the world. While in the rest of Europe four glacial stages have left their marks, only three ice invasions can be confirmed from the moraine structure in the USSR. During this period the affected areas resembled central Greenland, and the thickness of the ice exceeded 1½ miles. The presence of moraines, superimposed one on the other and separated by interglacial sediments of loess and peat, shows that temperate climatic intervals forced the continental glacier to retreat on at least two occasions. The Pleistocene glaciation left its unmistakable imprint on the topography of the region: festoons of terminal moraines extending parallel to the glacial front and separated by lake-filled and swampy depressions, gravel and boulder fields alternating with other glacial and fluvio-glacial sediments. The maximum extent was reached by the middle stage of the glacial invasions. It penetrated south to the middle Dnieper valley, curved north around the obstruction of the Central Russian upland, south again to the middle Don, and extended northeast along the Volga upland and the Northern Uvals, to the northern Urals and across northwestern Siberia to the Taymyr Peninsula. The ice radiated from three centers, the Scandinavian peninsula (the point of origin of the European ice sheet), Novaya Zemlya, and the Taymyr Peninsula. Increased precipitation and decreased evaporation greatly enlarged the Caspian Sea, which transgressed onto the lower Volga valley. Similarly, the White Sea covered the extreme northern European USSR with marine sediments. The ice of northwestern Siberia blocked the flow of the Ob' and Yenisey rivers, which flooded a large section of Western Siberia. This glacial lake, probably the largest fresh-water lake ever known, deposited the silt to which Western Siberia owes its extreme flatness. Pleistocene sediments include brick and pottery clays, quartz sands, gravel, limestone tuff, peat, and ores of lake and swamp origin.

STRUCTURE AND RELIEF

From the point of view of geomorphology, the USSR consists essentially of a vast lowland lying north of the high mountain and plateau belt which extends east and west across the center of the Eurasian continent. The larger portion of this plain, west of the Yenisey River, has an average elevation of less than 600 feet, while the higher eastern section ranges between 600 and 6,000 feet. Only one-twentieth of the total area of the USSR, situated along the southern border, reaches above an average elevation of 6,000 feet, with the highest points in Central Asia between 23,000 and 24,500 feet. At the other extreme from these lofty

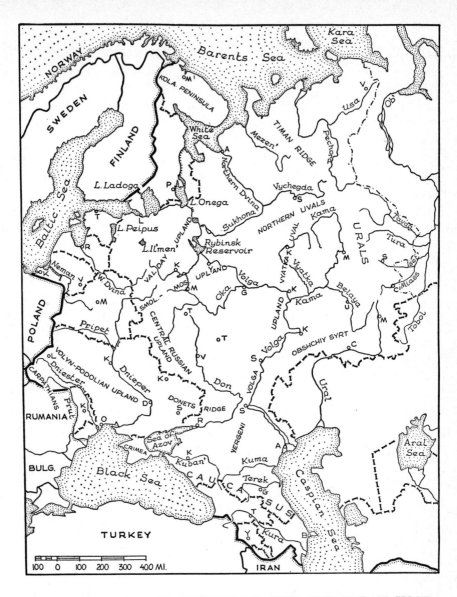

MAIN PHYSICAL FEATURES OF THE EUROPEAN USSR

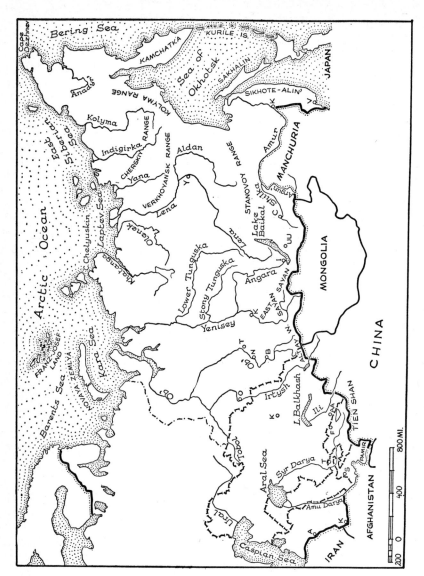

MAIN PHYSICAL FEATURES OF THE ASIATIC USSR

ranges are the low shores of the Caspian Sea at 92 feet below sea level, where the Batyr' Sink on the Mangyshlak Peninsula reaches a point 426 feet below sea level.

The relief of the USSR can be considered in three sections: (1) the East European plain west of the Urals and bordered in the south by the Carpathians, the Crimean mountains, and the Caucasus; (2) the West Siberian lowland, between the Urals and the Yenisey River, with its southern extension of the Turan lowland and the bordering ranges of the Kopet Dagh, Pamir-Alay, Tien Shan, and Altay mountain systems; (3) the highlands of Eastern Siberia.

The East European, or Russian, plain is a rolling lowland in which the heights do not exceed 1,500 feet. It consists basically of sedimentary deposits lying on the ancient Russian platform of Pre-Cambrian crystalline rocks, which have remained largely undisturbed through the periods of folding and mountain building. At the northwestern and southwestern rims of the platform the Pre-Cambrian rocks are exposed and form the Fenno-Scandian, or Baltic, shield, which includes the Kola Peninsula and Karelia, and the Azov-Podolian shield in the Ukraine. The Russian platform underwent many uplifting and subsiding actions in the course of its geologic history, with the ensuing transgression and regression of shallow seas and the deposition of marine sediments ranging from the Silurian to the Tertiary periods. These epeirogenic movements were occasionally accompanied by faulting and folding, which left their imprint on the present relief. These features include the Kursk-Voronezh horst, extending northwest-southeast across the Central Russian upland, the horst of the Ufa plateau at the western foot of the central Urals, the Stavropol' plateau on the northern edge of the Caucasus, and the Ust'-Urt plateau between the Caspian and the Aral seas. These raised sections of the Russian platform, which also include the Zhiguli Mountains on the Volga, constitute windows of older resistant formations among the recent Pleistocene deposits left by the continental glaciers in the northern half of the East European plain and by the latest marine transgressions in the extreme north and the southeast.

Ice radiating from Scandinavia covered the northwestern and middle sections of the East European plain as well as the adjoining North German lowland. The southern boundary of the glacier formed two bulges in the Dnieper and Oka-Don lowlands and joined the Novaya Zemlya-Urals glacier in the northeast. The advancing and retreating ice polished, scoured, and denuded the ancient rocks and deposited vast amounts of boulders, sand, gravel, and clay, forming terminal moraines along its edge. South of the terminal moraines, which extend in several parallel festoons across the northwestern portion of the East European plain, lies a belt of wind-borne loess, a fine-grained, dust-like clay of glacial origin. It is this easily eroded loess cover that is partly responsible for the characteristic ravine and gully relief of the southern part of the European USSR. Coarser deposits of sand and clay were left by glacial streams which carried these fluvio-glacial sediments from the retreating ice south to the valleys of the Pripet, Dnieper, Oka, and Tsna rivers.

In the course of the marine transgression which followed the Ice Age, the waters of the Arctic Ocean joined the Baltic Sea and formed a strait across the lakes Ladoga and Onega. The sea washed out most of the glacial deposits in this area, with the exception of a few resistant terminal moraines. In the south, the regressing Caspian Sea left sand and clay deposits in the Lower Volga Region, and numerous salt flats and lakes between the sand hills of the Caspian lowland.

In the northern part of the East European plain, most of the uplands are formed by terminal moraines. The notable exceptions are the Khibiny Mountains (3,930 feet) in the Kola Peninsula, a complex of Pre-Cambrian rocks, and the eroded Timan ridge, dating from the Caledonian revolution. The principal hills in the terminal moraine zones are the Valday, the Smolensk-Moscow, and the Lithuanian-Belorussian uplands. They consist generally of a base of ancient sedimentary rocks covered by glacial deposits. The Valday upland is the main watershed of the East European plain and gives rise to such important streams as the Volga, the Dnieper, and the Western Dvina. This divide continues northeastward as the Northern Uvals, a series of low hills extending toward the Urals.

In the southern section of the East European plain lies a succession of uplands separated by the valleys of the Dnieper, the Don, the Oka, and the Volga rivers. These are the Volyn'-Podolian, Central Russian, and Volga uplands and the Obshchiy Syrt. Further south the Dnieper and the Oka-Don lowlands merge to form the Black Sea lowland, and the eastern portion of the Oka-Don lowland joins the Volga valley to form the Caspian lowland. The Black Sea and the Caspian lowlands, in turn, are connected by the Kuma-Manych depression, the bed of the former strait between the Caspian and the Black seas.

In the southwest, the south, and the east, the East European plain is bordered by mountain ranges. Of these, the Carpathians, the Crimean mountains, and the Caucasus date from the Alpine revolution, while the lower Urals, in the east, were formed during the Hercynian mountain-building period.

South of the Urals, the East European plain merges with another vast level area known as the Turan lowland in the south and the West Siberian lowland in the north. The two sections are separated by the Kazakh upland, an eroded region of Hercynian origin, and are joined by a depression in the Hercynian folded zone, known as the Turgay Gates. The northern section of the West Siberian lowland was covered by an ice sheet radiating from Novaya Zemlya and reaching as far south as the Ob'-Irtysh confluence. The surface deposits in this region are largely of glacial origin; further south they consist of sands, pebbles, and loess-like clays, while, in the Turan lowland, the erosive action of the winds on the alluvial deposits of old rivers and the ancient sedimentary rocks resulted in the formation of sand deserts.

South of the Turan and West Siberian lowlands are a series of mountain ranges: the Kopet Dagh and the Pamir-Alay system, dating from the Alpine revolution, and the Tien Shan and Altay systems, which arose out of the Ural-Tien Shan geosyncline during the Hercynian orogeny. The highest peaks of the USSR lie in the Tien Shan (Pobeda Peak, 24,400 feet) and in the Pamir-Alay system (Stalin Peak, 24,595 feet).

The East Siberian highlands, between the Yenisey River and the Pacific Ocean, constitute a sparsely populated and little-explored section of the USSR. The Central Siberian plateau, which lies between the Yenisey and the Lena rivers, includes the Pre-Cambrian outcrops of the Aldan and the Anabar shields. To the south are the Sayan-Baykal and the Transbaykal mountain systems and the Stanovoy Range, which were uplifted during the Caledonian revolution, peneplained by erosion, and rejuvenated in a more recent period. The highest point lies in the Sayan Mountains at the peak Munku-Sardyk (11,500 feet).

The ranges in the northeast include the arc-shaped Verkhoyansk, Cherskiy, Anadyr' and Kolyma ranges, of Alpine orgin. The Verkhoyansk and the Kolyma ranges enclose the Yana, the Indigirka, and the Kolyma lowlands, which open north onto the Arctic Ocean. Other young ranges extend north and south along Sakhalin and the Kamchatka Peninsula. The latter continues to be the site of considerable volcanic activity, which is also evident in the Kurile Islands, to the south. The highest active volcano on Kamchatka, the Klyuchevskaya Sopka, rises to nearly 16,000 feet.

HYDROGRAPHY

In spite of certain climatic and relief characteristics which have reduced the degree of usefulness of the water network of the USSR, the various river systems have long played a vital role in the life of the country. From the earliest time, they have served as important navigation routes in the steppes as well as in the forests. Low, short portages, later partly replaced by canals, have welded the individual basins into a single system connecting the Baltic and the Arctic seas in the north with the Caspian and the Black seas in the south. The conquest of the outlying sections of European Russia and, especially, the drive through Siberia in the sixteenth and seventeenth centuries were effected by means of these interconnecting water routes. Most of the large cities of the USSR were founded on rivers, particularly on the high right bank, where they were in some measure protected from the perennial floods. The settling of the newly won areas proceeded along the river courses, especially in the Arctic North and the southern desert regions, where the watershed areas are nearly devoid of permanent settlements. After the middle of the nineteenth century, when railroad construction reached its full development, the importance of the waterways decreased considerably. During recent years, however, such developments as the use of hydroelectric power, the construction of new canals and the modernization of older ones, the damming of the rivers and the construction of reservoirs and not least the exploitation for navigation of the streams of the Far North have given the waterways of the USSR a new and important role in the economy of the country.

Because of the mountainous terrain along the southern border of the USSR, many of the important rivers, such as the Ob', the Yenisey, and the Lena, flow northward to the Arctic Ocean. More than one half of the territory is thus drained into seas which are frozen during the greater part of the year. One quarter of the area forms part of closed inland basins draining mainly into the Caspian and the Aral seas. Only the remainder, less than one quarter of the total area, relates to the basins of the open Atlantic and Pacific oceans and their seas. While a number of features, such as the large size of the river basins, the great length of the main rivers, the weak incline and slow flow of their courses, and the high spring and low winter stages, are common to most of the streams, certain characteristics are to be noted individually for the rivers of the East European plain, of Siberia, and of Central Asia.

Most of the important streams of the European USSR rise in the main European divide, formed by the Lithuanian-Belorussian and Valday uplands, the Northern Uvals, and which reaches its maximum elevation in the Valday upland at 1,053 feet. As a result, the European rivers are uniformly marked by a gentle slope and a slow flow. They freeze in the winter for a period varying from two to three months in the extreme southwest of the European USSR (Dniester River, lower Dnieper River) to more than seven months in the extreme northeast (lower Pechora River). As a rule, the thaw is followed by high water in the spring and by a lower water level throughout summer, autumn, and winter. Because of greater precipitation and less evaporation inherent in the climate of the north, the rivers there generally carry a greater volume of water than do those in the south. In the area of the resistant crystalline shields, rapids are often formed along the course of the rivers. This is especially true of the streams of the Fenno-Scandian shield in the Kola Peninsula and in Karelia and of the Dnieper, Southern Bug, and Dniester in the Azov-Podolian shield of the Ukraine. Of the more important rivers of the East European plain, the Northern Dvina and the Pechora enter seas of the Arctic Ocean, the Neva, the Western Dvina, and the Neman flow into the Baltic Sea, the Dnieper, Don, Dniester, and Kuban' rivers into the Black Sea, and the Terek, Volga, and Ural rivers into the Caspian Sea.

The rivers of Siberia differ from those of the European USSR chiefly in their greater length and volume. The Ob', the Yenisey, the Lena, and the Amur are among the longest streams of the world and drain some of the most extensive basins. The Ob'-Irtysh system is generally considered to rank fourth, being 3,200 miles long, after the Mississippi-Missouri, the Nile, and the Amazon. The Siberian rivers rise in high mountain ranges and carry a large volume of water supplied by the melting snow and ice. The Ob' and the Yenisey attain a width of about two or three miles in the middle course and of fifteen or twenty-five miles in their lower reaches, where the depth is 50–65 feet. The Lena River already has a width of nearly 20 miles in the area of Yakutsk (middle course), and its major affluents, the Aldan and the Vilyuy, exceed many of the large European rivers in length. Because of the severity of the climate, the Siberian rivers are frozen for a period of five months in the southwest and for more than nine months in the northeast. Tremendous floods occur in the spring, when the upper course is freed of ice, before the thaw sets in in the lower reaches. The Amur River, which, unlike all the north-flowing tributaries of the Arctic Ocean, flows into the Pacific basin, is characterized by its individual regime. The heavy summer rains inherent in the prevailing monsoon climate create a high-water stage in July and August, rather than in the spring. It remains ice-free as long as 7 months of the year.

Except for the affluents of the Ob'-Irtysh system, the rivers of Central Asia drain into closed inland basins. They also rise in high mountain ranges (Tien Shan and Pamir-Alay systems), where they are fed by melting snows and glacier ice. The upper course is usually precipitous and offers excellent possibilities for hydroelectric development. In their lower reaches these rivers flow through deserts and are most important for irrigation and the supply of fertile alluvial mud. High water occurs propitiously during the summer months, when the demand for irrigation water is at its peak. Except for the Syr Darya and the Amu Darya, which flow to the Aral Sea, the rivers of Central Asia generally lose their water through evaporation and irrigation and disappear into the sands.

Lakes abound throughout the USSR, notably in the regions once covered by the continental glacier, where they occupy depressions scooped out by the glacier or were formed as the result of the morainic obstruction of a stream. Such glacial lakes are found in the northwestern European USSR, in northern Siberia, and in some high mountain ranges. Many lakes were formed through the fracturing and faulting of the earth's surface and the formation of a so-called graben. Of this type is Lake Baykal in Eastern Siberia, whose 5,710 feet make it the deepest inland body of water in the world. Also formed by faulting were the northern portions of lakes Ladoga and Onega, most of the lakes in the Fenno-Scandian shield (Kola Peninsula, Karelia), the lake Issyk-Kul' in the Tien Shan, and Teletskoye Lake in the Altay. All the lakes connected in some manner or other with Pleistocene glaciation contain fresh water. Salt-water lakes, however, were formed in the dry steppes and deserts once covered by the Tethys sea. The largest are the Aral Sea, Lake Balkhash, in which salification is still proceeding, and a number of lakes in the Caspian lowland and in the southern portion of the West Siberian lowland. Many of these lakes contain thick salt deposits, which, for example, reach a depth of more than one hundred feet in the case of Lake Baskunchak in the Caspian lowland.

CLIMATE

Except for such relatively small sections as the southern Crimea (mediterranean) and Transcaucasia (subtropical), as well as the monsoon region of the Far East, the climate of the USSR is distinctly of a uniformly continental type. This continentality is characterized by the weakness of moderating oceanic influences, a low precipitation, which occurs chiefly in the summer, a wide range between summer and winter averages, and short spring and autumn seasons.

A primary factor responsible for the type of climate prevalent in the USSR is its location in the vast land mass of Eurasia, between the frozen Arctic Ocean in the north and the dry desert plateaus of Asia in the south, and its great distance from the temperate Atlantic and Pacific oceans. The continental aspect may manifest itself in various ways according to regional conditions; Eastern Siberia, for example, has winters with very low temperatures and a thin snow cover, while Central Asia experiences extremely dry and hot summers. The location on the shores of the Arctic Ocean and the absence of any mountain ranges of an east-west direction leave the major portion of the USSR open to the invasions of Arctic and Polar air masses, while the mountains and the high plateaus of the south bar access to warmer air from the Indian Ocean.

The single tempering influence in this field of extreme climatic conditions is that of the Atlantic Ocean. Although situated several hundred miles west of the USSR, across peninsular Europe, the Atlantic succeeds in sending warm, humid cyclones through the Baltic Sea gap and makes its influence felt throughout the European USSR, Western Siberia, and even as far as Eastern Siberia. Its moderating effect is manifest in a gradual eastward increase in the difference between January and July average temperatures: from about 70° F at the western frontier of the USSR, the difference increases to 95° in the Urals, to 115° on the Yenisey River, and to as much as 150° in Eastern Siberia, in the area of Verkhoyansk and Oymyakon, the coldest towns of the world. The changing effect of the Atlantic Ocean is also noticeable in the gradual reduction of precipitation from west to east and southeast. The influence of the warm winds from the Atlantic Ocean is important, especially in the winter, when the isotherms do not extend along the parallels, but rather in an inclined northwest-southeast direction, indicating a gradual lowering of the temperature along the same parallel.

Another vital factor in determining the climate of the USSR is the subpolar continental high-pressure area, especially well defined during the cold season, which extends from the area of the cold pole of Verkhoyansk-Oymyakon past Lake Baykal and roughly along 50° N past Ural'sk, Saratov, and Khar'kov and joins the outliers of the Azores high-pressure area farther west. This anticyclonic area forms a well-defined climatic boundary during the winter, when it generally limits the influence of the Atlantic to the region lying to the north, where warmer, more humid winters prevail. It maintains itself somewhat in the western part of the USSR during the summer months, when it separates a humid, cool climate to the north from a drier and warmer climate to the south. In Eastern Siberia, however, it is replaced by a low-pressure area, which plays a vital role in the monsoon exchange in the Far East.

The monsoon climate of the Pacific littoral of the USSR represents the full extent to which the Pacific Ocean participates in the climatic picture of the country. Because of the mountainous terrain along the coast, this influence does not extend far inland and is restricted largely to the southern Far East.

The climate of the East European plain receives the most direct effect of the moderating cyclones from the Atlantic Ocean; here the continentality is at its weakest. The Atlantic influence is at its strongest during the winter season, when the warmer winds from the ocean considerably raise the temperature and create the northwest-southeast alignment of the January isotherms. During the summer, however, warm winds from the heated interior of Asia counteract the Atlantic moderation and produce a slight southwest-northeast inclination of the July isotherms. The precipitation, largely of Atlantic origin, decreases from west toward the northeast and the southeast. It is highest in the region of the upper Dnieper River (26 inches) and lowest in the southeastern Caspian lowland (8 inches); in the northeastern Pechora tundra it is about 12 inches. In the north rainfall is distributed rather regularly among the summer months, while in the south nearly half the precipitation occurs in late spring and early summer. Snowfall is heavier in the north. North of the high-pressure area, centered in the Saratov-Khar'kov area, the prevailing westerly winds bring humid air from the Atlantic Ocean, cool in the summer and warm in the winter with respect to the local conditions. South of the high-pressure area the prevailing easterlies are dry and hot in summer and cold in winter.

A separate climatic region is formed by the southern Crimea and

Transcaucasia, where high mountain barriers bar access to the cold blasts from the north. Here moderate and even warm winters are the rule, with January temperatures 40° at Yalta and 43° at Batumi. Precipitation occurs mainly in autumn and spring; summers are dry and cloudless. Most of the famous health and seaside resorts of the USSR are located along the southern coast of the Crimea and the Black Sea littoral of the Caucasus.

In Western Siberia, beyond the Urals, the continentality becomes more accentuated. The influence of the Atlantic is reduced, and the winter isotherms take a sharp turn southward. While the winter becomes much colder, frosts of 13–22° below 0° F being common even in the south, the summer temperatures are as high as in the European USSR and increase gradually toward the Turan lowland in the south. Precipitation is reduced and occurs in the summer. In the extreme south it amounts to only 12 inches yearly.

The climate of Central Asia, that is, that section of the Turan lowland lying south of 47° N and bordered in the north by the Kazakh upland, is characterized by very high summer temperatures, winters which are unusually cold for the latitude concerned, and very low precipitation. These features are caused by the location of the area near the center of the Eurasian continent, its distance from the Atlantic Ocean, and the easy access for the cold air masses from the north. The prevailing winds blow from the north and northeast; they bring polar air masses which undergo a decrease in relative humidity in moving toward the warmer climate and therefore carry little potential rainfall. Except for the extreme south and southwest (Krasnovodsk, Ashkhabad, and Termez), the polar air succeeds in producing January temperatures below freezing throughout Central Asia. The northern part of the Aral Sea, Lake Balkhash, and the lower reaches of the Amu Darya become covered with ice. Precipitation is negligible, except on the slopes of the Pamir-Alay and the Tien Shan systems, where the rainfall feeds the numerous glaciers. In the lowland, however, the annual rainfall varies between four and ten inches. As a result of the low humidity, as many as 180 days a year are cloudless in the Turan lowland.

Of all the parts of the USSR, Eastern Siberia has the most continental climate. This is due not only to the very tenuous influence of the Atlantic Ocean but also to the proximity of the Arctic seas along the northern and the eastern shores. Especially characteristic for Eastern Siberia are the extremely low winter temperatures coupled with a relatively warm summer. The northern part of the region is the coldest area of the world, with the so-called cold pole in the vicinity of Verkhoyansk and Oymyakon reporting occasional extreme minima below –90° F. The January averages are below –59° F, while in western Norway, which is on the same latitude, but exposed to the moderating influence of the Gulf Stream, they are about 32°. The July average at Verkhoyansk sometimes reaches 60°, with an extreme maximum of 93°. Thus the difference between the extremes exceeds at times 180°. Precipitation is even lower than in Western Siberia and occurs chiefly in July and August.

The Amur and Maritime regions, in the extreme southeast of the USSR, lie within the Far Eastern monsoon belt. The wet monsoon blowing from the Pacific Ocean brings with it as much as 40 inches of rain, which fall mainly during July and August. The dry, winter monsoon, which originates in the high-pressure area of Eastern Siberia, brings cold air masses which produce unusually low January temperatures and only a thin snow cover.

SOILS AND VEGETATION

The recent geologic history and the climate of the USSR are fully reflected in the pattern of latitudinal soil and vegetation zones extending across the country. The luxuriant subtropical and tropical vegetation which prevailed in the USSR during the Tertiary epoch disappeared as a result of the gradual cooling and remains now only in western Transcaucasia, along the southwest coast of the Caspian Sea, and in isolated sections in the Caucasus, the Crimea, and the mountains of Central Asia. It was succeeded by a new type of vegetation better adapted to the cold climate of the Ice Age: a tundra with dwarf birch and willow. After the retreat of the glacier, the freed territory was invaded by deciduous trees from Western Europe and by conifers from Mongolia and the Altay, while steppe and desert vegetation moved from the foothills of the Altay and the Caucasus. In this manner, the contemporary vegetation pattern took on shape. The tundra followed the edge of the retreating ice to its present location in the extreme north; the vast forests occupied the central reaches, while in the drier south, steppes and deserts were formed. At the present time, an imperceptible, and gradual, cooling of the climate is slowly displacing the vegetation zones toward the south.

The tundra belt lies along the coasts and on the islands of the Arctic Ocean; it is at its widest in northern Siberia on the Kara Sea and reaches

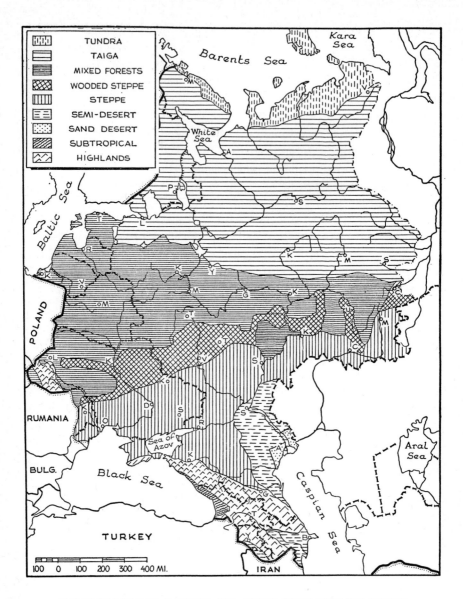

VEGETATION ZONES OF THE EUROPEAN USSR

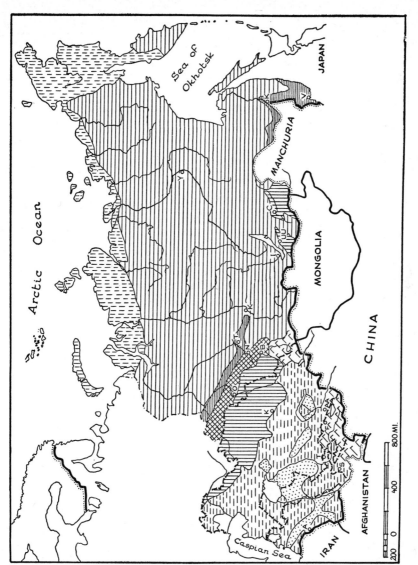

VEGETATION ZONES OF THE ASIATIC USSR

as far south as 60° N at the neck of the Kamchatka Peninsula. It covers more than 10 percent of the total area of the USSR. Its chief characteristic is the absence of forest vegetation. The extremely low temperatures hinder the development of physical and chemical decay of the scanty plant cover and produce only a thin top layer of humus above the permanently frozen subsoil. The short growing season (2–2½ months, with no monthly mean above 50° F), the low annual mean temperature (below 32°), the low precipitation (8–12 inches), and the thin, though extended, snow cover make it very difficult for plants to exist. Dwarf birches and willows hug the ground, where warmer temperatures prevail. Lichens and berry-bearing types are found in dry sandy areas, while moss and sedge occur in damper low-lying locations. On south-facing slopes, small flowers come to life during the short summer. In the south, the wooded tundra forms a transition to the true forest. Typical animals are reindeer, lemming, hare, and the Arctic fox and ermine, which are of special value for their furs. The white partridge and the Arctic owl are the most characteristic birds. During the summer, masses of water fowl nest on the cliffs along the coast.

South of the tundra lies the vast forest zone which occupies more than one-half the USSR. The light gray podsolized soils are typical for this zone. They consist of a top soil layer, three to six inches thick, of a white-to-gray color and containing about 2 percent of humus. Below it is an ash-colored horizon, up to twelve inches thick, which contains a considerable amount of silica and has been leached of most of the plant food. The lowest layer, a brownish zone, colored by iron hydroxide, contains the material washed out from the upper horizon and lies on the unaltered parent material, which is usually clay or sand. The podsol-forming process is speeded by the abundance of moisture and the consequent leaching of the soil. These conditions are best met by a clay base and a correspondingly high water table, while on sandy parent material, where ground water lies deeper below the surface, the process is developed to a lesser extent.

The wooded tundra gradually becomes denser and turns into the taiga or coniferous forest. This vast belt, comprising about one-third of the forest lands of the world, extends through the northern part of the European USSR across the Ural Mountains and over most of Siberia. In the European USSR pine and spruce are the common species. Toward the Urals they merge with Siberian larch, fir, and stone pine. The most widespread species in Eastern Siberia is the larch, which penetrates farther north than any other tree into the tundra and provides an unbroken cover over the mountains. The subzone of the mixed and deciduous forests extends in the form of a wedge from the western frontier of the USSR to the Ural Mountains. In Siberia its extent is negligible. Side by side with the coniferous types, the mixed forests include elm, oak, maple, and ash. The linden extends furthest north of all the deciduous types. A separate mixed forest zone in the Amur-Ussuri region is characterized by a mixture of northern conifers (spruce, pine, larches, and fir) with Manchurian walnut, oak, and elm, as well as wild apricot and peach. Large sections of the forest zone are covered by marshes and peat bogs. This is especially true of Western Siberia, where considerable precipitation and a poorly developed watershed area produce marshes extending over tens of thousands of square miles. Large mammals such as elk, reindeer, and other deer are common in the forest zone. The brown bear and the lynx are the principal carnivores, while rodents such as squirrels, rabbits, and beavers are also widespread. Typical birds are the woodpecker and the grouse.

The steppe zone extends in an uninterrupted belt from the western border of the USSR to the Altay Mountains. It is characterized by a grass cover and very limited tree growth and covers about 12 percent of the total area of the USSR. The transition between forest and steppe is very gradual and gives rise to the so-called wooded steppe. The characteristic soil is the black earth (Russian *chernozem*), which is one of the most productive of the world and accounts for two-thirds of the arable land of the USSR. It is generally developed on loess or loess-like loam; its color varies from black to chocolate brown, and the thickness of the layer varies from three to five feet. The highly developed root system of the steppe grasses is favorable to the formation of humus, which, thanks to the dryness of the climate, is not leached from the top soil and accumulates on the loess base. The humus content of the black earth varies between 5 and 10 percent and even reaches 20 percent in some areas. It is this circumstance which renders the black earth so remarkably fertile. Along the edges of the black-earth belt, the humus content shows a gradual decrease, and the black earth changes into gray forest soil in the north and chestnut and brown soils in the south. The principal causes for the limited tree growth are low precipitation, occasional droughts, and the deposition of mineral salts below the humus layer. In the wooded steppe the scattered tree clusters consist of oak in the European areas and birch in Siberia. To-day there remain few large expanses of virgin steppe. Most of the black earth has been put under cultivation. In the few remnants, meadow grass occurs only in the northern wooded portion of the steppe, while elsewhere fescue grass and feathergrass are typical.

To the south and the southeast the steppe is succeeded by the desert zone, where vegetation is scattered or wholly absent. The scanty growth is due mainly to the low rainfall and the excessive summer temperatures. The zone includes the northern and the eastern shores of the Caspian Sea and the Turan lowland, and it extends to about 51° N, where it meets the mountains of Central Asia. Covering about 18 percent of the USSR, the desert belt is divided into the northern subzone of the dry steppe and the southern subzone of the desert proper. The dry steppe, or semi-desert, is another transition area, similar to the wooded tundra and the wooded steppe. The climate becomes progressively drier, rainfall averages eight inches yearly, and bare areas appear amidst the patches of grass. The humus content of the brown soils decreases, while the salinity shows a definite increase. In many areas where the salt is washed to the surface, salt marshes (Russian *solonets* and *solonchak*) are formed. Characteristic plant forms are wormwood and in the saline soils, saltwort. In the desert proper, rainfall is sometimes less than four inches annually. Winters are short, though relatively cold, and the summers become unbearably hot, the temperature reaching 120° F in the shade. Stony and clayey desert flats are nearly devoid of vegetation. The sandy deserts have some wormwood and sage growth, and thickets of *saksaul* bushes are common. The gray desert soil contains considerable quantities of carbonate of lime and yields rich crops when properly irrigated.

Subtropical forest vegetation is confined to the western and the eastern sections of Transcaucasia and to the slopes of the Crimea, the Caucasus, and the mountains of Central Asia. In these areas forests have continued to exist since the Tertiary period. They are usually a mixture of deciduous and coniferous types, accompanied by a luxuriant undergrowth. Except in Transcaucasia, where conditions of warmth and moisture continue to approach the climate of the Tertiary period, the numerous varieties of plants have undergone a selective process resulting in the dominance of a few types which are better adapted to the changed climatic conditions. These are generally trees such as oak, hornbeam, and beech in the Crimea and the Caucasus, and maple, pistachio, almond, nut, and apple in the mountains of Central Asia. The lateritic yellow and red soils in these regions have also remained from the Tertiary period. They contain no calcium, only a little silica, and a large proportion of clay and may represent the remains of weathering of volcanic rocks.

High mountain or Alpine vegetation occurs below the snow line throughout the mountain regions of the USSR. The lower limits of the Alpine meadow belt vary from 1,000 feet in the northern Urals, where they tend to be replaced by tundra, to 8,000–9,000 feet in the Pamir-Alay mountain system in the south. The elevation of the snow line, which represents the upper limit of the Alpine zone, varies with the precipitation and the location of the slopes. In the mountains of the Far East and Eastern Siberia, Alpine meadows are entirely absent. The forest cover extends virtually to the summits and leaves only the highest elevations covered with mountain tundra. Less than 0.5 percent of the total area of the USSR falls within the Alpine vegetation zone.

MINERAL RESOURCES

Prior to the Bolshevik Revolution, the known reserves of the mineral resources of the USSR were only a fraction of the mineral wealth which has been charted up to the present time. The intensive field work carried on during the period between the First World War and the Second uncovered new deposits and enlarged the boundaries of previously known reserves. Before 1917 the Russian Empire accounted for 1 percent of the world's reserves of iron and phosphorites and 3 percent of the coal. No nickel, potassium, borate, sulphur, or bauxite had been located. Since then the known reserves of such vital minerals as coal, petroleum, zinc, lead, iron, and copper have increased manyfold.

With estimated reserves of 1,654 billion tons of coal as of 1937, the USSR has 20 percent of the world's reserves and is second to the United States. The caloric content of the deposits, in which bituminous coal amounts to about 85 percent, is said to exceed that of the United States deposits. The most extensive reserves are those of the Kuznetsk Basin, in Western Siberia. Originally estimated at 13 billion tons, they are now estimated at 450 billion tons of the best coal in the Union. They are distinguished by a high caloric content, low ash and sulphur values, and thick seams at moderate depth, making for cheap exploitation. Important deposits are also in the Donets Basin, where they are estimated at about 90 million tons. This coal field has coking coal in the west and anthracite in the east. At one time it was thought to have been entirely

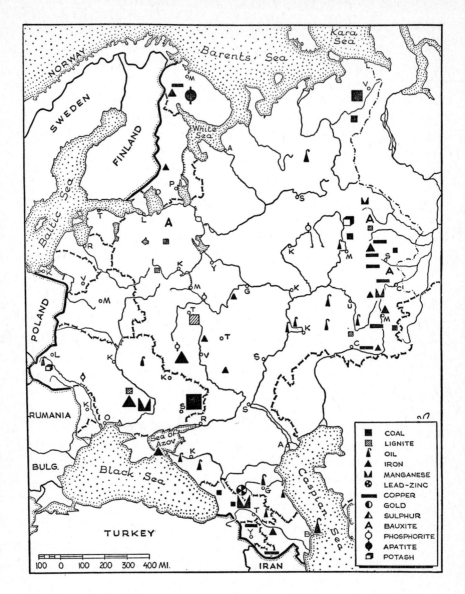

100 0 100 200 300 400 MI.

MINERAL RESOURCES OF THE EUROPEAN USSR

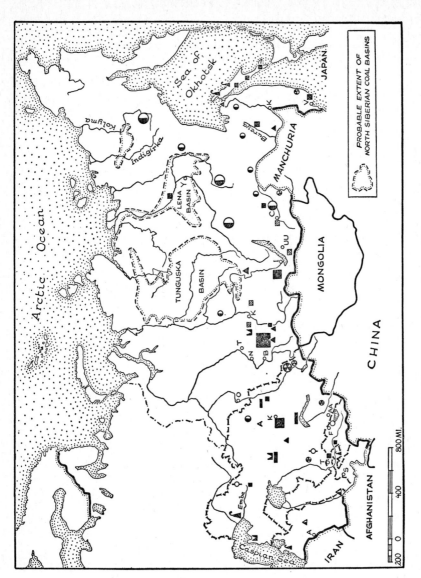

MINERAL RESOURCES OF THE ASIATIC USSR

explored; however, later study revealed reserves totaling one-and-one-half times the original estimates. In central Kazakhstan, Soviet geologists have explored the Karaganda field of good coking coal. On the site of a small mine which at one time only provided coal for a local copper smelter, reserves of more than fifty billion tons have been surveyed. South of Moscow, in the area of Tula, lies the Moscow Basin, a lignite area of Lower Carboniferous origin. Other coal fields are the Pechora Basin, in the northern European USSR, the Kizel and Chelyabinsk basins, in the Urals, the little explored Tunguska and Lena basins, in Eastern Siberia, and near Irkutsk the important Cheremkhovo field. The Bureya reserves in the Far East are said to exceed those of Karaganda. Coal is also present near Vladivostok (at Suchan and Artem) and on Sakhalin. In Central Asia, extensive deposits occur in the Fergana valley and at Angren, near Tashkent.

Estimates of the petroleum reserves of the USSR, as far as these have been surveyed, amount to about 8 billion tons, or according to Soviet sources more than one-half the world total. The most important producing fields are in the Caucasus at Baku in the Azerbaijan SSR, at Groznyy and near Maykop. The Baku field has been in operation for eighty years. In spite of the long exploitation, the deposits had not been entirely explored before the Revolution. As a result of the exploration of deeper horizons and the enlarging of the boundaries of the field, about 90 percent of the present production is derived from strata surveyed since 1917. While most of the production comes from wells on or near the Apsheron Peninsula at Baku, oil fields have also been developed at Neftelan near Kirovabad and near the Kura River mouth at Neftechala. On the Apsheron Peninsula wells go to a depth of 13–16,000 feet; other wells lie up to four miles off shore in the Caspian Sea. During the last two decades Soviet geologists, led by the petroleum expert Gubkin, have surveyed a vast new oil-bearing region between the Volga and the Urals, which has become known as the "Second Baku." Petroleum was struck accidentally in 1929 along the upper Kama River at Verkhne-Chusovskiye Gorodki, an event which confirmed Gubkin's guess regarding the presence of extensive oil reserves in the Russian platform. The first productive well was drilled in 1932 at Ishimbay; this was followed by strikes at Krasnokamsk, Tuymazy, and Buguruslan. In 1937 petroleum was discovered along the Volga at Syzran', Stavropol', and Saratov. Since most of the petroleum came from Carboniferous and Permian horizons, the search was pressed for older oil deposits in Devonian strata. In 1944 the first rich Devonian strike was achieved at 5,000 feet on the Volga in the Zhiguli Mountains, later also at Severokamsk and in the Tatar Autonomous SSR. The "Second Baku" is already expanding; new deposits have been surveyed on the Siberian slopes of the Urals, and signs point to the presence of oil west of the Volga. Other major petroleum fields are along the Emba River in western Kazakhstan, in the foothills of the Carpathians, and on Sakhalin.

Not quite one half the world's resources of peat lie in the forested zone of the USSR. A cheap fuel with a low caloric value, peat is used mainly to feed power stations in the northwestern and the central European USSR. Oil shales, which like peat had not been exploited prior to the Revolution, are found mainly along the southern shore of the Gulf of Finland and along the Volga. They are converted into gas and liquid fuel. Natural gas occurs on the Volga near Saratov, in the Northern Caucasus, and in the foothills of the Carpathians.

The iron ore reserves of the USSR amount to 10.9 billion tons. Including the low-grade ferruginous quartzite of the Kursk magnetic anomaly, the deposits total 267 billion tons—over one half the world reserves. The main deposits occur at Krivoy Rog in the Ukraine and at Kerch' in the Crimea, near Lipetsk and Tula, south of Moscow, in the Urals, at Magnitogorsk and Nizhniy Tagil, in the Kola Peninsula, Siberia, and the Far East. The most spectacular deposits are those of the Kursk magnetic anomaly. Although compass deviations had been observed since the 1870's, it was not until 1923 that magnetite-bearing quartzite was encountered, at a depth of 531 feet. Mining activities at the Gubkin mine, west of Staryy Oskol, were begun in 1939, interrupted by the Second World War, and again activated during the current Five-Year Plan.

Of the important manganese ores, the USSR has one third of the world reserves. The largest deposits are at Nikopol' in the Ukraine and at Chiatura (formerly called Chiatury), in the Caucasus. The occupation of the Nikopol' deposits during the Second World War stimulated the exploration of new manganese sites in the Urals, in Kazakhstan, and in Eastern Siberia. Copper reserves were greatly enlarged by surveys during the past two decades. The largest deposits were revealed in Kazakhstan at Kounradskiy near Balkhash, at Dzhezkazgan, and Boshchekul', and in the Uzbek SSR, at Almalyk. Other deposits are in the central

Urals and in Transcaucasia. Lead and zinc reserves are important in the Altay Mountains of Kazakhstan, near Dzaudzhikau in the Caucasus, in Eastern Siberia, and in the Far East.

Nickel reserves are the second largest in the world. The metal occurs in the Urals, on the Kola Peninsula, and in northern Siberia at Noril'sk. Bauxite, the mineral for aluminum, is found at Boksitogorsk (Leningrad Oblast), in the Urals, and in Siberia. The huge nephelite deposits of the Kola Peninsula are also regarded as an important aluminum source. Tin reserves have been explored in Transbaykalia, the Yakut Autonomous SSR, and in Kazakhstan. Among the rare metals, molybdenum occurs in the Caucasus, Kazakhstan, and the Far East, tungsten in the Urals, Kazakhstan, and Transbaykalia, and vanadium and chromium in the Urals. There are rich gold deposits in Siberia, the Far East, Kazakhstan, and the Urals, and platinum is found chiefly in the Urals.

Of special interest are the large reserves of nonmetallic minerals. In the Khibiny Mountains of the Kola Peninsula, Soviet geologists have prospected deposits of two billion tons of mineral apatite, which contains 30 percent of phosphoric acid and serves as a vital source for superphosphate fertilizer. The exploration of the deposit raised the USSR into first place with respect to phosphate reserves. Superphosphate is even beginning to be exported from that country. Associated with the apatite is nephelite, a raw material used in the manufacture of glass, ultramarine dyes, and enamel, as well as of aluminum. In addition to apatite, large phosphorite reserves in Kirov and Moscow oblasts, in Kazakhstan, and in the Ukraine are also converted into superphosphate fertilizer. Potash is secured chiefly at Solikamsk, in the Urals, where the deposits aggregate 18.4 billion tons. These reserves, which were discovered in 1925, together with the lesser deposits in the Ukraine, give the USSR a share of 80 percent of the potassium salt reserves of the world. Of vast proportions are also the common salt deposits. In Lake Baskunchak, of the lower Volga, one of the main producers of the USSR, a salt stratum of 130 feet in thickness has been discovered. Sulphur, which was formerly imported, is now mined extensively in the Kara-Kum desert of the Turkmen SSR. Construction materials, such as limestone, granite, and marble, abound, as do gems and precious stones in the Urals and kaolin and refractory clays in the Ukraine. Mercury is found in the Donets Basin, in the Urals, and in the Kirghiz SSR. Also to be mentioned are arsenic and antimony, feldspar and mica, cadmium and cobalt, indium and radium, and corundum and graphite.

CHAPTER 2

The Political Framework

UNDERLYING the principal features of the political framework of the USSR is its characteristic multi-national population pattern. Although the Russian element, together with the Ukrainians and Belorussians, constitutes by far the bulk of the population, the existence of the many non-Slavic minorities is thoroughly reflected in the system of Soviet administrative-territorial divisions, as well as in the toponymics of vast sections of the country.

POPULATION

Since the last general census of the USSR, which returned a population of more than 170 millions, the country has experienced the Second World War and many territorial changes, events which have not failed to affect the population data. The official prewar estimate of 1940, following the acquisition of the Baltic States, northern Bukovina, Bessarabia, and the Finnish territories, was 193 millions. Unofficial postwar estimates have ranged from 193 to 200 million inhabitants. On the basis of the number of election districts created in connection with the general election of 1950, the hypothetical population of the USSR was 201,300,000. The average rate of growth of the population of the USSR in the intercensus period 1926–39 amounted to 1.23 percent per year. This rate was far above the increase characteristic of most western European nations and the United States, but remained below that of the Philippines, Puerto Rico, Mexico, and some other countries.

The average density of population is 23 persons per square mile. The distribution is very irregular however. In the European part of the USSR the density is 65 and as high as 250 in the black-earth belt. In Eastern Siberia and the Far East, the average is 3–5 per square mile; only along the Trans-Siberian Railroad does the density rise to 50. The same contrast is maintained in Central Asia where nearly uninhabited desert areas are broken by oases with population densities of 375 to 400 per square mile.

The urban population of the USSR was 61 millions in 1940 and represented 32 percent of the total. The industrialization drive which began in 1928 resulted in a rapid increase in the urban population. Hundreds of new urban centers grew up in a trend which is continuing into the postwar period and remains the outstanding and controlling factor in the redistribution of the population of the Soviet Union. The largest new cities are Karaganda, the coal-mining center of the Kazakh SSR, which rose from a village of a few hundred to a city of 165,937 during the period 1926–39, Magnitogorsk (1939 population, 145,870), Stalinogorsk, and Komsomol'sk. Other cities which showed an increase of more than tenfold in the intercensus period are Stalinsk, the Kuzbas metallurgical center, Stalinabad, capital of the Tadzhik SSR, Murmansk, the largest city of the world north of the Arctic Circle, Dzerzhinsk, a new chemical center west of Gor'kiy, and Prokop'yevsk, a coal-mining city in the Kuzbas.

Population displacement during the Second World War also played an important role in the changing population pattern. The previous migration from the European areas toward the Arctic shores, the Urals, and Siberia was accelerated under the threat of the advancing Germans. The displaced persons were relocated in large numbers in the Volga Region, the Urals, Western Siberia, Kazakhstan, Central Asia, and in the Far North. Everywhere their settlement marked a sharp increase in the industrial production and in the sown area, and even the creation of entirely new industries.

The USSR is a country of many nationalities. Eleven important ethnic groups include more than one hundred separate peoples. The Eastern Slavs form by far the most important group, totaling three fourths of the population of the USSR and including about 100 million Russians, 36 million Ukrainians, and 10 million Belorussians. The Russians live chiefly in the northern, central, and southeastern sections of the European USSR, in southern Siberia along the Trans-Siberian Railroad, and in the Far East. The Ukrainians are located in the southwestern European USSR, and the Belorussians in the western section. The second most important ethnic group, the Turkic stock, numbers about 17 million people. It includes the Volga unit of Tatars, Chuvash, and Bashkir, the Azerbaijani Turks, the large Turkic block of Central Asia, including the Kazakh, Kirghiz, Uzbek, and Turkmen nationalities, and in Siberia, the Yakuts, Khakass, Tuvinians, and the Altay group, which comprises the Oyrot and related units.

The Ugro-Finnic ethnic group, which numbers about 5 million people, includes the Baltic units, among which the Estonians and Karelians are the main representatives, the Volga-Ural units, which comprise the Mordvinians, the Udmurt (Votyaks), the Mari (Cheremiss) and the Komi (Zyryan and Permyak), and the smaller Siberian units, the Nentsy (Samoyeds), the Khanty (Ostyaks), and the Mansi (Voguls). Most numerous among the western, or Baltic, Finns are the Estonians, with about 1 million people; the Mordvinians, with nearly 1.5 million people, are the chief east Finnic nationality.

The Slavonic-Baltic group, on the Baltic Sea, includes about 1.5 million Latvians and Latgals and 2.2 million Lithuanians, which were annexed to the USSR in 1940. In the Caucasus and Transcaucasia are several groups speaking Japhetic languages. They include the two major Georgian and Armenian nationalities, each numbering about 2¼ million people, and smaller mountain groups, such as the Lesghians and Avars, of Dagestan, the Kabardinians, and the Cherkess. To the Iranian group belong the 1¼ million Tadzhiks of Central Asia and more than 350,000 Ossetians in the middle Caucasus. Other important groups are the Moldavians, of Bessarabia, numbering more than two million people, the Buryat-Mongols (over 200,000) of Eastern Siberia, about two million Jews located chiefly in the western and the southwestern European USSR, and the many small tribes of Siberia, including more than 35,000 Evenki (Tungus), and the lesser Paleoasiatic units of the Luoravetlany (Chukchi), Nymylany (Koryaks), Itel'meny (Kamchadals), Nanay (Golds), Nivkhi (Gilyaks), and Eskimos.

ADMINISTRATIVE-TERRITORIAL DIVISIONS

The administrative-territorial structure of the USSR is characterized by an instability seldom encountered in the organization of the civil divisions of other countries. A close examination of the parallelism of the economic administrative units and of the national autonomous divisions is useful not only because it is a guide to the territorial changes which keep the political map in constant flux but also because these changes often reflect matters of economic and nationalities policies of the government.

Prior to the Bolshevik Revolution, the country was divided into ordinary administrative units called *guberniyas*, which in turn were divided

DISTRIBUTION OF CITIES OF THE EUROPEAN USSR

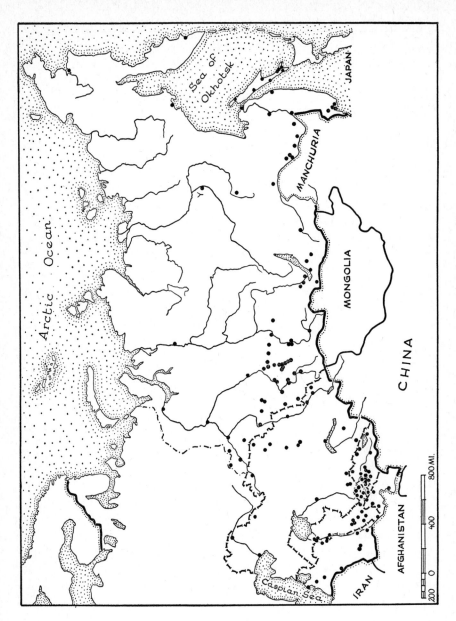

DISTRIBUTION OF CITIES OF THE ASIATIC USSR

into *uyezds* and *volosts*. This arbitrary and economically shapeless administrative structure dated from 1708, when it was initiated by Peter the Great with the formation of the first eight *guberniyas* of Moscow, Ingermanland (renamed St. Petersburg in 1710), Arkhangel'sk, Kiev, Smolensk, Kazan', Azov, and Siberia. The number of units increased steadily through the eighteenth and the nineteenth centuries, and in 1917, on the eve of the Revolution, the Russian Empire was divided into 101 *guberniyas*, 812 *uyezds*, and 16,760 *volosts*. Typical of the lack of political and economic planning in the Tsarist administrative structure is the case of Ivanovo-Voznesensk (now called Ivanovo), a major textile center, which was relegated to the rank of a minor provincial town in Shuya *uyezd* of Vladimir *guberniya*, but which has since become an oblast capital.

Following the "Declaration of the Rights of the Peoples of Russia," made in the very first days of the Revolution of 1917, the national autonomous units were the first to herald the present administrative structure. The Russian SFSR and the Ukrainian SSR were first proclaimed in 1917; in 1919 the Belorussian SSR and the German Volga and Bashkir autonomous republics were organized. When, in December, 1922, the Russian and the Transcaucasian SFSR and the Ukrainian and the Belorussian SSR joined to form the Union of Soviet Socialist Republics, about twenty autonomous oblasts and republics had been created.

In 1922 began the gradual transition from the structure of *volost-uyezd-guberniya* to the organization of *rayon-okrug-oblast* (or *kray*). By 1930 the last *guberniya* had been abolished. The administrative okrug (not to be confused with the national okrug, an autonomous unit which began to be formed in 1929) had served essentially as a provisional unit and was almost entirely suppressed in 1930. A number of administrative okrugs (averaging about ten) continued to exist for a time in those areas of the country requiring a separate integrated administration. The last such unit, Aldan okrug of the Yakut Autonomous SSR, which had been created in 1939 to serve the special needs of an important gold-mining region, was abolished in 1947. As a result of the abolition of the administrative okrug, the rayons were subordinated directly to the oblast, kray, or republic.

The principle of national autonomy governs the division of the USSR into its first-order units, the so-called union republics. These republics, according to the Soviet constitutions (Article 4 of the 1924 Constitution and Article 17 of the 1936 Constitution), form a voluntary union of nations and reserve the right of free secession. Of course, not one of the union republics has ever raised or is likely to raise the question of secession. The number of union republics has increased from four at the time of the formation of the union, to eleven according to the original 1936 Constitution, and to sixteen in 1940, with the formation of the Karelo-Finnish and Moldavian republics and the accession of the Estonian, Latvian, and Lithuanian republics. According to the official terminology, all except the Russian SFSR are called Soviet Socialist Republics. In the early years of the USSR the forms "Soviet Socialist" and "Socialist Soviet" were used indiscriminately; the former order has now been standardized. The Russian SFSR, which is the leading and the most important republic in every respect, is a federation of a number of nationalities associated with the Russian nation and is therefore known as a Soviet Federated Socialist Republic. The principle of national cultural autonomy also determines the formation of lesser autonomous units. The so-called nationalities' ladder descends through the autonomous SSR, autonomous oblast, and national okrug to the national rayon and national local Soviet (council). The rank occupied by any given nationality or ethnic group depends on the number of people, cultural and economic progress, and similar considerations. In theory, each national group within the confines of the USSR may, according to its growth and its cultural and political development, climb the rungs of this ladder to become a constituent republic. In practice, however, no group has ever risen more than two rungs of the ladder, and, except for the Karelian and Moldavian autonomous republics, which achieved the status of union republics in 1940, no promotion has occurred since the promulgation of the 1936 Constitution. The most successful advances were those of the Kirghiz Autonomous Oblast (formed in 1924), which became a union republic in 1936, and of the Cherkess autonomous unit, which as a result of the partition of the Karachay-Cherkess Autonomous Oblast in 1926 was first made a national okrug, only to be raised to the level of autonomous oblast in 1928. The great majority of promotions involved simply the advance of an autonomous oblast to the status of autonomous SSR.

The autonomous republics are administratively under the immediate jurisdiction of the union republics. They began to be created in 1919, and their number rose to twenty-two in 1936; seventeen republics formed part of the Russian SFSR. Since that time, however, the number has been reduced to sixteen (of which twelve are in the Russian SFSR). The reduction was due to the promotion of the Karelian and Moldavian republics and the abolition in 1941–45 of the German Volga, Kalmyk, Chechen-Ingush, and Crimean republics which had been accused of collaboration with the German invaders.

The autonomous oblasts are subordinated directly to the kray within the Russian SFSR and to the republic in the case of the lesser union republics. Their number, which reached seventeen in 1925, has been steadily decreasing ever since, primarily because of the raising of their status to that of autonomous SSR. At the present time they number only nine. In 1943 Karachay Autonomous Oblast was also abrogated, as a result of alleged collaboration with the Germans. The Tuva People's Republic, which had had the status of a quasi-independent Soviet protectorate, was incorporated into the USSR in 1944. It was assigned the status of autonomous oblast, a rather low level of autonomy for a former semi-independent republic. However, its position was enhanced by the fact that it was not included in a kray of the Russian SFSR, but was placed under the immediate administrative jurisdiction of the union republic on a level equal to that of an autonomous SSR.

The national okrugs constitute the lowest major type of autonomous unit. Their formation dates from 1929, when the Komi-Permyak administrative okrug was converted into a national okrug. National okrugs occur only within the Russian SFSR and are under the jurisdiction of the oblast or kray in which they are located. They are largely populated by minor Siberian ethnic groups. The national rayons and local Soviets are of minor importance and are formed locally on the basis of small ethnic groups living in the territory of a more important nationality. Unlike the national okrugs and other national autonomous units, these small divisions do not send any representatives to the Soviet of Nationalities, one of the chambers of the Supreme Soviet of the USSR.

The main administrative divisions other than the national autonomous units are the oblast and the kray. The dominant principle governing the formation of these units is the creation of well-integrated economic units. An oblast or kray is usually organized in such a manner as to include in it a well-coordinated economic region centering on an important industrial and commercial center and specializing in the production of some particular commodity, while striving for regional self-sufficiency in the greatest possible degree. Considering the nature of these divisions and the criteria on which they are based, the great instability of the administrative structure becomes instantly clear. The economy of the USSR is in a state of constant flux. New industrial regions are being developed, railroad construction opens new mining regions to exploitation, reclaimed farm lands are put under cultivation. As these developments occur, the administrative structure of the country varies accordingly. New divisions are created in newly populated and developed regions, large unwieldy divisions are split into more efficient units, unsuitable divisions are abolished and replaced by better integrated units. The territorial organization, at least within the nonautonomous sphere, is thus entirely subordinated to the requirements of an economy which is itself extremely dynamic. Principles defining the formation of oblasts and krays were formulated in 1921, and in 1923 the first such division, Ural Oblast, was created. While earlier plans had contemplated the creation of a limited number of large economic regions (thirteen in 1930), the decision to abolish the intermediate okrug division necessitated the splitting up of the large economic regions into a greater number of smaller units. At the present time there are six krays and fifty oblasts (including two intra-kray oblasts) in the Russian SFSR, twenty-five oblasts in the Ukrainian SSR, twelve in the Belorussian SSR, four in the Turkmen SSR, nine in the Uzbek SSR, four in the Tadzhik SSR, sixteen in the Kazakh SSR, six in the Kirghiz SSR, as well as four in the Lithuanian SSR. Krays, which occur only in the Russian SFSR, are identical to the oblasts, but are usually larger in area. The term "kray" is given to those divisions which contain autonomous oblasts. Until 1936 even autonomous republics were sometimes included in the kray administration. The single exception in this terminological scheme is Maritime Kray, which contains no autonomous oblast and is itself properly speaking an oblast. The name was retained even after Maritime Kray lost (in 1939 and 1943) its two internal oblasts by abrogation. Khabarovsk Kray is the single such division containing at the present time internal or intra-kray oblasts. Intra-kray oblasts numbered fifteen in 1934, but since then have been constituted generally into separate oblasts. Amur Oblast (formerly of Khabarovsk Kray) was most recently thus constituted in 1948.

Local government resides in the rayon, the village, and other local Soviets. The rayon, which was first formed in 1924, is in reality a miniature oblast. The same economic principles guide its creation. All oblasts and krays and all major autonomous divisions (national okrugs, oblasts,

and republics), as well as most of the lesser union republics are divided
directly into rayons. The size of the rayon varies greatly throughout
the USSR. In the sparsely settled tundra of the Far North are units
with an area of nearly 150,000 square miles (Ilimpiya Rayon of the
Evenki National Okrug); in the Ukrainian SSR, in the densely populated black-earth zone, are rayons including less than 100 square miles.
The rayons are divided into village soviets, nomad soviets, and other
types of local councils, each of which comprises a number of villages,
hamlets, and other small populated centers and constitutes the smallest
type of rural administrative unit in the USSR.

Urban local government resides in the cities, city-type settlements,
and workers' settlements, which are generally directly subordinated to
the rayon. Just as in the case of the previous divisions, economic criteria guide the formation of these urban centers. The establishment of
a new industry or the opening of a new mine will furnish the basis for
the creation of an urban center, usually a workers' settlement or city-
type settlement. As the locality grows and its population increases, it
may be converted into a city, which may be of rayon, oblast, or kray
subordination and, as is the case in the very large cities, of republic subordination. The rise of the urban centers of the USSR is thus an excellent guide to the economic development of the country. The criteria
for the formation of urban centers vary for each union republic. In the
Russian SFSR the workers' settlements, which were first formed in
1927, should have a minimum population of 400 adults; 65 percent
of them should be salaried workers or employees, an indication of the
industrial character of the locality. Special provision was also made
for the creation of health resorts (*kurortnyy poselok*) and residential
summer resorts (*dachnyy poselok*), which began in 1929. Cities may
be formed in the Russian SFSR with a population of 1,000 adults, not
more than 25 percent of which should be engaged in agricultural occupations. Similar provisions exist with respect to the other union
republics. The low population requirements explain the extraordinary
urbanization of the last two decades. The creation of a new industry
furnishes an excuse for the formation of a new urban center; a new steel
mill is the nucleus around which a new city rises. Another important
factor is the policy of the incorporation by the city of surrounding
suburban areas. An extreme case of this type of urban aggrandizement
is that of Baku. Although the city of Baku proper is an urban center
of modest proportions on the southwestern shore of the Apsheron Penin-

sula, this entire peninsula, one of the major oil fields of the USSR, comes within the Baku city limits. Cities of oblast, kray, or republic subordination are frequently divided into city rayons (boroughs).

TOPONYMY

The general instability of the administrative-territorial structure and various political and economic developments are closely reflected in the place names of the USSR. One of the principal difficulties for any student of Soviet geography is the facility and suddenness with which administrative divisions and populated places adopt new names. It should, nevertheless, be realized that considerations characteristic of the Soviet system generally underlie these seemingly annoying and purposeless changes.

One feature of Soviet toponymy is simply linguistic and relates to suffixes. As a locality rises from a small village to a large village and then to a workers' settlement, a town, or a city, the suffix of the name (if such a suffix exists at all) may change successively from *skaya* to *skoye* to *skiy, o,* or *sk.* A hypothetical small village named for Stalin would thus be successively known as Stalinskaya, Stalinskoye, Stalinskiy, Stalino, and Stalinsk as it passes through the phases of growing urbanization. These changes in suffixes are due to changes in gender of the words signifying village (feminine *derevnya*, neuter *selo*), workers' settlement (masculine *rabochiy poselok*), or city (masculine *gorod*). Names which are entirely lacking in suffixes are also encountered and are generally applied to sizable cities, such as Molotov, Kirov, Kalinin, and Voroshilov. Suffixes signifying "town" or "city," such as the Russian *grad* (a variant of *gorod*), Armenian *akan*, Iranian *abad*, also occur frequently, in names such as Leningrad, Leninakan, Leninabad.

As has been seen, names of Soviet political figures occupy a fair share of the place names of the USSR. It has been remarked that the popularity of a given personality can be gauged by the number of cities named in his honor. Among the deceased leaders, the foremost place is occupied by Lenin. Figures formerly prominent in the Soviet regime, such as Dzerzhinskiy, Sverdlov, Frunze, Kuybyshev, Ordzhonikidze, Kirov, Kalinin, and Zhdanov, have large numbers of places named after them. Among the living, Stalin, Molotov, Voroshilov, Kaganovich, Beriya, and Budennyy are most frequently honored. Among the foreign political figures, Engels, Marx, and the German communists Ernst Thaelmann and Rosa Luxemburg are named. Such nonpolitical Soviet personalities as Maxim Gor'kiy, the Kazakh bard Dzhambul, the celebrated pilot Chkalov, and the partisan leaders Shchors and Chapayev have larger centers named in their honor. Finally, many places are named for such Soviet institutions and concepts as the soviets (councils), in Sovetskoye, Sovetsk, and similar place names, the Komsomol youth organization, in Komsomol'sk, the Red Army, in Krasnoarmeysk, the First of May, in Pervomayskoye, the October Revolution, in Oktyabr'skoye, and the collective farm, in Kolkhoznoye.

Cities named for Soviet leaders who came into disfavor and were purged or exiled were given new names. Among the outstanding examples of cities affected by the changing fortunes of their name patrons are Yelizavetgrad, successively named Zinov'yevsk, Kirovo, and Kirovograd; Yenakiyevo, successively named Rykovo, Ordzhonikidze, and again Yenakiyevo; Ivashchenkovo, successively named Trotsk and Chapayevsk; Gatchina, successively named Trotsk, Krasnogvardeysk, and again Gatchina; Batalpashinsk, successively named Sulimov, Yezhovo-Cherkessk, and Cherkessk; and Aulie-Ata, successively named Mirzoyan and Dzhambul. These changes closely reflect the fate of purged national and local leaders such as Trotskiy, Zinov'yev, Rykov, Yezhov, Sulimov, and Mirzoyan. Even cities named for figures seemingly in favor are not always unaffected. Stavropol', which had been renamed Voroshilovsk, was again given its original name apparently in order to avoid confusion with another Voroshilovsk in the Donets Basin. The abrogation of the names of several cities so called in honor of Sergo Ordzhonikidze, still a revered Bolshevik leader, occurred in 1944 without any apparent reason. Ordzhonikidzegrad reverted to its former name, Bezhitsa, as did Orzhonikidze (formerly Yenakiyevo) and Sergo (formerly Kadiyevka) in the Donets Basin. Ordzhonikidze in the Caucasus, formerly called Vladikavkaz, adopted a new Ossetian name, Dzaudzhikau.

Another characteristic toponymic development concerns the adoption of non-Russian place names in national autonomous areas. These changes affected such large cities as Tbilisi (formerly Tiflis), the capital of the Georgian SSR, Yerevan (formerly Erivan'), the capital of the Armenian SSR, and Alma-Ata (formerly Vernyy), the capital of the Kazakh SSR. The capitals of lesser autonomous units and other non-Russian localities were affected. Verkhneudinsk, of the Buryat-Mongol Autonomous SSR, became Ulan-Ude; Petrovsk, of the Dagestan Au-

tonomous SSR, became Makhachkala; Ust'-Sysol'sk, of the Komi
Autonomous SSR, was renamed Syktyvkar; Tsarevokokshaysk (later
Krasnokokshaysk), of the Mari Autonomous SSR, was renamed
Yoshkar-Ola; Obdorsk, of the Yamal-Nenets ·National Okrug, became
Salekhard; and there were many other similar changes. This policy in
favor of non-Russian names was reversed for the national groups which
lost their identity as a result of alleged collaboration with the Germans
during the Second World War. In the Volga German Autonomous SSR
the abrogation was accompanied by the disappearance of all German
place names. Marksshtadt (Marxstadt) was shortened to Marks; Unterval'den (Unterwalden) was translated to Podlesnoye'; Bal'tser
(Balzer; formerly called Golyy Karamysh) was now again changed to
Krasnoarmeysk; and names such as Mariyental' (Mariental) and Fridenfel'd (Friedenfeld) were dropped in favor of the standard Soviet
appellations Sovetskoye and Komsomol'skoye.

In the Kalmyk Autonomous SSR, another abrogated autonomous
unit, native names such as Elista, Ulan-Erg, and Yashkul' were changed
to common Russian names, as Stepnoy, Sadovoye (garden town), and
Krasnoye (red town). Similar name changes took place in the territory
of the former Chechen-Ingush Autonomous SSR and Karachay Autonomous Oblast in the Caucasus. There, however, the native names
were changed not only to Russian forms but also to the languages of
neighboring national divisions which annexed portions of the suppressed
areas. Thus, the capital of Karachay Autonomous Oblast, Mikoyan-
Shakhar, was ceded to the Georgian SSR and given the Georgian name
Klukhori. In the Crimean Autonomous SSR, founded on the Tatar ethnic
minority, changes of place names of Tatar origin even preceded the
abrogation in the summer of 1945. Only the names Balaklava and
Bakhchisaray were retained, probably because of their fame in Russian
history and literature.

Toward the end of the Second World War a number of cities and villages with names of German origin were renamed upon the request of
the local population. The best-known names were associated with cities
in the Leningrad area and dated from the time of Peter the Great. In
1944 Shlisselburg (Schlüsselburg) became Petrokrepost', Petergof
(Peterhof) was changed to Petrodvorets, and near-by Dudergof (Duderhof) to Nagornoye. In 1948 the city of Oranienbaum was renamed
Lomonosov. Only Kronshtadt (Kronstadt) has retained its name, again

probably out of deference to its historical revolutionary significance. In the Ukrainian SSR several isolated Jewish communities, such as Kalinindorf and Stalindorf, were named Kalininskoye and Stalinskoye.

The acquisition of German and Japanese territories after the Second World War was also marked by characteristic Soviet name changes. In the northern part of East Prussia, which was adjudged to the USSR by the Potsdam Conference, all German place names were changed to Russian toponymics. Since there were no historical names of Russian origin, names of war heroes, descriptive forms, and other Soviet stereotypes were adopted. Königsberg was changed to Kaliningrad, Insterburg to Chernyakhovsk (for the general Chernyakhovskiy), Tilsit to Sovetsk, Pillau to Baltiysk (for the Baltic Sea), Friedland to Gvardeysk (for the Guard divisions of the Red Army), the rail center of Gerdauen to Zheleznodorozhnyy (railroad town), and so forth. In southern Sakhalin and the Kurile Islands the Russians also replaced all the Japanese names. They resorted partly to old Russian names in use before the cession of the territory to Japan in 1905, partly to descriptive and standard Soviet names. Among the historic names are Korsakov (Japanese *Otomari*) and Poronaysk (Japanese *Shikuka*); other new names are Uglegorsk (Japanese *Esutoru*), named for the coal mines near by, and Yuzhno-Sakhalinsk (Japanese *Toyohara*).

Many descriptive place names of the USSR are guides to the type of economy established in the towns. Nebit-Dag and Neftegorsk are Turkmen and Russian versions of "petroleum mountain." Boksitogorsk is a major bauxite-mining center near Tikhvin. Vagonoremont (near Moscow) has railway-car repair shops. Elektrostal' manufactures high-grade steels in electric furnaces. Fosforitnyy mines phosphorite near Yegor'yevsk and Elektroperedacha (now called Elektrogorsk) has a power station. Many towns named Lesozavodsk and Lesozavodskiy are the sites of lumber mills. Kant, which is the Kirghiz word for "sugar," is a beet-sugar refining center in the Chu valley of the Kirghiz SSR. Temir-Tau, which is Turkic for "iron mountain," is the name of an iron-mining town in the Kuznetsk Basin and the site of the new metallurgical works near Karaganda, Kazakh SSR. Asbest is an asbestos-mining center in the Urals, and Izumrud, near by, has emerald mines.

The greater part of the oblasts and krays of the USSR are named for their administrative centers. Only Kamenets-Podol'skiy Oblast (capital, Proskurov) of the Ukrainian SSR is named for a city other than the administrative center. Several divisions are named for physical features

(Altay Kray, Issyk-Kul' Oblast, Crimean Oblast, Surkhan Darya Oblast), and for regions (Khorezm Oblast, Maritime Kray, Transcarpathian Oblast). About 90 percent of the rayons are also named for their administrative centers. When the center is changed, the rayon is often renamed accordingly. National autonomous units are generally named for the ethnic group upon which they are founded. In several cases the old conventional Russian name of a nationality has been replaced by the name used by the national group itself. Thus, Zyryan became Komi; Votyak or Vot was changed to Udmurt; the Cheremiss were renamed Mari; the Kara-Kirghiz became Kirghiz; the people formerly known as Kirghiz are now called Kazakh. Among the lesser Siberian tribes, the Tungus are now known as Evenki, the Samoyeds as Nentsy, and the Ostyaks and Voguls as Khanty and Mansi. In 1948 the Oyrot Autonomous Oblast was renamed Gorno-Altay (mountainous Altay) Autonomous Oblast in a logical adjustment of nomenclature. The Oyrot national group (once known as Oyrat) is, properly speaking, only part of the so-called Altay ethnic group, which also includes several other mountain tribes. The larger Altay group includes only about 35 percent of the population of the area, the Russians constituting over 50 percent. There was little reason, therefore, to identify the autonomous oblast specifically with the Oyrots, which represented only a small minority of the population.

CHAPTER 3

The Economic Pattern

STATE PLANNING is the essence of the Soviet economic pattern. Since private enterprise is nonexistent, all agricultural and industrial activities are centrally directed. State control manifests itself in the characteristic features of the economy, such as the introduction of new crops into the USSR and the redistribution of old crops to new areas, the relocation of industry in order to bring processing plants closer to the sources of raw materials and closer to the consumer, and finally the attempt to obtain regional quasi-self-sufficiency in consumer goods.

AGRICULTURE

The vast range of climatic and soil conditions in the USSR permits the cultivation of a large variety of crops, ranging from hardy grains grown in the tundra zone to tea and citrus fruits grown in the humid subtropical belt. Only plants that thrive in purely tropical conditions, such as coffee, cacao, or bananas, have not been acclimatized in the Soviet Union. In spite of the vast extent of the country, however, only about one third of the area can be considered potential agricultural land. About 10 percent could be made available for crops, 2.5 percent for meadows and grassland, and 15 percent for pastures. The remainder of the country is covered by forests, tundra, deserts, mountains, and marshes, which will probably never be developed agriculturally because of the forbidding climatic and soil conditions.

Since the beginning of collectivization in the early 1930's, the organization of Soviet agriculture has undergone extensive changes. In 1928 there were more than twenty million individually owned farms, with an average sown area of about eleven acres. By the late 1930's, when individual holdings had been reduced to an insignificant number, the agricultural area was distributed among 250,000 collective farms with an average sown area of about 1,200 acres and about 4,000 state farms with an average sown area of 7,500 acres. The latter are usually located in newly developed agricultural land, where harsh conditions prevail, and have the benefit of more thorough mechanization and scientific methods.

Soviet agriculture has shown certain definite trends since the execution of collectivization and the introduction of planned economic methods. There has been an increase in the area under cultivation, a sharp rise in the acreage under industrial crops, continuing introduction and acclimatization of new crops, redistribution of old crops to new areas, and a rise in productivity. The area under cultivation in the USSR increased from 260 million acres in 1913 to 370 million acres in 1940. This gain was achieved through the expansion of the sown area from the basic agricultural black-earth belt into the forest area to the north and into the dry steppe and desert areas of the south. Meliorative measures, such as drainage of swampy areas and irrigation of dry steppe and desert regions, and the development through selective and crossbreeding processes of resistant crop types adapted to the more exacting climatic conditions were the principal factors that made this expansion possible. Characteristic of Soviet agricultural policy has also been the sharp increase in the acreage under industrial, fodder, and garden crops. In order to widen the variety of the agricultural products, new crops were introduced from foreign areas and native wild-growing plants were adopted for systematic production. Among the most important indigeneous plants that were domesticated are *kendyr'*, a fiber plant from Central Asia used in the manufacture of very resistant cloth, and the rubber-bearing varieties of *kok-sagyz* and *tau-sagyz*, which were discovered in 1930–31 in the Tien Shan mountain system. Foreign plants introduced into the USSR and now cultivated on a commercial scale include the ramie, or Chinese nettle, which furnishes a silk-like fiber, *kenaf*, an Indian substitute for jute, the tung tree from China, which furnishes a valuable ingredient of varnishes and lacquers, the soybean, introduced from Manchuria and now cultivated extensively in the Soviet Far East, in Moldavia and the Ukraine, grain sorghums from Palestine, easily adapted to a dry climate, and such widely assorted plants as the cork oak from Algeria, the guttapercha tree from Indonesia, the pecan nut from the United States, the sweet potato from the West Indies, and citrus fruits, including lemons, oranges, tangerines, and grapefruit. In their search for new industrial applications of old crops, the Soviets discovered that citric acid could be obtained from tobacco, that the cotton tree furnishes natural dyes, ranging from cream to brown and from light blue

CHIEF AGRICULTURAL AREAS OF THE EUROPEAN USSR

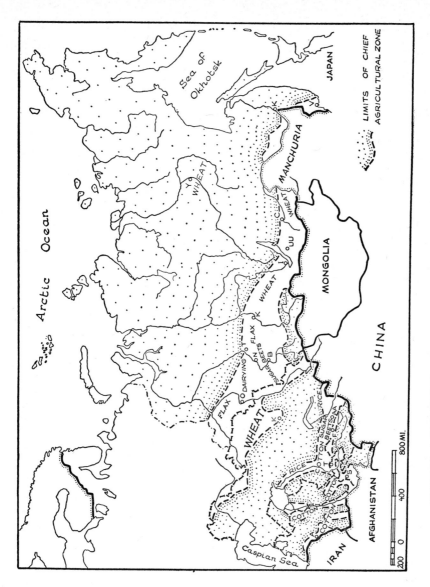

CHIEF AGRICULTURAL AREAS OF THE ASIATIC USSR

to dark green, that as many as 150 uses were possible for corn, and that paper and soap could be manufactured from the wheat stalk. A veritable campaign was begun to raise the yield of plants and the productivity of the soil. Wherever possible scientific farming methods were introduced. In dry areas, deep tilling of the soil (up to 10 inches, instead of the previous 4 inches), the conservation of the winter snow, and the planting of tree shelter belts helped to preserve moisture in the ground. Mineral fertilizer was extensively used to improve deficient soils; peat was used for nitrification, lime was used in podsols, and gypsum was applied to salty soils in the desert regions. Crop rotation, alternating for example alfalfa and cotton or millet and sorghum with wheat, was extensively introduced, and selection produced quick-ripening wheat which matures in the dry steppe before the advent of the hot, dry winds from the deserts and also barley capable of ripening during short northern summers beyond the Arctic Circle.

In October, 1948, the Soviet government proclaimed a grandiose plan of shelter-belt planting to be effected during the period 1949–65. This program was intended to combat the periodic drought danger existing mainly in the southeastern European USSR and extending into the Lower and Middle Volga regions, the Northern Caucasus, the Central Black-Earth Region, as well as the Crimea and the southeastern Ukraine. The plan features the planting of eight huge tree shelter belts to protect the drought-ridden agricultural areas from the hot, dry summer winds blowing from Kazakhstan and Central Asia. It provides for the strongest belt system of six rows of trees, each row 200 feet wide, to extend along the banks of the Ural River from Vishnevaya Mountain (in the southern Urals north of Orsk) to the mouth at Gur'yev on the Caspian Sea. Lesser belts are to be planted along the Volga (below Saratov), the Northern Donets (below Belgorod), and the Don (below Voronezh). Other belts are to extend cross-country on the left Volga bank, between Chapayevsk and Vladimirovka, on the right Volga bank, between Kamyshin and Stalingrad, from Stalingrad via Stepnoy to Cherkessk, and from Penza to Kamensk-Shakhtinskiy on the Northern Donets. The total length of these shelter zones is to be 3,500 miles. In addition to the planting of these great belts by the state, the plan calls for small-scale shelter-belt planting by collective and state farms, not only for protection against the dry southeasterlies, but also to prevent erosion and conserve soil moisture. It is planned that the total area to be planted in farm shelter belts will be more than 23,000 square miles.

Of great importance in the campaign for increased production was the geographical displacement of crops throughout the USSR. Wheat had been traditionally grown within the triangular black-earth belt and covered no more than about six hundred thousand acres north of the Kiev-Tula-Gor'kiy line, roughly the northern limit of the rich agricultural zone. Before the Second World War as many as 7½ million acres lay under wheat north of that line, and the northern limit of wheat cultivation had been pushed from 56° N to 60° N and beyond. During the war, when a large section of the black-earth zone was occupied by the Germans, it was to a large extent the newly developed wheat belt to the north and east that supplied the grain. Many areas which previously had relied on long-haulage grain were forced to grow their own wheat supplies. Even in Central Asia, where wheat in irrigated areas had generally been replaced by cotton, and relegated to the higher dry-farming zone, the growing of grain in the lowlands were reinstated temporarily during the war emergency. While the new wheat areas in Central Asia are generally being replanted with cotton since the end of the war, the newly won grain belts in Kazakhstan and Siberia continue to be an important asset in the wheat supply picture of the country. Winter wheat is commonly grown in areas with sufficient snowfall, such as the Ukraine and the Kuban' district in the Northern Caucasus. Spring wheat, however, predominates in the Volga Region, the Urals, Western Siberia, and northern Kazakhstan, where the snow rarely attains a sufficiently thick protective cover.

The USSR has effected a considerable shift in the geography of rice. Once restricted to the irrigated valleys of Central Asia, southern Kazakhstan, and Transcaucasia, this semi-tropical grain has gradually penetrated northward into the flood plains of the lower Kuban' and Dnieper rivers, the swampy Volga delta and has been introduced into the Far East in the vicinity of Lake Khanka. Currently, acclimatization experiments are being carried on in the oblasts of Kuybyshev, Kursk, Ryazan', and Poles'ye, 1,500 miles north of the former cultivation zone. Corn has been displaced from subtropical Transcaucasia to make room for such newly introduced crops as oranges, lemons, tea, and bamboo. It is now grown mainly farther north, in the wooded steppe of the European USSR and Siberia. The acreage under rye and oats has been greatly enlarged in Siberia, especially during the Second World War, and rye is extensively grown in higher altitudes and latitudes. Finally, both millet and sunflowers, two drought-resistant crops, have advanced into the dry steppes of the southeastern European USSR and northern Kazakhstan.

Among the industrial crops, cotton has moved northward from 43° to 47° N. Although its original irrigated areas in Central Asia and southern Kazakhstan remain the chief producers, the plant has been successfully acclimatized in the dry steppe belt extending from the mouths of the Danube through the Ukraine, the northern Crimea, and the Northern Caucasus (lower Kuban' and Terek valleys) to the valley of the lower Volga River. Dry farming prevails in the new cotton belt, and although the area includes one fourth of the total cotton acreage, it produces less than 10 percent of the total yield. The Uzbek SSR remains the principal producer in the irrigated cotton district, where the area under long-staple Egyptian cotton is gradually being expanded. While the cotton plant migrated northward, the sugar beet retraced this path toward the cotton homeland and has now been adapted to irrigated farming in the Kirghiz SSR, southern Kazakhstan, and the Uzbek SSR. Sugar beets are now also grown in southern Siberia, in the Altay and Minusinsk steppes and in Transbaykalia, in southern Maritime Kray of the Far East, and in the new Soviet areas of the Baltic Region and the Karelian Isthmus. In spite of the wide distribution, the new areas account for only 10 percent of the total acreage, while the great bulk of the beet continues to be produced in the Ukraine and Kursk Oblast of the Russian SFSR. In the podsol oblasts of Moscow, Vologda, and Gor'kiy the sugar beet serves for the manufacture of jams and syrups, and experimental thrusts have been effected into the Far North to Arkhangel'sk Oblast and the Nenets National Okrug.

The growing of another fiber plant, flax, is commonly associated with dairy farming. Due to the rapid exhaustion of soils sown with flax, it is commonly rotated with fodder crops (alfalfa) which present an obvious basis for the rearing of dairy cattle. Flax is commonly grown for fiber production in the forested zone, where humid, cool summers predominate. The original flax-growing area was restricted to the northwestern European USSR, including the oblasts of Smolensk, Kalinin, Velikiye Luki, and Pskov, the Belorussian SSR, and the Baltic republics. In recent years new areas have been sown with flax in the Urals and in Siberia. Flax for the production of linseed oil is grown somewhat farther south in the black-earth belt. Hemp, the fiber of which is used in making coarse fabrics, ropes, and nets, requires more warmth than flax and is grown farther south. The basic hemp regions are the quadrilateral Chernigov-Bryansk-Orel-Kursk, at the meeting point of the Russian SFSR and the

Belorussian and Ukrainian SSR's, and the triangle Penza-Ryazan'-Gor'kiy, centered on the Mordvinian Autonomous SSR. Of the recently introduced fiber plants, *kenaf* was first cultivated in the Adige Autonomous Oblast of the Northern Caucasus, but is now widespread throughout Transcaucasia, the Crimea, the Ukraine, and Central Asia, and ramie is grown in the humid subtropical conditions of the Batumi and Lenkoran' littorals of Transcaucasia. Aside from the sunflowers of the dry and sunny steppes, the oil-bearing plants of the USSR include the mustard plant, grown chiefly in the lower Volga valley, and the castor bean which prevails in the Northern Caucasus. The soybean of well-known numerous applications was first introduced into the Soviet Far East by Chinese and Korean farmers. Now it is also grown in the Ukraine and the Northern Caucasus. The potato crop, also of almost universal application, is channeled to the consumer as food, to the stock raiser as fodder, especially for hogs, and to industry as an important raw material for alcohol, starch, and derived products. Other notable industrial crops are the yellow Turkish tobacco, which thrives in the humid foothills of Abkhazia (Georgian SSR), near Maykop (Northern Caucasus), and on the southern coast of the Crimea, the Russian *makhorka* tobacco, grown in the Ukraine from Chernigov to Poltava, in Tambov Oblast, and on the lower Volga, the tea plant, which is restricted to the red lateritic soil of the subtropical Batumi littoral and the Caspian coast at Lenkoran', and the rubber-bearing *kok-sagyz* and *tau-sagyz* and the imported *guayule*, which are cultivated in the southern Ukraine, Transcaucasia, and Central Asia.

One of the most notable accomplishments of Soviet agriculture is the progressive exploitation of the agricultural potential of the vast desert regions of Kazakhstan and Central Asia. While the areas under irrigation are being enlarged, the possibility of introducing dry farming is being studied. Experimentation showed that careful tilling of the soil, coupled with crop rotation and seed selection, may make feasible the introduction of such drought-resistant plants as millet and barley into the desert. The use of ditches is intended to protect the plants from the burning winds and to bring them nearer to the ground-water level. Aside from the prospect of dry farming of grain, the exploitation of the desert is already proving economically feasible. Wild-growing wormwood varieties furnish valuable vermicides, such as santonin; vegetable dyes can be extracted from a number of desert plants, and the *saksaul*, a gnarled desert tree, can be successfully planted to furnish scarce firewood and form protective tree zones around cultivated areas. Finally, it is thought that the sowing of fodder crops will increase to a very large extent the potential pastures for the grazing of livestock, particularly karakul sheep.

The importance of irrigation in the Soviet agricultural scheme becomes clear if one considers that one seventh of the area of the USSR receives less than ten inches of rain annually. With the help of irrigation, the fertile gray desert soil permits the maturing of the poplar in five to six years and furnishes up to seven yields of alfalfa per year. The chief irrigation schemes have been established in Central Asia in the valleys of the Syr Darya, the Amu Darya, the Chu, and the Murgab. Irrigation changed the lower Vakhsh valley of the Tadzhik SSR from a desert into one of the major cotton areas of the USSR and the construction of the Fergana canals in 1939 considerably raised the cotton yield of the Fergana Valley. In the Azerbaijan SSR, the construction of the Samur-Divichi Canal, which is continuing during the current Plan, will bring water from the mountain streams of the eastern Caucasus to the arid Apsheron Peninsula and Baku. Olive groves and vineyards will then rise in the irrigated areas. Grandiose projects are scheduled in the postwar Five-Year Plan. In the Azerbaijan SSR, the Kura River is being dammed above Yevlakh, by a dam 250 feet high, to form the second largest reservoir of the USSR, the Mingechaur Sea, with an area of about 290 square miles. As a result of this construction, which will also involve the building of a powerful hydroelectric station, the lower Kura valley will be transformed into fertile irrigated farmland for the cultivation of cotton, wheat, orchard crops, essential-oil-bearing plants, and tung trees. Another large-scale irrigation project is being completed in the Zeravshan valley of the Uzbek SSR. The Uzbek Sea, a reservoir south of Katta-Kurgan, with a capacity of 777 billion cubic yards, is intended to collect the spring flood waters of the Zeravshan River and to discharge them for cotton irrigation during the dry summer months. Other irrigation projects to be initiated during the current Five-Year Plan are the construction of the Orto-Tokoy Reservoir, on the Chu River, in the Kirghiz SSR, the dam on the Syr Darya, near Kzyl-Orda, intended mainly for rice cultivation, and the spectacular Kara-Kum Canal, which will flow 250 miles from the Amu Darya, near Kerki, through the desert of Kara-Kum, to the Murgab oasis, near Mary, and will open vast desert stretches for cultivation. A future extension of the canal to the Tedzhen oasis is contemplated, and its possible connection with the Caspian Sea has been discussed. A major role in future irrigation schemes is played by the Volga River. A series of dams along its middle course and its lower course is intended to regulate its system of irrigation of the dry steppes along its banks. To supply a regular flow of water, another large reservoir will be constructed in the northern European USSR on the watershed of the Vychegda, the Pechora, and the Kama rivers, diverting a portion of the northern waters to the Volga basin. While these plans are, however, still far from realization, another important irrigation project in the Northern Caucasus has been completed. Here, the construction of the Nevinnomyssk Canal diverts water from the Kuban', a Caucasus mountain stream, to the Manych River, and its affluent, the Yegorlyk, which lack sufficient water reserves. With the help of the canal, a large area in the dry steppes north of Stavropol' has been brought under irrigation.

While a considerable effort is spent in supplying large sections of the USSR with irrigation water, other areas, again, require drainage projects to rid them of excess moisture. These marshy sections include the Pripet Marshes in the Belorussian SSR, the Yakhroma valley north of Moscow, the Kuban' delta in the Northern Caucasus, and the Colchis lowland in the Georgian SSR. The draining and drying of these areas is attained by the construction of drainage canals and the planting of such water-absorbing plants as the eucalyptus in Georgia.

The raising of livestock in the USSR is closely related to the supply of fodder, which may consist of natural meadow or pasture and of fodder grasses, silage, root crops, grain feed, and the waste products of such industrial processes as distilling, sugar refining, starch-making, and vegetable oil extraction. As is the cultivated area, the major portion of the livestock is found in the European USSR. Depending upon the type of available fodder, the distribution of livestock places emphasis on the rearing of hogs in the west, dairy farming in the north, and the raising of sheep in the dry southeast. Dairy farming is developed especially in the middle and northern reaches of the European USSR, as well as in Western Siberia, and relies chiefly upon alluvial meadows and other permanent pasturage in the north, and upon fodder grasses in the west. Milk production is emphasized in the vicinity of the large urban and industrial centers, while in Vologda Oblast and in Western Siberia about 50 percent of the milk is made into butter. Cheese-making is a specialty in the Caucasus and in the Altay. The raising of meat cattle is chiefly developed in the steppe belt of Kazakhstan, Western Siberia, and Transbaykalia on the basis of natural grazing land, while in the Caucasus and the Ukraine a more intensive form of meat-cattle breeding depends upon grain and root crops and waste products of the agricultural industry. Hog-raising has as its chief source of fodder the potato crop, which is most strongly developed in the Belorussian SSR and the middle reaches of the European Russian SFSR in the oblasts of Smolensk, Kaluga, Moscow, Tula, Kursk, and Orel. In the Ukraine, however, hogs are fed chiefly on grain and waste products, and in the Caucasus on corn. The rearing of sheep for wool and meat is centered in Kazakhstan, Central Asia, and in Transbaykalia. In the stock-breeding regions and at focal points of the transportation system, large meat-packing plants and refrigerating points have been established. Other packing plants gravitate toward large meat-consuming centers such as Moscow and Leningrad.

Horses, which remain the principal draft animals, are bred mainly in the Ukraine, the Northern Caucasus, and the Lower Volga Region side by side with draft-oxen. Important horse-breeding farms are also located in the Central Black-Earth Region, especially in Voronezh Oblast. In Transcaucasia buffaloes are often used, and in the desert regions of Kazakhstan and Central Asia the camel replaces the horse. In the tundras of the north the reindeer serves as the universal domestic animal, furnishing food (milk and meat), clothing (leather, fur, and wool), and draft power. Poultry is raised in grain-growing areas, especially where the lack of extensive pasturage does not favor the breeding of stock, such as in certain parts of the Ukraine and the Central Black-Earth Region, in Kuybyshev Oblast, and the Tatar and Bashkir Autonomous SSR. Sericulture is practiced in Transcaucasia and in Central Asia.

As in agriculture, in livestock breeds and the rationalization of stock breeding considerable progress has been made. As the result of cross-breeding, the excellent Kostroma milk cow was developed. In Kazakhstan the crossing of the merino sheep, known for its fine fleece, with a local fat-tail breed resulted in a sheep suitable for long-distance treks and notable for its fine wool and meat. Another breed, derived from the merino sheep and a local mountain ram, is strong, resistant, and able to endure the severe conditions of high-altitude grazing, although continuing to furnish a fine wool. The principal change in the nomadic type of stock-raising in the deserts of Kazakhstan and Central Asia involved the adoption of a semisedentary mode of life. The constant migration in search of forage was abandoned in favor of the establishment of permanent settlements and semiannual treks from the winter pastures in the desert lowland to the summer grazing land in the higher altitudes of the Tien Shan and Altay mountains.

Hunting of fur-bearing animals is a major occupation of the population in areas where there is little or no agriculture or other types of rural economy. This is true especially of the Far North and the forest zone of Siberia, and to a lesser extent of the desert regions of Central Asia and the bordering mountains. Furs, which are a major Soviet export item, are collected principally in Eastern Siberia, the Far East, and the European North. Minor fur-producing regions are the Urals, Western Siberia, and Kazakhstan. In order to prevent the complete extermination of fur-bearing animals, conservation measures have been adopted. While wolf-hunting is unrestricted, animals such as squirrels can be trapped only in specified seasons, and the hunting of elk, spotted maral reindeer, and white heron is entirely prohibited. In order to replenish depleted fur resources, the Soviets introduced into the USSR such valuable animals as the North American mink and muskrat and the Argentine coypu, or nutria.

The major fishing areas of the USSR are the Caspian and Far Eastern waters. In the Caspian Sea, which receives organic matter from such rivers as the Volga, the Ural, the Terek, and the Kura, conditions for breeding and feeding fish are very favorable in the shallow coastal reaches. The chief processing center is Astrakhan', which receives its salt supply from near-by Lake Baskunchak. The development of the Far Eastern fishing industry has been hampered by its distance from the main consumption centers, the lack of labor (due to the sparseness of the population), and the absence of salt. In recent years salt has been shipped from the rich deposits near Nordvik, on the Laptev Sea of the Arctic Ocean, and the population of the Far East has been steadily increasing. The main fishing centers lie on the shores of the Kamchatka Peninsula, especially on the west coast and near the mouth of the Amur River. While the Caspian catch goes mainly for domestic consumption, the Far East largely exports its fisheries' production. Next in order of importance are the Murman Coast of the Barents Sea, with its center at Murmansk, the waters of the Black Sea and the Sea of Azov, the Aral Sea, the mouths of the large Siberian rivers (Ob', Yenisey, Lena), the Baltic Sea, and the limans of the Black Sea coast.

As is industry, agriculture has been attempted by the USSR on a regional quasi-self-sufficient basis. At the same time, efforts have been made to develop regional specialization depending on local conditions.

This specialization is not intended to develop into monoculture, but rather to emphasize the production of a given number of interrelated branches of the economy. This would involve, for example, the simultaneous development of activities such as flax growing, the sowing of fodder grasses (in rotation), and the rearing of dairy cattle. Thanks to specialization, the particular characteristics of a region can be exploited to their fullest extent, mechanization can be adopted successfully, labor becomes more specialized, hence more skilled, and the intensive pursuit of a given activity or set of activities favors the local establishment of related processing industries, thus saving the cost of transportation of raw materials.

From the point of view of specialization, four main agricultural belts can be distinguished in the USSR, each one being subdivided into zones. The northernmost zone, in the tundra and taiga belt, depends on reindeer-raising, hunting, and fishing. A small-scale replica of the southern stock migration involves the trekking of the reindeer herds between the summer pastures in the tundra and the protected winter pastures at the northern edge of the forest. Agriculture has been introduced only in recent years and is furthered on a small scale by the use of hothouses, the long hours of summer daylight, and the specially developed frost-resistant seeds and plants. To the south, in the taiga, cattle are reared in alluvial meadows along the rivers, and hardy grains and vegetables are cultivated in the clearing. However, agriculture is generally subordinated to lumbering, mining, hunting, and fishing.

Further south, in the mixed forests of the middle belt, lies the extensive flax and dairy-farming zone. Here flax is grown in rotation with fodder crops, which in turn support the dairy cattle. Potatoes are also grown to some extent and serve as fodder for hogs. The flax and dairy zone includes the old industrial centers of the European USSR. One of its principal problems is the gradual introduction of wheat into its growing scheme. Adjoining in the south and extending through the wooded steppe from the Baltic Sea to the Middle Volga Region is the grain-hemp-potato zone. While grain (especially spring and winter wheat) is important throughout this zone, local specialization emphasizes any of the associated crops (hemp, potatoes, and sugar beets) and related dairy- or hog-farming. In the western portion of the wooded steppe the humid climate and the long, warm summers favor the cultivation of sugar beets and winter wheat. Stock-raising is carried on intensively on the basis of grain feed and waste products of sugar refining. In the east, beyond the

Volga, agriculture is much less intensive. Grain predominates, and cattle-rearing is based on natural pasture. In Western Siberia, between the Urals and the Altay, the emphasis on grain, mainly wheat, is still stronger. Flax and hemp are secondary crops. Extensive areas not yet plowed under serve as grazing land for meat and dairy cattle.

In the southern belt, the western portion corresponds to the grain-sunflower zone, where wheat, barley, corn, and other grains are grown side by side with industrial crops, of which sunflowers are the most important. As in the wooded steppe to the north, the raising of hogs, poultry, and meat and dairy cattle is very intensive. In the southern section of this zone, cotton is a new feature in the dry-farming scheme. In the east of the steppe belt, the dry farming of grain and fodder crops is less intensive. In this zone, which corresponds to the dry regions of the Volga steppes and the Northern Caucasus, cattle are reared mainly for meat, and sheep for wool. It is in this area that droughts present the greatest peril to agriculture and irrigation is most energetically applied. The desert and mountain pastures of the south correspond to the zone specializing in the raising of livestock for meat and wool. The natural pastures support sheep, camels, and cattle on an extensive scale. Agriculture is of secondary importance. In certain isolated areas, such as the mountain pastures of the Caucasus, stock-raising assumes a more intensive character and is also directed toward milk production. In the foothills of the Crimea and the Caucasus, where the relief is not favorable to field crops, orchards, vineyards, and tobacco plantations are favored by the warm, mild climate. Special mention must be made of the subtropical Black Sea littoral, where the frostless climate permits the cultivation of tea, citrus fruits, and the tung tree. In the foothills of southern Kazakhstan and northern Kirghizia lies a complex zone of industrial and grain crops, where irrigated cultivation of sugar beets, southern hemp, and rice alternates with the dry-farming of grain. Stock-raising depends partly on alfalfa crops, partly on desert and mountain pastures.

In the eastern belt the grain and dairy and meat cattle zone corresponds to the best-developed sections of Eastern Siberia and the Far East. Natural meadows and grazing grounds are extensive. The southern section of the Far East is characterized by a warm, humid summer and represents a rice, soybean, and sugar-beet zone with wide potentialities for future development.

Not connected with any of the foregoing agricultural specialty belts are the truck- and dairy-farming areas near large urban and industrial centers throughout the country, which supply the city population with produce, milk, berries, fruits, and potatoes.

The policy of intensive industrialization, which was adopted by the USSR in the middle 1920's, has had a tremendous impact on the industrial geography of the country. Among the most significant trends are the emphasis on industrial production, in particular the manufacture of machine tools and machines, and the radical shift of the industrial center of gravity toward the eastern sections of the Union.

At the start of the First Five-Year Plan, in 1928, the share of industry in the total production was 58.7 percent. Of the total industrial output, heavy industry accounted for 39.7 percent. In 1940, on the eve of the Soviet entry into the Second World War, the part of industry in the country's production had grown to 84.7 percent; heavy industry produced at that time 61.2 percent of the industrial output. Under the impetus of the war, when the products of heavy industry played a significant role in making victory possible, the distortion of the Soviet industrial pattern was accentuated still further. In 1945 heavy industry was producing 76.1 percent of the total industrial output. So great was the emphasis given heavy industry during the war, that the Fourth Five-Year Plan provides for a sharp increase in the output of consumer goods and a reduction of heavy industry production to about two thirds of the total industrial output.

The new characteristic location pattern of Soviet industry evolved from two major principles. Industrial centers were to be established near the sources of raw materials and near the consumers, and each major national unit (union republic) was to achieve a high degree of self-sufficiency in industrial production, while developing its own specialization. Prior to the shift of the geographic pattern, the great majority of industrial enterprises were concentrated in the Central Industrial Region (mainly textile), in the Ukraine and the Urals (mainly mining and metallurgy), and at Leningrad (machinery). Then, simultaneously with the modernization and further development of the old industrial sites, new industrial regions were created in Siberia, the Far East, and Central Asia. The most spectacular example of industrial development was the formation of the Ural-Kuznetsk *kombinat*, which provided for the exchange of coal and iron ore between the Urals and the Kuznetsk Basin. During the Second World War the industrialization of the eastern regions of the USSR was forced to a still greater degree. During the four war years, 1941–45, industrial output increased 3.6 times in the Urals, 2.8 times in Siberia, and 3.4 times in the Volga Region.

Soviet industry now produces numerous items which formerly had to be imported from abroad. Among these products are automobiles, tractors, textile, printing, and paper-making machinery, steel-rolling mills, powerful hydraulic turbines, excavators, and internal combustion engines. New technical processes have been developed, such as hydraulic and cutting techniques in peat working, the use of peat as fuel for electric power stations, the underground gasification of coal, and the manufacture of synthetic rubber. Industry in the USSR is characterized moreover by large enterprises; more than 60 percent of the industrial workers are employed in plants with more than one thousand employees. The large size of many industrial enterprises facilitates the mechanization of the work, reduces overhead expenses, and facilitates the utilization of byproducts. The extreme concentration of a number of industries involved extended periods of construction, however, and necessitated abnormally long haulage of the products to certain consumer areas. In view of these setbacks, a policy of smaller-scale industrial construction, said to have been directed against megalomania, was adopted on the eve of the Second World War. Among the larger enterprises, the so-called *kombinat*, or combine, is typical. This type of establishment may be engaged in making a number of products based upon the same raw material; it may be concerned with various industrial applications of the same raw material; or it may follow through all stages of a given manufacturing process from the raw material to the finished product. Thus, a lumber *kombinat* of the most complete type would engage in sawmilling, manufacturing prefabricated houses, veneering, pulp and paper milling, and distilling wood for methyl alcohol and other chemical products. The lignite of the Moscow Basin is used at Stalinogorsk as fuel for the electric power station and as a raw material for the nitrate fertilizer plant. Finally, a textile *kombinat*, such as the one at Tashkent, engages in all processes of the textile industry, from the spinning of the cotton yarn, through the weaving and dyeing, to the production of the finished fabric. The advantages inherent in the *kombinat* type of industrial enterprise can be resolved into the fullest and the most rational utilization of the raw material and consequent reduction of production costs, the lowering of the transportation costs which are generally incurred in carrying the raw materials or semifinished products between various processing stages,

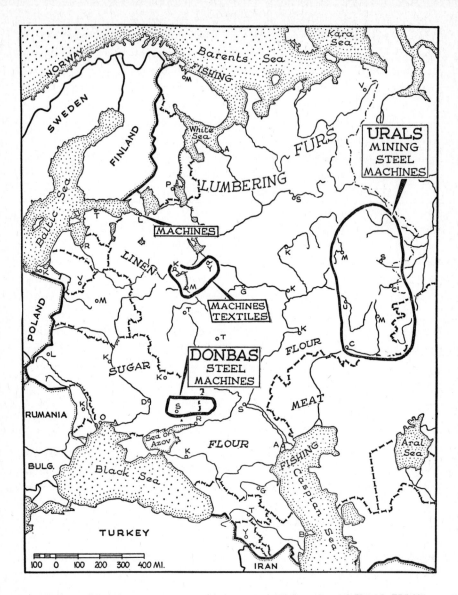

CHIEF INDUSTRIAL AREAS OF THE EUROPEAN USSR

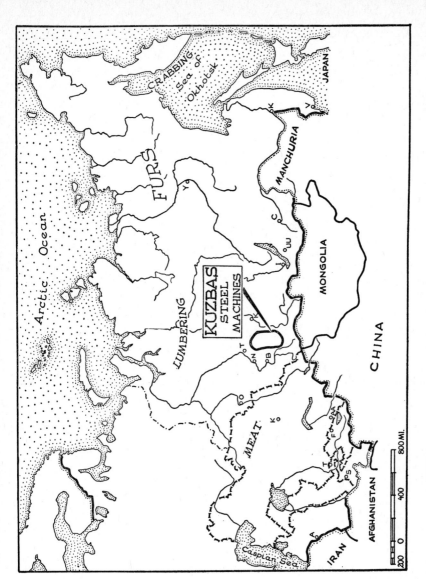

CHIEF INDUSTRIAL AREAS OF THE ASIATIC USSR

and also the overall acceleration of the production processes due to their centralized localization.

Coal, petroleum, wood, peat, hydroelectricity, and oil shale are the most common sources of power in the USSR. There coal accounts for about 80 percent of all fuel resources, while in the world as a whole its share is 90 percent. The importance that the Soviets attach to the development of sources other than coal is clearly in keeping with their rational use of other resources. While the USSR contains only 20 percent of the world's coal reserves, it has 55 percent of the petroleum, 40 percent of the peat, and 35.7 percent of the hydroelectric power reserves. Because of the vast extent of the country and the cost of long-distance haulage of fuel, efforts are constantly being made to develop local power resources and to approximate also in this field as high a degree as possible of local self-sufficiency. High-grade fuels, such as anthracite and coking coal from the Donets Basin and petroleum from Baku, are necessarily carried to regions deficient in industrial fuels. However, such local resources as lignite, peat, oil shale and hydroelectricity are being developed essentially for local consumption. Although nearly every oblast or kray offers some sources of power, specific types of fuel are distributed very irregularly throughout the Union; no notable petroleum deposits, for example, appear to be east of the Urals in Siberia, and in the south, due to zonal geographic factors, lumber and peat reserves are negligible.

A summary regional survey shows that Siberia abounds in coal (Kuznetsk, Cheremkhovo, Bureya, and other basins), in hydroelectric potentialities (along the Ob', the Yenisey, the Angara, the Lena, and the Amur), and in lumber. Peat is found only in Western Siberia, and petroleum in Sakhalin and the Kamchatka Peninsula. In Kazakhstan and Central Asia lumber and peat are almost entirely lacking. There are considerable coal reserves (mainly at Karaganda), oil at Nebit-Dag, along the Emba River, and in the Fergana Valley, and there are hydroelectric resources along the upper Irtysh, Syr Darya, and Amu Darya. In the European USSR, fuel resources are concentrated in the south, where there are the coal reserves of the Donets Basin, the petroleum of the Caucasus, and the water power of the Dnieper and the Caucasus streams; in the north they are based on the Pechora coal and the peat and hydroelectric power of the northwest. One of the major problems connected with the fuel supply is the relatively poorly provided Central Industrial region of the European USSR. Although the local reserves of lignite in the Moscow Basin, and of peat and lumber, are being developed to the greatest extent possible, they have been proved to be insufficient for the fuel demands of the highly industrialized areas of Moscow, Ivanovo, and Gor'kiy. Almost two thirds of the fuel still remains to be hauled more than one thousand miles from the Baku oil field or from the Donets Basin. The long haulage of fuel is gradually being reduced, as new hydroelectric plants are developed along the upper Volga River (at Ivan'kovo, Uglich, Shcherbakov, and near Gor'kiy) and the oil fields of the "Second Baku" are opened along the middle Volga nearer to the major consumers in the Central Industrial Region.

Coal accounts for about 75 percent of all fuels consumed by the Soviet economy, as against 12 percent of wood and about 7 percent of petroleum. Less than 5 percent each are represented by peat and oil shale. In the Soviet economic scheme the importance of a coal basin is determined by such factors as the size of the reserves, the mining conditions, the quality of the coal, and the location of the basin with respect to consumer areas and transportation facilities. The most important coal-mining area of the USSR continues to be the Donets Basin, located on the Northern Donets, an affluent of the Don, and extending from the eastern Ukraine into Rostov Oblast of the Russian SFSR. This basin, which covers an area of 10,000 square miles, furnishes coking coal to the metallurgical industry of the southern European USSR, raw materials for the chemical plants of the region, and fuel for the large-scale industries in the southern, central, and Volga regions of the European USSR. Moreover, it services the rail lines of the Ukraine and adjoining sections of the Russian SFSR. Aside from its importance in the economy of the European USSR, the Donets Basin typifies the eastward trend of the industrial center of gravity of the USSR. Despite more than a threefold increase in production since 1913, its proportion of the national output has declined from 87 percent in 1913 to 57 percent in 1940, because of the rise of the new fields in the east. The decline of the Donbas was speeded by the German occupation during the Second World War. In 1945 production was reduced to 25 percent of the national output, and although by 1950 prewar production is expected to be equaled, the share of the Donbas in the USSR coal output is not expected to rise above 35 percent.

The Kuznetsk Basin, the coal field of the USSR second in importance, lies along the upper Tom' River, an affluent of the Ob' in Western Siberia. An area as large as the Donets Basin, its reserves are five times as great as those of the Donbas. The thick seams, which represent about 30 percent of the total coal reserves of the USSR, lie close to the surface and furnish some of the best coal of the Union. The basin was almost untouched before the first Five-Year Plan and furnished fuel only to the adjoining sections of the Trans-Siberian Railroad. After the creation in the early 1930's of the Ural-Kuznetsk *kombinat*, it became the major supplier of coal to the new metallurgical industries at Stalinsk and Magnitogorsk; from 1928 to 1940 its production rose from 2.75 million tons to about 20 million tons. Due to the loosening of the Ural-Kuzbas link and the gradual replacement of Kuznetsk coal by Karaganda fuel, the output of the Kuznetsk Basin now services chiefly the industries of Western Siberia.

The third coal base of the USSR, the Karaganda Basin, in central Kazakhstan, lies half way between the Kuznetsk Basin and the Urals. Its reserves of more than fifty billion tons are used mainly to supply the metallurgy of the Urals with coking coal, as well as the ferrous and nonferrous metallurgy and the railroads of the Kazakh SSR itself. The Moscow Basin, the fourth largest producer, furnishes low quality coal, which is used principally in the chemical and the electric power plants of the Central Industrial Region. Other basins important for their coking coal are those of the Pechora, Kizel in the Urals, and Tkvarcheli and Tkibuli in the Georgian SSR. Among the principal new fields scheduled for development during the current Plan are the Bureya deposits in Khabarovsk Kray, the Ekibastuz location in the Kazakh SSR, the Kuyurgaz (or Babay) field in the Bashkir Autonomous SSR, and the Uzgen basin in the Kirghiz SSR. Throughout the Union local deposits are to be developed in order to reduce long-distance haulage of fuels.

Petroleum plays a major role in the Soviet economy. Because of its importance as a fuel for internal combustion engines, it is replaced wherever possible by other fuels, such as oil shale, coal, and peat. A number of power plants which formerly operated on petroleum products have been converted to the use of coal in recent years. Although the industry is undergoing a significant shift in emphasis in its geographic pattern, the fields of the Caucasus (Baku, Groznyy, and Maykop) continue to be the principal producers. The Baku oil field, for example, which produced 83 percent of the total output in 1913, is scheduled to furnish only 48 percent in 1950 according to the Plan. It should be noted, however, that this major decrease is not due solely to the rise of new fields elsewhere in the USSR. Production at Baku decreased from a high of nearly

24 million tons on the eve of the Second World War to slightly more than one half that output in 1945. The scheduled 1950 production is pegged at 17 million tons. It is speculated that the limited resources of the Baku field and the current dearth in drilling machinery have contributed considerably to the shift toward the development of new potential producers such as the "Second Baku," which should furnish more than 7 million tons of oil in 1950. In addition to this field, which occupies such a favorable site near the central reaches of the European USSR, attention is currently being devoted to the development of fields in the Turkmen and Uzbek SSR, in Sakhalin, and in the Ukraine.

Peat represents only 3 percent of the fuel resources of the Union; in the central and the northwestern sections of the European USSR, however, it is one of the principal sources of energy. By far the greatest portion of the output serves as fuel for electric power stations constructed on the sites of the peat bogs or in their immediate vicinity. Among the more spectacular peat-fed power stations are those of Shatura and Elektrogorsk (near Moscow), Kaganovich (near Ivanovo), Gidrotorf (near Gor'kiy), Karintorf (near Kirov), Dubrovka (near Leningrad), and Orekhovsk (near Orsha, Belorussian SSR).

The extraction of combustible shale, another fuel intensively developed by the Soviets, is carried on mainly in Estonia, in the vicinity of Kokhtla-Yarve, and in the Volga Region, near Syzran'. It is converted partly into gas and partly into gasoline and other chemical products. The postwar Five-Year Plan saw the construction of a pipe line carrying shale gas from the Estonian field to Leningrad, as well as of pipe lines for natural gas connecting Dashava (Drogobych Oblast, Ukrainian SSR) with Kiev and Yelshanka (near Saratov) with Moscow. Coal gas, obtained by an underground coal-gasification process, is being piped from Tula to Moscow.

In order to economize high-grade fuels, local low-quality resources are generally utilized in electric power plants. In addition to the peat-powered stations, a plant at Akhtme (Estonia) is served by shale, the stations at Stalinogorsk, at Kaganovich (near Kashira), and at Chelyabinsk utilize lignite, while in the Donets Basin, in feeding the power plants of Zuyevka and Shterovka, anthracite dust is used.

Hydroelectric potential is highest along the upper course of streams rising in the mountain periphery of the USSR. Only one sixth of the potential lies in the European USSR, of which the Caucasus share is one half. The remaining hydroelectric resources lie in the Asiatic USSR, where they are still almost undeveloped. The construction of the Volkhov hydroelectric station and of the Zemo-Avchala plant near Tbilisi (Georgian SSR) inaugurated the building of large-scale water-power projects shortly after the Bolshevik Revolution. Among the largest installations completed prior to the Second World War are the Dnieper dam at Zaporozh'ye, the stations at Uglich and Shcherbakov, on the Volga, the Tuloma and Niva plants on the Kola Peninsula, the Svir' works at Podporozh'ye and Lodeynoye Pole, and the stations at Chirchik (Uzbek SSR), on the Rion River (Georgian SSR), and at Kanaker, on the Zanga River, in the Armenian SSR. During the Second World War, in connection with the speeded shift of industries to the Urals and Siberia, hydroelectric plants in those areas were built or enlarged. During the current Plan, the most spectacular projects are those of Farkhad, on the Syr Darya (Uzbek SSR), Mingechaur, on the Kura River (Azerbaijan SSR), the series of stations on the Zanga River, and the Ust'-Kamenogorsk plant on the upper Irtysh River (Kazakh SSR). To be completed during the next few years are large installations at Kaluga, on the Oka, at Gor'kiy, on the Volga, and at Molotov, on the Kama. Finally, projects are being worked out for the exploitation of the rich potential on the Angara and Yenisey rivers, in Siberia.

Like all other branches of Soviet industry, metallurgy has undergone considerable expansion, productively and geographically, during the Five-Year Plans and the Second World War. The trend, which is basic to the entire industrialization program, is continuing under the present Plan. The development of the industry was effected by reconstructing and modernizing old plants and constructing new mills in areas which were previously undeveloped, but rich in raw materials. The foremost metallurgical area lies in the southern section of the European USSR, including the eastern Ukrainian SSR and the Crimean and Rostov oblasts of the Russian SFSR. This area, which before the Second World War produced about two thirds of the total pig-iron output and more than one half of the steel, will probably continue to play a leading role in the metallurgical scheme, due to its favorable location and in spite of the great destruction wrought by the German invasion. The southern metallurgical region is based upon the coking coal of the Donbas and the iron ore of Krivoy Rog and of Kerch', in the Crimea. Most of the iron and steel mills are in the Donbas itself, where the major establishments, Stalino, Makeyevka, Yenakiyevo, and Voroshilovsk, and flux materials lie in close proximity to the coal mines. A second group of plants is located along the Dnieper, at Dnepropetrovsk, Dneprodzerzhinsk, and Zaporozh'ye, and at the Krivoy Rog mines. A third and smaller group lies on the northern shore of the Sea of Azov, at Zhdanov and Taganrog, and at the Kerch' mines. Because of the relatively high sulphur content of the Donbas coke, the southern steels are generally of the ordinary type. High-grade metal is produced only in the electric furnaces of the Zaporozh'ye steel plant. The metallurgical industry of the Central Industrial Region and adjoining areas is on a small scale and scattered in widely separated plants. A few mills, such as those near Tula, at Lipetsk, Vyksa, Kulebaki, and Tashino, in Gor'kiy Oblast, are supplied partly by local iron ore and partly by imported scrap. Once fueled by charcoal, they have now been converted to Donbas coke. High-grade steels are produced from scrap in such mills as the Red October plant at Stalingrad, the Hammer and Sickle and Elektrostal' plants at and near Moscow, respectively, and the plant at Leningrad. The most spectacular achievement in the metallurgical field was the creation of the Ural-Kuzbas *kombinat*, utilizing the iron ore of the Urals and the coke of the Kuznetsk Basin. These two areas, separated by a distance of more than 1,200 miles, nevertheless supplemented each other successfully in the creation of giant metallurgical plants, such as those of Magnitogorsk and Stalinsk. In the Urals, in addition to the reconstruction of the old charcoal-burning mills of Zlatoust, Lys'va, Beloretsk, and others, new steel mills were constructed by the Soviets at Nizhniy Tagil, and during the Second World War, at Chelyabinsk. The lack of good local coking coal in the Urals is a problem; however, on the basis of the local iron ore of good quality, the presence of alloys (manganese, nickel, chrome, and others), and the supply of coal from Karaganda, the Urals have come to specialize in the production of high-grade steels and ferroalloys. In connection with the loosening of the Ural-Kuznetsk link, the metallurgical industry of the Kuznetsk Basin is relying increasingly on iron ore from the Gornaya Shoriya to the south and near Abakan to the southeast. In addition to the mills in the basic metallurgical regions, isolated steel mills have been and are being constructed throughout the USSR. Among them are the steel mill of Komsomol'sk, which is to be supplied with blast furnaces during the postwar Five-Year Plan, the mill at Rustavi, in the Georgian SSR, at present under construction, which will operate on a complete pig-iron, ingot, and rolled-steel cycle, the steel mills of Temir-Tau (Kazakh SSR) and Begovat (Uzbek SSR), to which blast furnaces are to be added at a later stage. Other construc-

tion projects provided for by the current Plan are the creation of chrome
and nickel-steel metallurgy in the city of Novo-Troitsk near Orsk (Chkalov Oblast) and the establishment of a metallurgical base for Leningrad
and the European Northwest on the basis of Pechora coke and iron ore
from Yena, in the Kola Peninsula, and Gimoly, in the Karelo-Finnish
SSR. The construction of this steel mill, intended to fill the requirements
of Leningrad's industry (10 percent of the USSR output), is being
started at Cherepovets (Vologda Oblast). Projects of the future involve
the creation of a link between the Pechora coking-coal fields and the
metallurgy of the northern Urals, as well as the establishment of a powerful metallurgical region in Eastern Siberia, based on Cheremkhovo coal
and Angara-Ilim iron ore.

Nonferrous metallurgy plays a vital supporting role in heavy industry, and metals such as copper, lead, zinc, nickel, and aluminum, individually or as alloys, are important in electrotechnical, precision-
instruments, automobile, and aircraft industries. In the production of
copper, the smelters and refineries of Balkhash and Dzhezkazgan (Kazakh SSR) are rapidly outdistancing the former leading producers
of the Urals (Krasnoural'sk, Kirovgrad, and Revda). Copper is also
produced at Alaverdi (Armenian SSR), and a new refinery is being
constructed at Almalyk (Uzbek SSR). Lead-zinc ores (often associated
with silver, gold, and other metals) are worked in Kazakhstan (mainly
at Achisay, Tekeli, Leninogorsk, and Zyryanovsk), in the Caucasus at
Sadon, in the Urals, Western Siberia (Kuznetsk Basin), and in the Far
East at Tetyukhe. Chimkent (Kazakhstan) leads in the production of
lead, and Dzaudzhikau (North Ossetian Autonomous SSR) and Belovo
(Kemerovo Oblast) in the production of zinc. Aluminum is generally
worked near sources of hydroelectric power, because of the large power
supply required for its production. The principal works are at Volkhov,
Zaporozh'ye, Krasnotur'insk, Kamensk-Ural'skiy, and Kandalaksha.
Everywhere bauxite is the raw material, except at Kandalaksha, where
Khibiny nephelite is processed. Nickel is smelted at Verkhniy Ufaley
(Urals), Monchegorsk (Kola Peninsula), and Noril'sk (northern Si-
beria). Manganese is mined near Nikopol' (Ukraine), Chiatura (Geor-
gia), Dzhezdinskiy (Kazakhstan), and near Achinsk (Western Siberia).
Other metals, such as tin, mercury, antimony, tungsten, and molybdenum,
are also mined, principally in Transbaykalia, Central Asia, the Altay
Mountains, the Northern Caucasus, and the Urals. Tungsten-

molybdenum ores are given special attention in the development provided for during the postwar period.

The construction of machinery constitutes one of the most rapidly developing industrial branches in the USSR. While since 1913 the value of the output of heavy industry as a whole has increased twelvefold, in the same period the machine-building industry has increased its total production nearly fifty-five times. Before the Revolution machine construction was restricted to Moscow, Leningrad, and the Ukraine. The Soviets expanded the industry in developing the production of new articles, such as automobiles, tractors, machine tools, and airplanes, and also in emphasizing rational locations when establishing new plants. New production items were introduced into the industry by means of long-established enterprises: Leningrad was the first to manufacture tractors, a Moscow auto repair plant converted to the production of automobiles, Sormovo (near Gor'kiy) initiated the production of Diesel engines, and Kolomna developed new types of locomotives. The experience and skill gained by these producers were then applied to the newly created production centers. Decentralization was the dominant principle governing their location. While heavy machine tools continue to be produced in the main mining and metallurgical areas (Sverdlovsk for the Urals and Kramatorsk for the Donbas), and while precision instruments are made in Moscow and Leningrad because of the easy availability of skilled labor there, other new machinery works are scattered throughout the country. Thus, agricultural machines and tractors are produced in the main grain belt and near metallurgical centers, railway cars are manufactured on sites close to steel and lumber sources, and gold dredges are made at Krasnoyarsk and Irkutsk, near the Siberian gold fields. Vladimir, which produces auto parts, and Kirzhach, where automobile lights are made, lie roughly in the center of the triangle formed by the three automobile cities of Moscow, Yaroslavl', and Gor'kiy. In Ivanovo and Kalinin oblasts, regions of numerous textile mills which are fueled by peat, factories produce textile-milling and peat-extracting machinery. In the Crimea, where the canning industry is important, canning equipment is produced. In Central Asia an agricultural machinery plant produces mainly cotton-picking and cotton-ginning equipment. The Second World War and the German occupation of the machinery production centers of the Ukraine necessitated further development of the industry in the eastern sections of the USSR. Metalworking and machine production increased sixfold in the Urals during the years 1941–45, and the share of the industry in the total production of the Urals rose from one half to three quarters. Typical of the change in emphasis is the case of Nizhniy Tagil; it was formerly mainly a mining and metallurgical center, but now 80 percent of its total output is connected with the machine-building industry. New tractor plants were built at Rubtsovsk (Altay Kray), Vladimir, and Lipetsk to offset the loss of the plants in the occupied regions and to service the newly developed agricultural areas in the east. A new auto plant was constructed at Miass in the Urals, and the postwar Plan is indicative of the continuing emphasis given to the industry in providing for new automobile works at Moscow, Dnepropetrovsk, Novosibirsk, Kutaisi, Ul'yanovsk, and Minsk.

Chemical industry is often associated with metallurgy in the rational use of by-products of the steel mills and coking plants. In addition to this association, chemical plants utilize coal, petroleum, combustible shales, and peat for the production of gasoline and other liquid fuels; they base the manufacture of wood pulp and paper and artificial fiber on such waste products of the lumber industry as sawdust, and they produce alcohol and synthetic rubber from potatoes. The industry also processes such specific chemical raw materials as phosphorite, apatite, salt, potash, mirabilite, sulphate, pyrite, and chrome ores. Geographical dispersion of the new chemical plants has decentralized the production which was formerly centered on Leningrad and Moscow. Superphosphate plants are now located at Leningrad (based on Khibiny apatite), at Voskresensk (near Moscow), Dzerzhinsk, Konstantinovka (Ukraine); others are being erected in the Kazakh SSR and in Central Asia on the basis of the rich phosphorite deposits of Chulak-Tau near Dzhambul. Potash fertilizer is processed in the chemical works of Berezniki (Molotov Oblast) and in the western Ukraine, while nitrate is synthesized from Kizel coal at Berezniki, from Moscow Basin lignite at Stalinogorsk, from Donbas coal at Gorlovka, and by nitrogen fixation at Dzerzhinsk. Synthetic rubber is obtained from potatoes at Yaroslavl' and Kazan', from limestone at Yerevan, and from petroleum at Baku.

With one third of the country in the forested zone and a constant need for construction timber, the USSR has developed an important lumbering industry centered mainly in Arkhangel'sk Oblast, the Karelo-Finnish SSR, the northern Urals, and Siberia. Formerly the greater part of the production was exported through such sawmilling centers as Arkhangel'sk, Onega, and Mezen'. The diversion of most of the present output to domestic markets has given rise to new inland lumber centers, such as Kotlas, and to a large number of sawmills at the intersection of rail lines and rivers flowing out of the forested belt. Aside from export and construction uses of the Soviet lumber, a good part is processed into paper, veneers, matches, alcohol, and various chemical products. Paper mills are concentrated mainly in the northern European USSR (Leningrad Oblast, Karelo-Finnish SSR, and Arkhangel'sk Oblast) which produces two thirds of the total output. During the last two decades large sawmilling centers, such as Igarka and Lesozavodsk, have grown up in Siberia and the Far East.

The textile industry is the principal consumer branch. Before the Revolution, its activities were concentrated overwhelmingly in the areas of Moscow and Ivanovo-Voznesensk, and to a lesser extent at Leningrad. Raw material, in the case of cotton, was shipped from the cotton-growing areas of Central Asia and was returned there for the consumer in the form of finished textile goods. The Soviets built new cotton mills closer to the sources of raw cotton, in Central Asia and Transcaucasia. Following the cotton-grain exchange between Western Siberia and Central Asia via the Turksib Railroad, cotton mills were also built in Barnaul, Novosibirsk, and Kansk. In spite of the new construction, the former cotton mills of the Central Industrial Region, now enlarged and modernized, continue to be the main producers. The cotton mills of the USSR employ about one half of the textile workers of the country. In the central and western sections of the European USSR are the main linen-milling centers of Vyazniki, Kostroma, and Smolensk. Woolen mills, which were formerly located only in Moscow and Leningrad (fine cloths) and in the central European USSR (coarse cloths), are now being built nearer the sheep-raising regions of the USSR. As a result of the continuing construction during the postwar Plan, the Central Industrial Region is expected to lose its textile monopoly, and long-distance haulage of raw materials and textile goods will be considerably reduced.

The location of the food industry depends essentially on the position of the agricultural resources and the position of the consumer centers. These factors determine the rational location of new plants. Thus, agricultural products which decrease in bulk after processing are generally treated in the crop areas; this refers to distilling, wine-making, canning, and especially sugar-refining industries. On the contrary, a product, such as grain, which is converted into food of a type unsuitable for transportation (macaroni and bakery products) or of great bulk (bread) is generally processed in the consumer area. Aside from the foregoing principles, the economic independence of each area (with regard to products such as dairy and meat products, grain, bakery goods, and beverages) is considered in locating the various parts of the food industry.

TRANSPORTATION AND COMMERCE

Several features peculiar to the geography of the USSR have attributed exceptional importance to the development of a suitable transportation network. Proper transportation facilities have become indispensable between widely scattered industrial centers and sources of raw materials and between industrial and agricultural districts which supplement each other in their economy. Thus, the treeless south is opposed to the forested north in the exchange of lumber and grain; the major producing regions of coal and oil, the Donbas and Baku, are separated by distances of 1,000–1,500 miles from the major industrial consumer areas of Moscow and Leningrad; and the Kuzbas and the Urals exchange their coke and iron over a distance of more than 1,200 miles. In addition to the economic factors, the vast distances also affect considerably the transportation network within the country; the low average population density, the extremely irregular distribution of the population, and the continuing process of industrialization and development, which keeps the country in constant flux, are other complicating factors.

The waterways served as the first major transportation routes. Rivers played an important part early in the development of the Russian state. Rising at moderate heights within the confines of the original Russian settlement area between Kiev, Moscow, and Leningrad, the rivers were connected at an early date by portages extending over the low watersheds. Across the entire East European plain and later across Siberia, the rivers served as the main arteries and ways of expansion. Thus, in a country of long winters which render navigation impossible for as long as nine months every year, the rivers have traditionally played a major role in the development of the economy. Even after the coming of the railroads, the first lines were clearly subordinated to the waterways and merely served as links over portage routes. One of the first railroads was the Kalach-Tsaritsyn (now Stalingrad) line, which connected the Don and the Volga rivers at their nearest approach. Of relatively early date also was the construction of the Perm' (now Molotov)-Tyumen' railroad, which linked the basins of the Volga and the Ob' rivers across the Urals. With the further industrialization of the country, however, the railroads rapidly assumed an importance of their own, and at the present time they have the major role in the transportation economy of the USSR.

The first important rail line connected St. Petersburg (now Leningrad) and Moscow. Other railroads were built from Moscow toward the Volga cities of Yaroslavl', Nizhniy-Novgorod (now Gor'kiy), and Saratov, and they soon established the pattern of radiating lines centered at Moscow which became the dominant feature of the prerevolutionary railroad geography of the country. The construction of rail lines was also dictated by the grain export, which resulted in the building of lines from the chief grain areas (Ukraine, Volga Region) to the ports of the Baltic Sea and the Black Sea. Other lines connected the industrial centers of the south (Krivoy Rog, Donbas) and the Urals with the Moscow and Leningrad industrial areas. Only a few widely separated railroads penetrated far into the outlying areas, serving Siberia (Trans-Siberian Railroad), Central Asia (Trans-Caspian Railroad), and the Caucasus (Trans-Caucasian Railroad). Their function was chiefly the shipment of raw materials to the processing centers of European Russia and the return of the finished products to the outlying areas.

Under the Soviets, which inherited a network of 36,300 miles, the rail transportation pattern underwent a drastic change. A great reduction in foreign trade lessened the importance of rail lines leading to the western borders and to the major exporting ports. While the load on the short western lines was considerably reduced, the loadings on the long eastern lines underwent a sharp increase. In spite of the fact that Soviet policy provided for the local processing of a large proportion of cotton, lumber, ores, and other raw materials, the great increase of production during the Five-Year plans maintained and even exceeded the former flow of goods to the industrial areas of the central European USSR.

Realizing the importance of the railroads in the industrialization of the country, the Russians adopted an ambitious construction program which raised the railroad mileage to 67,000 at the eve of the Second World War. During the war itself a further 6,000 miles went into operation, and during the current Plan 4,500 miles of construction have been scheduled. In the building program economic considerations are of primary importance. Railroads destined chiefly for the shipment of raw materials are penetrating into many areas which formerly appeared as blank regions on the railroad maps. Other lines are constructed to create short cuts, by-passes, or direct links between important related areas.

The Moscow-Donbas railroad, of which the major northern portion consists of reconstructed lines, only the southern section south of Valuyki having new track, established a direct link between two major industrial regions and carries coal and steel to the north and lumber and manufactured goods to the south. The North Pechora railroad, which was completed in 1942, connected the vital Vorkuta coal district and the Ukhta petroleum area with the rest of the USSR, causing a sharp increase in the production of the two newly-developed regions. Connections between the Moscow area and the East were considerably improved under the Five-Year Plans, with the construction of the Kazan'-Sverdlovsk and Gor'kiy-Kotel'nich lines, which filled vital gaps in the transportation network. Further work is being done during the current Plan to electrify the Chelyabinsk-Ufa section and to double-track the Omsk-Sverdlovsk-Kotel'nich-Gor'kiy route.

In the Urals, which lacked suitable north-south communications, the construction of the Sos'va-Alapayevsk section in 1945 completed the Chelyabinsk–Kamensk-Ural'skiy–Serov connection, the only modern north-south link on the eastern slopes of the mountains. The older Chelyabinsk-Sverdlovsk-Karpinsk line is scheduled for electrification during the current Plan. Taking into consideration the war-time construction of the Orsk-Kandagach section and the possible future connection of the northern Urals with the Vorkuta area, one can envision for the first time a continuous rail link along the entire chain of the Ural Mountains.

One of the most spectacular railroad construction projects of the current Plan is the South Siberian Railroad. This line, which is intended to ease the load of the old Trans-Siberian, will extend from the area of Kuybyshev across the Urals to Magnitogorsk. Following the already operating Magnitogorsk-Kartaly-Akmolinsk line, the South Siberian will continue through the northern Kazakh steppes through Pavlodar and Kulunda to Barnaul and through the Kuznetsk Basin to Abakan. The last section of this major trunk line, from Abakan to Tayshet, on the Trans-Siberian, leads through difficult mountain country and is to be completed after 1950. This railroad, of tremendous economic significance, will connect and help to develop the mining region of the Bashkir Autonomous SSR, the steel mills of Magnitogorsk, the grain steppes of Kazakhstan, the salt of Kulunda, the coal of Ekibastuz, the Kuznetsk Basin, and the lumber and iron resources of the Kuznetsk Ala-Tau. While this work proceeds south of the Trans-Siberian Railroad, this old line is also being rejuvenated in its western section. With the electrification during the current Plan of the Stalinsk-Omsk-Chelyabinsk-Ufa section, the Trans-Siberian Railroad and its western extension to Ufa will become the longest electrified railroad in the world.

Typical of the region in which the railroads were the dominant factor in the industrial development is the Kazakh SSR. Before its railroad era, Kazakhstan was traversed only by the Trans-Caspian Railroad in the west and touched by the Trans-Siberian in the north. The construction of the Turksib Railroad (1927–30) was the first chapter in the development scheme. This line, whose primary function was to connect the Siberian and the Central Asian domains and to provide a route for the exchange of Siberian coal, grain, and lumber for Central Asian cotton, incidentally also developed the entire eastern part of Kazakhstan. From it vital spurs penetrate into the rich mining areas of the Altay Mountains, to the lead mines of Tekeli, the phosphate of Chulak-Tau, and the coal of Lenger. Along its route, irrigation has opened vast areas to agricultural production. Other lines were constructed during the 1930's to the coal mines of Karaganda, the copper deposits of Balkhash and Dzhezkazgan, and the petroleum of Emba. During the current Plan the construction of the Mointy-Chu section will complete a north-south line through the center of the Kazakh Republic.

Also initiated during the current Five-Year Plan will be the realization of the long-projected railroad between Aleksandrov-Gay in the Volga Region and Chardzhou on the Trans-Caspian Railroad in the Turkmen SSR. This line will ease the load of the old Trans-Caspian Railroad (through Kandagach-Tashkent) and provide a direct link between the Lower Volga Region and Central Asia. The first section from Chardzhou to Kungrad near the Aral Sea is scheduled for completion by 1950.

During the Second World War considerable construction was carried on in the Volga Region. This area, which had an excellent water route in the Volga River during the summer, was without north-south communication during the winter months. Such a north-south railroad was built during the war along the right bank of the Volga River, between Ilovlinskaya (near Stalingrad) and Sviyazhsk (near Kazan'). Of great importance also is the direct Volga-Caucasus link along the northwestern shore of the Caspian Sea, between Astrakhan' and Kizlyar, which was completed during the war.

In addition to the economic factors, other considerations in the

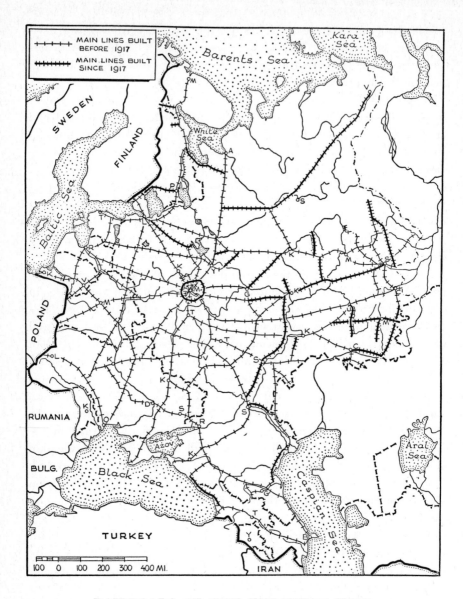

RAILROADS OF THE EUROPEAN USSR

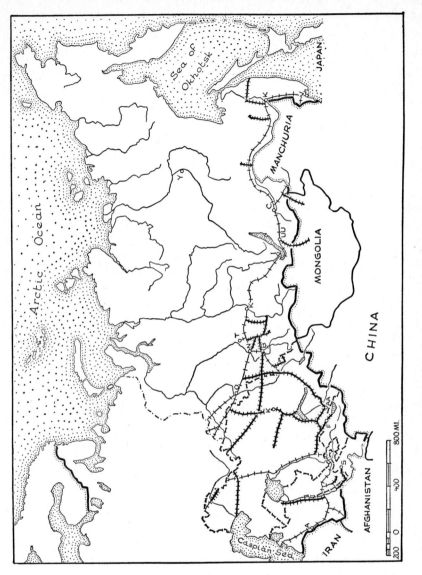

RAILROADS OF THE ASIATIC USSR

railroad-building program have involved the creation of rail service for the capitals of autonomous national units. Among the centers which received rail connections under the Soviet regime are Stalinabad, Sukhumi, Stalinir, Yoshkar-Ola, Cheboksary, Cherkessk, and Abakan. The formation of new railroad centers of major proportions, such as Chelyabinsk and Novosibirsk, has necessitated the construction of by-pass lines for the use of transit freights. Moscow itself, still the premier rail hub of the country, received a circular by-pass route during the Second World War, circling the capital at a distance of about fifty miles.

A number of projected rail lines on which construction had begun prior to the Second World War were abandoned in favor of more important projects. Among these railroads are chiefly minor sections, such as the Kazan'-Chistopol'-Bugul'ma railroad through the Tatar Autonomous SSR, the Ufa-Magnitogorsk line, and the spur into the Caucasus to Mikoyan-Shakhar (now Klukhori). Also affected, however, was the much-discussed Baykal-Amur trunk line, which represented the eastern section of the grandiose new Siberian railway from Magnitogorsk to the Pacific Ocean. This controversial link, which during the Second World War was the subject of much speculation, had been scheduled for construction during the third Five-Year Plan. Beginning at the western terminus of Tayshet, the work had proceeded at least as far as Ust'-Kut at the eve of the Second World War. However, during the conflict construction apparently subsided in favor of more vital projects. The Baykal-Amur line failed to be listed in the fourth Five-Year Plan as one of the major construction jobs, and it would appear that work on the line, if it is in progress at all, is no longer forced, in view of the major effort exerted on the South Siberian Railroad, the western part of the overall Siberian project. In connection with the Baykal-Amur project, a few auxiliary lines did see completion. These are the Komsomol'sk-Sovetskaya-Gavan' line, the Izvestkovyy-Chekunda-Ust'-Niman line into the Bureya Basin, and the spur from the area of Skovorodino to Tyndynskiy.

The USSR is fortunate in possessing a river network of major proportions, including such great streams as the Amur, the Lena, the Yenisey, the Ob', and the Volga rivers, having some of the most extensive basins of the world. In spite of the short periods of navigation, the waterways assume especially great importance in areas where no other communications are available, particularly in Siberia. Bulky freight for distant destinations (a common feature of Soviet domestic commerce) generally is shipped by water routes. The principal goods which fall within this category are lumber products, petroleum, building materials (cement, stone, and so forth), grain, salt, and coal. The total length of the waterways has been calculated at about 250,000 miles, of which only one fourth is navigable. By 1950 the total length of navigable waterways is to be raised to 71,000 miles. Among the rivers which have been opened to navigation in recent years are the northern Siberian rivers, the Pyasina, the Khatanga, the Anabar, the Olenek, the Yana, and the Indigirka.

The greatest development of the waterways has taken place in the European USSR. The most important streams of this section of the country rise in the Central Russian upland and flow toward the Baltic, the Black, and the Caspian seas. The upper course of the Northern Dvina and Neva systems also lies in close proximity to the Volga basin. These geographical factors and the low watershed elevation has made it possible to combine the various river basins of the European USSR into a unified water network. The principal canals involved in this scheme are the Mariinsk system, which connects Leningrad and the Volga at Shcherbakov and which will undergo reconstruction during the current Plan, the Moscow Canal (until 1947 the Moscow-Volga Canal), and the White Sea–Baltic Canal. The rivers of the Asiatic part of the USSR present a quite different picture. All the major streams rise in the high mountain ranges along the southern border and flow northward, parallel to each other, to the Arctic Ocean. Only their affluents, which generally flow in an east-west direction, approach each other in their upper reaches and present the possibility of an overall water route. From the point of view of navigation only the Amur, which flows generally from west to east into the Pacific Ocean, is of much importance; least valuable are the rivers of the Caucasus and Central Asia, partly because of their mountainous character, but also because they often belong to closed inland sea basins (the Caspian and the Aral seas).

The Volga River and its affluents carry nearly one half of all the freight carried on the waterways of the USSR. The Volga is the largest river of the European USSR and flows through a densely populated, highly developed economic region, having a population of about 50,-000,000 (one third of the total population of the European USSR). Its basin extends from Leningrad in the north (through the connecting Neva system) to Astrakhan' on the Caspian in the south and from

Moscow in the west to Molotov in the east. The Caspian Sea provides an outlet toward Central Asia and Iran. The chief freight items are lumber (downstream) and grain, fish, salt, and oil (upstream).

Although the USSR is the most continental Great Power of the world, both ocean and coastal shipping are of considerable importance. As much as 90 percent of the foreign trade passes through the ports. This distribution of the foreign trade was true chiefly prior to the Second World War, when the chief customers of the USSR, Great Britain, the United States, and France, were overseas countries. Since the war, however, a larger proportion of the foreign trade proceeds by railroad to the countries of eastern Europe. Long-distance coastal shipping (that is, between the ports of different seas) is of relatively little importance for the USSR chiefly because of the great distances. However, cement is shipped from Novorossiysk on the Black Sea to Leningrad and Arkhangel'sk, and sugar from Odessa to Arkhangel'sk and Vladivostok. Local coastwise shipping, on the contrary, has been developed to a large extent on the Black Sea and especially on the Caspian, where the shipping of petroleum from Baku to Astrakhan' is one of the chief features of Soviet maritime commerce. Coastwise navigation can also be expected to assume greater importance on the Baltic Sea in view of the great expansion of the Soviet coast during the Second World War.

The Black Sea handles more than 50 percent of all overseas exports. Together with the Sea of Azov, it represents the chief maritime navigation region of the USSR. Its importance is due chiefly to the ice-free ports, the proximity of the rich grain areas of the Ukraine and the Northern Caucasus, of the Donbas industrial area, and the Caucasus oil exports. The main ports are Odessa, Nikolayev, Zhdanov, Novorossiysk, Poti, and Batumi. Navigation on the Caspian Sea is limited by its inland location and by the shallowness of its northern section. However, it serves as a convenient link between the riparian districts of the Caucasus, the Lower Volga, Kazakhstan, and Central Asia, and to a lesser degree, Iran. Petroleum shipping between Baku and Astrakhan', the two chief ports, is the principal activity. The Baltic Sea has become important for the USSR as a direct route to the Atlantic Ocean. In addition to Leningrad, the main ports were all acquired since 1940. They are Tallin (Tallinn), Riga, Liepaya (Liepāja), Ventspils, Klaypeda (Klaipéda), and Kaliningrad.

The Arctic Ocean is rapidly gaining in importance in view of the development of the Northern Sea Route. This maritime link, which is the outcome of a practical realization of the long-sought Northeast Passage, began to be developed as a normal transportation route in the middle 1930's. In order to derive the greatest benefit possible from the brief navigation period, the Soviets constructed special ships able to withstand the pressure of ice floes, charted the yearly movement of ice in the seas of the Arctic Ocean, established such vital navigation aids as lighthouses, meteorological and oceanological observation posts, and secured the assistance of icebreakers. During the current Five-Year Plan the final stages of normal development of this Arctic route are scheduled to be achieved. Among the chief ports which have been developed along the Northern Sea Route are Murmansk (which is icefree because of the influence of the Gulf Stream, Arkhangel'sk, Nar'yan-Mar, Amderma, Novyy Port, Dikson, Igarka, Nordvik, Tiksi, Ambarchik, and Anadyr'. The freight consists largely of lumber exports and of finished products in coastwise shipping. The Soviet Pacific ports on the Sea of Okhotsk and the Sea of Japan are handicapped by their remoteness from the chief economic centers of the country and, except for Vladivostok, by paralyzing ice conditions. Their position has been considerably enhanced since the end of the Second World War, when the USSR acquired the former Japanese section of Sakhalin and the Kurile Islands. The USSR thus obtained direct access to the open Pacific. The concession of the joint Sino-Soviet naval base at Port Arthur also has added to the importance of the Soviet Pacific coast. Other Soviet naval bases are Sovetskaya Gavan' and Petropavlovsk, on Kamchatka. Coastwise shipping in the Sea of Okhotsk supplies the city of Magadan and its hinterland, the Kolyma gold fields.

Because of the lack of good highways, automobile transportation is of limited importance in the USSR. It is restricted to short-distance hauls, to traffic in metropolitan areas, and the approaches to rail heads, stations and river landings. In areas lacking rail and river transportation, long-distance auto connections have, however, assumed greater importance. Among such areas are the greater part of Siberia, Kazakhstan, and Central Asia. In Siberia and the Far East the chief highways are found in locations where railroad construction presents great difficulties, such as mountainous areas along the southern border and permanently frozen soils in the north. To be noted are the Chuya highway from Biysk (Altay Kray) through the Altay into Mongolia, the Aldan highway, which serves the Aldan gold fields of the Yakut

Autonomous SSR, and the Kolyma highway, which extends from the port of Magadan northward into the Kolyma gold fields. In the mountains of Central Asia, the main roads are the Pamir highway, between Osh and Khorog, and the Stalinabad-Tashkent highway, which crosses the Gissar, Zeravshan, and Turkestan mountain ranges. In recent years, highway construction has also become important in the European USSR. First to be completed was the Moscow-Minsk highway, prior to the Second World War. During the current Plan, highway construction is to be emphasized in the European USSR, chiefly in the Ukraine. The principal roads will connect Moscow and Khar'kov with the Crimea and the Northern Caucasus. More than seven thousand miles of highways are scheduled for this period.

The importance of aviation is obvious in the case of such a vast country as the USSR. It is especially vital in outlying areas devoid of other means of transportation, such as the Far North during the winter months. Aviation is widely used in fields other than transportation: as emergency service in the Siberian areas, for sowing sandy desert areas with grass seed, for surveying ice conditions in the Arctic, for spraying mosquito-infested marshes, and so forth. Regularly scheduled air lines are to aggregate a total of 110,000 miles by 1950.

PART TWO

Regional Survey

Russian Soviet Federated Socialist Republic (Russia)

Capital, Moscow (Moskva); area, 6,501,500,
population, 111,000,000

THE RUSSIAN SFSR is the largest, most populous, and economically
the most important union republic of the USSR, extending over nearly
four fifths of the total area and including more than one half the total
population of the Soviet Union. Its frontiers coincide with those of the
USSR in the north and east, along the seas of the Arctic Ocean and the
Pacific. Only in the southwest and west do the other union republics
intervene between the territory of the Russian SFSR and the international border of the USSR. Since the acquisition of the northern half
of East Prussia, the Russian SFSR extends over the vast distance of
nearly 7,000 miles, from the area of Kaliningrad (20° E) to the tip
of the Chukchi Peninsula (170° W). From north to south, the maximum
extent varies from 1,500 miles in the east to 2,500 miles in the west.

The Russian SFSR has essentially a lowland relief, consisting of the
East European plain and, beyond the Urals, of the West Siberian lowland and bordered by mountain systems in the east (Central Siberian
plateau and peripheral ranges) and in the southeast (Altay and Sayan
mountains). In the southwest, the Russian SFSR extends to the crest
of the Greater Caucasus. The principal rivers of the USSR flow through
this republic: the Volga and the Don rivers in the south of the European
part, the Onega, Northern Dvina, and Pechora rivers in the north, and
in Siberia the Ob' (with its chief affluent, the Irtysh), the Yenisey, the
Lena, the Yana, the Indigirka, and the Kolyma rivers; all these streams
flow north into the seas of the Arctic Ocean. Only the Amur River has
an easterly course, emptying into the Sea of Okhotsk of the Pacific
Ocean.

The Russian SFSR includes the entire polar belt of the USSR, with the Arctic islands of Franz-Josef Land, Novaya Zemlya, Severnaya Zemlya (North Land), the New Siberian and Vrangel' (Wrangel) islands, and so forth. Along the shores of the Arctic seas lies the tundra zone, which was settled by the Russians more than 700 years ago in its western (European) section, but only in recent years in its eastern (Asiatic) section. The taiga, in the south, occupies the major portion of the territory of the republic. Consisting largely of evergreens, the forest belt also has deciduous-tree zones, particularly in the European part. Farther south lies the black-earth belt, at first covered with a wooded steppe vegetation, but gradually changing into the steppe proper. The extreme south is a dry steppe, in which chestnut soils predominate; these are, however, only slightly inferior to the black earth with respect to fertility. Subtropical vegetation occurs only on the southern shore of the Crimea and along the Black Sea littoral of the Caucasus.

Because of its extensive coal and petroleum resources, the Russian SFSR is best supplied with power-producing minerals. Two of the largest coal basins of the world lie within the confines of the Asiatic portion of the republic: the Kuznetsk Basin, along the upper Tom' River, between the Salair Ridge and the Kuznetsk Ala-Tau, and the Tunguska Basin (as yet unexploited), along the lower Yenisey River, largely north of the Lower Tunguska, its right affluent. Lesser basins in Siberia are near Minusinsk and Cheremkhovo and along the Bureya River, while the Moscow and Vorkuta basins are most important in the European part. The Russian SFSR also includes the eastern section of the Donets Basin, the major portion of which lies within the Ukrainian SSR. An important petroleum zone extends throughout the European part of the Russian SFSR, beginning on the Arctic Circle in the Pechora River basin, along the western slopes of the Urals, past Molotov and Ufa, widening westward to the middle Volga in the area of Kuybyshev and Syzran', passing through the Gur'yev-Emba area of the Kazakh SSR, and reappearing north of the Greater Caucasus range at Makhachkala, Groznyy, and Maykop. In the very center of the European section of the Russian SFSR lies about one-half of the world's reserves of iron ore. Here more than 200 billion tons of low-grade ore lie buried in the Central Russian upland, east and southeast of Kursk, in the so-called Kursk magnetic anomaly. Other iron deposits occur in the Kola Peninsula, near Kerch' in the Crimea, in the Urals, and in Siberia.

Other important mineral resources are phosphorite and apatite deposits in the Kola Peninsula and along the Vyatka-Kama divide, oil shale in the Volga Region and Leningrad Oblast, natural gas near Saratov, peat and building materials in many sections of the European part of the Russian SFSR. In the Urals, in addition to petroleum and coal, potash, salt, and copper are found on the western slopes, iron, nickel, chrome, and platinum in the central ranges, and magnetite iron ore, copper, zinc, bauxite, and precious stones on the eastern slopes. In addition to coal, gold abounds in the Asiatic portion, in the Lena River basin and along the Kolyma River, and there are important tin deposits in Eastern Siberia, as well as lead, silver, and graphite.

The population of the Russian SFSR amounts to about 111 millions. The greatest population density occurs in the black-earth belt of the European section and in the regions of century-old settlement, including the watershed between the upper Volga and the Oka, the cradle of the Muscovite state, and the districts adjoining the northwestern lakes, Il'men' and Peipus (Chudskoye), and the upper course and left affluents of the Dnieper River. In these areas the concentration reaches 125 to 150 per square mile and as much as 250 and higher in the Moscow area. In the black-earth region of Siberia the density decreases to 60–90 persons per square mile. North of this belt the population rapidly decreases to 10–25 per square mile in the European North and as little as one person for every 2 square miles in the taiga of Siberia. Only in the valleys of the northern rivers (Northern Dvina, Pechora, Ob', Yenisey, Lena, with the Aldan and the Vilyuy, Yana, Indigirka, and Kolyma) does the population density rise to about 25 per square mile. The urban population is distributed mainly throughout the European part of the Russian SFSR: between the Volga and the Oka rivers, on the Baltic Sea and the Volga, and in the industrial Urals. The Siberian cities extend along the Trans-Siberian Railroad and lie usually at its intersection with the principal Siberian rivers. A great urban concentration has taken place in connection with the industrial development of the Kuznetsk Basin.

The Russians are the basic national element of the Russian SFSR and number about three fourths of the total population. They live principally in the black-earth belt, mixed forest, and taiga of the European section. The great number of minorities are found mainly along the middle Volga, on the western slopes of the Urals, on the northern slopes of the Greater Caucasus, and in the mountainous sections of Western and Eastern Siberia. In the Middle Volga Region live the Mordvinians and the Mari of the Finno-Ugric group and the Tatars and the Chuvash of the Turkic group; on the western slopes of the Urals are, from north to south, the Komi, the Komi-Permyak, and the Udmurt, all belonging to the Finno-Ugric group, and the Bashkirs, members of the Turkic group. On the northern slopes of the Greater Caucasus live a wide variety of peoples, including the Avars, the Darghins, the Lesghians in the east, and the Circassian tribes in the west. These national elements belong to the Caucasian linguistic group, of which Georgian is also a member. The Ossetians, who live in the central part of the Greater Caucasus, belong to the Iranian group. In Western Siberia, in the valleys of the Altay system, are other representatives of the Turkic group: the Altay tribes (a group of several small national elements), the Khakass, and the Tuvinians. In Eastern Siberia, the two principal nationalities are the Buryat-Mongols of the Mongolian group and the Yakuts of the Turkic group. A large number of small elements in the extreme north of the Russian SFSR belong to the Finno-Ugric, the Tungus-Manchu, and the Paleoasiatic linguistic groups.

Prior to the Bolshevik Revolution, industry within the present confines of the Russian SFSR was located in the Central Industrial Region between the Volga and the Oka, with specialization in the milling of cotton, silk, woolen, and linen textiles. The Petrograd (now Leningrad) industrial district was the chief area engaged in machine construction, while the metallurgical industry in the Urals was still on a small scale. During the Five-Year Plan period industrialization progressed rapidly throughout the republic, with particular emphasis on the Volga Region, the Urals, Western Siberia and the Far East. The Central Industrial Region largely developed heavy machinery construction, the manufacture of precision tools, and the production of chemicals, while maintaining its previous importance as a textile-milling region. The Leningrad industrial district continues to be a machine-construction center. However, in contrast to the prerevolutionary period, when raw materials were usually imported, it now uses local mineral resources, that is, copper, nickel, apatite, nephelite (an aluminum ore), from the Kola Peninsula; coal and petroleum, from the Pechora River basin; bauxite, lignite, and oil shale from the vicinity of Leningrad itself. Power is obtained from hydroelectric plants on the Volkhov and the Svir' rivers. An entirely new industrial region was created on the Volga. This river serves as one of the principal transportation routes of the Russian

SFSR, linking the Moscow industrial district via the Oka River and its own upper course, the Ural industrial district on the Kama River, the lumbering region along the Vyatka, the grain-producing areas along the middle Volga, the Donets coal and metallurgical district, west of Stalingrad, and finally the rich fisheries of the northern Caspian Sea. Among the principal goods transported on the Volga are: downstream, machines, textiles, fertilizers, metal from the Urals, and lumber; upstream, petroleum and cotton from Transcaucasia and Central Asia, fish, salt, melons, pumpkins, and grain. By rail, coal and iron arrive at the Volga from the Donbas, and coal, iron, and nonferrous metals from the Urals and Siberia. Recently extensive petroleum fields ("Second Baku") and natural gas deposits have been developed along the Volga, furnishing the basis, in addition to the goods brought by rail and water, for the establishment of important machine construction, chemical, woodworking, and food industries.

In recent years the Urals have been turned into one of the largest industrial and mining regions of the world. Huge metallurgical establishments have been built at Magnitogorsk, Nizhniy Tagil, and other cities. Other mills process copper, zinc, aluminum, magnesium, and nickel ores. Large chemical and paper mills have risen along the Kama River. Important rail centers, such as Sverdlovsk, Chelyabinsk, Molotov, and Ufa, have turned into top-ranking machine-construction centers. One of the longest high-voltage power lines of the USSR links the several power plants and industrial sites of the region.

The main industrial district of the Siberian realm is the Kuznetsk Basin. On the site of extensive coal mines, ferrous and nonferrous metallurgy and machine construction have developed to a very great extent. The iron and steel mills of the Kuzbas work on the basis of local coal supplies and iron ore, partly of local origin, partly from the Urals. The once all-important Ural-Kuznetsk *kombinat*, involving the exchange of coal and iron ore between the two industrial regions, is gradually losing its importance as local iron ore deposits are being further developed in the Kuznetsk Basin. The principal industrial sites are Stalinsk (steel milling and machine construction), Kemerovo (coal and chemicals), Novosibirsk (machine building), and Belovo (zinc metallurgy). Another industrial region has been created in the Far East, with the principal centers at Vladivostok, Khabarovsk, and Komsomol'sk. Shipbuilding, oil refining, and machine construction are the principal activities.

The Russian SFSR is the site of the principal lumbering regions of the USSR. In the European section the lumber industry is centered in the Northern Dvina River basin and its affluents, the Sukhona and the Vychegda rivers, as well as along the Kama and the Vyatka rivers, to the southeast. In Siberia the chief lumbering districts are along the right bank of the Yenisey and in the basin of the Ussuri River, an affluent of the Amur. The principal fisheries of the Russian SFSR lie in the European North where herring and cod are caught on the banks of the Barents Sea, in the northern Caspian Sea and the Volga delta (zander, herring, and especially sturgeon), and in the Far East along the Sea of Japan coast and the Kamchatka Peninsula (salmon and herring).

The basic agricultural areas are in the black-earth belt. Most important is the Northern Caucasus (Kuban' Steppe), where wheat, corn, tobacco, and sunflowers grow excellently on black-earth and chestnut soils. The Northern Caucasus is also one of the foremost livestock-raising areas of the USSR. The Central Black-Earth Region, along the upper Don and the Oka rivers, is the chief sugar-beet district of the Russian SFSR, while the Volga Region and the steppes beyond the Volga specialize in wheat growing. The black-earth section of Siberia produces hard-grained spring wheat, which keeps for several years and is highly valued on the world market, and is also important for its highly developed dairy industries. In the forested belt of the Russian SFSR, new areas are being plowed under and drained for the introduction of grain crops, which now grow as far north as the 60th parallel. In the European forests, flax and hemp are the principal crops, and dairy farming, the dominant pastoral activity. The best flax is grown in the areas of Pskov, Smolensk, Kalinin, and Vologda, the latter being also the chief dairying center.

The transportation network linking these regions consists primarily of a well-developed railway system, which is densest in the European section. The main through-traffic lines join at Moscow, Leningrad, Sverdlovsk, Kirov, Vologda, Bryansk, and other centers. Throughout the European section, rail transportation operates in close conjunction with river and sea routes. The Volga River leads in the amount of freight carried on its course. It is connected with Moscow via the Moscow Canal and with the Neva and Leningrad via the Mariinsk waterway, the Tikhvin and the Vyshne-Volotsk canals. The chief seaports are Leningrad, Murmansk, Arkhangel'sk, Rostov, Sevastopol', and Astrakhan'. In Siberia the rail network is restricted to the Trans-Siberian trunk line and its many branches and spurs. The large rivers handle the north-south traffic during their ice-free season. The Ob', the Irtysh, the Yenisey, and the Amur intersect the Trans-Siberian Railroad, while the Lena is connected with it by a series of good highways. The Northern Sea Route is the basic route serving the Arctic coast of Siberia. This route through the seas of the Arctic Ocean was developed as a permanent transportation route as late as the third Five-Year Plan, after a large number of polar stations reporting on weather and ice conditions had been set up along the route. Its principal ports are Novyy Port, at the mouth of the Ob' River, Igarka, Dudinka, and Ust'-Port, in the lower reaches of the Yenisey, Nordvik, at the mouth of the Khatanga River, Tiksi, near the Lena delta, Ambarchik, near the mouth of the Kolyma River, and Anadyr', at the mouth of the Anadyr' River. The principal ports along the Pacific coast of the Far East are Vladivostok, Sovetskaya Gavan', Magadan, and Petropavlovsk on Kamchatka. The highway network is especially well developed in the European section of the Russian SFSR. The roads generally run parallel to rail lines and converge at Moscow. In Siberia, highways serve to open up newly developed areas not reached by the rail network; this is particularly true of the extensive gold-mining areas of Eastern Siberia and the Far East.

The Russian SFSR exports to the other union republics: machines, steel, petroleum, lumber, paper, textiles, and grain, and imports from them pig-iron, grain, sugar, cotton, livestock, and fruits.

Due to the large number of non-Russian ethnic groups within the Russian SFSR, the union republic has been organized into a Soviet Federated Socialist Republic, in contrast to the other union republics which have a more homogeneous national composition. The Russian SFSR was organized in 1917 and became one of the original four republics which united to form the USSR in 1922. The present territorial-administrative scheme was inaugurated with the creation of the Ural Oblast in 1923. Thereafter the newly created oblasts and krays rapidly replaced the former *guberniyas*. The more advanced non-Russian ethnic groups, such as Tatars, Bashkirs, Buryat-Mongols, Yakuts, and others, were constituted into the autonomous republics which, together with the basic Russian group (73 percent of the total population), form the so-called Russian Federation, or Russian SFSR. The territory with a predominant Russian population has been divided into oblasts and krays, which are purely administrative divisions. National minorities within these divisions have their own autonomous or national units. The most important minorities form autonomous oblasts within the krays, while lesser ethnic groups form national okrugs or even national rayons within oblasts or krays. At present the Russian SFSR includes 12 autonomous republics, 6 krays, and 50 oblasts.

In order to facilitate the study of the geography of the Russian SFSR, the republic has been divided into the following geographical regions on the basis of common physico-economic characteristics.

Central Industrial Region
  Moscow (Moskva) Oblast
  Vladimir Oblast
  Ivanovo Oblast
  Yaroslavl' Oblast
  Kostroma Oblast
  Ryazan' Oblast
  Tula Oblast

Central Black-Earth Region
  Orel Oblast
  Tambov Oblast
  Voronezh Oblast
  Kursk Oblast

European West
  Bryansk Oblast
  Kaluga Oblast
  Smolensk Oblast
  Velikiye Luki Oblast
  Kalinin Oblast

European Northwest
  Novgorod Oblast
  Pskov Oblast
  Leningrad Oblast

European North
  Murmansk Oblast
  Arkhangel'sk Oblast
  Komi Autonomous SSR
  Vologda Oblast

Volga Region
  Forest section
    Gor'kiy Oblast
    Kirov Oblast
    Mari Autonomous SSR

  Wooded-steppe section
    Tatar Autonomous SSR
    Chuvash Autonomous SSR
    Mordvinian Autonomous SSR
    Penza Oblast
    Ul'yanovsk Oblast
    Kuybyshev Oblast
  Steppe section
    Saratov Oblast
    Stalingrad Oblast
    Astrakhan' Oblast

Crimean Oblast

Lower Don and Northern Caucasus
  Rostov Oblast
  Krasnodar Kray
  Stavropol' Kray
  Kabardinian Autonomous SSR
  North Ossetian Autonomous SSR
  Groznyy Oblast
  Dagestan Autonomous SSR

Urals
  Molotov Oblast
  Udmurt Autonomous SSR
  Bashkir Autonomous SSR
  Chkalov Oblast
  Chelyabinsk Oblast
  Sverdlovsk Oblast

Western Siberia
  Kurgan Oblast
  Tyumen' Oblast
  Omsk Oblast
  Novosibirsk Oblast
  Tomsk Oblast
  Kemerovo Oblast
  Altay Kray

Eastern Siberia
  Krasnoyarsk Kray
  Tuva Autonomous Oblast
  Irkutsk Oblast
  Buryat-Mongol Autonomous SSR
  Chita Oblast
  Yakut Autonomous SSR

Soviet Far East
  Amur Oblast
  Khabarovsk Kray
  Maritime Kray
  Sakhalin Oblast

Kaliningrad Oblast, see Baltic Region, Chapter 26.

CHAPTER 5

Central Industrial Region

THE CENTRAL INDUSTRIAL REGION owes its economic importance not so much to the presence of raw materials and power resources as to its central location in the middle of the East European plain. It was to this area between the upper Volga and the Oka rivers that the Russian center of gravity moved after the decline of the Kievan state in the southwest. The first Russian settlers were later joined by refugees fleeing from the Tatars in the south, the Germans and Swedes in the northwest, and the Lithuanians and Poles in the west. In the thirteenth century Moscow assumed a commanding position and became the nucleus of the growing Russian state that spread steadily along the waterways radiating from the Volga-Oka watershed.

The region extends over an area of more than one hundred thousand square miles in the middle of the European USSR. Although far removed from the sea, it is linked with all coastal waters of eastern Europe, thanks to its location near the sources of important streams. Its two principal rivers, the Volga and the Oka, drain into the Caspian Sea; the Don, which flows to the Sea of Azov, rises near Stalinogorsk, and the Volga connects, via the Mariinsk and the Northern Dvina canal systems, with the Baltic and the White seas. The northern lowlands are level or slightly hilly, having clay and sand ridges left by the retreating ice sheet. Many sections are forested and swampy. The river banks are smooth and level, and the absence of clearly defined river valleys causes the spring floods to spread over relatively large areas. Settlements are concentrated on sandy ridges along rivers and lakes, while the marshy watersheds are sparsely inhabited. One such forested, swampy area is the Meshchera (or Meshchora), in the large left-bank bend of the lower Oka River.

North of Moscow lies the eastern continuation of the Smolensk-Moscow moraine upland. It is most sharply defined between the towns of Klin and Dmitrov and is there called the Klin-Dmitrov ridge, rising

CENTRAL INDUSTRIAL REGION

almost to 1,000 feet. A hilly, deeply-gullied plateau in its higher sections, this feature breaks off abruptly toward the Volga in the north. It continues eastward in isolated heights toward Ivanovo and sends an outlier across the Volga just east of Kostroma. The left bank of the Volga is generally level and consists predominantly of sandy deposits of glacial origin. Marshes and peat bogs abound amid the fir forests which are watered by the Unzha, a left affluent of the Volga River.

The climate of the Central Industrial Region has much in common with that of the European North. Winters are of only slightly shorter duration (4–5 months), but the summers are also warmer. Spring is generally cooler than the autumn. Precipitation occurs throughout the year and decreases gradually toward the southeast. It totals 22–26 inches yearly and has clearly defined maxima in July and August. The annual mean temperature decreases toward the northeast.

The region lies within the mixed-forest zone and the podsol soil belt, which constitute a transition between the coniferous taiga in the north and the wooded steppe in the south. More than one half the low area beyond (north of) the Volga is covered with virgin evergreen taiga. The landscape is characterized by fir forests in the lower humid sections and pine woods in the drier areas. Extensive peat marshes are found among the fir. Only northwest of Vladimir is there an important treeless area, the Opol'ye, with dark soils similar to those of the southern steppes. South of the Oka River the terrain becomes higher and drier, the forests have been largely cut, and the remaining copses contain a greater variety of deciduous types. Along the banks of the Oka, sandy and limy soils support some steppe vegetation and indicate the nearness of the black-earth belt in the south.

Among the chief mineral resources are peat, found mainly east and northeast of Moscow, the lignite of the Moscow Basin south of the Oka River, iron ore near Tula and in the vicinity of Kasimov, and phosphorite near Voskresensk, southeast of Moscow.

The Central Industrial Region has a population of more than eighteen millions, which is almost entirely Russian in ethnic origin. The high density (180 per square mile) is due to the great urban concentration of its industrial population. Leading in density and urban settlement is the watershed area between the Oka and the Volga rivers, where more than 250 persons are counted per square mile and 70 percent of the population lives in urban centers. Both population indexes are further exceeded in the metropolitan districts of Moscow and Ivanovo. In the wooded section north of the Volga the population density drops to less than 75 per square mile, but the urban share remains rather high due to the sparse rural settlement. In the wooded steppe south of the Oka, on the contrary, the density remains high, but the urban concentration is low, as a result of the large rural population.

Among the cities of the Central Industrial Region are the former capitals of old Russian principalities, characterized by kremlins, churches, and trading rows. Some centers of this type have become industrialized and, like Moscow, Serpukhov, and Kolomna, have assumed, at least partially, a modern appearance. Other feudal seats, however, such as Vereya, west of Moscow, and Suzdal', north of Vladimir, have been overwhelmed in the industrial upheaval and are now merely relics of a glorious medieval past. Also to be found are new cities of the type that has become familiar in newly developed outlying sections of the country. They may be the result of a steady outgrowth of industrial villages, such as Ivanovo and Orekhovo-Zuyevo, or the dynamic product of the Soviet planned economy, such as Stalinogorsk.

The region contains no national autonomous units and, in addition to Moscow Oblast, is divided administratively into the oblasts of Yaroslavl', Kostroma and Ivanovo northeast of Moscow, Vladimir east of Moscow, and Ryazan' and Tula south of the capital.

Because of the forested character of the region, the absence of fertile soils, and irregular rainfall during harvest time, the population engaged early in artisan industries based on local supplies of flax, skins, wool, lumber, and iron. With the advent of the Industrial Revolution, textile milling became the dominant industry, employing two thirds of the labor power in the processing of local flax and wool and imported cotton and silk. The Soviet regime brought about an important shift in the regional specialization and introduced new industries; among them the machinery and the chemical branches are paramount. A new industrial orientation of machine, chemical, and textile production was thus given to the once one-sided textile-milling region. In this process, development of the textile industry was largely restricted to the construction of new spinning mills intended to balance the large number of weaving centers previously in existence. The Central Industrial Region produces about 25 percent of the total Soviet output in large-scale industry.

Machine construction has become the most important industry. Most of the plants are concentrated in Moscow, which produces automobiles, all types of electrical equipment, machine tools, ball-bearings, precision instruments, and watches. Locomotives, tramway and railway cars, and agricultural machinery are manufactured in the vicinity of Moscow, at Mytishchi, Lyubertsy, and Kolomna. Elsewhere in the region, specialization in the production of machinery proceeded in accordance with the local conditions. Thus, Shcherbakov, a large port on the upper Volga and the Rybinsk Reservoir, has become a major shipbuilding center, Yaroslavl', admirably situated as a distributing center, manufactures and ships trucks and trolley buses, and Ivanovo, a textile center in a peat-producing district, makes peat-working and textile machines.

Although iron and steel for the many machinery works have to be largely imported from the Urals and the Donets Basin, small-scale local metallurgical industries mill iron ore at Tula or work scrap into high-grade steels at Moscow and Elektrostal'. The new chemical industry uses local phosphorite, lignite, and industrial alcohol in the production of phosphates (Voskresensk), nitrates (Stalinogorsk), and synthetic rubber (Yaroslavl' and Yefremov).

Among the textile raw materials, flax and to some extent wool are of local origin, while cotton and silk are imported. Since the creation of new textile mills near the sources of cotton and silk, the Central Industrial Region has come to specialize in the production of fine, high-grade cloth and industrial fabrics. Knitwear, clothing, and shoe industries are also highly developed. Food industries are largely oriented toward the needs of the large industrial population and furnish bakery products, confectionery, flour, and meat products. Only in the wooded steppe south of the Oka are local agricultural products processed into flour, alcohol, vegetable oils, starch, and molasses.

The lumber industry is of secondary importance in the over-all industrial scheme of the region, but is nevertheless fully represented from sawmills north of the Volga to furniture factories at Moscow. In connection with the intensive industrial and housing construction, the production of building materials (cement, bricks, lime) is well developed.

Power for the industries and other economic needs is supplied by long-haul coal from the Donets Basin and petroleum from the Caucasus. However, with the development of local power stations based on peat and lignite resources, the long-distance fuel imports have been reduced in recent years. Further economy has been achieved since the completion of hydroelectric stations on the upper Volga, at Uglich and Shcherbakov.

Also to be noted in the economy of the Central Industrial Region are the characteristic handicraft industries, which range from the production of toys at Zagorsk to the textile home industries near Ivanovo and the artistic painting of lacquered wooden objects at Palekh.

Although far less important than industry in the economic integration of the region, agriculture plays a significant role in supplying the large industrial population with milk and dairy products, vegetables, potatoes, grains, and some meat, and in furnishing flax and potatoes to industry.

According to agricultural specialization, three distinct economic regions can be distinguished within the Central Industrial Region. The watershed area between the upper Volga and the Oka rivers contains the major urban centers and is largely engaged in truck and fruit gardening, dairy, poultry, and hog farming. An intensive truck-garden district is that of Rostov (Yaroslavl' Oblast) on Nero Lake. In the lumber region north of the Volga River agriculture in the occasional clearings is devoted to the growing of flax and dairy farming. Due to the great distance from the milk-consumption centers, most of the milk is converted into dairy products (butter and cheese). On the right bank of the Oka River, in Tula and Ryazan' oblasts, the orientation is toward grain and potato cultivation. Fodder and beet crops are grown in rotation, and sunflowers, hemp, and sugar beets supply the agricultural industries. Livestock is raised for meat and milk products.

The dense railroad network radiates from Moscow and is supplemented by numerous lateral lines. Eleven trunk routes, like so many spokes of a wheel, connect the capital with all sections of the country. Direct connections exist with Leningrad, Riga, Kaliningrad, Minsk, and the western frontier, Kiev, Khar'kov, the Donets Basin and the Crimea, Saratov, the Caucasus, the Urals, Siberia, Arkhangel'sk, and the upper Volga. Highways replace railroads over short distances, serve as access routes to the rail lines, and handle a considerable portion of the interurban traffic. Waterways are important as a result of the central watershed location of the region. The construction of the Moscow Canal (called Moscow-Volga Canal until 1947) completed the formation of a river navigation ring of which the Moskva, the Oka, and the Volga rivers form the remaining sections. The region also contains the greater portion of the Rybinsk Reservoir (filled in 1941), which constitutes the southernmost component of the Mariinsk canal system linking the Volga and the Leningrad industrial area.

The Central Industrial Region imports industrial raw materials (iron, steel, lumber, cotton), fuels (coal, petroleum), lumber, grains, and salt. Its exports consist largely of machines, textiles, and printed matter.

Moscow Oblast
Capital, Moscow (Moskva); area, 18,500, population, 9,450,000

Situated in the west central section of the Central Industrial Region, Moscow Oblast occupies the most populous and urbanized area of the central European USSR. In the south its border passes along the Oka River and sends a narrow panhandle across the river to the headwaters of the Don in the area of Stalinogorsk; in the north the oblast reaches nearly to the upper Volga. It is drained by two left affluents of the Oka: the Klyaz'ma River, on which lie most of the textile centers, and the Moskva, which flows past Moscow.

Essentially hilly, the relief is accentuated in the north by the Klin-Dmitrov ridge, an eastern extension of the Smolensk-Moscow upland. Yearly precipitation is 22–24 inches, and the monthly mean temperatures range from 12° F in January to 66° F in July. The vegetation is of the mixed deciduous and coniferous type on a base of podsolic soils; the forests have been largely cleared, and in accordance with a conservation plan further deforestation has been prohibited. Among the mineral resources, the lignite of the extensive Moscow Basin (of which only a small portion lies within the confines of Moscow Oblast) is of first-rank importance in relieving Moscow, at least partially, of its dependence on long-haul Donets Basin coal. Peat is extracted east of Moscow and serves as fuel for the production of electric power, while phosphorite deposits at Fosforitnyy in the area of Voskresensk constitute a raw-material basis for the chemical industry. Brick clays, cement rock, and other building materials occur in many locations.

About one half the total population, of which more than 95 percent are Russians, lives within the city limits of Moscow, where representatives of nearly every national group of the USSR can be encountered. The oblast includes, in addition to Moscow, about 150 cities and workers' settlements, leaving only one fifth of the inhabitants to rural environment.

A remarkable concentration of industry was the prime factor in the urbanization of the oblast. On an area only 1/400 that of the USSR, the region produces nearly one fifth of the country's industrial output. The industrialization drive of the last two decades has brought about a sharp change in the specialization of the industry, from the former emphasis on textiles to the present predominance of machines and chemicals. Because of lack of large-scale metallurgical production, the machine-building industry puts out chiefly precision machines, requiring skilled labor, but less metal than does bulky machine construction. However, some imported pig-iron and scrap are treated in the *Serp i Molot* (Sickle and Hammer) plant in the eastern part of Moscow and in the electric furnaces of Elektrostal', where special high-grade steels are milled. The majority of the machinery works are located in Moscow, while outside the city tramway and subway cars are made at Mytishchi, locomotives and rolling stock at Kolomna, agricultural implements at Lyubertsy, oil-cracking equipment at Podol'sk, and machine tools at Klin, Dmitrov, and Yakhroma.

Of great importance in the economy are the chemical plants. Foremost are those of Voskresensk, producing superphosphate, phosphate meal, and sulphuric acid on the basis of the local phosphorite deposits, and Stalinogorsk, which uses the lignite of the Moscow Basin as a raw material for its nitrogen derivatives. Near Stalinogorsk are the lignite-mining centers of Donskoy (with the satellite mines of Zadon'ye and Novougol'nyy) and Uzlovaya, a rail junction, and the near-by Dubovka mines.

Textile milling is carried on in Moscow itself and in large cities extending especially eastward toward Orekhovo-Zuyevo. Cotton goods and industrial fabrics are the staple products of large mills at Noginsk (including the noted Glukhovo textile mill), Pavlovskiy Posad, Orekhovo-Zuyevo, Yegor'yevsk, Serpukhov, and lesser centers. Silk cloth (at Stalinskiy), woolens (at Pushkino), and knitwear are also produced. In addition to the large-scale industry, many handicraft co-operatives engage in the manufacture of toys (Zagorsk), art objects, woven goods, footwear, and other apparel.

Electric power for the many industrial enterprises of the oblast is furnished by a few powerful stations, based partly on the extensive peat resources (Shatura, Elektrogorsk, Orekhovo-Zuyevo), partly on the Moscow lignite basin (Stalinogorsk and Kaganovich, near Kashira), and on long-haul Donets Basin coal. In spite of the resources of the Moscow Basin, the demand on coal from the Donets Basin is so great that a special coal trunk railroad was constructed in the late 1930's connecting the Donets Basin directly with Moscow.

Agriculture is mainly designed to supply Moscow and the other large urban agglomerations with fresh milk, vegetables, fruits (especially berries), and potatoes. These products, which are grown on truck and dairy farms, are transported by trucks to the consumption centers. Road transport is well developed and rivals the railroads as a local freight carrier. Long-haul transportation to the other regions of the USSR relies on the rail lines radiating from Moscow and to an increasingly greater extent on the waterways. The construction of the Moscow Canal (called Moscow-Volga Canal until 1947) was completed in 1937 and provided a link between the upper Volga and the Moskva River at Moscow. The canal leaves the Volga in the Volga Reservoir (also known as the Moscow Sea) at Ivan'kovo and extends 80 miles south through marshy terrain to the Klin-Dmitrov ridge, across this feature by means of an elaborate lock and pumping system, and on to Moscow via the waters of the Klyaz'ma and several minor rivers. The construction raised the level of the Moskva River and turned Moscow into a major inland port. The oblast exports machinery, machine tools, automobiles, precision instruments, chemicals, textiles, printed matter, cosmetics, and cigarettes and imports grain, meat, and sugar from the Ukraine, grain and meat from Siberia and the Volga Region, iron and nonferrous metals from the Urals and the Ukraine, coal from the Donets Basin, oil from the Caucasus, cotton from Central Asia, lumber from the upper Volga, and fish and salt from the lower Volga.

Moscow is the capital of the Russian SFSR and of the USSR, the political, economic, and cultural center of the Union, and one of the foremost cities of the world. The city is located on the meandering Moskva River, which is here connected with the Volga River by the Moscow Canal. Its port facilities consist of the northern port or Khimki Reservoir on the Moscow Canal, the western port or Fily embankment on the Moskva River, and the southern port, a four-square-mile reservoir on the Moskva River, at the southeastern city limits. This far-flung inland port is accessible by water from the Baltic, the White, and the Caspian seas. With the projected construction of the Volga-Don Canal, establishing a connection with the Sea of Azov and the Black Sea, Moscow will truly become a "Port of the Five Seas." It is the largest rail hub of the USSR; its eleven converging lines are linked by an inner ring, following roughly the city limits, and an outer ring (completed in 1942) which circles the city at a distance of some fifty miles, passing through Aleksandrov and Voskresensk in the east and Kubinka and Povarovo in the west. Suburban lines are electrified and multiple tracks are common in the metropolitan area. Modern highways radiate from the city, and air lines connect it with the remotest parts of the Union.

Moscow's share in the industrial output of the USSR is nearly one sixth of the total production. The city produces automobiles (identified by the letters ZIS for *Zavod imeni Stalina*, or Stalin Works), motorcycles, trolley buses, airplanes, and has locomotive and railway-car repair shops. Other plants manufacture high-grade steels, machine tools, ball bearings, electrical goods, precision instruments and watches. Among its light industries are the textile mills, including the Trekhgornaya mill, shoe and leather factories, food and tobacco processing plants. The publishing of books and periodicals is of considerable importance. Power for its industries is received from the generating stations of Stalinogorsk, Kaganovich (near Kashira), Shatura, Elektrogorsk (called Elektroperedacha until 1946), and from the new hydroelectric stations of Uglich and Shcherbakov. A gas pipe-line from the natural-gas wells near Saratov was completed during the postwar Five-Year Plan. Moscow is the seat of the Central Committee of the All-Union Communist Party, of the legislative and executive bodies of the USSR and the Russian SFSR (which are housed in the Kremlin), the Academy of Sciences of the USSR (brought here in 1934 from Leningrad), Moscow University, Lenin Library, Tret'yakov art gallery, and other scientific and cultural institutions, including museums, theaters, and motion-picture studios.

Located in rolling terrain on both banks of the Moskva River, the city extends concentrically around its ancient citadel, the Kremlin, which rises on the left bank between two affluent creeks, the Neglinnaya (now enclosed in underground pipes) and the Yauza. Founded in 1147, the expanding city was successively surrounded by several outer walls, which have been replaced by circular boulevards. Streets developed in a radial pattern with the arterial thoroughfares leading through the "rings" onto intercity highways. In 1935 a vast reconstruction project was begun, involving the construction of a subway (*metro*) network, of wide arterial streets, bridges, and residential quarters, and aiming at the ultimate incorporation of several suburban cities of more than fifty thousand inhabitants (Kuntsevo, Lyublino, Perovo, Mytishchi, and Babushkin) into a greater Moscow. Vast amusement parks were developed, including the Gor'kiy Central Park on the right bank of the Moskva, in the southwest, the Sokol'niki and Dzerzhinskiy (Ostankino) parks in the north, and the Stalin (Izmaylovo) Park in the east. During the postwar Plan the fourth section of the subway (of which the first three sections were completed in 1935, 1938, and during the Second World War) linking the remaining lines along one of the circular boulevards will be constructed. Several skyscraper buildings, the highest of thirty-two stories, to be located in the Lenin Hills on the Moskva River, in the southwestern part of the city, are also planned for the postwar period.

In the metropolitan area are the residential and industrial satellite cities of Kuntsevo (aircraft, textiles), Tushino (chemicals, textiles), Babushkin (locomotives), Mytishchi (electric coaches, tramways, and subway cars), Perovo (railway coaches), Lyublino (transport machinery), Lyubertsy (agricultural implements, electrical goods, plastics, petroleum products).

The main textile centers of the oblast extend east from Moscow along the Klyaz'ma River. They are Orekhovo-Zuyevo (cotton goods, artificial silk, plastics), Noginsk, with the large Glukhovo cotton mill, and Pavlovskiy Posad.

Serpukhov, on the Oka River, south of Moscow, is another textile center, processing cotton, wool, and flax. It also produces paper and motorcycles.

Podol'sk, another industrial center on the Moscow-Serpukhov highway, has electrolytic refining works and manufactures airplane motors, sewing machines, chemicals, and cement.

Kolomna is a major railway rolling-stock producer and puts out locomotives, freight cars, Diesel motors, phonographs, and textile machinery. An old city situated on the Oka at the mouth of the Moskva River, it has a kremlin and many churches.

Kashira, another old city on the Oka, south of Moscow, has become the center of an industrial district. Kashira itself has only lumber, shoe, and other light industries. Northward, across the Oka, however, lies the metallurgical city of Stupino (formerly called Elektrovoz), where electric locomotives are manufactured. Just east of Kashira is the great lignite-fed power station of Kaganovich, which supplies Moscow with electricity.

Stalinogorsk (formerly called Bobriki), which developed after 1930 in the Moscow lignite basin, has a large power generator connected with Moscow and a chemical industry producing explosives, fertilizer, and

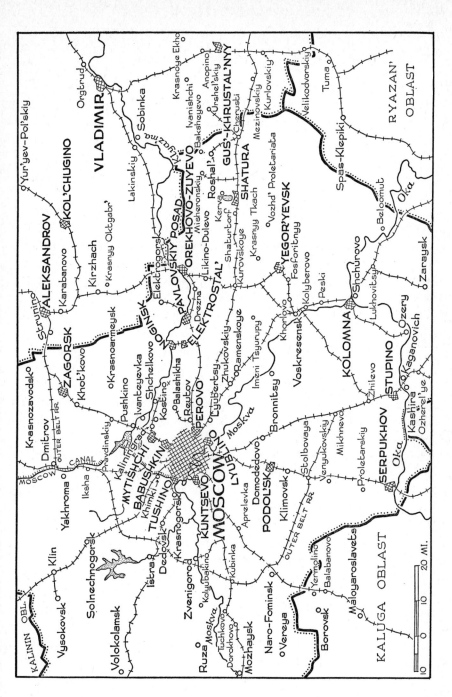

MOSCOW AREA

sulphuric acid. The city consists of the industrial borough in the north and the residential district some five miles to the south.

Yaroslavl' Oblast
Capital, Yaroslavl'; area, 14,250, population, 1,500,000

Yaroslavl' Oblast is situated on Rybinsk Reservoir and on the upper Volga River, in a wooded plain in which only the terminal moraines of the Uglich upland and the Danilov ridge rise above the level terrain. The Volga enters the oblast in the southwest and flows northward into the Rybinsk Reservoir, from which it emerges in a southeasterly direction. The river plays an all-important role in the economy of the oblast, not only as an excellent waterway, but also as a supplier of hydroelectric power. The region lies in the forest zone, which has been cleared to a large extent on the right bank of the Volga, but remains relatively dense on the more sparsely settled left bank. The podsolic soils have a sandy base (favorable for the growing of potatoes) in the southeastern section and are predominantly sandy in the remainder of the oblast, where flax is the principal crop in the forest clearings. A characteristic feature of the oblast are alluvial soils extending along the river courses, where they support rich meadows and grazing lands. In the neighborhood of lakes Nero (near Rostov) and Pleshcheyevo (near Pereslavl'-Zalesskiy), extensive truck gardens are fertilized by means of sapropelic mud raised from the bottom of the lakes. Peat and building stone are the chief mineral resources.

The physical configuration of the oblast, as well as its economy, underwent a radical change in 1941 with the damming up of the Volga River and the formation of the Rybinsk Reservoir. This body of water flooded about 2,000 square miles of alluvial lands between the Sheksna and the Mologa rivers, covering a large number of inhabited localities, including the sawmilling town of Mologa, at the Volga-Mologa confluence. The "Rybinsk Sea," as it is sometimes called, became the largest artificial lake of the USSR. It changed the living habits of the local inhabitants, who found themselves suddenly confronted with this wide expanse of water, and provided the base for new fishing and shipbuilding industries.

Until the Revolution, the textile industry dominated in the economy of the oblast. Unlike Ivanovo Oblast, where small-scale home industries formed the basis of the present textile mills, the Yaroslavl' textile mills were organized originally as large enterprises in the urban centers of the region. Linen milling is the principal textile industry and is located chiefly at Yaroslavl', Tutayev, Gavrilov-Yam, and Rostov. Since the Revolution, the rise of the machine-building and shipbuilding industries has gradually changed the emphasis to these new activities, which are now established at the two main industrial centers of the oblast, Yaroslavl' and Shcherbakov (formerly Rybinsk). Caucasus petroleum carried up the Volga River is refined at the oil-cracking plant of Konstantinovskiy. Handicraft industries are widespread and produce sheepskins near Tutayev, wood articles on the left bank of the Volga, headwear, jewelry, and other articles. Two large hydroelectric plants on the Volga provide most of the electric power to the industries of the oblast. The station of Shcherbakov received its first turbine in 1941 after the filling of the Rybinsk Reservoir in the spring of that year. The plant at Uglich had been completed previously. A power plant based on peat is operating at Yaroslavl'.

In agriculture, intensive crops such as flax, potatoes, and garden products predominate. Flax is grown in all areas where clay soils prevail, particularly on the left bank of the Volga and in the western section of the right bank. Numerous retting mills prepare the fiber for the large textile enterprises. Throughout the flax area dairy cattle are raised on fodder crops, which are sown in rotation with flax, and on the natural alluvial meadows along the rivers. Potatoes thrive on the sandy soils of the southeast. They are of industrial importance and provide the raw material for the synthetic rubber works at Yaroslavl', several distilleries, and starch factories. Truck farming is concentrated around the large centers (Yaroslavl', Shcherbakov) and in the area of Rostov and Lake Nero. Grains, mainly wheat, are grown to a lesser extent, and are important only in the Opol'ye, which penetrates into the extreme south portion of the oblast. Chicory is a secondary crop in the potato region.

The Volga River handles the major portion of the freight, which consists of incoming iron and steel (from the Urals and the Ukraine), petroleum, cotton, alcohol, machines, and grain, and of the outgoing machinery, automobiles, tires, rubber products, lacquers, linen goods, lumber, vegetables, and starches.

Yaroslavl' lies at the intersection of the Volga with the Moscow-Arkhangel'sk railroad, at the mouth of the Kotorosl' River. It is the oldest Russian city on the Volga (founded in 1024) and was a rival of Moscow in the twelfth to the fifteenth centuries. The most important enterprises are the automobile plant (trucks, trolley buses), synthetic rubber and asbestos works, which produce tires, rubber footwear, and asbestos products, lacquer and paints factory, electric motor, brake and machinery works. There are shipyards and railroad shops, the large cotton mills of Krasnyy Perekop and Krasnyy Pereval, linen mills, shoe and tobacco factories, flour mills, and sawmills. In recent years, the city has expanded considerably and now extends over fifteen miles along the Volga River.

Shcherbakov (called Rybinsk until 1946) is an important port and industrial center on the Rybinsk Reservoir at the issue of the Volga River. It produces printing and road-building machinery, has shipyards, match factories, and sawmills. Since 1941 the city has become a major supplier of hydroelectric power.

Uglich (founded 1148) is an important river port on the Volga, having paper mills and sawmills. Its hydroelectric station (in operation since 1940) supplies power to Moscow.

Other centers are the historical cities of Rostov (founded 864) in a truck-garden region on Lake Nero, and Pereslavl'-Zalesskiy (founded 1152) on Lake Pleshcheyevo, site of the first shipbuilding experiments under Peter the Great.

Kostroma Oblast
Capital, Kostroma; area, 22,400, population, 1,050,000

Lying east of Yaroslavl', Kostroma Oblast is bordered in the north by the moraine features of the Northern Uvals and is drained by the Kostroma and the Unzha rivers, as well as by the upper Vetluga. It is a densely forested region, which has been partly cleared in the west, and where agriculture is restricted to occasional clearings. Flax is the main crop throughout the region. Fodder crops are sown in rotation and support dairy-cattle herds. Secondary products are wheat near Soligalich (north) and Nerekhta (southwest), potatoes near Makar'yev (south), and garden crops on the lakes of Galich and Chukhloma. Dairy farming is most important in the northeast, in the area of Vokhma.

Lumbering and associated industries are the mainstay of the economy. Sawmills and veneering works are strung along the Vologda-Kirov railroad (the main through line of the oblast), the principal sites being at Shar'ya, Manturovo, Neya, Galich, and Buy. The rural population engages in woodworking, distilling, and flax retting. The large industrial centers Kostroma and Nerekhta in the southwest have linen mills, which are powered by peat from Kosmynino (northeast of Nerekhta). The oblast imports chiefly grain and machines and exports lumber and linen goods.

Kostroma, on the left bank of the Volga River, at the mouth of the Kostroma, was founded in 1152. It has long been a major linen-milling center, and also produces machinery, ships, shoes, and starches. There are lumber and paper mills, and the agricultural products of the region are processed into flour, tobacco products, alcohol, and linseed oil. Its importance as a river-rail transfer point will be considerably enhanced by the construction under the current Plan of the Kostroma-Galich railroad.

Nerekhta has linen-milling and woodworking industries. Shar'ya and Buy are important lumber towns.

Ivanovo Oblast
Capital, Ivanovo; area, 9,500, population, 1,500,000

Ivanovo Oblast lies northeast of Moscow on a level plain between the Klyaz'ma and the Volga rivers. It slopes almost imperceptibly toward the Volga valley and is watered by the Nerl', the Uvod', and the Teza, all left affluents of the Klyaz'ma. The Volga, which traverses the extreme northeast and is the principal waterway of that portion of the oblast, receives on the left the Unzha River, important chiefly for timber flotage.

The dominant podsolic soils support deciduous forests mixed with conifers. These have, however, been largely cleared, except for the northeast, where conifers prevail in the area of the Volga-Unzha confluence. The chief mineral resources are peat (which is used to feed electric power stations and serves as fuel for textile mills), phosphorites (in the area of Kineshma on the Volga), and some quartz.

The oblast is the leading textile-producing region of the USSR. While its textile industry ranks second to that of Moscow Oblast in amount of production, it plays proportionately a far more important role in the economy of the oblast. The industrial needs of the textile mills are filled by the output of several associated industries producing chemicals (acids, alkalis, and dyes), textile machinery, and starch. Also connected with the industry are handicraft co-operatives, which weave factory-produced thread into cloth, engage in embroidery, and make wooden weaving shuttles. The cotton mills are clustered around Ivanovo, the "Soviet Manchester," at Kokhma, Shuya, Teykovo, Rodniki, Vichuga, and Furmanov (formerly Sereda), and there is linen milling at Privolzhsk and Puchezh on the Volga. Sawmills along the Volga, mainly at Kineshma and Novaya Slobodka, process local timber resources or lumber floated down on the Unzha River.

In recent years Ivanovo acquired machine-building industries, which are now producing textile machinery to be sent to the new mills of Central Asia and Transcaucasia, and peat-working machines, of special importance in a region relying on its peat resources for fuel.

Handicraft industries specialize in embroidery near Puchezh, in the making of felt boots near Kineshma, and in artistic wood carving and decoration at Palekh and Kholuy in the southeast.

Electric power is furnished by a large station at Komsomol'sk, west of Ivanovo, which is based on the rich peat deposits in that district. Other important peat works are located in the southeast, near Yuzha.

Agriculture supplies the industrial centers with truck produce (vegetables and potatoes) and dairy products; tobacco and chicory are secondary crops in the west, while wheat, fodder crops, and flax are grown mainly in the east.

Trade passes over the Volga and the rail network, and Kineshma serves as the principal river-rail transfer point. The oblast imports raw cotton, iron, steel, grain, and petroleum and exports cotton goods and textile machinery.

Ivanovo, which dates from the fourteenth century, lies on the non-navigable Uvod' River. It was developed from a small trading village into a commercial and manufacturing center as early as the beginning of the seventeenth century. The first textile mill was founded in 1751. It combined with the left-bank town of Voznesensk in 1871 and became the city of Ivanovo-Voznesensk. Before the Revolution it was subordinated administratively to Shuya, the uyezd center, which it far outranked in economic importance. In 1929 it became an oblast capital in accordance with its leading economic position. One of the largest cotton-milling centers of the USSR, it also produces textile and peat-working machines and has flax-retting, clothing, and food industries. In recent years the city expanded and was largely rebuilt.

Other important centers are Kineshma, the river port for Ivanovo and site of cotton mills, lumber plants, and chemical works, and Shuya, the largest of the cotton-milling satellites of Ivanovo. The construction of the 60-mile Shuya-Yuzha-Il'ino railroad (projected for the postwar Plan) will establish a direct link between Gor'kiy and Ivanovo.

Vladimir Oblast

Capital, Vladimir; area, 10,350, population, 1,350,000

Adjoining Moscow Oblast in the east, Vladimir Oblast lies in a low forested region watered by the lower course of the Klyaz'ma River and bordered by the Oka in the southeast. The rivers play an important role in the economy of the area in providing cheap transportation routes and furnishing the large textile mills with the all-important water supply. The predominant podsols support mixed forests and are not favorable to agricultural development. Fertile black-earth-like soils do occur west of Vladimir between the Nerl' and the Kirzhach, two left affluents of the Klyaz'ma, in the so-called Opol'ye, a vast clearing in the wooded region. The oblast is poor in mineral resources except in the south, where there are large deposits of quartz sand and peat.

Metalworking, machinery, and textile industries are located in the north, while in the south glassworking and peat extraction are carried on. The main engineering plants are at Vladimir; electrical goods are made at Kirzhach, motorcycles at Kovrov, and radio equipment at Aleksandrov. Kol'chugino is the site of an old refinery of nonferrous metals, based chiefly on copper ores from the Urals. The textile industry is centered at Vyazniki, the principal city of an important linen-milling region, and at the cotton mills of Vladimir, Sobinka, and at Karabanovo and Strunino, near Aleksandrov. The glass and crystal works, based on the high-grade quartz sand in the south, are centered at Gus'-Khrustal'nyy. In recent years the making of glass fiber has also been begun. Paper is milled at Krasnaya Gorbatka, and there are sawmills throughout the southern part of the oblast, where lumbering is still engaged in by the population. Like Moscow Oblast, Vladimir is famous for its handicraft industries—the weaving of linen goods near Vyazniki and silk fabrics near Kirzhach and artistic wood carving and decorating at Mstera.

Except for the fertile Opol'ye, where wheat, tobacco, and rubber-bearing plants are grown, the main crops are flax and potatoes, which thrive on the poor sandy soils. A truck-farming and dairy-cattle zone extends along the industrial centers, and the cherries of Vladimir are well known.

By means of its river routes and a dense rail network, the oblast imports cotton from Central Asia, flax from the neighboring oblasts to the east, iron and steel from the Urals, and wheat and petroleum. It exports finished cotton and linen goods, glass products, and lumber to the other parts of the USSR and its machine parts and electrical equipment to the auto plants of Moscow, Yaroslavl', and Gor'kiy.

Vladimir, one of the historical centers of the region, was founded in 1116 and became a rival of Moscow in the twelfth and the thirteenth centuries. Long noted only for its cathedral, churches, and other monuments built of white stone in the original Vladimir-Suzdal' style, the city was industrialized after the Revolution and now produces automobile parts, precision instruments, phonographs, plastic products, cotton goods, and canned cherries. A tractor plant was built here during the Second World War.

Kovrov, on the Klyaz'ma River, is an industrial center manufacturing motorcycles, excavators, machine tools, and linen textiles.

Murom, a river port on the Oka River, has shipyards and locomotive works and produces linen textiles and canned foods.

The oblast also includes the once leading centers of Suzdal' (founded 1028), Yur'yev-Pol'skiy (founded 1152), Gorokhovets (shipyards), and Sudogda, now relegated to the rank of second-rate towns.

Ryazan' Oblast
Capital, Ryazan'; area, 18,200, population, 2,100,000

Ryazan' Oblast lies in the southeastern section of the Central Industrial Region, astride the middle course of the Oka River, and represents a transitional zone to the Central Black-Earth Region in the south. North of the Oka, it includes the forested and swampy Meshchera (or Meshchora) depression, and, in the south, the agricultural wooded steppe with black-earth soils. Unlike Tula Oblast to the west, Ryazan' has few natural foundations for an industrial economy and is generally one of the least developed regions of the Industrial Center.

Its principal natural resources are lumber and peat on the left bank of the Oka, rich alluvial grazing lands in the valleys of the river and its affluents, and on the right bank, black earth and the easternmost wing of the Moscow lignite basin. The lignite mining activities are centered at Skopin, with the principal mines at Pavelets, Pobedinskiy, and Oktyabr'skiy, to the west and south of Skopin. Peat is worked in the Meshchera, and there are phosphorite deposits along the Oka River. Iron deposits in the area of Kasimov form the basis of metalworking industries in near-by towns. Ryazan' is the center of the machine-building industry, which specializes in the production of agricultural implements.

Sawmills process the lumber of the north, and cement is milled at Oktyabr'skiy, west of Mikhaylov.

Of all the oblasts of the Central Industrial Region, Ryazan' has the greatest portion of the sown area under grain (wheat, rye, and oats). In addition to the grain crops, the south grows sugar beets, tobacco, and rubber-bearing plants. Some hemp is produced in the east. In the raw Meshchera section the poor soils support mainly potatoes. Hogs are raised in the potato and grain areas, while the flood valley of the Oka produces excellent hay and fodder crops for the raising of dairy cattle. Poultry farms are common, and there are many apiaries. The agricultural products form the basis of extensive agricultural industries, such as flour milling, distilling, and the making of starch and molasses. The principal processing centers are Chaplygin (until 1948, called Ranenburg), Ryazhsk, Lebedyan', and Mikhaylov.

The commercial orientation of the oblast is mainly toward Moscow, which it supplies with lumber, livestock, truck produce, and grain.

Ryazan', which was founded in 1094 at a point thirty miles to the southeast and moved to the present site on the right bank of the Oka in the thirteenth century, is an engineering and agricultural center. It produces agricultural machines, cash registers, electric light bulbs, shoes, and clothing and engages in flour milling, fruit canning, tanning, and woodworking.

Kasimov, the former capital of a Tatar principality, lies on the Oka River and produces linen goods, metalware, alcohol, and clothing. It is the site of several relics of the Tatar domination, including a minaret and a mausoleum of Tatar princes.

Tula Oblast
Capital, Tula ; area, 9,300, population, 1,500,000

Tula Oblast lies south of Moscow in the northern section of the Central Russian upland and is bounded by the Oka River in the north and west and by the upper reaches of the Don in the southeast. It constitutes a transition zone between the forest and the wooded steppe belts ; it is slightly hilly, and the soils are predominantly of the leached black-earth type. Both the precipitation and the tree density decrease gradually toward the southeast. Because of their proximity to the industrial complex of Moscow, the mineral resources of the oblast assume special importance. It includes the major section of the Moscow lignite basin, with the mining centers of Bolokhovo, Kaganovich, Bogoroditsk, and

Shchekino along the rail lines west and south of Stalinogorsk. Iron is mined at Kireyevka and Ogarevka, east and south of Tula. In addition, construction materials such as marble, refractory clays, gypsum, and gravel are present in large quantities. On the basis of the local iron deposits, small-scale metalworking and metallurgical industries have been in operation since the eighteenth century. However, it was only after the Revolution, when the necessity of supplying Moscow with local lignite and iron became paramount, that heavy industry was developed earnestly in the Tula Oblast. The old metallurgical works of Kosaya Gora (south of Tula) were reconstructed and a new plant was built at Novotul'skiy, east of the city. Many small metalworking centers in the vicinity of Tula specialize in the production of ironware and agricultural implements. Although no major power plants are in operation in the oblast, Tula lignite helps to fuel the great electric stations of Stalinogorsk and Kaganovich (near Kashira) in adjacent Moscow Oblast, which furnish power in return. Gas produced by an underground coal-gas plant is piped directly to Moscow.

The basic crops are hardy grains, such as rye, oats, and barley. In recent years, however, the wheat acreage was increased perceptibly, and larger areas are now under industrial crops, including potatoes (in the central section), sugar beets (southeast), rubber-bearing plants (south), and flax (west). On the basis of the potato crop, hog raising has assumed importance and synthetic rubber is being produced at Yefremov. Rural industries engage in flour milling, distilling, and sugar refining.

The basic function of the oblast in the over-all economic picture of the Union is to supply the industrial conglomeration of Moscow to the north with lignite, iron, steel, and building stone.

Tula, which lies on the Upa River (a right affluent of the Oka), is located in the Moscow lignite basin and near the iron mines which supply its satellite metallurgical works of Novotul'skiy (east) and Kosaya Gora (south). It is a five-way rail center and has long been famous as a producer of arms, samovars, agricultural implements, and ironware.

CHAPTER 6

Central Black-Earth Region

THE OBLASTS of the Central Black-Earth Region are distinguished by several common physical and economic characteristics. The region lies in the upper reaches of the Oka, the Don, and the Seym rivers and is bounded by the Central Industrial Region in the north and by the Ukrainian SSR in the south. It has an inland location about 600 miles from the Baltic Sea and 350 miles from the Black Sea. Its total area is about 70,000 square miles.

Its relief has a generally level character, slightly raised and hilly in the west, within the confines of the Kursk and Orel oblasts, where it forms the Central Russian upland. In the east the level Oka-Don lowland extends through the Tambov and Voronezh oblasts at an average elevation of 300 to 600 feet. The entire area is traversed by deep, meandering river valleys, characterized by steep right banks, and low swampy left banks, with ox-bows and flood basins. The rivers are shallow, flow quietly, occasionally barred by sand banks, and are unsuitable for navigation or water-power production. The principal streams are the Oka, with its tributary, the Tsna, the Don and its affluents, the Voronezh and Bityug on the left, and the Sosna on the right, and the Seym, an affluent of the Desna. The watersheds are marked by numerous gullies and ravines, which are typical regional land-forms. Their extraordinary development and ramification in this area is due chiefly to the easy erosion of the loess soils, the early clearing of the forests, and the plowing of the land by the original steppe inhabitants. Since these ravines offer serious obstacles to transportation, reduce the area under cultivation, and occasionally block river courses, a regular campaign against their spread is being carried on.

Due to its distance from the sea, the Central Black-Earth Region has a rather continental type of climate. The winters are shorter than in the Central Industrial Region to the north, but quite as cold. For example, January temperatures in Voronezh fall just as low as in Moscow;

only the southwestern section has more moderate winters. Summers are long and hot, and the intensive insolation makes possible the growing of a large variety of crops. Spring arrives early in this region, and the melting of the snow proceeds rapidly, due to the lack of forest cover. This season is warmer here than in the north, having temperatures approximating those of the autumn months. Dry winds blow frequently from the southeast and often cause destructive droughts, especially in the southeastern sections. Precipitation varies from 24 inches yearly in the northwest to 16 inches in the southeast, and occurs mainly in the summer in occasionally stormy downpours, leaving the harvest season comparatively drier.

The soils in the center and the south are ordinary black earths; in the north the black earth has been degraded under the influence of the advancing forests, and in the east the rich black-earth type prevails. The vegetation form is typical wooded steppe, with a gradual transition to the true steppe in the southeast. There are frequent birch and oak clusters and isolated pine woods. In the early historic period deciduous forests covered the entire area. Their extent can still be determined by the character of the soils, i.e., the degraded black earth with less than 6 percent of humus content. In the sections which have always had steppe vegetation, the humus content reaches 10 percent and higher. Most portions have been cleared of the original forests, and at the present time only about 7 percent of the total area is wooded, lying in the northwest and the northeast. The southern sections have already been converted into typical steppe.

The lack of timber resources in the Central Black-Earth Region is paralleled by the poor supplies of mineral fuels. Negligible peat deposits are found in the northeast in the vicinity of Tambov, and in the southern section of Voronezh Oblast, an outlier of the Donets Basin provides some coal resources. In the southeast, some oil shale has been located. All these deposits, however, are of limited importance. Of far greater significance are the iron ore deposits near Lipetsk (Voronezh Oblast), and especially the Kursk magnetic anomaly of colossal proportions (about 100 million tons of reserves), which is still in the very first stages of exploitation. Phosphorites are mined near Shchigry (Kursk Oblast), and building materials are quarried throughout the area.

Like that of the Central Industrial Region, the population of the Central Black-Earth Region is almost entirely Russian, without any autonomous national groups. Only in the south, along the border of the

CENTRAL BLACK-EARTH REGION

Ukrainian SSR, are there some Ukrainian minorities. The total population of the region is about 9,500,000, giving an average density of 135 per square mile. This is one of the highest rural population densities in the USSR, exceeded only by that in the right-bank wooded steppe of the Ukraine. The greatest concentration exists in the central part of the region and in the southwestern sugar-beet districts of Kursk Oblast. The inhabitants live in large rural communities, extending sometimes for miles along the banks of rivers and ravines. The size of the villages increases progressively from the northwestern wooded steppe, where a well-developed river network prevails, toward the steppe proper, where the rivers are scarcer and serve as population concentration points. Administratively, the Central Black-Earth Region is divided into the oblasts of Kursk, Orel, Tambov, and Voronezh.

Before the Bolshevik Revolution this region was quite impoverished and suffered from the extremely wasteful farming methods of that time. Large sections of the arable land were plowed under to the detriment of pasture ground, of which a relatively small acreage was available. Instead of cattle, sheep were raised by the peasants of the region, because they generally required less fodder. As a result of the absence of large herds of cattle, little natural fertilization of the soil took place, and its fertility diminished gradually. The three-field rotation system prevailed, and rye was the basic grain crop. After the Revolution and the collectivization of the farms, this situation changed radically. The three-field strip system was replaced by the multi-field system, the acreage under industrial crops rose from 10 percent (in 1913) to 25 percent of the total sown area; the collectivization led to the destruction of the boundary field strips, which not only reduced the potential cultivated area to a considerable extent, but served also as hotbeds of weeds and pernicious insects; finally, the collectivization brought about widespread use of agricultural machinery, such as mechanized plows, tractors, combines, and other implements.

Wheat has now become the basic grain crop, winter wheat in the Kursk Oblast and spring wheat in the Voronezh Oblast; in addition, millet is extensively grown in Voronezh and buckwheat in Kursk. Rye and oats are also important. The industrial crops are distributed in the following manner: flax and potatoes in Orel Oblast, sugar beets primarily in Kursk Oblast, sunflowers in Voronezh Oblast, and tobacco and potatoes in Tambov Oblast. Among the new crops introduced in recent years are soybeans, corn, and essential-oil and rubber-bearing plants. Fodder crops, chiefly alfalfa and clover, supplement the normal residue of food industries in the feeding of livestock, of which pigs and poultry are most important. Voronezh Oblast is famed for its horse-breeding farms.

Among the industries, food-processing activities based on the local produce are in first place; they include flour milling, sugar refining, sunflower-oil extraction, flax retting, distilling, and the production of tobacco, essential oils, and plant rubber. Among the principal metal and light industries are metallurgy of local iron ore and the manufacturing of tractors at Lipetsk, synthetic rubber production at Voronezh, textile milling, tanning, and shoemaking.

The chief destination of the export products from the Central Black-Earth Region is the Central Industrial Region to the north; the most important goods are grains (wheat, oats, rye), eggs, poultry, pigs, vegetable oils, and other agricultural produce.

The region lies astride the principal rail lines linking Moscow and the Central Industrial Region with the areas in the south of the European USSR. The direct Moscow-Khar'kov line passes through Orel and Kursk; Tambov lies on the railway to Saratov and the Volga Region, while the main connection of Moscow with Rostov and the Caucasus touches the city of Voronezh.

Orel Oblast
Capital, Orel; area, 12,200, population, 1,500,000

Orel Oblast lies in the Central Russian upland and is drained by the upper Oka River in the west and by the Sosna (an affluent of the Don) in the east. The black earth of the wooded steppe predominates and supports mainly crops of potatoes in the east and hemp in the west. In secondary position is the acreage under wheat, coarse grains, rubber-bearing plants, and sugar beets. Because of the relative humidity, sunflowers are almost entirely absent. Fruits (especially apples) and truck produce are grown in the vicinity of the urban centers. Hogs and horses are extensively raised.

Rural industries engage in hemp retting and milling, distilling, and the production of starches. Metalworking and food-processing industries are located at the principal centers of Orel, Yelets, and Livny.

Orel, a rail hub and industrial center on the upper Oka River, produces textile and agricultural machinery, and has flour mills, meat plants, distilleries, breweries, clothing, and shoe industries.

Yelets, east of Orel, on the Sosna River, is a rail and road center, with iron foundry, woodworking, and food industries. It trades in grain, lumber, livestock, beeswax, and honey. Iron is mined near Argamach, just northeast.

Tambov Oblast
Capital, Tambov; area, 13,200, population, 1,650,000

Tambov Oblast lies east of Orel in the Oka-Don lowland, extending between the Central Russian upland and the Volga upland in the east. This region, which descends to an elevation of about 250 feet above sea level, is rather flat and dissected by few ravines and gullies. It is drained mainly by the north-flowing Tsna River, of the Oka system, and by the Vorona, which flows south to the Khoper, an affluent of the Don River. The banks of the streams, which are generally suitable only for timber flotage, are bordered by narrow forest belts. During the postwar period the Tsna was rendered navigable between Tambov and Morshansk by an elaborate system of locks and reservoirs. The soils are of the black-earth type, with a high humus content in the south and merging with the ordinary and degraded types to the north.

In this important agricultural region the principal grain crops are rye, oats, and millet. The oblast is the principal millet producer of the USSR. Tobacco is raised in the area of Morshansk, potatoes along the sandy banks of the Tsna River, legumes in the east, sugar beets in the north, and hemp throughout the oblast. Cattle is reared for meat production, and there is considerable hog raising. In the south are several horse-breeding farms.

The industries, flour milling, distilling, and meat packing, are based mainly on the local agricultural production. Imported raw materials constitute the foundation of the old textile industry, which specializes in the milling of coarse cloth at Rasskazovo and Morshansk, and of the new engineering works at Tambov and Michurinsk.

Tambov is situated on the Tsna River at the crossing of the Moscow-Saratov railroad. A branch leaves the main line here for Kamyshin, on the Volga. The central location of the city in the rail network of the southern half of the European USSR contributed to the establishment of industries producing railroad accessories, including lighting equipment and electric motors. A plant for the production of synthetic rubber was built here at the eve of the Second World War. The city also has aircraft and explosives plants and a varied food industry, engaged in flour milling, distilling, and tobacco processing. In 1940 the southeastern industrial section and adjacent suburbs of Tambov were constituted into the separate city of Kotovsk.

Michurinsk (called Kozlov until 1932) is known for its horticultural experimental station, founded by the plant breeder Michurin. It is a rail center and manufactures locomotives and tractor parts; it also produces meat, and canned foods.

Morshansk (glass, wood distillation products, metal goods, coarse cloth) and Rasskazovo (cloth, wool, and leather mills) are other regional centers.

Voronezh Oblast
Capital, Voronezh; area, 26,400, population, 3,450,000

Voronezh Oblast, the largest and most populous of the Central Black-Earth Region, is drained by the Don River and its affluents and is oriented toward the dry steppes of the Lower Volga Region. It has a drier climate and a lower population density than the other black-earth oblasts. Hilly in the southwest and level in the northeast, it is the only oblast of the Central Black-Earth Region where wheat acreage exceeds that of rye. About one fourth of the total tilled area is under wheat, as opposed to one sixth for Kursk Oblast and about one tenth for the other black-earth districts. Voronezh is mainly a spring wheat oblast, due to the relatively light precipitation. However, in recent years efforts have been made to develop winter wheat in the western sections adjoining Kursk Oblast.

As is the case with all dry wheat regions, sunflowers are the most important industrial crop; they are sown side by side with wheat. Other crops are potatoes and sugar beets in the north, in the vicinity of Voronezh. The northern potato crop is used partly to feed the hogs, while in the drier south, sheep are reared. The section along the Bityug is famous for its breed of heavy-duty horses, which are raised especially at the breeding farm of Khrenovoye.

The agricultural products of the oblast have laid the foundation for a well-developed industry engaged in sunflower-oil extraction, flour milling, distilling, and the processing of starches and molasses. The intensive cultivation of potatoes also led to the establishment of a synthetic rubber plant at Voronezh.

The iron deposits near Lipetsk have been the basis, since the eighteenth century, of a metallurgical industry in that city. Machinery is produced at Voronezh. The deposits of refractory clays, marl, and limestone supply cement and brickworking plants, of which Semiluki, near Voronezh, is the main site.

Voronezh is an important industrial center on the high right bank of the Voronezh River. It was founded in the sixteenth century as a fortress. Under Peter the Great it became a base for the wars against the Turks, and a Russian war fleet was constructed here. In recent years engineering industries grew up in the city, and it produces now agricultural, textile, and flour-milling machinery, excavators, bridging equipment, Diesel motors. It has locomotive and car repair works, synthetic rubber, radio, and oil-cracking plants. Its large food-processing plants engage in flour milling, meat packing, sunflower-oil extraction, and fruit and vegetable canning. A university and several agricultural research institutes are located there.

Lipetsk, on the upper course of the Voronezh River, has an old metallurgical plant, which dates from the time of Peter the Great and was reconstructed after the Revolution, and a new mill, built in 1936, which produce pig iron, iron alloys, and cast-iron pipes. Both establishments use near-by iron deposits. A tractor works was built in the Second World War. In the vicinity of Lipetsk is a health resort with mineral springs and mud baths.

The chief agricultural centers, which produce chiefly flour, sunflower oil, and meat, are Buturlinovka, Borisoglebsk, Kalach, and Ostrogozhsk.

Kursk Oblast
Capital, Kursk; area, 19,600, population, 3,000,000

Kursk Oblast is situated south of Orel in the Central Russian upland and is drained by streams of the Dnieper basin, including the upper courses of the Seym, the Psel, the Vorskla, and the Oskol rivers. It is characterized by relatively moderate and humid continental climate and by a high population density.

The climatic conditions encourage the growing of sugar beets, of which the oblast is the principal producer in the Russian SFSR, and of winter wheat, mainly in the east. Secondary crops are hemp and potatoes in the north and truck produce near the cities. In recent years the acreage under leguminous crops (peas, beans, and lentils) has undergone a marked increase. Hogs are raised on the by-products of sugar refining, and there are many poultry farms in the oblast.

Industry is concerned chiefly with the processing of agricultural products and engages in flour milling, sugar refining, distilling, and tanning. There are fruit and vegetable canneries and poultry-meat packing plants. Mineral resources are utilized by the phosphate works of Shchigry, brick and tile works, and the chalk works of Belgorod, which produce about one half of all the writing chalk of the USSR. Of the greatest potential importance are the magnetic iron deposits known as the Kursk magnetic anomaly, a vast ore belt, 90 miles long and 10 miles wide, which had long been known because of the erratic behavior of compass needles, but which is only now being developed as a potential metallurgical base. In 1939 the first large iron mine was sunk at Gubkin, west of Staryy Oskol.

Kursk, a rail center on the Moscow-Sevastopol' and Kiev-Voronezh lines, lies on the upper Seym River. An old city dating from the 9th century, it has become an important industrial center and produces agricultural and spinning machinery, electrical apparatus, synthetic rubber, clothing and shoes. Among its varied processing plants are flour mills, distilleries, tanneries, and tobacco factories.

Belgorod, on the right bank of the Northern Donets River, is situated at the foot of chalk hills, which gave the city its name (white city). Until the eighteenth century, it was one of the southern fortified points of the Moscow domain. The main industries are connected with flour milling and the quarrying of chalk.

Other important agricultural centers are Staryy Oskol, Novyy Oskol, the rail hub of L'gov, and Shebekino.

CHAPTER 7

The European West

THE EUROPEAN WEST (western section of the European Russian SFSR) lies between the Belorussian SSR in the west and the central regions of the European USSR in the east. Its five oblasts, Bryansk, Kaluga, Smolensk, Velikiye Luki, and Kalinin, have many natural and economic features in common with the Belorussian SSR, which is discussed separately in Chapter 25.

The region, which aggregates more than 85,000 square miles, has a relief for the most part of glacial origin and a climate which is less continental and hence more humid than that prevailing farther east.

In the north, the Valday upland (also known as the Valday hills) is the principal feature of a series of moraine ridges extending in a general NE-SW direction and rising to 1,055 feet. The area contains a large number of glacial lakes, up to 150 feet deep, with high, deeply dissected shores and a multitude of islands. The largest are Lake Seliger and the upper Volga lakes. The upland, which constitutes the watershed between the Baltic and the Caspian drainage basins, merges toward the north with the Baltic lowland, where marshes and peat bogs take the place of the lakes. The Valday lake district gives rise to two important streams of the European USSR, the Western Dvina, which flows to the Baltic, and the Volga River, which drains into the Caspian Sea. The southernmost feature in this glacial moraine region is the Smolensk-Moscow upland, which is the central section of a long ridge known as the Lithuanian-Belorussian upland in the west and the Klin-Dmitrov upland in the east.

The Central Russian upland, which occupies the southern part of the European West, is primarily a rolling plateau with a few low hills and marshy depressions. The highest and best-defined portion is the watershed between the affluents of the Oka and the Volga, on one hand, and the tributaries of the Dnieper and the Western Dvina, on the other. Here the Dnieper rises together with its left affluent, the Sozh. In the north among occasional limestone formations, karst relief is found in

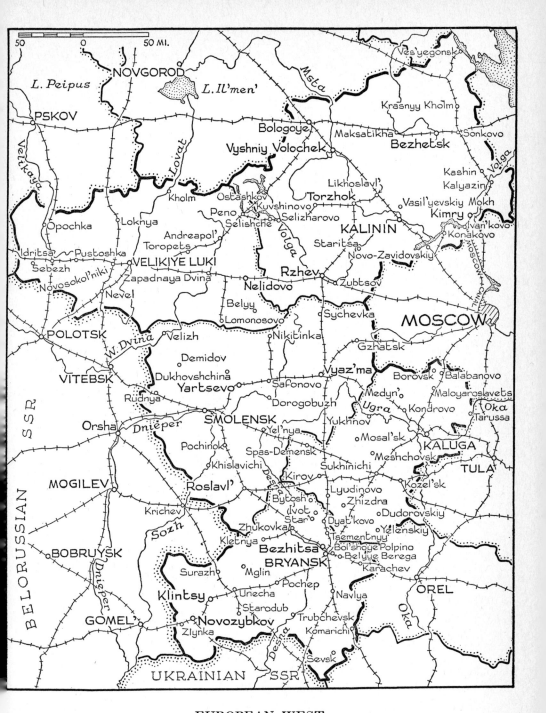

EUROPEAN WEST

the form of sink holes and underground streams. The western section of the Central Russian upland is less eroded than the deeply-gullied eastern portion in the Central Black-Earth Region.

As a result of its position in the western USSR, being nearer the moderating influence of the Atlantic Ocean, the European West has a less severe type of continental climate than the central regions to the east. Winters are somewhat warmer, summers cooler, and the mean annual temperature rises toward the west. Precipitation is noticeably greater (26 inches yearly at Smolensk), especially during the summer months.

The increased humidity, the lower summer temperatures, the impermeability of the clay subsoil, and the low watershed pattern are responsible for the formation of extensive marshes. Forests cover 20 to 30 percent of the area and include a great variety of trees, resulting from the meeting of the coniferous northern types (fir, pine), birch from the east, oak from the south, and maple and ash from the southwest. Favorable climatic conditions produce a good quality of timber, which is in great demand in the adjoining treeless regions of the USSR. Agriculture, especially the cultivation of wheat, suffers from the excessive humidity, which favors, however, the growth of hay meadows and fodder crops. The cool summers (July temperatures drop below 65° F) and the clay soils are ideal conditions for the raising of fiber flax.

Mineral resources are of secondary importance. The western wing of the Moscow lignite basin penetrates into Kaluga and Smolensk oblasts, and some iron ore is found near Zhizdra. Of greater economic importance are the lignite deposits near Selizharovo and at Nelidovo, which are mined for the Leningrad industrial area. The chief minerals are peat, which serves as the principal local fuel, building materials, and phosphorites.

The population totals more than 7,500,000 and is 95 percent Russian. The main minorities are Ukrainians, Jews, Latvians, and Poles. The average density of 90 per square mile is lower than in the central European USSR, Kalinin Oblast having the greatest urban concentration.

Flax is the agricultural specialty. Fodder crops, which are sown in rotation, support large dairy-cattle herds. The by-products of the dairy industry, in turn, aid in the rearing of hogs. The interlocking agricultural series (flax—fodder crops—dairy farming—hog raising) is typical of the economy of the European West. While 16 percent of the cultivated area is under flax in Kalinin Oblast and 13 percent in Smolensk Oblast, potatoes also constitute a major crop as food, fodder, and industrial raw material for the distilling industry. The industrial crops (flax, potatoes, and fodder crops) occupy 50 percent or more of the total cultivated area. Grain crops are represented mostly by rye and oats. Wheat acreage is being increased and reaches about 7 percent of the area under cultivation. Hog and cattle raising, as well as lumbering, complete the nonindustrial side of the economy.

Processing industries are based mainly on the local agricultural production and engage in butter and cheese making, distilling, meat packing, flour milling, tanning, shoe manufacturing, the retting, spinning, and weaving of flax and, to a lesser extent, hemp. The timber resources furnish raw material for sawmills and plywood mills, furniture and woodworking industries, paper and match factories. Construction materials, glass, porcelain, and chemical fertilizer are produced on the basis of the mineral resources. Large-scale industries operating with imported raw materials and producing especially cotton textiles and machinery are centered in the industrial districts of Kalinin and Bryansk.

The largest cities, such as Kalinin and Smolensk, lie on important rail lines, including the Moscow-Leningrad trunk railway and the routes linking Moscow with the Belorussian SSR, Poland, and the Baltic republics. The territory of the European West once lay on the old trade route from the Baltic to the Black Sea and contained most of the important portages connecting the river routes across the watershed. The Vyshne-Volotsk Canal (now in repair) was constructed on the site of one of these portages. The rivers, which penetrate only in their upper reaches into the region, have now lost their former importance and are used chiefly for timber flotage. Only the Volga, enhanced since the construction of the Moscow Canal, represents an important shipping route.

Bryansk Oblast
Capital, Bryansk; area, 13,400, population, 1,800,000

The southernmost oblast of the European West, Bryansk borders on the Belorussian and Ukrainian SSR in the west. It is drained by streams of the Desna River basin and forms part of the mixed forest zone.

The basic crops are hemp, which is grown throughout the oblast, with coarse grains and potatoes in the west. Also grown are sugar beets in the area of Komarichi, buckwheat in the poor soils of the west, and tobacco. Truck produce is important in the Bryansk industrial area. Hog raising is associated with the cultivation of potatoes.

The principal mineral resources are peat, which provides the fuel for several electric power plants, phosphorites, and quartzite. Heavy industry is centered in the area of Bryansk and neighboring Bezhitsa. The local iron foundries, which operated originally on local low-grade iron resources and charcoal, now receive pig iron and coal from the Ukraine. Locomotives, machinery, and metal products are made here. North of Bryansk are a large cement mill (Tsementnyy) and a glassworking district around Dyat'kovo, with the main plants at Bytosh', Ivot, and Star, northwest and west of Dyat'kovo. Sawmills operate along the rail lines; there is a paper mill at Surazh, and match manufacturing plants at Novozybkov and Zlynka.

The agricultural production forms the basis for hemp retting and milling (Karachev is one of the main hemp-shipping points of the USSR), for distilling, starch, and tobacco industries.

Bryansk is a port on the Desna River and a six-way rail center. The city was founded in the twelfth century on the high right bank of the river, and it gradually expanded to the low left bank, the present site of the rail junctions and industrial suburbs: Uritskiy (rolling stock), Imeni Volodarskogo, Imeni Tolstogo, and Imeni Fokina (sawmills). The city also produces rope, cement, artificial slate, and clothing. Superphosphate is milled in the outer eastern suburb of Bol'shoye Polpino, and a large peat-fed power plant is in operation at Belyye Berega, five miles east.

Bezhitsa (called Ordzhonikidzegrad from 1935 to 1943), on the Desna River, just northwest of Bryansk, is an important locomotive and rolling-stock manufacturing center, with metallurgical and coking plants.

Unecha is a rail center (with a paper mill) in the western part of the oblast; near-by Klintsy mills rope products and woolen textiles.

Kaluga Oblast
Capital, Kaluga; area, 11,600, population, 1,050,000

Kaluga Oblast lies between the Smolensk-Moscow upland in the north and the Central Russian upland in the south and is drained by the Oka River and its left affluent, the Ugra River. It is in the mixed forest zone with predominating sandy soils.

The basic crop consists of coarse grains (rye and oats), with some wheat and potatoes in the northeast, hemp in the south, fodder grasses, fruits, and vegetables. Dairy cattle and hogs are reared. On the basis

of the agricultural production, the rural industries engage in fruit canning, dairying, flour milling and distilling.

The mineral resources supply peat, quartzite for glassworks at Dudorovskiy and Yelenskiy, kaolin for porcelain making at Kirov, and phosphorite for fertilizer plants. In the northeast (toward Moscow) are
textile mills at Borovsk (woolens) and Balabanovo (cotton). There are
several woodworking plants and a paper mill at Kondrovo. Metalworking and engineering industries are centered at Kaluga and at Lyudinovo
(steam-tractor works).

Kaluga, an old city and head of navigation on the Oka River, produces railroad hand cars, steam-generating, telephone, and telegraph
equipment, weights, and measuring devices. It has a varied food-
processing industry. A hydroelectric station is under construction as
part of the postwar Five-Year Plan.

Smolensk Oblast
Capital, Smolensk; area, 18,900, population, 1,800,000

Smolensk Oblast lies in the Smolensk-Moscow upland, which forms here
the watershed area between the basins of the Western Dvina, the Volga,
and the Dnieper. The chief waterway is the upper course of the Dnieper
River, which is only suitable for timber flotage within the confines of the
oblast. The moderate continental type of climate favors the vegetation
of the mixed forest zone on clayey and sandy podsols. Peat and building
materials are the chief mineral resources; lignite is mined near Dorogobuzh.

The oblast has a specialized flax economy, cultivating the plant in an
intensive manner for fiber and linseed-oil production. Fodder grasses
play an important role as a rotating crop and provide the basis for the
rearing of dairy cattle. The by-products of the dairy industry in turn
support the raising of hogs. The most common grains are rye and oats.
In recent years, wheat has been introduced in order to reduce the imports
of this bread grain.

The rural industries engage in flax retting, dairying, tanning, sawmilling, and woodworking.

Smolensk is a four-way rail center and the head of navigation on
the Dnieper. It is an old city, dating from the ninth century, and played
an important role in the trade between Kiev and Novgorod. Till the end
of the seventeenth century it was a prize in the wars between Russia and

Poland. The kremlin and the powerful walls of an old fortress are preserved. Its main industrial establishments are a linen mill, machinery works (textile machines, road graders), and clothing plants. There are flour milling, distilling, brewing, sawmilling, and woodworking. The city acts as an important distributing center for lumber, flax, and grain.

Yartsevo is a cotton-milling town northeast of Smolensk, and Vyaz'ma and Gzhatsk are industrial centers on the way to Moscow.

Velikiye Luki Oblast
Capital, Velikiye Luki; area, 17,300, population, 900,000

Velikiye Luki Oblast lies in a lake-studded moraine region, drained by the Western Dvina, Lovat', and Velikaya rivers and bordered by the Valday upland on the east. It has sandy and clay soils and a dense forest cover in the eastern sections.

The principal crops are flax, potatoes, and fodder crops. Dairy cattle and hogs are extensively raised. Industry is based largely on the processing of agricultural products (flax retting, distilling, dairying) and on the forest reserves. There are sawmills at Kholm, Nelidovo, Zapadnaya Dvina, and Peno, most of which are situated at the crossing of rivers and rail lines. Rural handicrafts produce carts, sleds, and wagon wheels.

Velikiye Luki, a rail junction on the Lovat' River, has railway shops, clothing mills, and light industries of local importance.

Nelidovo has been developed in the postwar period as a lignite-mining center serving Leningrad.

Kalinin Oblast
Capital, Kalinin; area, 25,500, population, 2,250,000

Kalinin Oblast is situated in the Valday upland watershed area, in which many of the large rivers of the European part of the USSR have their source, flowing toward the Gulf of Finland, such as the Msta River, or toward the east, such as the Volga and its affluents, the Tvertsa, and the Mologa. This is a region of ancient portages linking important water trade routes, some of which were later replaced by canals, such as the Vyshne-Volotsk Canal, which joins the Msta and the Tvertsa rivers.

It is a district of clearly marked moraine characteristics. The many lakes, of which Lake Seliger is the largest, are deeply dissected and contain a large number of islands. Boulders and pebbles of varying size cover large expanses of the predominantly clayey and sandy soils. East of the Moscow-Leningrad railroad, which bisects the oblast from southeast to northwest, the moraine features are less evident. The glacier passed unobstructed over the level terrain in this area and left few deposits.

Forests cover about one third of the total area and are densest in the northeast, along the upper Mologa. The lumber reserves, which consist mainly of fir, pine, and oak, assume special importance due to their proximity to such important markets as the Moscow and the Leningrad industrial districts. The chief mineral resource is peat, which occurs mainly near Kalinin, where it is used as fuel in electric power plants, lignite, deposits of which are being increasingly exploited west of Selizharovo, and quartzite, the basis for the local glass industry.

Agricultural specialization is oriented toward the production of flax (of which Kalinin is the top-ranking supplier in the Russian SFSR), dairy farming, and the raising of potatoes and vegetables. Flax, which covers 16 percent of the sown acreage, is rotated with fodder crops. Potatoes occupy 10 percent of the total sown area. Altogether, 53 percent of the tilled land is under industrial crops, representing the largest percentage in the Russian SFSR.

Large-scale industry is still little developed here as compared with the Moscow and Leningrad regions. In first place is the milling of textiles. Cotton mills are strung along the Moscow-Leningrad railroad, with the largest establishments at Kalinin, Vyshniy Volochek, and Novo-Zavidovskiy. Linen is milled at Rzhev and at Bezhetsk, which also makes textile machinery. Other industries are connected with railway-car works, the manufacturing of peat-working and textile machines at Kalinin, tanning and shoemaking at Kimry, Torzhok, and Ostashkov, sawmilling (at many points along the rail lines), and paper milling at Kuvshinovo. Glassworking and the making of porcelain is also important. Handicraft and home industries are developed in the districts of Kimry (shoe making) and Ostashkov (net making).

The filling of the Volga Reservoir in 1937 (with the establishment of a hydroelectric plant at Ivan'kovo) and the construction of the Moscow Canal, which established a direct waterway to Moscow, have contributed considerably to the industrial development of the oblast. In the northeast it touches the new Rybinsk Reservoir.

Kalinin (known as Tver' until 1933), lies at the junction of the Volga River, its affluent, the Tvertsa, the Moscow-Leningrad railroad, and several main highways. It is the southern terminus of the Vyshne-Volotsk canal system (now in repair) and the head of regular navigation on the Volga. An old city (founded in 1135), it was an important trading center on the route from the Oka-Volga watershed area to the western cities of Novgorod and Smolensk and an early rival of Moscow, by which it was, however, absorbed in the fifteenth century. The main industrial establishments are the railway-car works, the plants of textile and peat-working machines, and three large cotton mills.

Vyshniy Volochek is a cotton-milling center on the former portage (now replaced by the Vyshne-Volotsk Canal), linking the Msta and the Tvertsa rivers.

Kimry, with near-by Kalyazin, are old footwear manufacturing centers on the Volga River. The former home industries have been consolidated into co-operatives and partly replaced by modern factories.

Torzhok, on the Tvertsa River, is a tanning center in the flax-growing region. It has a noted flax research institute and produces flax-retting machinery.

Ostashkov, the tanning center on Lake Seliger, is also important for newly developed fisheries and net-making industries and is becoming a health and tourist resort.

CHAPTER 8

The European Northwest

THE EUROPEAN NORTHWEST (northwestern section of the European
Russian SFSR) is a relatively small region of about 65,000 square miles,
lying south of the Gulf of Finland and Lake Ladoga. It includes the
strategic Karelian isthmus, located between these two bodies of water.
It is near the Atlantic Ocean and has a humid climate and a well-developed
lake and river network.

Basic crystalline rock formations underlie the glacial sediments left
by the retreating ice masses. In the south, terminal moraine ridges rise
above the surrounding terrain. In the north, a preglacial limestone
escarpment parallels the southern shores of the Gulf of Finland and Lake
Ladoga. River courses are featured by rapids where they cross these
terraces and become potential sites for hydroelectric projects. The surface relief of the region shows a hilly lowland with typical moraine land
forms: long ridges formed of clay, sand, and rock rubble, wide prev-
alence of pebbles and smooth boulders, numerous lakes in the depressions
and along the low watersheds, and slow-flowing rivers which occasionally
form rapids along their course.

The European Northwest, sometimes called the Lake Region, contains the southern sections of the lakes Ladoga and Onega, with their
flat, straight shores, and, further south, lakes Il'men', Peipus (Chudskoye), and Pskov. All these bodies of water are of glacial origin and
were formed by the melting of the continental glacier in depressions
which had been dammed up by glacial debris. All lakes are shallow, and
the smaller ones have a tendency toward marsh formation. Except for
the extreme southeast, the entire region drains into the Gulf of Finland
via the short, but important, Neva River, which joins Lake Ladoga to
the gulf. Lakes Onega and Il'men', in turn, empty into Lake Ladoga
through the Svir' and the Volkhov rivers. Only the southeastern section
of the region belongs to the Volga drainage basin and is watered by the
Mologa, an affluent of the Volga.

The proximity of the ocean and the abundance of inland waters tend to moderate the climate, but also render it raw and cool. Winters are warmer here than further east, but summers and especially spring are much cooler. West winds coming from the sea blow with great force, notably in the autumn, and occasionally cause the Neva River to back up into Lake Ladoga producing floods in Leningrad itself. These winds also create heavy storms on Lake Ladoga and throw the water onto the eastern shores.

Forests cover a large portion of the area: one half in the average and as much as three fourths in the northeast. The prevailing podsol soils with heavy clay or sand bases are not very permeable and render necessary extensive drainage work and careful treating of the soil for agricultural use.

The European Northwest is relatively poor in mineral resources. The principal deposits are lignite, near Borovichi, the eastern extension of the Estonian oil-shale district, between Gdov and Veymarn, and the bauxite of Boksitogorsk, near Tikhvin. Various types of construction materials (stone, clay, quartz) are quarried south of Leningrad and near Borovichi.

With a total population of more than 6,500,000, the region has an average density of 100 per square mile. The basic ethnic element is Russian (80–95 percent). The centrally located Russian nucleus is surrounded by various Finnish groups, including the Finns and Karelians in the north and the Estonians in the west. Smaller nationalities of Finnish origin form isolated population islands in the region. These are the Veps, south of Lake Onega, the Ingrians (original inhabitants of Ingermanland, along the south coast of the Gulf of Finland), and the small group of the Vots, just south of the Ingrian settlement area.

The center of gravity of the economy lies in the city of Leningrad, where 80 percent of the industry is concentrated. Its development is due largely to the favorable geographical location on the Gulf of Finland astride important river and rail routes. The industries produce machines, ships, electrical equipment and chemicals, textiles, food, and lumber products. In addition to the industrial suburbs of Leningrad (Sestroretsk, Kolpino, Petrokrepost', Dubrovka, and Gatchina), the areas of Volkhov (aluminum, water power), Borovichi (refractory materials, lumber, paper, linen), and Vyborg (lumber, machines) are the centers of production. Lumbering and associated industries are important in the forested areas. Power supply rests mainly on imported coal and petro-

EUROPEAN NORTHWEST

(Leningrad Area is shown in detail on p. 153.)

leum and on local oil-shale, peat, lumber, and water-power production. The most important power stations are in Leningrad, Dubrovka, Volkhov, and along the Vuoksi and Svir' rivers.

The cultivation of oats and flax is characteristic for the poor soils of the region. Winter rye is the principal bread grain. The raising of dairy cattle is favored by the abundance of meadowland. The southern and southwestern sections, with their sandy and clayey soils and humid climate, are the chief flax-growing areas. Potatoes are cultivated mainly in the belt north and west of Lake Il'men'. Agriculture in the vicinity of Leningrad is intended to feed the great urban centers and to supply them with truck produce and dairy products. Because of the large city population, the region is still a grain importer. Although the wheat acreage is constantly being increased, fodder grains (barley, oats) and grasses far exceed the bread grains in this area.

Leningrad is a major transportation center at the junction of the important rail, highway, and water routes of the European Northwest. By means of the Neva River and the Mariinsk canal systems, the city is connected with the upper Volga. The Baltic–White Sea Canal provides a connection with the White and Barents seas and the Kola Peninsula.

Novgorod Oblast
Capital, Novgorod; area, 20,700, population, 1,050,000

Novgorod Oblast includes the northern section of the Valday upland in the east and the Lake Il'men' depression in the west. It is drained by the Msta, the Lovat', and the Volkhov rivers, all of which form part of the Lake Il'men' system. Forests cover about one half the total area, with marshes, clayey, and sandy arable soils in the remainder of the oblast.

The principal mineral resources are concentrated in the area of Borovichi. They include lignite, mined at Komarovo and Zarubino, in the furthest northwestern extension of the Moscow Basin, which is of special importance for the Leningrad industrial district. Limestone and refractory clays are quarried in the same area, which also has several peat works.

Lumber industries constitute the chief branches of the economy. There are numerous sawmills along the railroads; paper is milled at Vel'giya, near Borovichi, and at Parakhino-Poddub'ye; matches are made at Chudovo and near-by Gruzino. Staraya Russa and Parfino, to the east, have plywood works and produce prefabricated houses. The ceramics industry is well represented in the area of Chudovo, with large glass works at Imeni Kominterna, Malaya Vishera, and Bol'shaya Vishera, and a porcelain plant at Krasnofarfornyy. Glass is also worked at Proletariy, near the northeast shore of Lake Il'men'.

The chief crop is flax, and some areas are under wheat and potatoes. Dairy cattle are raised extensively on the alluvial meadows along the rivers and on fodder crops sown in rotation with flax. Rural industries engage in flax retting, distilling, and flour milling. There is a linen mill at Kulotino, west of Borovichi. Fisheries and small-scale boatbuilding industries are active on the shores of Lake Il'men'.

Novgorod, on the Volkhov River, near its issue from Lake Il'men', is one of the oldest cities of the USSR, dating from 862. It has been dubbed "museum city" because of the numerous architectural relics from the early Middle Ages. The city flourished during the thirteenth and the fourteenth centuries as a major trading point and the political center of a vast territory embracing the northwest and the north of European Russia. It is now an agricultural center, with distilling, meat-packing, and flour-milling industries.

Borovichi is the principal industrial center of the oblast. It specializes in the production of refractory and acid-resistant ceramic products (bricks, pipes, etc.), and makes prefabricated houses. Its cotton-spinning mills supply the knitting handicrafts, important home industries in that vicinity. Paper is milled at near-by Vel'giya (east), as well as at Parakhino-Poddub'ye (west). Linen is milled at Kulotino, and near-by Uglovka has important limestone quarries.

Chudovo, a rail junction near the Volkhov River, has cement and match manufacturing works, glassworks and metalworks. Near by, across the Volkhov River, are the industrial settlements of Gruzino (matches), Imeni Kominterna (glass), and Krasnofarfornyy (porcelain).

Staraya Russa, an old Russian settlement on the Polist' River, near the southern shore of Lake Il'men', has woodworking and agricultural machinery plants. Near by is a health resort, having salt springs and mud baths.

Pskov Oblast
Capital, Pskov; area, 12,200, population, 900,000

Pskov Oblast lies on lakes Peipus and Pskov and borders on the Estonian and Latvian SSR's in the southwest. From these republics the oblast received, in 1944, certain Russian-majority districts in a transfer which constituted the first territorial change affecting Estonia and Latvia since they became independent nations, in 1920. The area around the Estonian city of Petseri became Pechory Rayon; the Latvian towns of Abrene (formerly Jaunlatgale) and Kačanava were renamed and became the centers of Pytalovo and Kachanovo rayons of Pskov Oblast.

The region has clayey glacial soils and a humid climate and is one of the most important flax-growing areas of the USSR. The intensive cultivation of this crop and the growing of wheat and potatoes in the few drier, sandy sections form the basis of the rural flax-retting, flour-milling, and distilling industries. Dairy farming is also important.

Peat is worked near Ostrov and Porkhov, and limestone and dolomite are quarried near Novorzhev. Oil shale is found near Gdov. Lumbering in the north is the basis of the match manufacturing industry at Chernevo.

Pskov, on the Velikaya River, near its mouth in Lake Pskov, dates from 903. It was originally an outpost of Great Novgorod, later became independent, and was finally absorbed by Moscow. It is the center of the flax-raising area and has linen and rope mills, agricultural and textile machinery works, and railroad shops, in addition to other agricultural industries.

Porkhov, Ostrov, and Pechory are agricultural centers; they process the local produce (flax, potatoes, grain, dairy products, and hides).

Dno is an important rail junction.

Leningrad Oblast
Capital, Leningrad; area, 32,800, population, 4,800,000

Leningrad Oblast lies in a well-preserved moraine region bordering on the Gulf of Finland and Lake Ladoga and extending from Lake Peipus, in the west, to Lake Onega, in the east. It is watered by one of the densest lake and river nets of the USSR, including the Luga, the Neva, the Volkhov, and the Svir' rivers. Since 1940, when Finland lost the Karelian isthmus and the northern Ladoga littoral to the USSR, Leningrad Oblast has expanded onto the isthmus. Originally (in 1940) it acquired merely the southern portion as a protective zone for the city of Leningrad, while the northern half (north of the Primorsk-Vuoksi River line) was incorporated into the Karelo-Finnish SSR. In 1944, for strategic and economic reasons, the northern section was also added to Leningrad Oblast. It includes the cities of Primorsk (Koivisto), Priozersk (Käkisalmi or

Kexholm), and Vyborg (Viipuri or Viborg), as well as the hydroelectric stations of Svetogorsk (Enso) and Raukhiala (Rauhiala) on the Vuoksi River, two of the main electric power suppliers for the Leningrad industrial district. The oblast also underwent a slight boundary adjustment in 1944 along the Estonian frontier, where it acquired the narrow border zone on the right bank of the Narva River thus relocating the Russian-Estonian border along the river from Lake Peipus to the Gulf of Finland.

The nearness of the sea constitutes a moderating influence on the climate of the region, especially in its western section. The city of Leningrad, although located 4° farther north than Moscow, has a higher January mean than the capital (20° F as against 12° F). Precipitation amounts to 24 inches annually, and the coolness of the summer and the general cloudiness lead to the formation of marshes.

The mineral resources of the oblast include the eastern extension of the Estonian oil-shale belt between Slantsy and Veymarn, peat in the vicinity of Leningrad, bauxite at Boksitogorsk, near Tikhvin, marble and dolomite near Volosovo, brick clays and building stone. In the past the huge Leningrad industrial complex had to rely mainly on long-haul Donets Basin coal and petroleum from the Caucasus for its fuel supply. In recent years, however, the exploitation of newly developed deposits of petroleum and coal in the European North and the construction of new hydroelectric stations in the vicinity of Leningrad have altered considerably the fuel supply scheme for the Leningrad industries and have reduced, at least partially, the need for long-distance transportation. The trend to make the Leningrad area self-sufficient in fuel resources is being intensified during the current Five-Year Plan with the development of lignite deposits near Borovichi (Novgorod Oblast), Selizharovo (Kalinin Oblast), Nelidovo (Velikiye Luki Oblast), and Dorogobuzh (Smolensk Oblast). A gas pipe line has been constructed from the Estonian oil-shale fields at Kokhtla-Yarve to Leningrad. Shipments of petroleum from Ukhta and coal from Vorkuta are also being increased. Hydroelectric power is furnished by the stations of the Svir' River (at Svir'stroy and near Podporozh'ye), the Volkhov River (at Volkhov), and the Vuoksi River (at Svetogorsk and Raukhiala). Along with the development of fuel resources, steps are also being taken under the current Plan to give the Leningrad Oblast its own metallurgical supply base. Construction of an iron and steel works is scheduled to begin at Cherepovets, on the basis of Vorkuta coke, iron ore from Yena in the Kola Peninsula and Gimoly in the Karelo-Finnish SSR, and local flux materials. Since

Leningrad requires about 10 percent of the total steel production of the USSR, the new steel mill will free the production of many other mills for use elsewhere in the Union.

As one of the oldest machine-building centers of the USSR, the city of Leningrad played a vital role in the industrialization of the country during the first Five-Year Plans. Its well-equipped plants and skilled labor supply served to develop and to introduce into other industrial areas of the Union the manufacture of machinery never before produced in the USSR, including such items as tractors, steam turbines, rolling mills, textile, tobacco- and food-processing machines, counting and printing machines, fishing trawlers, motorcycles, photographic, telephone, and radio apparatus. Leningrad is still the only producer in the USSR of such specialized products as large hydroelectric turbine installations, special machine tools and others. Similar pioneering work was done by the Leningrad chemical industry, which was the first to develop the methods of production of synthetic rubber from potato alcohol. Among the other important industries centered at Leningrad are textile mills, producing linen, cotton, and knitted goods, clothing mills, food-processing and printing plants.

With the exception of the aluminum industry at Volkhov, based on Boksitogorsk bauxite, agriculture and lumbering comprise the economy outside of the Leningrad industrial complex. A large part of the lumber is exported through the port of Leningrad; however, a large percentage of the timber is also processed into pulp, paper, matches, and wood-distillation products. Many timber-processing plants are located on the Karelian Isthmus: at Krasnoostrovskiy (until 1948, B'yërkskiy), near Primorsk (until 1948, Koivisto; sawmilling), at Sovetskiy (until 1948, Johannes; site of a cellulose and paper mill), at the paper and sulphate-cellulose works of Svetogorsk, and at the cardboard mill of Priozersk. Paper is also milled at Syas'stroy, at Dubrovka on the Neva River and near Kingisepp, while sawmills are established along the rail lines.

The agricultural economy supplies the vast urban district of Leningrad with truck produce and dairy products. In the immediate vicinity of the industrial district, vegetables are raised and dairy cattle reared on fodder crops. Beyond this zone, potatoes form the dominant crop. Bread grains occupy less than one third of the sown area and are less important than the coarse grains (oats, barley) and fodder grasses.

The oblast occupies an exceptional position from the point of view of transportation facilities. It is here that the Atlantic Ocean reaches its easternmost extension into the Eurasian continent in the form of the Gulf of Finland of the Baltic Sea. In addition to this open access to foreign countries, the region is connected with the White Sea by the Baltic–White Sea Canal, with the Volga (and the Caspian Sea) by the Mariinsk Canal system, and, by means of a dense rail network radiating from Leningrad, with the remaining sections of the Union.

Leningrad, the second city of the USSR and the northernmost city of comparable size in the world, lies in the delta of the Neva River on the Gulf of Finland. It was founded by the Peter the Great in 1703 in order to give the backward Russian nation a "window on Europe." From 1713 until 1918 the city was the capital of Russia, in place of Moscow. Originally named St. Petersburg, it was renamed Petrograd in 1914, and finally Leningrad in 1924. The city is the main port of the USSR, the foremost shipbuilding center, and one of the principal entry points of the country. A dredged deep-sea canal (built in 1875–93) leads from the port to the naval fortress of Kronshtadt on Kotlin Island, which was once the outer commercial port of the city, but is now of only military significance. Leningrad is a major rail hub, with direct lines to Murmansk, the Urals, Moscow, and the Ukraine. An industrial center rivaling Moscow, Leningrad produces slightly more than 10 percent of the total industrial output of the USSR, specializing in the production of machinery and electrical equipment at the leading Kirov, Elektrosila, Baltic, and Stalin works. The Skorokhod plant is noted for its shoes, and Krasnyy Treugol'nik (red triangle) manufactures rubber products. Even though the city is no longer the political capital of Russia it does continue to play a major role in the life of the country. Its working population has become the avant-garde of Soviet labor and frequently takes the initiative in such Soviet labor measures as Socialist competition, the Stakhanovite movement, sponsorship of new construction, and similar projects. Recently it initiated a movement to stimulate the completion of the postwar Five-Year Plan by the end of 1949. Leningrad boasts a large number of higher educational and research institutions and museums, including the Hermitage, with its picture and sculpture collections, Peter and Paul fortress, St. Isaac cathedral, the Admiralty, and the Winter Palace. In recent years the city has expanded considerably, and now it incorporates the seaside resorts of Sestroretsk and formerly Finnish Zelenogorsk (until 1948, Terijoki) within its city limits. To speed transportation within the city, construction of a subway system is being started under the postwar Plan.

Of special note in the metropolitan area are the former Tsarist residences of Pushkin (formerly Tsarskoye Selo and Detskoye Selo), Petrodvorets (formerly Petergof and Peterhof), Lomonosov (until 1948, Oranienbaum), Gatchina (formerly Trotsk and Krasnogvardeysk), and Pavlovsk (formerly Slutsk). The main industrial suburbs are Kolpino, site of the noted Izhora works, producers of naval equipment, machine tools, steam engines, and steel-rolling equipment, Dubrovka, with peat-fed power station and paper and pulp mills, and Petrokrepost' (formerly Schlisselburg or Schlüsselburg), with cotton-milling and explosives plants. Peat is obtained in the vicinity of Leningrad at Lakhtinskiy (northwest), Rakh'ya (northeast), and Sinyavino (east).

Volkhov, on the Volkhov River, is the site of the first large hydro-electric station constructed in the USSR in 1926. It is an important rail junction on the rail lines from Leningrad to Murmansk and to the Urals and produces aluminum on the basis of the bauxite from Boksitogorsk. Formed by the union of the two towns of Zvanka and Volkhovstroy in the middle 1930's, it was called Volkhovstroy until 1940.

Vyborg, the former Finnish city of Viipuri, became part of Leningrad Oblast in 1944. It is an important timber port for the hinterland served by the Saimaa Canal and produces agricultural implements, electric instruments, furniture, woolen textiles, and netting. Much of its deep-sea traffic is handled by the outer port of Vysotsk (until 1948, Uuras).

Tikhvin, on the Tikhvin canal system, is a sawmilling and woodworking center. To the southeast are the large bauxite mines of Boksitogorsk (developed 1935) which furnish raw material for the aluminum works of Volkhov and Zaporozh'ye.

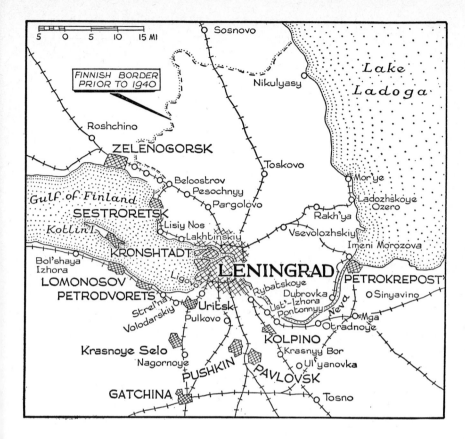

LENINGRAD AREA

CHAPTER 9

The European North

THE EUROPEAN NORTH (northern section of the European Russian SFSR) is bordered in the west by Finland, in the east by the northern Urals, and in the south by the watershed of the East European plain extending along the main moraine ridges in the west and the Northern Uvals in the east. In the north, the European North opens onto the seas of the Arctic Ocean and includes such important island groups as Kolguyev, Vaygach, Novaya Zemlya, and, far to the north, in 80° N latitude, Franz-Josef Land. The Karelo-Finnish SSR, which is occasionally treated as part of this region, shall be discussed in Chapter 27. The total area of the European North, not including the Karelo-Finnish SSR, is 500,000 square miles, making it the largest natural region of the European part of the Russian SFSR.

Nearly one-quarter of the region lies north of the Arctic Circle, a geographic factor which determines many of its physical and economic characteristics. This is a region whose shores are washed by Arctic seas covered even during the summer months by drifting ice, a region of the Arctic and subarctic tundras, of dense conifer forests, extensive marshes and peat bogs, a region of abundant streams with long winters and light summer nights. It is a region still in the early stages of economic development and inhabited by a correspondingly sparse population. It is rich in natural resources, such as timber, furs, reindeer, fish, seals, and minerals, including apatite, nephelite, lead, iron, coal, and petroleum.

The European North is divided into the Kola Peninsula in the extreme northwest, the Dvina-Pechora lowland, the centrally located, most extensive section, the northern Urals in the east, and the islands of the Arctic Ocean.

The Kola Peninsula is formed of crystalline rocks, which represent a geologic extension of the Scandinavian Peninsula. The relief bears evidence of recent glaciation: elevations with rounded summits, frequent depressions, smoothly polished boulders, and the ubiquitous moraine

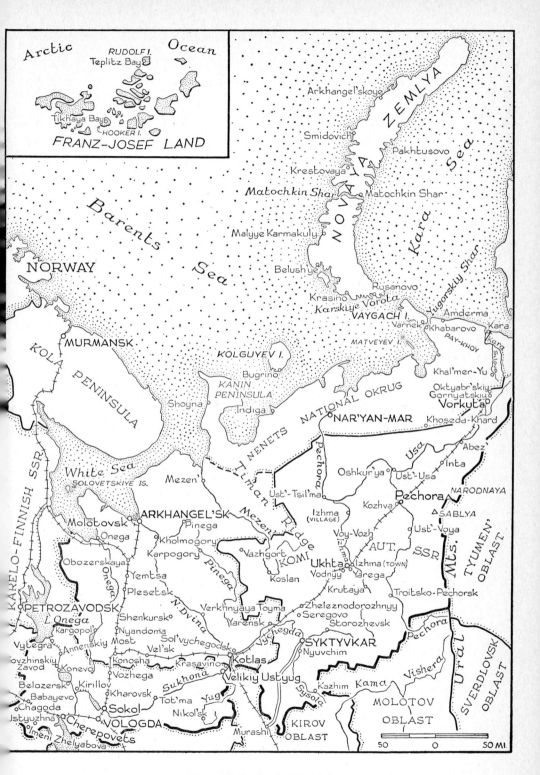

EUROPEAN NORTH

formations. The depressions, which had been formed as a result of geologic faulting, were subsequently deepened and smoothed by the action of the glacier ice and are now usually occupied by lakes. The Khibiny Mountains, the highest of the peninsula, lie roughly in its center and rise to 3,930 feet. They abound in a great variety of important minerals, including apatite, a major raw material of mineral fertilizers. The largest lake, Imandra, empties into the Kandalaksha Bay of the White Sea via the Niva River. To the north, the Tuloma River flows into the Kola Gulf of the Barents Sea. These rivers are characterized by an abundant regime and a rocky course which make them excellent sources of hydroelectric power. The shores of the peninsula are high and rocky in the west, where they form inlets similar to the fiords of Norway. In the east, beyond the section known as the Murman coast, the shores become progressively lower and less indented.

The extensive Dvina-Pechora lowland has a nearly featureless relief. The original glacial deposits have been partially washed away by the once-expanding waters of the Arctic Ocean and have remained only in the western and northern portions. The lowland slopes gently from the watershed of the Northern Uvals northward toward the shores of the Arctic Ocean and is traversed by broad river valleys. The low Timan ridge, an eroded range of ancient sedimentary rocks, divides the lowland into the eastern Pechora basin and the western plain, watered by the Northern Dvina. The Timan ridge continues northward into the heights of the curiously shaped Kanin Peninsula. Thanks to the low southern watersheds the waters of the Northern Dvina have been connected by canals with the Volga and the Neva rivers. The Timan ridge itself offers no serious obstacle to transportation and is crossed by several portages connecting the Pechora and the Northern Dvina rivers. The rivers of this region are characterized by an abundant regime and are navigable over long distances. The Northern Dvina, together with its main left branch, the Sukhona River, which emerges from Kubena Lake, form a continuous waterway about 650 miles in length. The Vychegda, the principal right branch of the Northern Dvina, as well as the Pechora River, are equally important for navigation and timber flotage. These rivers empty into funnel-shaped inlets of the Barents Sea.

The northern Urals, the highest, most rigorous, and most inaccessible section of the Ural Mountains, lie between the European North and the northern part of Western Siberia. They begin about 25 miles from the

Kara Sea, where the height of Konstantinov Kamen' rises abruptly from a nearly level tundra. Northwest of this point lies the range Pay-Khoy, which continues on into the uplands of Vaygach Island and Novaya Zemlya. The Ural Mountains themselves extend from Konstantinov Kamen' in a general southwesterly direction to 65° N latitude where they reach their highest point (6,183 feet) at Mount Narodnaya. South of near-by Sablya massif (5,405 feet), the Urals continue south in two parallel ranges. The northern Urals rise in a narrow belt from the surrounding tundra. Their wild, treeless rockiness softens south of 67–65° N. lat., where coniferous forests gradually cover the slopes. Here and there, snow remains in sheltered spots through the entire summer, and recent expeditions have located small glaciers up to half a mile in length.

Of the islands of the Arctic Ocean, Kolguyev, the southernmost, is an extension of the Dvina-Pechora lowland, while Vaygach Island and Novaya Zemlya are mountainous. The latter rises to 3,640 feet and is indented by a large number of deep fiords. The narrow, fiord-like strait Matochkin Shar separates the northern and the southern islands of Novaya Zemlya. Vaygach Island, to the south, is separated from Novaya Zemlya by the strait Karskiye Vorota (Kara Gates) and from the mainland by the strait Yugorskiy Shar. These straits and their ice conditions are of great importance for navigation on the Northern Sea Route connecting the European North with the Arctic coast of Siberia.

The climate of the European North is extremely rigorous, notably in the northeast. Long winters are marked by average January temperatures of a few degrees below 0° F in the Pechora basin, and 200 days in the year they have temperatures below the freezing point. In the southern sections, winters are equally cold, but are relieved by short, warm summers. The rivers remain frozen late into the spring. A large portion of the region, north of the Arctic Circle, experiences the Arctic night in December and January, when the sun remains below the horizon and a faint noontime twilight appears only for two to three hours. This is the season of the northern lights and of Arctic blasts, blowing south from the ice-covered sea. During June and July, however, when the midnight sun constantly remains above the horizon, nature revives. Even in the zone where the sun briefly dips below the horizon, the night is light enough to permit reading. Along the Murman coast the warm ocean current has a moderating influence on the raw climate and produces increased precipitation, cloudiness, and frequent fogs. This area is marked by a cold spring, cool, raw summer, warm, foggy autumn, and a snowy winter, arriving as early as the end of October.

The greater part of the European North is covered with coniferous forests, which have been considerably cleared in the west and the south-west, but have maintained their virgin density in the northeast. Large expanses are covered with lichen swamps. North of the forest zone lies the tundra in a uniform, occasionally rolling lowland. During the summer the widespread swamps, which develop due to the lack of ground-water drainage, are covered with patches of peat bogs and clusters of dwarf birch and willow and serve as breeding grounds for swarms of mosquitoes. During the winter the tundra becomes still more lifeless under its snow cover and is visited by snowstorms lasting as long as two or three days. The principal tundras are the Bol'shezemel'skaya (Great Land) Tundra, east of the mouth of the Pechora River, and the Malozemel'skaya (Little Land) Tundra, to the west. These areas have large sections of permafrost. Tundra also covers the Kolguyev and Vaygach islands, large portions of Novaya Zemlya, and a few spots of Franz-Josef Land outside of the glaciated area.

The European North is the most sparsely populated section of the European USSR, its population of nearly 3,500,000 scattered through the region with an average density of 7 per square mile. The concentration is lowest in the center of the Kola Peninsula, in the Pechora basin, and on the islands of the Arctic Ocean. In addition to the basic Russian population, numerous indigenous national groups form sizable minorities in the European North. They are organized into political units ranging from autonomous SSR (Komi) through national okrug (Nentsy) to national rayon (Saami).

Because of the poor climatic and soil conditions in the European North, agriculture has been developing only in recent years thanks to the application of modern farming methods. The most important crop is flax, which prospers especially in the southwest and produces a very good type of fiber. The sown area under flax, as well as that under coarse grains (rye, barley, oats), is constantly being expanded. Agriculture is being introduced more and more into the northern belt, where spring wheat appears to be the most suitable crop. Rich meadows in the river flood valleys offer excellent grazing land for livestock, raised principally for dairy products and meat.

The region is being industrialized at a rapid pace on the basis of the natural resources. Forests cover three fifths of its area; the Arctic Ocean, the inland lakes, and the rivers abound in fish; seals are hunted along the coasts, and the tundras offer great possibilities for the raising of reindeer. Among the main mineral resources are coal and petroleum in the Pechora basin and lead on Vaygach Island. The Khibiny Mountains harbor such vital minerals as apatite, nephelite, many rare metals, and iron ore.

The lumber industry and its allied activities are by far the most important. Sawmills have increased in number, and the lumbering processes have largely been mechanized. Due to the limited needs of the region itself, the lumber is largely exported to the central and southern regions of the European USSR, as well as abroad. The principal exporting and sawmilling center is the port of Arkhangel'sk (Archangel). Together with the sawmilling industry, paper milling, match manufacturing, and wood distilling are also gaining in importance.

Fishing is centered off the coast of the Kola Peninsula, with Murmansk the principal port and canning base. Trawler fleets operate throughout the Barents Sea, and air reconnaissance is extensively used in locating new seal herds. Large urban centers have grown up around the newly developed mineral deposits: Kirovsk, at the Khibiny apatite and nephelite mines, near-by Monchegorsk (nickel), Nikel' near Pechenga (nickel), Ukhta, in a newly developed petroleum region, and Vorkuta, the center of the subpolar coal basin. On the basis of the iron ore reserves in the Kola Peninsula and the Vorkuta coal, the construction of a new iron and steel-milling center is to be begun during the current Five-Year Plan. This new metallurgical base, which according to preliminary investigations could be most suitably located at Cherepovets (Vologda Oblast), is intended to supply, above all, the needs of the Leningrad industrial region.

The European North plays an important role in the Union economy as an exporter of lumber, furs, and fish, and as a supplier of nephelite for the aluminum industry and of apatite for the production of mineral fertilizers.

The region is served by few rail lines of importance. Murmansk and Arkhangel'sk are heads of trunk lines going to Leningrad and Moscow; the Leningrad-Vologda-Kirov-Molotov-Sverdlovsk railway passes through the southernmost sections, and the new North Pechora Railroad, completed in 1942, provides an all-important exit route for the Vorkuta coal. In the extreme southwest the canals of the Mariinsk system and the Northern Dvina Canal play an important role in the water transportation scheme.

Murmansk Oblast
Capital, Murmansk; area, 57,800, population, 450,000

Murmansk Oblast includes the entire Kola Peninsula and the mainland strip to the west as far as the Norwegian and the Finnish borders. In accordance with the Treaty of Moscow (1940), Finland ceded to the USSR the western portion of the Rybachiy (Fisherman) Peninsula, thus placing the entire peninsula in Soviet hands. By the Finnish armistice of 1944, the USSR acquired the entire Pechenga (Petsamo) district, which had been ceded to Finland in 1920. A small boundary rectification in 1946 gave the USSR control over the area of Yaniskoski (Jäniskoski) and Niskakoski. These territorial acquisitions became part of Murmansk Oblast, which thus obtained a common frontier with Norway in the northwest and with Finland in the southwest.

A taiga forest covers the southern part of the oblast, while the north consists of tundra. Thanks to the Gulf Stream, the northern (Barents Sea) coast of the Kola Peninsula remains ice-free, and the climate of the northern littoral is considerably more temperate than that of the center of the peninsula.

The mainsprings of the economy are the spectacular mineral reserves in the Khibiny Mountains and in the Monche-tundra, to the west. In the Khibiny, a large-scale intrusion of nephelite syenite furnishes abundant quantities of apatite, a rare mineral processed into phosphate fertilizer, and of nephelite, which is a source of aluminum. In addition to these reserves, the Khibiny mountain mass incorporates as many as sixty elements differentiated from the magmatic intrusion. Across Lake Imandra, to the west, lies Monche-tundra, part of another glacier-scoured mountain of pre-Cambrian origin. Here are vast nickel and copper reserves which have been worked since the middle 1930's. Among the rare metals found in the area are titanium, vanadium, zirconium, and molybdenum. Magnetite iron deposits, important for the eventual establishment of an iron and steel base supplying Leningrad, are found southwest of Lake Imandra along the Yena River. Nickel mines, representing an extension of the Monche-tundra site, lie in former Finnish territory south of Pechenga at the town of Nikel'.

The mining, concentrating, and refining industries connected with the rich mineral resources of the oblast are located at Kirovsk, the center

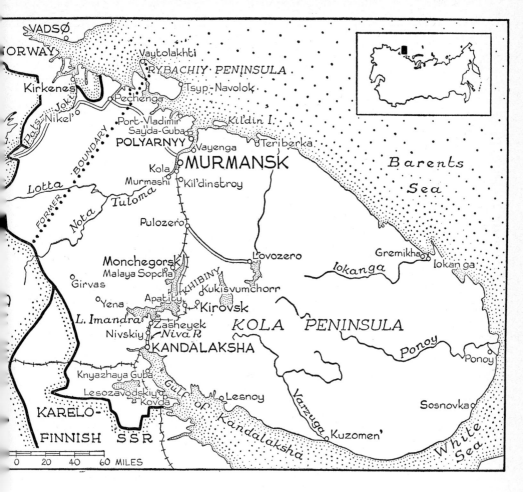

MURMANSK OBLAST

of the Khibiny mining district, at Monchegorsk, and at Kandalaksha. These industrial centers are supplied with power from the two hydro-electric installations of the oblast: the Tuloma station, the northernmost water-power scheme in the world, and the Niva River site, north of Kandalaksha.

Fishing is an important industry along the coasts of the Kola Peninsula. In the Barents Sea, the warm Gulf Stream favors the development of microscopic animal and plant life turning this region into one of the richest fisheries along the Arctic coast of the USSR. Herring, cod, and haddock constitute the major part of the catch, which is chiefly effected by trawler fleets. Fish canneries are located at Murmansk, Port Vladimir, Sayda-Guba, and Teriberka on the north coast, and at Kandalaksha, on the White Sea. Sawmilling and woodworking plants process the lumber from the southern half of the oblast at Lesozavodskiy, Lesnoy, Zasheyek, and the larger urban centers.

In spite of the unfavorable agricultural conditions, the long summer days are being used to develop hardy crops adapted to the rigorous climatic conditions. Truck and dairy farms along the Murmansk Railroad supply vegetables, berries, and fresh milk to the mining population. A pioneer among these polar farms is the Industriya state farm at Apatity station. Reindeer raising is the main occupation of the Saami (Lapp) population in the center of the peninsula.

Of primary importance in the development of the region is the Murmansk (officially known as Kirov) Railroad, the northernmost main line in the world leading 900 miles from Leningrad north to Murmansk. Built in 1916 as a war supply line from the port of Murmansk, the railroad has now been electrified in the Kandalaksha-Murmansk section. During the current Five-Year Plan the electrified section will be extended southward to Loukhi in the Karelo-Finnish SSR. From the main trunk line spurs lead to Kirovsk and Monchegorsk, as well as to the naval base of Polyarnyy, north of Murmansk, and to Kuolayarvi on the Finnish border.

Murmansk is an ice-free port on the east shore of the narrow, fiord-like Kola Gulf of the Barents Sea. It is the largest polar city in the world, situated within the Arctic Circle at the latitude of central Greenland. During the months of December through May it tends to replace the frozen port of Leningrad as the "window on Europe." It is the center of the fishing industry on the Murman coast and has shipyards, fish canneries, and refrigerating plants. It is the site of a polar biological research station. The port exports lumber, fish, and apatite, and imports machinery and coal, the latter from the Soviet coal-mining concession in Spitsbergen at Barentsburg and Grumantbyen. The city is the western terminus of the Northern Sea Route to the Pacific Ocean and played a vital role as a port for Allied supplies during the Second World War. Typical of the rapid growth of Soviet cities, the population increase was from 8,777 in 1926 to 117,054 in 1939. In the vicinity of Murmansk are the naval base of Polyarnyy, twenty miles north at the mouth of Kola Gulf, and the old commercial town of Kola, founded in the thirteenth century by Novgorod traders.

Kirovsk, the center of the Khibiny mining region, was founded about 1930 and now counts nearly 50,000 inhabitants. It lies among the apatite and nephelite mountains on the small glacial Lake Vud"yavr and is the site of concentrating and refining plants, a power station, botanical gardens, and a mineral museum. To the north is the large mining settlement of Kukisvumchorr.

Monchegorsk, founded about 1935, is a nickel and copper mining center on the west shore of Lake Imandra. Near by is the mining settlement of Malaya Sopcha.

Kandalaksha, on the White Sea, at the mouth of the Niva River, has an aluminum refinery and superphosphate works powered by the Nivskiy hydroelectric station to the north. It also engages in sawmilling and fish canning.

Komi Autonomous Soviet Socialist Republic
Capital, Syktyvkar; area, 156,200, population, 450,000

The territory of the Komi Autonomous SSR includes almost the entire basin of the Pechora River (except for its lower reaches in the Nenets National Okrug), the greater part of the Vychegda River basin, and the upper reaches of the Mezen' River. Except for the mountainous northern Urals, in the extreme east of the republic, the area is an almost featureless, wooded flat lowland, interrupted only in its center by the old Timan ridge. Nearly the entire region is forested; only a narrow strip in the extreme north enters within the wooded tundra zone. The eastern half of the republic lies in the zone of permanently frozen soils.

The rigorous natural conditions have been responsible for the lowest population density of any region in the European part of the USSR. The principal element, the Komi (formerly known as Zyryan), belongs to the Ugro-Finnic group. They are the most advanced of the so-called peoples of the north and frequently work as teachers, doctors, instructors, or agronomists among the lesser nationalities of the North European USSR and Siberia, which have been organized into national okrugs.

Until about 1940, the economy of the republic was quite in accordance with the existing natural conditions. The population was concentrated in the southern section and engaged mainly in lumbering along the Vychegda River. Agriculture had little importance and was possible only along the rivers, on the alluvial floodlands. Livestock was reared on the rich meadows, and some flax was raised in the extreme south. In the north the sparse population engaged principally in fur trapping, hunting, reindeer raising, and fishing, and to a lesser extent in lumbering along the Pechora River.

Since that time, however, spectacular advances were registered which converted the republic within less than a decade from one of the most backward regions of the European USSR into a vital supplier of coal and petroleum to the Leningrad industrial district. This development was brought about by the construction of the North Pechora Railroad from Kotlas northeast to Vorkuta. This line, one of the northernmost trunk railways in the world, went into operation in 1942, after two years of construction work, and opened for definite exploitation the rich Pechora coal basin and the Ukhta oil fields.

The Pechora basin, centered on the new city of Vorkuta, furnishes both excellent heating and coking coal. The former type occurs mainly in the Inta fields, southwest on the railroad, while coking coal is mined at Vorkuta itself and to the north in the Nenets National Okrug at the Khal'mer-Yu and Silova sites. Since 1940, when the coal was shipped laboriously over a short rail line to Ust'-Vorkuta and down the Usa and Pechora rivers to the sea, production has multiplied nearly fifteenfold and is contributing considerably toward the reduction of coal shipments from the Donets Basin to the Leningrad area. A distant project contemplates the construction of a railroad to the northern Urals in order to make the coking coal available there as well. The second large industrial district has developed around the new city of Ukhta and the surrounding petroleum fields. The high-grade fuels are refined locally and shipped to the Leningrad manufacturing region. The principal wells lie along the Ukhta River, an affluent of the Izhma, at Yarega and Vodnyy, as well as to the northeast, in the Kozhva area, at Pechora and Kanin.

Other industries are connected with the quarrying of grindstone at Ust'-Voya on the upper Pechora River, with the extraction of natural gas and asphalt rock at Krutaya, on the upper Izhma River, and the winning of salt at Seregovo on the lower Vym' River. Since the eighteenth century iron has been mined and worked at the smelters of Nyuvchim and Kazhim along the Sysola River. In recent years sawmills, woodworking plants, and wood distillation centers have been established along the Vychegda River, chiefly at Syktyvkar. In the north of the republic a chamois leather plant processes the hides of young reindeer at Ust'-Tsil'ma, and the meat of game and fowl is salted or canned at Ust'-Usa.

The republic was first organized as autonomous oblast in 1921, and it became an autonomous republic in 1936.

Syktyvkar (formerly called Ust'-Sysol'sk) lies on the Vychegda River, at the mouth of the Sysola, off the North Pechora Railroad, but connected by a good road with Murashi (Kirov Oblast) to the south. It was founded in the eighteenth century as the center of Russian colonization, and has now become a major lumber center, with sawmills, paper and pulp mills, and wood-distillation plants.

Vorkuta, the new sub-Arctic coal-mining center, was made a city in 1943 and has a population of about 30,000. The largest urban center within the Arctic Circle east of Murmansk, the city is the northern terminus of the North Pechora Railroad, which, however, is being extended northward toward the newly discovered coal site of Khal'mer-Yu and on to the Kara Sea. The mining towns of Gornyatskiy and Oktyabr'skiy are among the larger settlements which have mushroomed around Vorkuta.

Ukhta, the former town of Chib'-Yu, became a city in 1943. It is the center of an oil region producing high-grade fuels and the site of refining plants. Vodnyy, Izhma, and Yarega are the principal satellite oil towns along or near the North Pechora trunk line.

Vologda Oblast
Capital, Vologda ; area, 56,900, population, 1,500,000

Vologda Oblast, roughly rectangular in shape, extends almost 450 miles from the Mariinsk Canal system in the west to the basin of the Sukhona River in the east. The forest cover is dense in the east and the northwest, where numerous sawmills have been established along the Vytegra and Kovzha rivers. Excellent hay meadows occur in the alluvial flood valleys of the rivers and form the basis for a well-developed dairy industry. Peat deposits constitute the main mineral resource and are extensively exploited in the west.

The chief economic activities are linked to the raising of dairy cattle and the production of dairy products, such as canned milk and butter. The region is known for some of the best dairy stock in the USSR. Of almost equal importance is the growing of flax, which prospers in the relatively mild and wet climate of the oblast and provides the raw material for the large linen-milling center of Krasivino, north of Velikiy Ustyug.

The lumber resources are processed at the sawmills along the Kovzha River (at Annenskiy Most, Kovzhinskiy Zavod, and Konevo), at Cherepovets, and along the rail lines west and north of Vologda. North of this city is the large paper-milling and cellulose-manufacturing center of Sokol.

Minor industries include the distilleries at Belozersk and Ustyuzhna, which operate on the basis of potato and grain crops in the west, and the glassworks in the area of Chagoda (until 1939 called Belyy Bychek). The filling of the Rybinsk Reservoir in 1941 has changed considerably the economy of the shore areas within Vologda Oblast as well as in adjoining Yaroslavl' Oblast to the south. Fishing and shipbuilding industries have assumed special importance. Shipyards are operating at Cherepovets and Imeni Zhelyabova, southwest of Ustyuzhna. Among the handicraft industries, the making of lace ranks most important.

The oblast has long been in a region of important trade routes and to the present day transportation is principally of the transit type. The western section is served by the waterways of the Mariinsk Canal system, between Lake Onega and the Rybinsk Reservoir, and by the Northern Dvina Canal system, which links the Sheksna River with the Sukhona via Kubena Lake. In addition to these navigation routes, the oblast is served by the important Moscow-Arkhangel'sk and Leningrad-Kirov railroads.

Vologda, on an affluent of the Sukhona River and at the junction of the two main rail lines of the oblast, is a major transportation and industrial center. Founded in 1147, the city flourished as a trading center under Ivan the Terrible on the route to Arkhangel'sk and the foreign markets. It is the center of an important dairying region and has railroad shops, agricultural and timber machinery works, lumber, linen, and clothing mills, and distilling and food-processing industries.

Cherepovets, on Rybinsk Reservoir, at the mouth of the Sheksna River, has developed very rapidly since the filling of the reservoir, in 1941, which converted the city into an important inland port. Due to its excellent location on water and rail routes, it is the probable site of the iron and steel industry planned for the European North under the postwar Five-Year Plan. It has sawmilling, shipbuilding, distilling, and food industries.

Sokol, the paper and cellulose center north of Vologda, also boasts extensive sawmills and a condensed milk plant. It includes the former town of Pechatkino, the site of the cellulose works.

Velikiy Ustyug, on the Sukhona River, near the mouth of the Yug, was a flourishing trading center in the sixteenth and seventeenth centuries, noted also for its silver, woodworking, carving, and embroidery handicrafts. It produces hog bristles, alcohol, metal products, and has shipbuilding, clothing, and food industries.

Arkhangel'sk Oblast
Capital, Arkhangel'sk (Archangel) ; area, 229,400,
population, 1,050,000

Archangel'sk Oblast lies on the White and the Barents seas and is drained by the Onega and the lower Northern Dvina, Mezen', and Pechora rivers. The southern limit of the tundra zone passes through its northern portion parallel to the coast. Administratively, the oblast includes the Nenets National Okrug, entirely within the tundra zone to the northeast, the Arctic islands of Franz-Josef Land, Novaya Zemlya, Vaygach, Kolguyev, Matveyev, and the Solovetskiye Islands in the White Sea.

The oblast proper is served by only three railroads: the northern section of the Arkhangel'sk-Moscow trunk line, its branch (constructed in 1939–40) connecting with the Murmansk Railroad at Belomorsk, and the Konosha-Kotlas section of the North Pechora Railroad, also constructed on the eve of the Second World War. The scarcity of rail communications enhances the importance of the waterways, which serve not only as the basic transportation routes, but also constitute the main population sites. The river valleys abound in fertile alluvial soils and, thanks to natural drainage phenomena, are less marshy than the watershed areas. The alluvial soils permit some grain and flax farming and the existence of extensive meadows which support excellent dairy cattle (Kholmogory breed).

Some of the best timber of the European North grows along the Onega and the Northern Dvina rivers. These rivers and their affluents serve as excellent routes for lumber flotage to the sea and are supplied with sawmills at rail intersections and at their mouths. It is to these circumstances that the oblast owes its leading role in lumber production of the European USSR. Lumber is exported through the ports of Arkhangel'sk, Onega, and Mezen' and processed at plywood plants, pulp and paper mills, distillation plants, producing tar, resin, and methyl alcohol. It serves in the manufacturing of prefabricated houses and in shipbuilding. In addition to lumber products, furs, fish, and hog bristles are exported by the oblast.

Arkhangel'sk, the capital, lies at the head of the Northern Dvina delta, twenty-five miles from the White Sea. This largest sawmilling center of the USSR, with more than 150 sawmilling units, is also the principal lumber port of the country, handling one third of the Soviet lumber exports. As one of the supply ports of the Northern Sea Route, Arkhangel'sk is well supplied with shipyards, repair docks, and rope mills, and is a processing center for the White Sea fisheries and seal-hunting expeditions. On the right bank of the Northern Dvina and opposite the railway station, the city extends in a narrow band, backed by marshes, ten miles along the Maymaksa branch of the delta through the northern suburb of Solombala to the outer port of Ekonomiya, fifteen miles from the sea. Founded in 1583, following the first establishment of Anglo-Muscovite trade, Arkhangel'sk flourished as the only Russian port during the sixteenth and seventeenth centuries. It declined after the rise of St. Petersburg, but regained its importance with the construction of the railroad from Moscow, in 1897. During the First and Second World wars it served as a major supply port for Allied goods.

Molotovsk, a new city twenty miles west of Arkhangel'sk, is a shipbuilding and sawmilling center which developed after 1938. It has a large pulp mill based on the waste products of the sawmilling industry.

Kotlas, on the Northern Dvina River at the mouth of the Vychegda, was formerly the terminus of a railroad from Kirov. During the Second World War, it became a rail center on the North Pechora line and developed into a major lumber-processing center. It has shipyards, sawmills, and wood distilleries. To the southeast lie the pulp and paper mill and shipyards of Limenda.

THE NENETS NATIONAL OKRUG (capital, Nar'yan Mar; area, 67,300, population, 30,000) extends along the coast of the Barents Sea from the Kanin Peninsula to the Pay-Khoy range and includes the frozen wastes of the Malozemel'skaya Tundra, west of the lower Pechora River, and the Bol'shezemel'skaya Tundra, to the east. The population, which consists mainly of Nentsy (Samoyeds),* engages in reindeer raising, fishing, and seal hunting. Some dairy and truck farming has been introduced. Fluorspar is mined at Amderma, an air base and polar station in the extreme east, on the Kara Sea. The okrug includes the northern section of the Pechora coal basin, north of Vorkuta, with mines at Khal'mer-Yu and along the Silova River.

Nar'yan-Mar, a lumber port on the eastern arm of the Pechora River delta, has sawmilling and tanning industries. Near by is an experimental reindeer station.

The population of the Arctic islands, which cover a total area of 43,200 square miles, is less than 1,000. The northernmost archipelago of Franz-Josef Land has government obervation stations at Tikhaya Bay, on Hooker Island, site of the principal settlement, and on Rudolf Island, in the extreme north. Economic activity is restricted to fishing, seal hunting, and the collection of birds' eggs and feathers.

Novaya Zemlya, with a population of more than 400 and an area of 35,000 square miles, has its administrative center at Belush'ya Guba (also known as Belush'ye). The inhabitants, who live in about fifteen settlements located mainly along the indented west coast, engage in raising reindeer, trapping, and the collection of eider down. The Northern Sea Route passes through the strait of Matochkin Shar, between the two main islands of the group. The passage is equipped with Arctic research and observation stations.

Of the smaller islands, Kolguyev and Vaygach each has an area of about 1,400 square miles. Here the Nenets population engages in the common Arctic activities of fishing, seal hunting, and reindeer raising. Russians man several polar stations on the coast. On the south coast of Vaygach Island, in the vicinity of the Varnek observation post, a lead mine has recently been put into operation. The island is administratively part of the Nenets National Okrug. The main settlement of Kolguyev Island is Bugrino, on the south coast.

* Nentsy is the Russian plural form of Nenets.

CHAPTER 10

Volga Region

THE VOLGA RIVER, the most important waterway of the USSR, is the single unifying factor which makes the Volga basin a well-integrated natural and economic region. Only with respect to climate, soils, and vegetation does the basic complexion of the region vary. Consequently it is here divided into three areas for study: the Upper Volga Region (forest section), the Middle Volga Region (wooded steppe section), and the Lower Volga Region (steppe section).

The entire region, known in Russian as *Povolzh'ye,* includes twelve political-administrative units of the Russian SFSR (eight oblasts and four autonomous republics) situated on the middle and the lower courses of the Volga River and its tributaries. The region does not fully coincide, however, with the drainage basin of the Volga. The southwestern section forms part of the Don River drainage basin, while, on the other hand, the upper course of the Kama is included in the region of the Urals. The total area of the Volga Region is more than 300,000 square miles.

The two banks of the Volga River are differentiated rather sharply from the point of view of relief. The elevated right bank includes the Volga uplands, which extend along the river from Gor'kiy in the north to Stalingrad in the south and continue beyond this city as the Yergeni hills. The uplands represent old, pre-glacial formations altered by numerous faulted sections. The Zhiguli mountains, the most important of these faulted formations, lie in the Samara bend, a hairpin curve described by the Volga as it passes around this section of the uplands. The Zhiguli are strikingly picturesque, with their deep narrow valleys, odd limestone cliff formations, sharp escarpments, and dense forests, and they create the effect of mountains far exceeding their true height, 1,220 feet. The left bank of the Volga is in sharp contrast to the high, abrupt opposite bank and remains low and level along the entire course. Only in the southeast does it assume a rolling character, as it merges with the heights of the Obshchiy Syrt, an outlier of the Ural Mountains, characterized by a relief of wide river valleys and low, regular watershed areas.

The Volga River, which is also a major natural boundary of climatic, soil, and vegetation zones, is an impressive stream below its confluence with the Oka at Gor'kiy. At first about one mile wide and flowing in a valley which at its widest is 12 miles across, the Volga then widens considerably after it receives the Kama, its main left affluent. As a result of frequent changes in course throughout the flood valley, ranging from 12 to 25 miles in width, the river forms numerous islands, inlets, and sandbanks in its course and ox-bows and flood basins in the valley. The majority of its tributaries enter the Volga from the forested left bank. South of Stalingrad, it has hardly any affluents in the steppe zone and suffers considerable loss of water through evaporation. About three hundred miles from its mouth, in the vicinity of Stalingrad, the Volga forms a separate arm, the Akhtuba, which flows parallel to the main stream and is linked with it by a large number of branches. Their delta is a confused network of channels, branches, lakes, and islands, constantly changing in shape and size. The huge quantities of water which the Volga discharges into the Caspian Sea reduce the salinity in adjacent sections of the sea. This circumstance, coupled with the discharge of large amounts of organic matter and the formation of shallow banks, favors the existence of a rich fish-breeding area in this northern portion of the Caspian Sea.

In spite of the inland location of its outlet, the Caspian Sea, the Volga River is an all-important river route of the USSR. Through its far-flung tributaries and connecting canal systems it is linked with Leningrad, Moscow, and Molotov in the Urals and constitutes a continuous north-south route through the European USSR from the Baltic and the Arctic seas in the north to the Caspian in the south. The construction of the long-projected Volga-Don Canal would provide an outlet to the Black Sea. The Volga accounts for more than half the freight carried on the waterways of the USSR. Among its most important goods are lumber, which is floated downstream into the treeless steppes, and petroleum and grain which are moved up-current into the central sections of the European USSR.

One of the earlier Russian colonization areas, the Volga Region was first settled by the Slavs in the thirteenth century. Its conquest was completed with the subjugation of the Tatar holdings at Kazan' and

Astrakhan' in the sixteenth century by Ivan the Terrible. The original inhabitants of the Volga valley, of Turkic and Finno-Ugric origin, were dispersed by the Russian population influx that followed. Although the major nationalities along the middle Volga have been reconstituted by the Soviets into autonomous units, the Russians always represent at least one half the total population.

With a population of more than 21 millions, the Volga Region is one of the most thickly populated regions of the USSR. The average density is 70 per square mile, but the greatest concentration exists in the central wooded steppe section (nearly 100), followed by the forested north (about 80), and then the southern steppes (40). The Russians and to a lesser degree the Ukrainians constitute the basic section (75 percent) of the population. Among the non-Slav groups are the Mari (Cheremiss) and Mordvinians of Finno-Ugric origin and the Tatars and Chuvash of Turkic origin, all organized as autonomous republics. Until the Second World War the Volga Germans and the Kalmyks also shared the territory along the Volga as autonomous republics. Because of alleged collaboration with the German invaders, these national units were disbanded (in 1941 and 1943), and the ethnic groups concerned were resettled and lost their national identity. In addition to the autonomous republics, the Volga Region includes the oblasts of Gor'kiy, Kirov, Penza, Ul'yanovsk, Kuybyshev, Saratov, Stalingrad, and Astrakhan'.

Of the mineral resources of the region, the petroleum deposits of Kuybyshev Oblast are the most important. They form a portion of the "Second Baku," a new oil-bearing region extending from the Urals in the east to the Gor'kiy meridian in the west. Also important are iron ore, oil shale, phosphorite, natural gas, and salt. The presence of black-earth and chestnut soils throughout a large part of the Volga Region favors the development of agriculture. However, frequent droughts and dry, hot southerly winds often lead to crop failure. The chief crops are rye, oats, and wheat among the grains and sunflowers, hemp, tobacco, and mustard among the industrial plants. Vegetables, fruits, vineyards, and cotton fields prosper in the Volga valley. The industries, once based exclusively on the local mineral and agricultural production, now produce machinery, ships, petroleum products, especially as the result of development during the Second World War.

The economic future of the Volga Region is closely linked to the realization of the "Greater Volga" scheme. This project, formulated in the early 1930's, involves the construction of a series of large dams

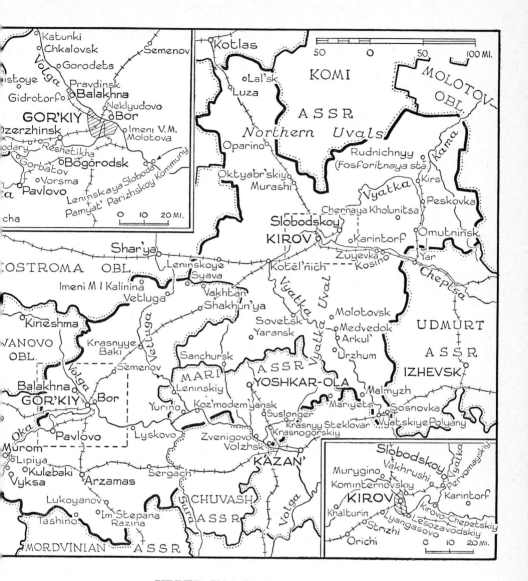

UPPER VOLGA REGION

with locks for the creation of a deep-water route along the entire course of the river, the generation of hydroelectricity, and the irrigation of drought-ridden areas. The first part of the project was put into effect with the construction of dams and power stations along the upper Volga River at Ivan'kovo (Kalinin Oblast) and Uglich and Shcherbakov (Yaroslavl' Oblast). Currently work is being started on large hydro-electric installations near Gor'kiy on the Volga and at Molotov on the Kama River. Future projects include the tapping of the waters of the upper Pechora and the Vychegda rivers. The construction of hydroelec-tric stations near Kuybyshev and Stalingrad has been scheduled for 1950–55 and 1951–56, respectively.

Of great importance is also the planting of tree shelter belts during 1949–65, especially the sections along the Ural and Volga rivers.

UPPER VOLGA REGION (FOREST SECTION)

THE FORESTED SECTION of the Volga Region extends along both banks of the river between the mouths of the Oka and the Sura rivers. It is bordered by the Central Industrial Region on the west and by the Urals on the east. In the north its boundary coincides with the watershed be-tween the Volga basin and the streams flowing north to the Arctic Ocean.

It is a lightly rolling plain rising to about 1,000 feet in the northeast, where the hills of the Northern Uvals form the main relief feature. The climate varies from the southwest, where the mean annual tempera-ture is 40° F, to the northeast, with an annual mean of 34° F. The southern limit of the forest zone passes south of the Oka River and then along the Volga, so that the greater part of the region lies in the forest zone, which has a wooded section amounting to 60 percent of the total area. This portion is characterized by poor podsolic soils and coniferous forests, predominantly fir. In the southwest lies a small area with black earth and deciduous (mainly oak) formations, where the tree density is only 25 percent.

Of the mineral resources to be noted are iron deposits in the south-west, along the Oka River, and in the northeast near Omutninsk, on the Vyatka-Kama watershed, peat formations in large sections of the Gor'kiy and Kirov oblasts, and oil shale and phosphorite, which lie in one of the richest Soviet sites near Rudnichnyy in the northeast.

The Russians represent about 90 percent of the population of the region, the remainder consisting of the Mari (formerly called Chere-miss), who are organized into their own autonomous republic, and of small splinter groups of Tatars, Chuvash, Udmurts (formerly called Votyaks), and Mordvinians. The average density is about 80 per square mile. The greatest concentration (100–150 per square mile) exists on the right bank of the Volga, in the oldest district of Russian colonization, where industries (Gor'kiy, Pavlovo) and agriculture (Arzamas) are most developed. Next follows the area along the middle course of the Vyatka River, including also the northeastern (agricultural) section of the Mari Autonomous SSR, where density of population varies between 50 and 100. The remainder of the region, largely forested, is sparsely populated. The percentage of urban population is below the USSR average, 20 percent and 32 percent respectively; it is highest in the Gor'kiy-Pavlovo industrial district and lowest in the Mari Autonomous SSR.

The economy of the region is affected by certain common traits, such as the favorable location on the Volga River on the route from the Urals to the Central Industrial Region, the valuable lumber resources and related industries, which send their products into the adjacent regions, and the highly developed handicraft industry. Regional specialization emphasizes the metalworking industries in the Gor'kiy-Pavlovo district, intensive agriculture in the Arzamas black-earth area on the right bank of the Volga, machinery, leather, and fur industries at Kirov, and the small-scale metallurgy of Omutninsk, on the left bank of the Volga. During the Five-Year Plans impetus was given to the development of automobile, locomotive, railway-stock, and shipbuilding industries at Gor'kiy and the satellite supply plants near by, machine and implements industry of Kirov, and the rational processing of lumber by mechanical and chemical means. Peat and timber are the main fuel resources, the former being fed to most power plants. Agricultural specialization on the right bank is in hemp, hog, and poultry raising, on the left bank in flax and dairy farming. Waterways and rail lines are of equal importance in transportation and radiate from the chief communications hub of Gor'kiy. In addition to the Volga, the Vetluga and the Vyatka rivers are open to navigation. The region is well served by the rail trunk lines Moscow-Gor'kiy-Kirov, Moscow-Kazan', and Leningrad-Kirov. The principal export items are locomotives, railway stock, ships, automobiles, machine tools, lumber (flotage of logs down the Volga and shipment of processed wood to the European Center), furs, leather, felt and leather footwear, phosphorites, oats, and flax. Imports consist chiefly of coal from the Donbas, petroleum from the Caucasus and recently from the "Second Baku," salt from the Lower Volga Region, textiles and machinery from the Industrial Center, and iron from the Urals.

Kirov Oblast
Capital, Kirov; area, 47,000, population, 2,250,000

Kirov Oblast occupies the basin of the Vyatka River, the major right affluent of the Kama. It is essentially a rolling plain sloping slightly toward the west and the southwest and bordered in the north by the hills of the Northern Uvals. Another upland, the Vyatka Uval, extends from the Kirov area southward across the plain to the area of Kazan', rising to 1,750 feet. The continental climate, with short, cool summers and long, cold winters and the sandy and clayey podsolic soils, are not very suitable for agriculture, especially in the northeast, where the humidity is greater. Large sections of the region are forested or covered with peat and other marshes. Of the rivers, only the Vyatka is navigable to any extent, while its affluents are suitable only for timber flotage. Peat, iron ore, and phosphorite constitute the principal mineral resources. The iron deposits in the northeast near Omutninsk have been worked since the eighteenth century. The reserves are large; however, the ore contains only 20–40 percent of metal and is scattered in many shallow layers, rendering the exploitation less economical than that of most of the other iron deposits of the USSR. The phosphate rock deposits, on the contrary, are among the best of the Union with respect to reserves and phosphoric acid content.

Formerly a predominantly agricultural region with a well-developed handicraft industry, the oblast has acquired a semi-industrial character during the Five-Year Plans. The old ironworks in the area of Omutninsk were rebuilt and re-equipped and are now furnishing iron and steel to the new engineering industry at Kirov and the industrial centers of Gor'kiy Oblast. They specialize in the milling of high-grade steels which are used in the making of instruments, automobiles, and tractors. Machines are also manufactured at Kirov itself. The construction of the rail branch Yar-Fosforitnaya through the iron milling region to the phosphate rock area at Rudnichnyy has given considerable impetus to the mining of the deposits, which are shipped for processing to the chemical and fertilizer plants of Molotov Oblast in the Urals.

Also important in the economy of the oblast are the fur-processing and leather industries of the Kirov-Slobodskoy area, which have long been operating on the basis of furs and hides brought from Siberia and are still producing about one third of the industrial output of the oblast. The lumber reserves of the northeast and other sections are exported to a large extent as uncut timber. Sawmills have been established at the intersection of rivers and rail lines, especially at Kirov and its suburbs, Kotel'nich, and Vyatskiye Polyany, which also manufactures prefabricated houses. Several lumber centers lie on the Kirov-Kotlas railroad; these include Murashi (whence a good highway leads to Syktyvkar), Oparino, and the city of Luza, which serves the neighboring paper center of Lal'sk. Paper mills are also operating at Zuyevka and near-by Kosino, at Kirovo-Chepetskiy, near the Cheptsa-Vyatka confluence, and at Murygino, on the Vyatka River, west of Kirov. Matches are produced at Kirov itself. Small-scale boatbuilding is carried on along the Vyatka River, south of Kirov, at the towns of Arkul', near Urzhum, and Medvedok, near Molotovsk.

The old handicraft industries have been organized into co-operatives and are growing alongside the modern plants. Woodworking (furniture and toys) and sheepskin processing are most important in the Kirov area; lacemaking is carried on in the district of Sovetsk, and felt boots are made at Molotovsk (until 1940, Nolinsk).

Most of the agricultural specialization of the oblast is in flax and dairy farming. The areas under flax are chiefly on the right bank of the Vyatka River, while coarse grains are grown on the left bank. The basic grain crops are rye and oats, but gradually wheat is also being introduced. The rearing of dairy cattle and the output of dairy products are centralized in the area between Kirov and Kotel'nich, where improved breeds have been developed.

The trade of the region is oriented mainly to the Urals and the Volga Region. The first rail line was built from Perm' (Molotov) to Vyatka (Kirov). Later construction linked the oblast with Kotlas and Leningrad, but it was not until the 1920's that the Kotel'nich-Gor'kiy line provided direct connection with the Central Industrial Region.

Kirov, called Vyatka until 1934, is an industrial and transportation center on the Vyatka River and the junction of the Leningrad-Urals railroad and the line to Kotlas. The city dates from 1174 and early was a center of Russian colonization of the region. The principal industries are the production of railroad equipment, matches (the "Krasnaya Zvezda" mill is one of the largest of the USSR), and visual teaching aids, of which it produces 30 percent of the USSR output. It has machinery works, fur-processing and shoe plants, meat works, and food-processing and distilling industries. Lumber and sawmills operate in the suburbs of Vyatskiy and Lesozavodskiy. Tanning and dairy industries are developed in the vicinity.

Slobodskoy, at the end of a rail spur, 20 miles northeast of Kirov, is an important tanning center. Shoes are manufactured at near-by Vakhrushi, on the railroad. Across the Vyatka from Slobodskoy lies the new peat power station of Karintorf, which supplies the Kirov-Slobodskoy district with electricity.

Omutninsk, the center of the small-scale northeastern metallurgical industry, is located on the new Yar-Fosforitnaya railroad, which leads to the Rudnichnyy phosphorite mines. The satellite iron and steel mills of Kirs and Peskovka, on the railroad to the north, and of Chernaya Kholunitsa, to the northwest, were converted to modern production methods in 1938.

Gor'kiy Oblast
Capital, Gor'kiy; area, 29,100, population, 3,600,000

Gor'kiy Oblast is situated astride the Volga River in the area of its confluence with the Oka River. It is a lightly rolling lowland rising gradually as it approaches the Northern Uvals in the northeast, where the climate is most severe. About two thirds of the total area lie in the forested zone north of the Oka and Volga rivers, which furnishes most of the lumber of the oblast. However, excellent wood (mainly oak) is also obtained in the southern wooded steppes, where the moderate climate and the occasional black earth offer suitable agricultural conditions. Among the principal mineral resources are iron deposits in the southwest (which have been worked since the eighteenth century) and peat in the neighborhood of Gor'kiy and Balakhna.

The region owes its important economic position to its location on the Volga waterway at the mouth of the Oka River, which provides a direct route into the central sections of the country; it is not far from the mouth of the Kama, which connects with the mining region of the Urals. On the basis of past economic development, the following regions can be distinguished: the highly industrialized Oka River district, extending from Gor'kiy itself past Dzerzhinsk (chemicals) and Pavlovo (metalworking), to the metallurgical works in the southwest, the agricultural wooded steppe, with prevailing grain crops, and the forested region, with flax and potato growing.

Metallurgy is represented by three works located at Vyksa, Kulebaki, and Tashino and dating from the eighteenth century. Originally these plants used local iron ore, but because of insufficient reserves Krivoy Rog ore and scrap metal became the principal basis for their operations. At the present time these renovated mills are producing high-grade steels for the machines and metal products of Gor'kiy and Pavlovo. Gor'kiy is the home of the famed Sormovo shipyards and locomotive and car-building works, as well as of the Molotov auto plant. Pavlovo and the near-by town of Vacha are the principal centers of an important metal-working region, which was constituted on the basis of handicraft co-operatives scattered throughout the area. The principal products are tractor and automobile parts, surgical instruments, and metalware (scissors, locks, and so forth). Shipyards are also established along the Oka at Doschatoye (near Vyksa) and Lipiya (opposite Murom) and on the Volga at Imeni V. M. Molotova (near Gor'kiy).

The rich lumber resources of the north were formerly exported without any processing. At the present time, however, they are partly converted into paper (at the mills of Balakhna and Pravdinsk, a supplier for the newspaper *Pravda*), rosin and other wood-distillation products (at Vakhtan and other plants in the Vetluga basin). Phosphorites, shale, limestone, gypsum, and peat are some of the local minerals which constitute the basis of the great chemical industry of Dzerzhinsk, producing phosphate fertilizer and many basic chemicals. Other industries are connected with the refining of imported petroleum at Gor'kiy, the manufacture of shoes at Bogorodsk, and the milling of rope and fishing-nets at Gorbatov and Reshetikha. Power for this vast industrial network is furnished by the peat-based power plant at Gidrotorf (near Balakhna) which supplies not only the industrial Oka valley but also the adjoining sections of Vladimir Oblast, including the linen-milling center of Vyazniki. Imported Baku oil and Donbas coal feed other power installations. The postwar Five-Year Plan provides for the construction of a new hydroelectric station on the Volga, at Gorodets, above Gor'kiy.

Of special significance in the industrialization of the oblast were the old home industries, which provided the necessary skilled labor for and in a number of cases formed the nucleus of the new modern industrial installations at Pavlovo and Bogorodsk. The art of woodworking is highly developed in the lumber region of the north, and the wooden spoons of Semenov are known throughout the entire Union.

Flax, potato, and dairy farming are the principal agricultural activities in the north, while in the southern wooded steppe wheat and hemp are grown, and hogs and poultry are raised. Rural industries engage in hemp and flax retting, distilling, flour milling, and meat packing.

The waterways, chiefly the Oka and the Volga, handle one half the freight carried in the oblast. There is a good rail network in the south, while the single Gor'kiy-Kotel'nich line serves the sparsely populated north. The region was organized as a kray in 1929 and became an oblast in 1936.

Gor'kiy, called Nizhniy Novgorod until 1932, was founded in 1221 as an outpost of the Vladimir principality. It rapidly developed into a dominating trading center, thanks to its excellent location at the confluence of the Volga and the Oka rivers, and in 1817 it became the site of the famed fairs (which were disbanded in 1930 in connection with the introduction of a planned economy). The city has grown rapidly during the last two decades, especially during the Second World War, when it was one of the few large industrial centers untouched by the fighting. The population increased from 644,116 in 1939 to an estimated 900,000 in 1946, and the city may have advanced to the rank of fourth largest urban center of the postwar USSR. The main industries are connected with machine building, the manufacture of locomotives and rolling stock, and the building of ships, airplanes, and automobiles. The city produces Diesel motors, metal goods, radio and telephone equipment, glass products, chemicals (oil gas, acids, petroleum products) and processes lumber, wool, and flour. The city proper, on the right bank of the Oka, is the site of a kremlin, a university, and other cultural institutions. It is connected by a bridge with the industrial section on the left bank. The automobile plant and the adjacent workers' settlement, six miles southwest of the city center, on the Oka, and the Sormovo shipyards and railway works, the same distance west on the Volga, all lie within the expanding city limits.

In the immediate vicinity of Gor'kiy are the paper mills of Balakhna and Pravdinsk, the power plant of Gidrotorf, and the chemical center of Dzerzhinsk (formerly called Rastyapino), one of the spectacularly growing cities of the USSR, rising from a population of 8,910, in 1926, to 103,415, in 1939.

Mari Autonomous Soviet Socialist Republic
Capital, Yoshkar-Ola; area, 8,900, population, 600,000

The Mari Autonomous SSR lies almost entirely on the left bank of the Volga River, opposite the Chuvash Autonomous SSR. It is a rolling plain, drained in the west by the navigable Vetluga River and in the center and east by the Bol'shaya Kokshaga, Malaya Kokshaga, and Ilet' rivers, which serve primarily for timber flotage. Mineral resources are restricted to limestone, marl, and gypsum; there are peat bogs in the western section, serving only local fuel needs.

Forests occupy about 60 percent of the total area and constitute the principal resource of the republic. The dominant fir and pine stands have a thin admixture of deciduous stock (oak, elm, birch, and aspen). Lumber is processed in sawmills along the Volga River at points near Koz'-modemyansk, at Zvenigovo, where it is used for shipbuilding, and at Volzhsk, the site of a pulp and paper mill. Other sawmills lie on river intersections along the Zelenodol'sk—Yoshkar-Ola railroad at Suslonger and Krasnogorskiy. Woodworking plants associated with the sawmills produce prefabricated houses, railway ties, furniture, musical instruments, and distillation products (tar, turpentine, and rosin). There are glassworks at Mariyets, Krasnyy Steklovar [red glassworker], and Leninskiy. At Yurino there is an old industry producing mittens and felt boots.

Agriculture is most developed in the northeast, where the population is most concentrated and specializes in grain, flax, and dairy farming. The ethnic distribution is 51 percent Mari, a group of Finno-Ugric stock formerly called Cheremiss, 44 percent Russian, and some Tatars and Udmurts. The Mari were first organized into an autonomous oblast in 1920. This unit was part of Gor'kiy Kray from 1929 until 1936, when it was raised to the status of autonomous republic.

Yoshkar-Ola, the terminus of a rail branch from Zelenodol'sk on the Moscow-Kazan' line, was known as Tsarevokokshaysk before 1918 and as Krasnokokshaysk until 1929. It has food-processing (meat, vegetable oil) and light industries, including a linen mill and a movie-projector factory.

Other important Mari centers are Koz'modemyansk, a lumber port founded in the sixteenth century on the Volga near the mouth of the Vetluga River, and the new industrial city of Volzhsk, which developed in the 1930's as a lumber and paper-milling center and was called Lopatino until 1940.

MIDDLE VOLGA REGION (WOODED STEPPE SECTION)

THE MIDDLE VOLGA REGION extends along both banks of the river between the mouth of the Sura in the north to the Samara Bend in the south. In this section the Volga receives the Kama River, its principal affluent, and is crossed by three railroad trunk lines at Kazan', Ul'-yanovsk, and Batraki (near Syzran'), respectively. Because of its location, the region is a major transit area for rail lines from Moscow and Leningrad to Kazakhstan and Central Asia, the Urals, and Siberia and for water routes from Leningrad and Moscow to the Caucasus (along the Volga) and from the Urals to the Caucasus and the Donets Basin (along the Kama and the Volga).

The region is in the wooded steppe, an intermediary belt between the forested zone in the north and the steppe in the south. The Vetluga, which enters the Volga at the northern limit of the Middle Volga Region, still is a typical forest river, while the Samara, at the southern border, has definite steppe characteristics. The only significant relief feature is the Volga upland, which reaches a height of 1,217 feet in the Zhiguli Mountains of the Samara Bend. It is of some importance as a climatic barrier in protecting the right bank from the dry southeasterly winds and in keeping the moist westerlies from the left bank of the Volga.

Striking differences can be observed between the two banks of the Volga River in the wooded steppe section. The right bank, with the Volga upland, is by far the hillier one and is noted here and there for picturesque relief features. It receives 16–22 inches of rain annually and has a relatively heavy forest cover, deciduous stock (oak and linden) predominating. Soils are generally of the degraded black-earth and the podsolic type. The left bank is a level lowland, rising toward the southeast, where it merges with the outlying hills of the Obshchiy Syrt. It receives a yearly precipitation of only 12–18 inches, has forests in the north beyond the Kama, black earth and isolated tree clusters in the center, and is almost entirely treeless in the south. The continentality of the climate increases from the northwest to the southeast, and the water network becomes gradually less developed in the same progression.

Petroleum resources have recently become a major factor in the local economy. The western outliers of the "Second Baku" have been tapped at Syzran', in the Zhiguli Mountains, and in the Tatar Autonomous SSR. Oil shale deposits are worked north of Ul'yanovsk, south of Syzran', and in the Obshchiy Syrt, while peat is important only in the north. Phosphorites lie adjacent to the oil shale, and various construction materials are to be found on the right bank of the Volga.

Russian colonization of the region after the seventeenth century displaced the local Mordvinians, Chuvash, and Tatars into separate ethnic

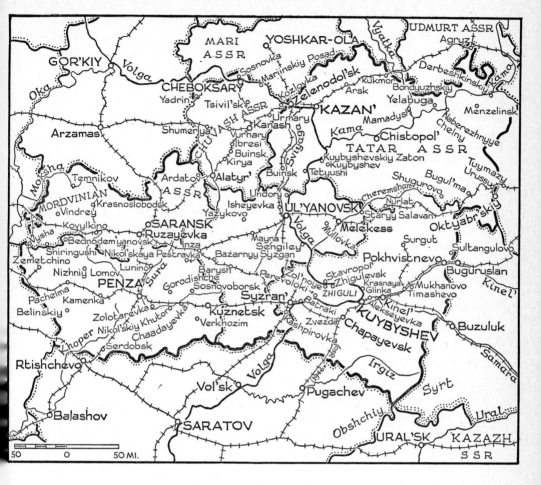

MIDDLE VOLGA REGION

"islands," where each is now organized into an autonomous republic. With some Mari and Bashkir minorities, the non-Russian population represents little more than 25 percent of the total. Population densities range from 125–150 per square mile on the right bank to 50–75 on the left bank.

The industrialization drive of the USSR completely altered the economy of the Middle Volga, especially during the Second World War. Heavy industry was introduced into all the large centers along the Volga, producing automotive and railroad equipment, chemicals, and construction materials, such as bricks, alabaster, asphalt, and glass. These industries, which require much fuel and electric power, are located on the river, where they can tap the passing lumber, coal, and petroleum freight. The chief industrial centers are Kazan' and Kuybyshev. During the Second World War the region also developed its production of airplanes, airplane motors, ball bearings, automobiles, and cables. Agricultural industries process local products and produce mainly flour, alcohol, starch, meat, tallow, soap, and candles. Sawmills, veneering, match factories, and paper mills are based on local right-bank timber and on lumber floated down the Volga River.

Agricultural specialization on the densely populated right bank assumed an intensive character. The area under fodder and industrial crops was sharply increased, with emphasis on potato and hemp production, and hog raising and dairy farming was furthered. Orchards, garden crops and poultry raising were introduced. On the sparsely populated left bank, where agriculture is more extensive and the danger of drought is always present, the cultivation of wheat and the raising of livestock for meat and wool are most important. Sunflowers and gourd-like crops are less significant.

The basic transportation routes are formed by the Volga River and the three east-west rail lines. During the Second World War a lateral line was built parallel to the Volga River, between Stalingrad, Saratov, Syzran', and Kazan'.

The Middle Volga Region exports grain, livestock, processed animal products (skins, felt boots, candles, and soap), construction materials, wood articles (made chiefly out of oak), ships, and railroad equipment. The main imported goods are coal, petroleum, machinery, and textiles.

Chuvash Autonomous Soviet Socialist Republic
Capital, Cheboksary; area, 7,100, population, 1,050,000

The Chuvash Autonomous SSR lies on the right bank of the Volga River, between the Sura on the west and the Sviyaga on the east. The relief is predominantly a ravine plateau at the northern end of the Volga upland. The climate is continental, with a yearly mean of 38° F and a precipitation of 16–18 inches. The wooded steppe, which covers about two thirds of the republic, changes into dense oak and linden woods in the southwest and the south. There are important phosphate rock deposits with some oil shale and limestone, which is well suited for the manufacture of cement.

The population, which is more than 80 percent Chuvash, 16 percent Russian, and includes some Mordvinians and Tatars, is engaged in agriculture and in lumbering, machine production, and light industries. The population density is between 125 and 150 per square mile throughout the agricultural area. The predominant grain crops, which once consisted mainly of rye and oats, have now been varied by the introduction of wheat, potatoes, fodder crops, and industrial plants such as hemp, flax, and tobacco. Flour milling, distilling, and other processing plants are scattered throughout the small towns and villages.

The share of industry has risen to about one half the total output. Most important are the sawmilling and woodworking establishments which process timber floated down along the Volga (in the north) and local wood resources in the southwest. Mariinskiy Posad and Kozlovka are the chief lumber centers on the Volga. Shipbuilding is carried on at Mariinskiy Posad. Local timber is cut at sawmills along the railroad between Alatyr' and Kanash (at Ibresy, Kirya, and Buinsk). One of the most significant industrial undertakings is the timber-processing plant at Shumerlya, a new city which developed during the 1930's, where furniture, veneers, flooring, and tannin are produced out of the local oak reserves. The chemical plant at Vurnary manufactures phosphate meal and other chemicals from the local phosphorite and oil shale deposits. At Urmary, on the site of the cement rock deposits, a projected cement plant may already have been established. The republic is well served by four rail lines radiating from Kanash, including a branch leading north to Cheboksary, which was constructed on the eve of the Second World War. Throughout the USSR, the Chuvash Autonomous SSR is known for its well-developed road network. Export items feature wood (mainly oak) articles, grains, and construction materials.

The Chuvash population was first constituted into an autonomous oblast in 1920; it became a republic in 1925. From 1929 to 1936 the autonomous republic formed part of Gor'kiy Kray.

Cheboksary, the Chuvash capital, lies on the Volga River, surrounded by lumber mills at near-by Sosnovka and Chapayevskiy. It produces flour, alcohol, and leather goods and is the site of a Chuvash regional museum. Under the postwar Plan, a textile mill, presumably based on the local flax crop, was to be opened in 1949. As part of the "Great Volga" scheme, a hydroelectric plant is projected to be built at a point a few miles below the city.

Alatyr', the largest city of the republic, has locomotive and car shops, metalworking and sawmilling industries, and produces clothing and knitted goods. It is a center of the grain-growing area.

Kanash, the main rail hub in the central part of the republic, has railway-car repair works and flour mills. Weaving handicrafts are found in the vicinity.

Mordvinian Autonomous Soviet Socialist Republic
Capital, Saransk; area, 10,100, population, 1,200,000

The Mordvinian (or Mordva) Autonomous SSR (sometimes erroneously called Mordovian Autonomous SSR) straddles the Moscow-Ryazan'-Ul'yanovsk railroad, west of the Sura River, and is drained in the west by the Moksha, an affluent of the Oka River. It is primarily a wooded steppe, with black-earth soils, but it is densely forested in the western section near the Moksha River.

The Mordvinian ethnic group was widely scattered, as a result of the Russian colonization of its territory, which at one time extended to the area of Ryazan' (in the west) and Arzamas (in the north).* At present only one third of the total Mordvinian population of the USSR resides in the autonomous republic, the remainder being distributed as minorities among the adjacent Russian and non-Russian administrative divisions. In the Mordvinian Autonomous SSR, the titular ethnic group represents only 37 percent of the total population of the republic, having more than 57 percent Russians and some Tatars. The unit was

* Both town names are derived from Erze, the name of one of the two principal ethnic divisions of the Mordvinians.

first established as an autonomous oblast in 1930 (as part of the Middle Volga Kray); it became a republic in 1934.

In addition to the usual grain crops (rye, oats, and wheat), industrial plants have appeared on the agricultural scene. Hemp, potatoes, and leguminous plants are cultivated throughout the republic, and flax is raised mainly for the production of linseed oil. Truck produce is grown in the vicinity of the urban centers of Saransk and Ruzayevka. Stock raising is restricted to cattle and sheep.

The agricultural industries operate throughout the farming region and engage in flour milling, distilling, hemp and flax retting, and the production of starch and vegetable oils. The chief agricultural centers, besides Saransk and Ruzayevka, are Ardatov, which also has sawmills, Krasnoslobodsk, which specializes in the processing of fiber plants, and Kovylkino. Peat is the chief fuel.

In the forest region in the west lie the sawmilling towns Vyshcha and Vindrey and the paper-milling center Temnikov. Shiringushi, in the southwest, manufactures woolen goods. Along the central trunk line and a north-south railroad crossing at Ruzayevka, the republic exports lumber, grain, hemp, starches, and canned milk.

Saransk, the capital, acquired machinery industries during the Second World War. It produces electrical goods, repairs motors, and manufactures agricultural implements. Among the enterprises processing agricultural products, a starch factory, a hemp mill, and a canned-milk plant may be noted.

Ruzayevka, the principal rail center of the republic and the second largest city, lies southwest of the capital on the main trunk line. Metal products and machinery represent the greatest part of its production. It has railroad shops and food-processing plants.

Tatar Autonomous Soviet Socialist Republic
Capital, Kazan'; area, 26,100, population, 2,850,000

The Tatar Autonomous SSR is in the area of the confluence of the Volga and the Kama rivers and extends from the lower Belaya River in the east to the Sviyaga, a right affluent of the Volga, in the west. This places it in a transition area between the true forest and the wooded steppe zones, with predominantly black-earth soils. The Volga and the Kama rivers divide the republic into three distinct natural regions: the right bank of the Volga, with a moderate continental climate, black earth, and deciduous (mainly oak) clusters, the right bank of the Kama, in the northern coniferous forest zone with a more extreme climate and podsolic soils, and the left bank of the Kama, with a moderate, dry climate and black-earth wooded steppe. Mineral resources are restricted to peat and recently discovered petroleum deposits, which form part of the "Second Baku."

The population is about one half Tatar, the other half being made up of large Russian elements and of Chuvash, Mordvinian, Udmurt, and Mari minorities. The republic was formed in 1920, one of the first units of autonomous republic rank to be established in the USSR.

Wheat is grown extensively throughout the area, especially in the northwest, where it is sown with sunflowers ; coarse grains are cultivated mainly in the southeast. Besides the introduction of large acreages under wheat, agricultural innovations include the increase in industrial crops, including leguminous plants in the north, and fodder crops in other sections of the republic. Dairy cattle are raised intensively on the alluvial pastures along the Kama River. Poultry farming is important, and orchards abound along the Volga River.

The exploitation of petroleum resources is passing through its initial stages as part of the development of the "Second Baku." The first wells are being developed at Shugurovo, west of Bugul'ma. Before the Revolution the industry of the region was restricted largely to the manufacture of candles, soap, and shoes. Under the Soviet regime the processing of animal products was further expanded. Wool is worked into coarse cloth, and there are tanning and sheepskin industries in many of the agricultural processing centers. Kukmor, in the north, specializes in the production of felt boots. In addition to the expansion of the old wool and skin processing industries, new branches were established in the republic, such as shipbuilding, at Zelenodol'sk and Kuybyshevskiy Zaton, south of the Volga-Kama influence, machine construction and the production of chemicals at Kazan', woodworking and the output of construction materials.

During the current Five-Year Plan a vital rail spur from Urussu (east of Bugul'ma) southward to Oktyabr'skiy (in the Tuymazy oil fields) will further develop petroleum deposits in the area. Exports of the Tatar Autonomous SSR consist essentially of furs, hides, shoes, river-going ships, grain, eggs, oak products, and chemicals.

Kazan', the capital of the Tatar Autonomous SSR and the Tatar cultural center of the Union, produces three fourths of the industrial output of the republic. It lies on the Kazanka, a small left affluent of the Volga, and extends about two miles westward to the port suburb on the Volga itself. It has shipyards, locomotive and railway-car shops, auto repair works, and produces aircraft, agricultural implements, typewriters, and calculating machines. Its old candle and soap works (dating from the nineteenth century) have been succeeded by a modern chemical industry, which produces synthetic rubber, photographic film, soap, cosmetics, and explosives. Kazan' processes about one half of all the furs of the USSR and has clothing, shoe, and felt-boot industries. In addition, it has extensive food-processing and woodworking plants. It is the seat of a branch of the Soviet Academy of Sciences, of a university, and the Tatar National Opera House. The kremlin, which was built in 1552 after the capture of the city by the Russians, is topped by the noted Suyumbeka tower.

Zelenodol'sk, a new industrial center on the Volga, west of Kazan', developed during the 1930's. It has large shipyards, lumber mills, wool and leather processing plants.

Chistopol', on the Kama River, is an agricultural center in the very midst of the republic. Its industries are connected with flour milling, woodworking, and the manufacture of clothing and knitted goods. Petroleum and asphalt deposits are being exploited near by.

Other important centers engaged in flour-milling, distilling, wood- and metalworking industries are Agryz (in the northeastern panhandle), Bugul'ma (mainly flour), Buinsk, Kuybyshev (formerly Spassk), Mamadysh, Menzelinsk, and Yelabuga.

Penza Oblast
Capital, Penza; area, 16,700, population, 1,500,000

Penza Oblast is in the western part of the Volga upland in the basin of the Sura River, an affluent of the Volga, which traverses the area in a deeply cut valley. The river divides the oblast into two districts: the left bank, with distinct black-earth agricultural characteristics, extensive cultivation, and few wooded areas, and the right bank, with sandy soils and forested upland slopes. The population is mainly Russian; however, there are sizable minorities of Mordvinians, Chuvash, and Tatars.

The type of agriculture which prevails in the oblast is similar to that practiced in the Central Black-Earth Region, with which the oblast is sometimes included. Rye and oats are the chief grain crops, while the acreage under wheat is increasing. Among the industrial crops, potatoes and hemp are important. Sugar beets are restricted to the extreme western section, adjoining Tambov Oblast. Fruits are widely grown. Cattle and hogs are raised by intensive methods.

Industries are based mainly on the agricultural and livestock products. They engage in flour milling, starch processing, distilling, meat packing (Chaadeyevka), hemp processing (Lubino, north of Penza), sugar refining (Zemetchino). The principal small agricultural centers are old cities such as Bednodem'yanovsk (formerly called Spassk), Belinskiy (until 1948 called Chembar), Gorodishche, and Serdobsk. Of some importance are the several small-scale textile centers manufacturing coarse woolens: Nikol'skiy Khutor, east of Penza, Verkhozim, southwest of Kuznetsk, Sosnovoborsk (formerly called Litvino), northwest of Kuznetsk, and Zolotarevka, southeast of Penza. The timber resources on the right bank of the Sura furnish raw material and fuel for numerous sawmills in the area, a glassworks at Nikol'skaya Pestravka in the northeast, and match mills at Nizhniy Lomov in the west. Phosphate rock is quarried in the vicinity of Pachel'ma, on the main east-west railroad.

Penza lies in the center of the oblast, at the intersection of two major rail lines. In addition to the old food-processing and sawmilling industries, it has acquired (notably during the Second World War) various metalworking industries, including the manufacturing of bicycles, watches, agricultural implements, textile-making, printing and calculating machines. Clothing mills are also located here.

Kuznetsk, the second city of the oblast, lies on the main east-west rail line east of Penza. It specializes in the production of leather and leather goods.

Ul'yanovsk Oblast
Capital, Ul'yanovsk; area, 14,400, population, 1,200,000

Constituted in 1943, Ul'yanovsk Oblast was the expression in territorial-administrative terms of the remarkable economic development of the Middle Volga Region during the Second World War. Formed out of sections of Penza and Kuybyshev oblasts, it lies mainly on the right bank of the Volga but also extends over a sizable portion of the left bank in the area of Melekess. The right bank is part of the hilly Volga upland and contains nearly all the forest reserves of the oblast. The left bank is a level lowland. There are oil shale deposits throughout a large area north of Ul'yanovsk, in the vicinity of Undory. Adjoining in the south along the Volga are extensive phosphorite reserves.

The economy is based on the timber reserves in the west and on the agriculture in the remainder of the oblast. The principal crops are grains, chiefly wheat, and sunflowers in the north and potatoes and fruits in the Volga valley. Coriander is grown and processed in the area of Mayna, on the railroad southwest of Ul'yanovsk. Flour milling, sunflower-oil extraction, distilling, and tanning are typical rural industries of the region. Timber cut in the western reaches of the oblast is processed at Inza, a vital rail junction for lines to Ul'yanovsk and Syzran', and at Barysh, to the southeast. Paper is manufactured at Bazarnyy Syzgan, southeast of Inza. In the same area are several small-scale woolen textile mills, at Gur'yevka, Izmaylovo, and Staro-Timoshkino, all clustered around Barysh, and at Yazykovo and Isheyevka, west and northwest of Ul'yanovsk, respectively. Another woolen mill lies at Mullovka, west of Melekess. On the Volga, south of Ul'yanovsk, lies Sengiley, the site of a cement mill and chalk-processing works. Peat is worked for fuel at Staryy Salavan, northeast of Melekess.

Ul'yanovsk, formerly called Simbirsk, lies on a 550-foot hill between the right bank of the Volga and the Sviyaga River, which here flows parallel to and in an opposite direction to the Volga.* At this point the Moscow-Ryazan'-Ufa railroad crosses the Volga, by means of a long bridge. An automobile plant was built here during the Second World War. It has important sawmilling, metalworking, and food (flour, meat) industries and acts as a major rail-river transfer point. The home of V. I. Lenin (whose real name was Ul'yanov), the city was renamed in his honor in 1923.

Melekess, a major agricultural center in the left-bank section of the oblast, produces flour, meat, and beverages and has sawmills and flax-processing plants.

Kuybyshev Oblast
Capital, Kuybyshev; area, 20,800, population, 1,950,000

Kuybyshev Oblast lies mainly on the flat left bank of the Volga, with only a narrow section extending across the river to Syzran' and the Zhiguli Mountains. This wooded range, which rises to 1,217 feet inside the Samara Bend, represents the most notable relief feature of the region. The left bank is essentially a dry black-earth steppe, wooded only in

---

* Ul'yanovsk is a geographical oddity with respect to its location. It is possible to leave the city by the Sviyaga and, floating northward to the Volga and southward along the Volga, to return to Ul'yanovsk by a continuous down-river route.

the northern section. Oil shale is available on the Volga south of Syzran', as well as in the outliers of the Obshchiy Syrt in the extreme southeast of the Oblast. Phosphorite deposits are found north of the Obshchiy Syrt. Asphaltite is mined in the area of Kuybyshev at Alekseyevka (to the east) and at Surgut. Construction materials, including limestone and gypsum, are quarried along the Volga, above Kuybyshev.

The fuel resources of the region are at present in their initial stages of development. Petroleum was first discovered at Syzran' in 1937. During the Second World War oil fields at Stavropol' (on the Volga) and at Zhigulevsk (until 1949, Otvazhnyy) and Zol'noye (in the Samara Bend opposite Stravropol') came under exploitation, as well as other oil fields at Kinel', Mukhanovo, and Pokhvistnevo. The construction of a vast hydroelectric power complex in the Samara Bend is still in the planning stage. It provides for the construction of a dam on the Volga at Krasnaya Glinka (above Kuybyshev) and of power installations there and at Perevoloki (on the south side of the Samara Bend), where the waters of the Usa River are to be diverted to the Volga.

The principal agricultural products are winter wheat and sunflowers in the dry left-bank steppes. Fruits are raised in the Volga valley, where alluvial pastures also support dairy cattle. Most of the livestock rearing, however, is on an extensive scale for meat and wool production. In addition to the usual agricultural industries (flour milling and distilling), woodworking plants and sawmills operate on the basis of lumber floated down the Volga River. Sugar beets are milled at Timoshevo, northeast of Kinel'.

Kuybyshev, on the left bank of the Volga at the mouth of the Samara River, was called Samara until 1935. Founded in 1596, it was the first Russian city on the left bank. In the late seventeenth century it developed into an important trading center and grain transfer point. After the Revolution it developed into an industrial center producing carburetors, automobile and tractor parts, machine tools, boilers, movie apparatus, and other machines. During the Second World War, the city received a renewed impetus. The population rose from 390,000 in 1939 to about 600,000 in 1946–47, and production increased elevenfold. In 1941–42 it became the refuge of a number of government departments evacuated from threatened Moscow. New industries were established: ball-bearing works, shipyards, oil refineries. Petroleum pipe lines lead here from the fields of Buguruslan (Chkalov Oblast) and from Zhigulevsk and Zol'noye, in the Samara Bend. Natural gas is also piped from Sultangulovo (east of Buguruslan). Kuybyshev is a major food-processing center for sunflower oil, meat, flour, and alcohol, and trades in lumber, cotton, grain, fats, and cattle. In 1943 it was separated from the oblast and became a city subordinated administratively directly to the Russian SFSR.

Syzran', on the Volga west of Kuybyshev, shared in the spectacular economic development of the region during the Second World War. Originally noted mainly for its food, sawmilling, and tanning industries, the city became the center of a petroleum district after 1937, and oil-cracking plants came into existence. During the war the city incorporated its satellite industrial towns, including Batraki in the north and Kashpirovka in the south, thus doubling its population to the present 150,000. Batraki, site of a long rail bridge across the Volga, has asphalt works and metal and woodworking industries. It is a major grain-transfer point. Kashpirovka is an oil-shale and phosphorite mining center, with processing works. Syzran' thus developed into an industrial center second only to Kuybyshev in the oblast. It has railway-car repair shops, leather, fur, and shoe industries, clothing factories and sawmills, canning, flour milling, and vegetable-drying establishments.

Chapayevsk, on the railroad between Kuybyshev and Syzran', is an agricultural center, formerly called Ivashchenkovo, later briefly known as Trotsk. It also produces chemicals and explosives.

Kinel', a rail junction east of Kuybyshev, is the center of a newly developed oil field, as is Pokhvistnevo, to the east.

Lower Volga Region (steppe section)

The Lower Volga Region extends along the lower section of the river from the wooded steppe to the Caspian Sea and from the Central Black-Earth Region in the west and the Northern Caucasus in the southwest to the Kazakh SSR in the east. Its general appearance is that of a dry steppe changing into semi-desert in the southeast. In the northwest the Volga upland parallels the river as far south as Stalingrad; it is then continued by the Yergeni hills south of that city. In the northeast are the low foothills of the Obshchiy Syrt. South and east of these hills lies the Caspian lowland, a level plain which formed the bed of an enlarged Caspian Sea in recent geologic times. The southern portion of the lowland, beginning at Kamyshin on the Volga River, lies below sea level. The salt lakes of Baskunchak and El'ton represent the remains of the former sea.

The climate of the Lower Volga Region is of the extreme continental type, due mainly to the influence of the adjoining dry steppes and deserts of Kazakhstan. Summer temperatures approximate those of the Crimea, and winter conditions remind one of Murmansk. Only in the extreme northwest can the wooded steppe be found. The great bulk of the region through Saratov and Stalingrad oblasts is a dry steppe with chestnut soils. In Astrakhan' Oblast the semi-desert predominates, with its light brown landscape and numerous sandy stretches, salt flats, and salt lakes. Due to the progressive increase in dryness, agriculture is gradually replaced by livestock raising for meat and wool. The effect of the decrease in precipitation on the density of the rural population is also quite characteristic of the region.

	Annual Precipitation In inches	Rural Population Per square mile
Northwest wooded steppe	18–12	100
Central steppe zone	12–6	35
Caspian semi-desert	Under 6	3.5

The population consists mainly of Russians, which account for three fourths of the total. The prewar German and Kalmyk ethnic groups were dispersed and resettled following their alleged collaboration with the Germans during the Second World War. They were largely replaced by Ukrainians. In the extreme north are Tatar, Mordvinian, and Chuvash minorities. While the population density decreases with the precipitation from the northwest to the southeast, it is always high along the Volga River. Because of the poorly developed water network, large villages are common throughout the region. About 60 percent of the urban population live in the three large centers of Stalingrad, Saratov, and Astrakhan'.

The region consists at the present time of the oblasts of Saratov, Stalingrad, and Astrakhan'. Before the Second World War it also included the Volga German and Kalmyk autonomous republics. Following the abrogation of the Volga German Autonomous SSR, its territory was divided in 1941 among the oblasts of Saratov and Stalingrad. The Kalmyk Autonomous SSR was abolished in 1943 and its bulk was attached to Astrakhan' Okrug of Stalingrad Oblast to constitute the new Astrakhan' Oblast. Small sections of the former republic were ceded to Stalingrad and Rostov oblasts and to Stavropol' Kray.

The economy is predominantly agricultural. Droughts are an ever-present danger because of the low precipitation, and measures have been

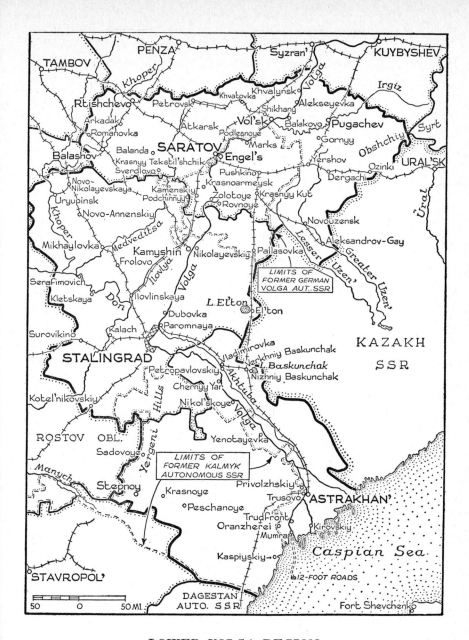

LOWER VOLGA REGION

initiated to combat the factors responsible for these conditions. Efforts are made to conserve moisture by accumulating winter snow and channeling rain water. Tree belts are planted to protect the cultivated areas from the scorching desert winds. The irrigation project connected with the "Great Volga" scheme will do much to promote the agricultural possibilities of the region. Crop specialization procedure has assigned intensive crops (sugar beets, potatoes, and forage crops) to the northwest and grain and sunflower to the central steppes, leaving the Caspian steppes for meat and wool production. The alluvial flood plain of the Volga River permits the intensive cultivation of orchard and garden crops and of cotton, sesame, and *kenaf* in the south.

The industries are based primarily on the local agricultural production and on raw materials passing in transit along the Volga. Oil shale, natural gas, cement clays, phosphorite, salt, and iron ore are the principal mineral resources. Fishing and its associated industries are important along the Caspian Sea.

Export items carried by the Volga and the several trunk railroads include grain, cattle, leather, wool, fish, salt, vegetable oil, and canned goods. Petroleum and lumber make up most of the transit freight along the Volga. Imports consist mainly of petroleum, coal, machines, textiles, and lumber.

Saratov Oblast
Capital, Saratov; area, 39,500, population 2,400,000

Saratov is the northernmost of the Lower Volga oblasts and extends about 350 miles, from Tambov Oblast in the west to the border of Chkalov Oblast, of the Urals, in the east. It is drained on the right bank of the Volga by two affluents of the Don, the Khoper and the Medveditsa, and on the drier right bank by the Bol'shoy Uzen' and the Malyy Uzen', which disappear in the semi-desert of northwestern Kazakhstan.

Once a backward agricultural area with a poorly developed industry based mainly on the farm production, Saratov Oblast has acquired a number of heavy industries since the 1920's and modernized its food-processing and light industries. As a result of agricultural reorganization, the area under cultivation was increased and weighted in favor of industrial and garden crops. Agricultural specialization proceeded in the following manner: On the right bank of the Volga, rye and oats kept their former dominant role, but the acreage under wheat was increased. Industrial crops, such as potatoes, sunflowers, and sugar beets, were emphasized. In the southern (drier) portion of the right bank and throughout the left bank, hard-grained export wheat became the dominant crop. Along the Volga in the vicinity of large urban centers, truck produce, garden crops, and dairy products are featured. Tobacco and mustard are grown on the territory of the former Volga German Autonomous SSR, in the area of Engel's. Cattle is raised for milk production on the alluvial pastures of the Volga flood plain and for meat on the drier left bank.

Agricultural industries engage in flour milling, sunflower-oil extraction, tanning, and soap making and are scattered throughout the region, mainly on the right bank. The principal centers concerned with food processing are Balashov, Atkarsk, and Petrovsk on the right bank and Pugachev, Balakovo, Novouzensk, and Engel's on the left bank. Dried fruits and vegetables are processed in Khvalynsk. Meat-packing plants are in operation at Rtishchevo, between Saratov and Tambov, and at Privolzhskiy, just south of Engel's.

The mineral resources of the oblast supply the large cement mills of Vol'sk with raw material. Oil shale is mined at Ozinki and at Gornyy, southwest of Pugachev. In 1942 rich natural gas deposits were discovered at Yelshanka, near Saratov. The available reserves far exceeded the immediate need in local industries, and a gas pipe line was laid from Saratov to Moscow, where the fuel found ample industrial and domestic applications. The construction of the line was completed in 1947. Glass is manufactured at Khvatovka, northwest of Vol'sk, and there are phosphorite deposits on the right bank along the Volga River.

The heavy metalworking, textile, and sawmilling industries are located on the Volga River, which serves as the main supply route for their raw materials. The main industrial center is Saratov, where nearly half the industry is concentrated. Other industrial cities are Marks (until 1941, Marksshtadt), which produces agricultural machines, clothing and knitted goods, tobacco and food products and Krasnoarmeysk (formerly Golyy Karamysh and, until 1941, Bal'tser), with cotton mills, clothing factories, and shoe plants. Cotton mills are also operating in a number of small towns in the area of Krasnoarmeysk and at Krasnyy Tekstil'-shchik, on the Volga, south of Saratov. Kamenskiy (until 1941, Grimm), near Krasnoarmeysk, manufactures tractor parts. Lumber floated down the Volga River is milled at a number of localities along the banks, principally at Rovnoye (until 1941, Zel'man).

The Oblast is well served by railroad lines, which were supplemented during the Second World War by the right-bank trunk line paralleling the Volga River. Saratov and Engel's are major river-rail transfer points on lines connecting the central European USSR with the southern Urals, Central Asia, and Astrakhan'. The rail branch leading to Aleksandrov-Gay on the border of Kazakhstan in the southeast is the northern section of the long-projected direct trunk line linking Saratov with Central Asia via Gur'yev. The Chardzhou-Kungrad section at the southern end of this line is under construction during the postwar Five-Year Plan and may mark the first step toward the ultimate realization of the entire railroad.

Saratov city, which in 1943 became subordinated directly to the government of the Russian SFSR, rose from a population of 375,860 in 1939 to about 450,000 in 1945, an increase of twenty percent in six years. Located on the right, elevated bank of the Volga, it is an important river port and transfer point for petroleum moving from Baku to the central European USSR and for agricultural products of the Lower Volga Region. A major center of agricultural industries (flour mills, vegetable oil presses, tallow and soap works, and tanneries), it also has lumber, textile, and metalworking plants. In the Second World War it acquired oil refineries, ball bearing works, and a large harvester-combine plant. It has a university and agricultural research institutions. Yelshanka, northwest of the city, is the point of origin of the natural-gas pipe line to Moscow.

Engel's, the former capital of the German Volga Autonomous SSR, lies on the Volga, opposite Saratov. It was formerly called Pokrovsk. Important as a grain and lumber-trading center, it also has Diesel motor works, chemical plants, sawmills and flour mills. A vast meat-packing plant lies in the southern suburb of Privolzhskiy.

Balashov, a rail junction and grain-trading center, in the western section of the oblast, has an airplane plant and extensive flour, dairy, and canning industries.

Rtishchevo, another rail center, northeast of Balashov, has machine and metalworking industries and a meat-packing plant.

Pugachev, formerly known as Nikolayevsk, lies on a lateral railroad joining the Saratov-Ural'sk line and Kuybyshev. It has quartz quarries, machine, flour, and distilling plants.

Vol'sk, on the Volga above Saratov, is one of the principal cement-milling centers of the USSR. It also manufactures leather goods, chemicals, and food products.

Stalingrad Oblast
Capital, Stalingrad; area, 49,100, population, 1,800,000

Stalingrad Oblast lies south of Saratov and between Rostov in the west and Kazakhstan in the east. It is essentially a dry steppe, with sand and salt flats along the Kazakhstan border. As elsewhere in the Lower Volga Region, precipitation decreases and mean summer temperatures increase from northwest to southeast.

An important agricultural region, it supplies chiefly wheat and sunflower crops. The acreage under cultivation is mostly in the north and on the right bank of the Volga. There wheat, sunflower, and mustard crops prevail, livestock raising being of secondary importance. Cotton is grown in the southwest, where dairy farming is also common. Vegetables, orchard crops, melons, and pumpkins are cultivated intensively in the northern Volga flood valley, while in the southern section cotton, *kenaf*, and other warm-climate crops prevail. On the left bank of the Volga, near the semi-desert of the Caspian lowland, sheep raising for meat and wool is the principal feature of the economy. Truck produce is grown in the Stalingrad metropolitan area.

Mineral resources in the oblast are restricted to iron deposits in the area of Uryupinsk, on the Khoper River, salt and gypsum in Lake El'ton, one of the vestiges of the once enlarged Caspian Sea and an extension of the Saratov phosphorite in the area of Kamyshin. Except for Stalingrad city, which developed into an industrial center during the Five-Year Plans, the industries are based mainly on the local agricultural production. Flour mills, tanneries, and vegetable oil presses are scattered throughout the farming districts. Among the most notable agricultural processing centers are Uryupinsk, northwest of Stalingrad on the Khoper River, which engages in meat packing, flour milling, and canning, and the flour-milling cities of Serafimovich, on the Don, Mikhaylovka, and Frolovo. Dubovka, a city on the Volga north of Stalingrad, is concerned primarily with lumber milling, but also processes flour and sunflower oil.

Two projects play a vital role in any future development of the oblast. As part of the "Greater Volga" scheme, a hydroelectric plant and dam are to be constructed in the area of Kamyshin. The realization of this project would provide much-needed electric power to the industries of Stalingrad, irrigation for the drought-ridden steppe of the left bank of the river, and would improve navigation conditions on the river itself.

Another plan, which has long been discussed, but still remains a project for the future, is the construction of the Volga-Don Canal. This would open a connection between the important Volga River and the open sea and remedy nature's mistake, which forces this all-important Russian stream into the closed Caspian Sea.

Since the eve of the Second World War, the territory of Stalingrad Oblast has undergone major changes on two occasions. In 1941, following the abrogation of the Volga German Autonomous SSR, the oblast annexed the southern portion of the liquidated division. In 1943 it absorbed sections of the Kalmyk Autonomous SSR, but at the same time, in its southeastern panhandle, gave up Astrakhan' Okrug, which furnished the basis for the creation of a new Astrakhan' Oblast.

The region exports wheat, food products, meat and cattle, tractors, and high-grade steels and imports textiles, petroleum, lumber, iron scrap, coal, and semi-manufactured goods.

Stalingrad city, of Second World War fame, lies on the right bank of the Volga, where the river approaches closest to the Don and the Donets Basin. A large river port and rail center, it plays an important role in the transshipment of petroleum, fish, lumber and coal. Its very industries are closely associated with its functions as a transit center. Extending about thirty miles along the Volga, the city includes the giant tractor works and the "Red October" metallurgical works in the north and chemical and lumber industries to the south. At the northeastern edge of the city are large oil tank and refining installations. The town of Krasnoarmeysk (formerly called Sarepta), a shipbuilding center, lies within the southern city limits, on the Volga River. A Russian fortress until the eighteenth century, Tsaritsyn, as it was then called, developed after the 1850's into a major lumber-trading center and transfer point for Baku oil shipments. Its population increased from 7,000 in 1861 to 133,000 in 1917. Due to the ravages caused by the Civil War and the ensuing famine conditions, the population decreased to 20,000 by 1920. As a result of the industrialization drive during the Five-Year Plans, Stalingrad's population rose to 445,476 in 1939. During the Second World War the city was besieged by the Germans for five months in 1942–43 and was almost entirely destroyed. Reconstruction began immediately after its liberation. A new railroad links the Volga just above Stalingrad with the Saratov-Astrakhan' line. Natural gas is piped here from the newly developed Archeda field near Frolovo.

Kamyshin, the second city of the oblast, lies on the Volga, halfway between Saratov and Stalingrad. It is a rail terminus and river port and trades in lumber, grain, and melons. Glass and varnishes are produced, and there are flour, meat-packing, canning, and distilling industries.

Astrakhan' Oblast
Capital, Astrakhan'; area, 35,600, population, 750,000

Astrakhan' Oblast was formed in 1943 following the abrogation of the Kalmyk Autonomous SSR. It was constituted out of the major portion of the former republic and Astrakhan' Okrug, which had existed within Stalingrad Oblast since 1937. Except for the Volga-Akhtuba flood plain, the region is a semi-desert lowland sloping gently toward the southeast. It is distinguished by a very low precipitation (4–8 inches) and extreme summer and winter temperatures of over 100° and less than 0° F.

The Kalmyks, who migrated to this area from Central Asia in the seventeenth century, were mostly nomadic livestock breeders. After the Revolution the Soviets introduced a sedentary mode of life among them. The raising of cattle and sheep for meat and wool production became the principal economic activity of the Kalmyk Autonomous SSR. Agriculture was practiced only in the relatively more humid western sections, where wheat, sunflowers and mustard were grown, and in isolated cultivated islands in the semi-desert, where drought-resistant millet became the staple crop. Cotton was planted in a coastal strip along the Caspian Sea. When the republic was abrogated, most of the western agricultural rayons were ceded to the oblasts of Rostov and Stalingrad. Because of the sharp reduction in the Kalmyk population, which engaged chiefly in livestock raising, the number of stock-raising rayons was also reduced from eight to four in 1944.

As a result of the foregoing changes in the economy of the region, agriculture and even livestock raising were relegated to the background by the dominant fishing industry of the Caspian Sea. In addition to wheat and sunflowers in the area of Stepnoy, in the west, and cotton and millet near the Caspian coast, the irrigated agriculture of the Volga-Akhtuba flood plain should be noted. With the help of dikes, it is possible to grow intensively melon and garden crops, vineyards, and new industrial crops such as cotton and *kenaf*. Besides the herds of cattle and sheep, raised mainly for meat and wool, camels play an important role in the semi-desert areas.

The fisheries in the delta of the Volga River and the adjacent shallow waters of the Caspian Sea make the oblast the most important and most

highly developed fishing region of the USSR. While the largest canneries
are concentrated in Astrakhan', there are smaller processing centers
throughout the delta and on the Caspian Sea. Among the principal
establishments are those of Mumra, Oranzherey, and Trudfront, at the
western end of the delta, southwest of Astrakhan', Kirovskiy, southeast
of Astrakhan', and Kaspiyskiy (until 1944 Lagan'), on the coast south
of the delta. Of great importance for the fishing industry are the salt
deposits of Lake Baskunchak in the northeast near the Kazakh border.
Salt and gypsum are worked on the lake at the town of Nizhniy Baskunchak. The salt is shipped to Astrakhan' by rail or, for transportation up
the Volga River, is taken by rail west to the river landing of Vladimirovka, where it is transferred to river vessels. Lake Baskunchak, another remainder of the enlarged Caspian Sea, furnishes about one fourth
of the total salt production of the USSR.

From the standpoint of transportation, the oblast is served by only
two highways, linking Stepnoy with Stalingrad, to the north, and with
Astrakhan', to the east. Astrakhan' itself is connected by rail northward
with Saratov. In the Second World War a new line was constructed
along the northwestern shore of the Caspian Sea, joining Astrakhan'
directly to the Caucasus.

Astrakhan' city, with a 1945 population of about 300,000, lies on the
left bank of the westernmost (main) branch of the Volga delta, 55 miles
from the sea. One of the chief ports on the Caspian Sea, it is also the
foremost fishing center of the USSR. It has shipyards, fish canneries
and processing plants, lumber and woodworking mills, food industries,
including meat-packing, flour-milling, and distilling plants. In addition
to the fish trade, it also deals in salt, cotton, grapes, fruits, and especially petroleum. Because of the presence of sand bars at the mouths of
the Volga, the transshipment of the petroleum of Baku to river-going
vessels is effected at the so-called "12-foot roads," an artificial island
port equipped with floating oil storage and transfer facilities in the
Caspian Sea 125 miles from Astrakhan'. A dredged channel leads from
this outer port to the city. The transfer of lumber to Caspian ships is
also effected at this point. Once a residence of Tatar khans, Astrakhan'
was annexed to Russia in 1556 by Ivan the Terrible. It developed gradually during the nineteenth century and rose from a population of 45,000,
in 1860, to 150,000, in 1914. Its growth during the Five-Year Plans
was less spectacular than was that of the new industrial centers of the
country. A rail bridge is under construction between Astrakhan' and

the right bank suburb of Trusovo, which was connected by rail with Kizlyar in the Northern Caucasus.

Stepnoy, until 1944 called Elista, was the former capital of the Kalmyk Autonomous SSR. A new city, founded in the late 1920's, it became primarily an agricultural center, with flour mills and other food-processing industries.

CHAPTER 11

The European South

THE EUROPEAN SOUTH is here taken to include two separate regions of the southern European Russian SFSR. These are the Crimean Oblast, which is coextensive with the Crimean Peninsula, and the regional complex known as the Lower Don and Northern Caucasus. While the Crimea and the Lower Don are each represented by a single administrative unit, the Crimean and Rostov oblasts, the Northern Caucasus comprises several Russian and autonomous non-Russian divisions.

Crimean Oblast
Capital, Simferopol'; area, 10,000, population 1,050,000

The Crimean Peninsula is the only natural geographical division of the USSR that is almost entirely bounded by the sea. It is attached to the continent only by the five-mile wide Perekop Isthmus. Washed by the deep Black Sea on the west and south and by the shallow Sea of Azov on the east, the Crimea has always been noted for the picturesque beauty of its southern shore, its subtropical climate, and the cloudless skies of this "Riviera" of the Soviet Union. Its northeastern shores consist of a complicated system of shallow inlets, straits, and sand bars, known by the common designation of Sivash (Putrid Sea). From the main body of the peninsula, the elongated Kerch' peninsula extends eastward toward the Northern Caucasus, from which it is separated by the Kerch' Strait.

From the standpoint of relief and physical geography, the Crimea can be divided into three divisions: the steppe plains of the north, which also include the Kerch' peninsula, the Crimean mountains, and the southern coast. The Crimean steppe, which comprises about three fourths of the total area of the peninsula, is a southern continuation of the steppes of the southern Ukraine. It represents a level lowland, rising gently toward the foothills of the Crimean mountains in the south and nearly devoid of water. Even the longest river of the Crimea, the Salgir, which rises in the mountains, evaporates in the steppe during the summer

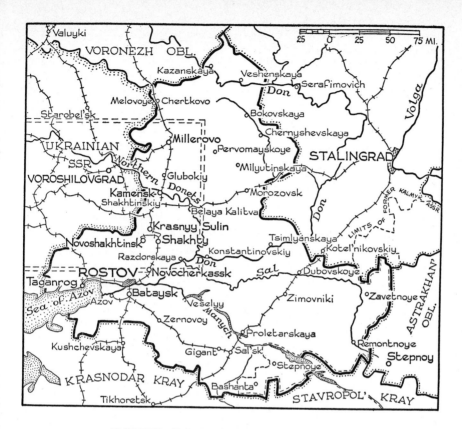

LOWER DON (ROSTOV OBLAST)

(Donets Basin is shown in detail on p. 451.)

CRIMEA

months. Water is obtained from artesian wells and from collection reservoirs for melting snow. Salt lakes abound along the shallow coast. The Kerch' peninsula rises in many low hill ranges, composed mainly of clayey schists which contain a number of mud volcanoes, similar to those found on the Apsheron peninsula near Baku. The Kerch' peninsula is the chief mineral region of the Crimea and contains vast deposits (about 3 billion tons) of phosphoric iron ore.

The Crimean mountains were formed in the Alpine orogenesis and extend 80 miles long and 30 miles wide along the south coast of the peninsula. They are composed chiefly of limestone. In the west they form three ridges; the lowest (northernmost) is considerably eroded and consists of crumbly yellow limestone. The central range, somewhat higher, consists of soft white limestone and has been dissected by river action into separate plateau blocks. The hard gray limestone formations of the southern range, which reaches the highest elevation at the Roman-Kosh (5,062 feet), break off nearly vertically at the south coast. The summits of the Crimean mountains are covered with steppe grasses and Alpine plants, which serve as excellent summer pastures for the stock of the lowland steppe. The southernmost ridge is commonly known by the name Yayla, a Tatar word for pasture. Like all limestone regions, the Crimean mountains contain extensive karst formations, including caves and sinkholes, which act as natural snow reservoirs. Being situated on the northern edge of the Black Sea fault, the range is subject to earthquakes. The last major quake occurred in 1927, when a number of buildings were destroyed in Yalta. The slopes of the main ridge are forested, conifers predominating in the north, and deciduous trees (mainly oak), in the south.

The narrow coastal plain extends from one to five miles wide between the mountains and the Black Sea. Consisting generally of clayey schist formations, its surface is broken by limestone bluffs protruding from the mountains toward the sea and by volcanic rocks in the vicinity of extinct volcanoes, such as the Kara-Dag in the east. The coast is poorly supplied with streams. Mountain torrents rage down the slopes following heavy rains and the melting of the snow in spring, only to become reduced rapidly to insignificant rivulets. The Mediterranean climate is the most characteristic feature of the littoral strip. Screened by the mountains from the cold northerly winds of the steppes and open to the mild, damp breezes from the south, the south coast of the Crimea is distinguished by mild winters, having a January mean of 39° F, and a hot, dry summer. Precipitation, which totals more than 20 inches annually, occurs mainly in the winter months. The natural vegetation is subtropical in character and includes Mediterranean trees and shrubs such as the olive, the cypress, the laurel, the magnolia, the oleander, and fan palms. In this section, one of the most beautiful sections of the European USSR, dark green forested slopes, broken here and there by the white buildings of health and tourist resorts, overlook fertile orchards, vineyards, and tobacco plantations.

Inhabited since the most ancient times, the Crimea has been a battleground throughout several centuries. On its shores Phoenicians, Greeks, and Romans established colonies in antiquity. They were later succeeded by the Italians (Genoese and Venetians) who were the last seafaring invaders of the Crimean shores. In the fourteenth century the Tatars, coming overland in the manner of the Scythians and Khazars centuries earlier, established themselves in the Crimea, at first independently, later under Turkish suzerainty. Following the Russian annexation of the peninsula in 1783, Russians and Ukrainians added to the multinational character of the population. In 1921 the Soviets broke through the last White Russian defenses in the Perekop Isthmus and organized the Crimean Autonomous SSR on the basis of the Tatar minority which, by that time, comprised only about 25 percent of the total population. Russians and Ukrainians represented the majority. There was a considerable German group of about 40,000 in the steppe farm lands and segments of Greeks, Bulgarians, Armenians, and Jews. During the Second World War the Tatar and German elements allegedly collaborated with the German occupying forces. Like other autonomous ethnic groups accused of similar acts, the Tatars and the Germans were resettled in other parts of the USSR and lost their national identity. The autonomous republic was abolished in June, 1945, and converted into an ordinary administrative oblast within the Russian SFSR. By December, 1944, all Tatar names of localities had been abrogated and replaced by run-of-the-mill Soviet appellations. Among the notable exceptions were the rail center of Dzhankoy and Bakhchisaray and Balaklava, famed in Russian literature and history. More than one half of the population is classified as urban, due to the importance of the industries, resorts, and ports.

Agriculture in the steppes of the Crimea specializes in the production of high-grade, quick-ripening wheat, mainly for export, cotton, tobacco, and garden crops. In the foothills and along the south coast large state

farms are covered with vineyards, fruit orchards, and tobacco plantations. Processing plants are located in the large cities and in the towns
of Sovetskiy (until 1944, Ichki-Grammatikovo) and Nizhnegorskiy (until 1944, Seytler), where flour is milled, in the rail center of Dzhankoy
(cotton ginning and flour milling), in Belogorsk (until 1944, Karasubazar), where fruits and vegetables are canned, and in Staryy Krym, where
various foods are processed. The principal wine centers are Yalta,
Balaklava, Alushta, and Sudak. Fisheries are important along the coasts.
Herring, mullet, mackerel, and goby, which make up the major portion
of the catch, are taken to Balaklava, Feodosiya, and Kerch' for processing.

The Crimea is poor in fuel resources. A small lignite mine is being
worked at Beshuyskiye Kopi, in the mountains north of Yalta, and there
are oil and natural gas deposits in the Kerch' peninsula. Of greater importance are the salt deposits along the shallow northern coasts. The
main bromine and saltworks are at Krasno-Perekop, on the isthmus, and
at Saki, a mud-bath resort east of Yevpatoriya. Construction stone,
marble and limestone, are quarried in the Crimean Mountains and in its
foothills at Balaklava.

On the basis of the phosphatic iron ore, which is mined in open cuts
southwest of Kerch', at Kamysh-Burun, a large-scale metallurgical industry has developed at Kerch' with the help of coal from the Donbas.
The ore has only 35 percent metal content, and treatment is laborious
because of the high proportion of phosphorus. However, waste products
serve for the manufacture of chemicals, notably phosphate fertilizer.
Because of the demand by the canning industry, the Kerch' steel mill
specializes in the production of tin plate.

Prior to the Second World War, the Crimea was connected with the
mainland by a single rail line, which crossed the Sivash Sea in the north
via a causeway and forked at Dzhankoy, sending one branch southward
to Simferopol' and Sevastopol', with a spur to Yevpatoriya, another
branch southeast to Feodosiya and Kerch'. During the war another
line was extended across the Perekop Isthmus to the Dnieper River at
Kherson. The peninsula has a good road network, especially along the
densely settled southern coast, where the many resorts are also connected by coastal steamers. Maritime connections also lead to Odessa
and the Black Sea littoral of the Caucasus. The chief export items are
iron ore, which supplies the steel mills of Zhdanov, salt (shipped through
Yevpatoriya), marble and other construction stone, as well as wine, to-

bacco, and canned goods (vegetables, fruits, and fish). Imports involve coal from the Donets Basin, petroleum from the Caucasus, lumber from Belorussia and the Caucasus, textiles from Moscow and Ivanovo oblasts, and butter from the European North.

Simferopol', the former capital of the Crimean Autonomous SSR and the present administrative seat of the oblast, lies in the center of the peninsula, amidst the forested steppe of the foothills. It has fruit- and vegetable-canning plants and produces canning machinery. Tobacco, fish, and wheat are also processed here.

Sevastopol', in the southwestern part of the Crimea, is an important naval base and possesses the best natural harbor on the Black Sea. Rail terminus and center for an electrotechnical industry of some importance, Sevastopol' is noted for the sieges of 1854–56 during the Crimean War and of 1941–42 during the Second World War. It became a city of republic rank in 1948, subordinated directly to the Russian SFSR government.

Feodosiya, or Theodosia, is a grain-exporting and fishing port on the southeast coast. It produces tobacco, flour, canned fish products, and wines. Known as Kaffa in the Middle Ages, it still possesses remains of Genoese walls.

Kerch', the metallurgical center at the east end of the Kerch' peninsula, also produces canning machinery, meat, tobacco, and canned fish. It ships iron ore that is mined at Kamysh-Burun, just southwest of the city.

Yalta, one of the most famous resorts of the USSR, lies on the subtropical south coast amid a large number of lesser year-round resorts. Extending eastward along the coast are Gurzuf, near the dome-shaped mountain of Ayu-Dag, and the wine-producing centers of Alushta and Sudak. To the west are Livadiya, scene of the Big Three conference in February, 1945, Gaspra, Koreiz, Alupka, and Simeiz. Adjoining Yalta are the famous vineyards of Massandra.

Yevpatoriya, or Eupatoria, a salt-shipping port on the west coast, engages in meat packing and has flour and clothing mills.

LOWER DON AND NORTHERN CAUCASUS

THE REGION known as the Northern Caucasus includes the northern slopes and foothills of the Greater Caucasus range and the level fertile steppes adjoining the Kuban' and the Terek rivers to the north. The steppes of the Lower Don are usually associated with the Northern

Caucasus not only because of their contiguity and common geographical factors but also because they were both settled by the Cossacks. The region is bounded by the Black Sea and the Sea of Azov in the west and by the Caspian Sea in the east. In the northeast its geographical boundary is the Kuma-Manych Depression, which once formed a connection between the Sea of Azov and the Caspian and is sometimes regarded as the natural dividing line between Europe and Asia. The combined area of the Lower Don * and the Northern Caucasus is more than 138,000 square miles.

North of the Kuban'-Terek line lies the steppe region of the Northern Caucasus, a level lowland which rises in the center to 2,715 feet in the Stavropol' upland, the northernmost outlier of the Greater Caucasus. West of the upland the steppes form a continuation of the Black Sea lowland; east of the elevation are the Caspian steppes and semi-deserts. The upland itself is deeply cut by numerous river valleys and ravines which divide it into separate plateau masses. South of the Stavropol' upland lies the northernmost of the three ranges which the Greater Caucasus forms in its western part, the so-called Black Mountains (Russian *Chernyye Gory*). These mountains are of the laccolite type, of partly eroded sedimentary formation; the highest points are Beshtau (4,725 feet) and Mashuk (3,940 feet). Connected with the volcanic character of these mountains are the famous mineral springs in the adjacent area of Pyatigorsk, Zheleznovodsk, and Kislovodsk.

The Greater Caucasus extends from the Apsheron peninsula in the Azerbaijan SSR 685 miles northwest to the Taman peninsula on the Black Sea. It has low hills at the two extremities and exceeds the highest Alpine peaks in its central section. At ten points it rises above the elevation of Mont Blanc. The gradual northern slopes and the abrupt southern side branch off into lateral ranges, which sometimes run parallel to the main divide. Many of the major peaks, including Mt. El'brus (18,476 feet), the highest point of the Caucasus and of Europe, lie in these lateral ranges. The western section of the Greater Caucasus, west of Mt. El'brus, is made up predominantly of limestone formations having an average elevation ranging from 2,000 to 12,000 feet and gives rise to the Kuban' River in the north and to several short streams in the south. In the central section occur Paleozoic crystalline formations, together with igneous rocks, which over large stretches are covered by snow fields

---

* The region of the lower Don River is discussed under Rostov Oblast, with which it is coterminous.

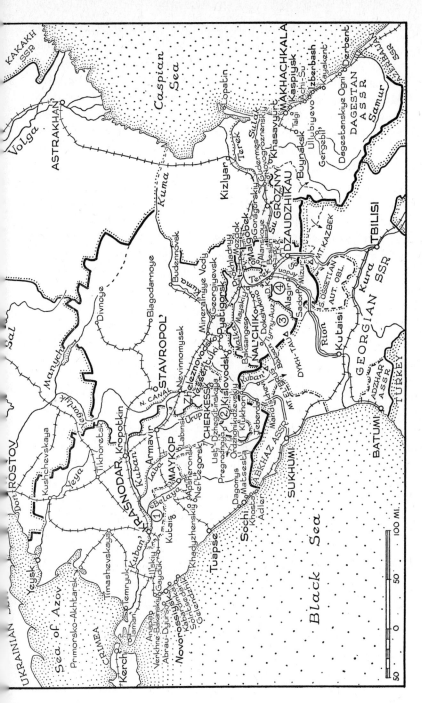

NORTHERN CAUCASUS

(1) Adyge Autonomous Oblast; (2) Cherkess Autonomous Oblast; (3) Kabardinian Autonomous SSR;
(4) North Ossetian Autonomous SSR

Su. Sundzha; **V,** Vinogradnoye; **KK,** Kosta-Khetagurovo; **DK,** Darg-Kokh; **G.,** Gizel'don
(Arrows indicate territorial changes.)

and glaciers. Here Mt. El'brus and Mt. Kazbek (16,541 feet), two extinct volcanoes, are evidence of the considerable volcanic activity which accompanied the folding processes. In this portion of the Greater Caucasus rise the Terek River, in the north, and the Rion River, in the south. East of Mt. Kazbek the main divide is formed primarily of Jurassic beds and nowhere exceeds 14,750 feet. The glaciers gradually decrease in size. They disappear altogether near the Caspian Sea, where the Greater Caucasus becomes a low range of hills rising to 1,075 feet. The northern spurs of this section of the Caucasus form an extensive mountain region known as Dagestan. The chief rivers here are the Sulak in the north and in the south the left affluents of the Kura River.

The Kuban' and the Terek are the main rivers of the Northern Caucasus. Due to their mountain origin, high water occurs in the summer when snow and ice melt in the high altitudes. The force of the current washes out the upper valleys, and in depositing the sediments in the lower course it forms sand banks, which render these streams useless for navigation. They are, however, important for irrigation and as a source of hydroelectric power. In their lower reaches these rivers form large swampy deltas, with many lakes and channels, overgrown with reeds and other marsh vegetation. The large quantities of sediment carried by the Terek act to enlarge the delta from year to year.

The climate of the Northern Caucasus is of the continental type and is exposed to a series of opposing air mass movements from the west, bringing moisture from the Black Sea and from the east, where they originate in the dry desert regions of Central Asia. Although the winters are short, they are severe, and frosts of below 0° F occur frequently. Spring arrives at the end of February and soon turns into a hot summer. Most of the precipitation occurs in the summer and is greater in the west and in the high altitudes. The heaviest rainfall takes place on the southern slopes of the Greater Caucasus near the Black Sea (up to 25 inches yearly); in the Kuma-Manych Depression to the northeast, precipitation is less than 12 inches a year. The climate of the Greater Caucasus range, while it varies, depending on the elevation and the location, is marked by a steady decrease of precipitation from west to east.

In accordance with the amount of precipitation, the type of vegetation varies throughout the region. The western ranges are covered with deciduous forests, with oak and beech, while the eastern highlands of Dagestan are nearly treeless. At lower altitudes begins the oak forest steppe, extending as far as the Kuban' River; north of that stream it follows the fertile black-earth steppe, which continues to the lower Don. In the northeast, however, the decrease in precipitation is evidenced by a gradual change to the dry wormwood steppe, with salt flats, shifting sands, and bitter-salt lakes, forerunners of the Caspian semi-desert in the east.

The population of the Lower Don and Northern Caucasus is more than 9 millions, giving an average density of 65 per square mile. The greatest concentration of the population is north of the Kuban'-Terek line, in the steppes, where Russians and Ukrainians predominate. These two ethnic groups came to this region from the north in the eighteenth and nineteenth centuries and constitute at present nine tenths of the total population. The Russians settled mainly in the eastern steppes, the Ukrainians along the Kuban' River. South of the Kuban'-Terek line live the indigenous mountain peoples of the Greater Caucasus; the Adyge (Cherkess or Circassians), Kabardinians, Ossetians, Avars, Laks, and others. The Slavic groups live in large administrative divisions, such as Rostov and Groznyy oblasts, Krasnodar and Stavropol' krays, while the many mountain peoples are organized in autonomous units, varying in importance and size, on the northern slope of the Greater Caucasus.

Four ethnic groups of the Northern Caucasus lost their national identity and were resettled in other parts of the USSR following their alleged collaboration with the Germans during the Second World War. The autonomous oblast of the Karachay was dissolved in 1943, and part of its territory was given to Stavropol' Kray, while the southern portion, including the capital, Mikoyan-Shakhar (now Klukhori), was ceded to the Georgian SSR. The Balkar nationality, which constituted 16 percent of the population of the Kabardino-Balkar Autonomous SSR, was dissolved in 1943, and a section of its territory, in the southwest of the republic, was transferred to the Georgian SSR. The republic became the Kabardinian Autonomous SSR. The Chechen-Ingush Autonomous SSR was also dissolved in 1943 because of the alleged fifth-column activities of its two main ethnic groups, the Chechen and the Ingush. The greater portion of the territory became part of the newly created Groznyy Oblast and the adjacent North Ossetian Autonomous SSR (west), Georgian SSR (south), and Dagestan Autonomous SSR (east) each received strips of land along the frontiers.

The Kuban' steppes are among the chief grain-producing regions of the USSR. The fertile black earth and sufficient rainfall favor the extensive cultivation of cereals such as wheat, barley, and corn, while of the industrial crops sunflower, cotton, *kenaf*, soy and castor beans are most important. Rice is grown in the swampy delta of the Kuban' River. In the drier eastern portion of the steppes and in the mountainous section of the Northern Caucasus the raising of livestock and allied activities are the main occupations of the rural population.

The industries are concerned primarily with the extraction and refining of petroleum (Groznyy, Makhachkala, and Maykop), the mining of polymetallic ores and molybdenum, and the production of hydroelectric power. In the steppes rural industries process the local products and produce vegetable oils, alcohol, sugar, and starches. Large cement mills at Novorossiysk are notable. Fishing and canning are well developed along the coast. An important role is played by health and tourist resorts, notably Kislovodsk and its satellites in the foothills of the Caucasus and the subtropical resorts of Sochi and Matsesta along the Black Sea littoral.

Two main rail lines serve the steppes of the region. Tikhoretsk is the junction for these two railways coming from Stalingrad and Rostov. The Stalingrad line passes through Krasnodar and on to the Black Sea port of Novorossiysk, while the Rostov trunk railroad runs parallel to the northern foothills of the Greater Caucasus and along the Caspian Sea to Baku. A line branching off at Armavir reaches the Black Sea oil port of Tuapse and continues along the coast past Sochi to the Georgian SSR through a rail link completed during the Second World War. Transportation across the Greater Caucasus range is maintained by three important highways: the Sukhumi military road (Cherkessk-Sukhumi), the Ossetian military road (Alagir-Kutaisi), and the Georgian military road (Dzaudzhikau-Tbilisi).

Rostov Oblast

Capital, Rostov on the Don; Area, 40,300, population, 2,550,000

Rostov Oblast is astride of the lower Don River, within the bend of the river in proximity to the Volga near Stalingrad. The southern section of the oblast is drained mainly by the Sal and the Manych, two left affluents of the Don. According to its relief, the region may be divided into the eastern end of the Donets ridge, the southeastern outliers of the Central Russian upland in the north and the wide Don steppe in the south.

The Donets ridge, the major portion lying within the Ukraine, penetrates the oblast between the lower Don and its right affluent, the Northern Donets. It is a plateau of limestone and sandstone, which is deeply dissected by river courses and ravines. On the higher points burial mounds of the ancient steppe dwellers are often found. The villages, normally surrounded by gardens and orchards, lie along the ravines and valleys of small streamlets. A similar landscape is represented by the outliers of the Central Russian upland to the north. The Don steppe, on the contrary, constitutes very level terrain. The wide river valleys, where streams proceed with a sluggish current, are often filled with salt lakes, and salt flats frequently break the expanse of black-earth and chestnut soils which characterize the region. Toward the east the relief gradually merges with the features of the Caspian lowland.

Normally the Don is not a very abundant river, but spring freshets raise its level considerably. At its mouth, on the Taganrog Gulf of the Sea of Azov, it forms a large delta, which, together with the shallow waters of the adjoining sea, abounds in fish of many varieties.

The climate is continental, with hot summers and severe, snowless winters. Precipitation varies from 16 inches annually in the west to 12 inches in the east and occurs chiefly in the summer months, in frequent heavy downpours. Easterly prevailing winds blowing in the spring and summer from the dry steppes and deserts of Central Asia and Kazakhstan present a serious danger of drought to the crops. Drought conditions are especially marked in the southeast, along the Sal River, where black earth is largely replaced by chestnut soils. In the well-watered flood plain of the lower Don, alluvial pastures are important for the raising of dairy cattle.

The eastern wing of the Donets Basin penetrates into the oblast along the Northern Donets River. Anthracite predominates in this area and represents about one fifth of the total reserves of the basin. The major coal-mining centers are Shakhty and Novoshakhtinsk. Other coal mines are concentrated in the areas of Gukovo, north of Krasnyy Sulin, and Gundorovka, west of Kamensk-Shakhtinskiy. In the Bogurayev coal field, at the intersection of the Northern Donets River and the Likhaya-Stalingrad railroad, coal is mined at Koksovyy (characteristically named for coke) north of the railroad and at Sinegorskiy to the south. Belaya Kalitva, at the center of this field, has limestone and glassworks. Anthracite dust from the mines is used to feed the power station of Artemovskiy, an eastern suburb of Shakhty, and the Nesvetay station in a southwestern suburb of Krasnyy Sulin. The former plays an important role in the mechanization of the coal-mining operations. Before the Second World War, more than 10 percent of the Donbas coal was mined within Rostov Oblast.

On the basis of the coal resources, heavy industry is operating metallurgical plants at Taganrog and Krasnyy Sulin. Rostov is the home of *Rossel'mash*, the largest agricultural machinery plant of the USSR. Agricultural implements are also manufactured at Morozovsk. Other centers engaged in the production of machinery and metal products are Taganrog, Novocherkassk, Glubokiy, and Likhovskoy (at Likhaya station).

In the northern grain-growing district, wheat and sunflower are the dominant crops. Toward the southeast, barley and mustard become important; further on, toward the Caspian Lowland, the emphasis shifts to stock raising. Horses and meat cattle are gradually replaced by sheep in the drier areas. Cotton is grown to some extent in the south and the southeast. Several Cossack villages along the Don River, notably Tsimlyanskaya and Razdorskaya, have extensive vineyards. In a wide zone through the urban and heavily industrialized section of Taganrog-Rostov-Shakhty, truck gardening and the raising of dairy cattle are the principal agricultural activities. The principal agricultural centers are Millerovo and Chertkovo in the north and Sal'sk (with near-by Gigant state farm, one of the largest grain farms of the USSR) in the southeast. These and other towns throughout the oblast mill flour, extract sunflower oil, and process tobacco. The fish catch of the Don delta and adjacent Taganrog Gulf is processed at Azov, a small port southwest of Rostov.

Rostov Oblast is settled by Russians and a Ukrainian minority. Prior to the Second World War some Kalmyk elements were organized into a Kalmyk national rayon, northwest of Zimovniki. In 1944, following the abrogation of the Kalmyk Autonomous SSR, the rayon was also abrogated, and presumably the population was resettled elsewhere. In this connection, Rostov Oblast also acquired the westernmost section of the former Kalmyk Autonomous SSR.

Rostov lies on the elevated, right bank of the Don River at the head of the delta. Thanks to its favorable location at the junction of trade routes between the Black Sea, the Volga, the Ukraine, the European Center, and the Northern Caucasus, it developed early into an important commercial center and transportation hub. With the construction of the

Rossel'mash agricultural machinery works, the city became an industrial center of first rank. It is the site of an auto-assembly plant, airplane factory, shipyards and machine-tool works, and produces a wide range of products, including foods (flour, vegetable oil, meat, canned goods), paints, cement, glass, shoes, furniture, and cigarettes. The city suffered considerably during the Second World War. Across the Don River lies Bataysk, a rail junction and aircraft center with two large airfields and repair shops. Northeast of Rostov, on the Aksay, a branch of the Don, lies the former center of the Don Cossacks, Novocherkassk, at present a machine-manufacturing city, with locomotive works.

Taganrog, the second city of the oblast, is a major coal and grain-shipping port on the Sea of Azov. A foremost industrial center, it has metallurgical and pipe-rolling mills, one of the largest boiler works of the USSR, and produces machines for the food and chemical industries. It manufactures agricultural implements, instruments, and shoes, and has an extensive food-processing industry. Shipbuilding and aircraft manufacturing are also important.

Kamensk-Shakhtinskiy, on the Northern Donets River and the Voronezh-Rostov railroad, has chemical works and lumber mills and produces flour and alcohol.

Shakhty (formerly called Aleksandrovsk-Grushevskiy) is the largest coal-mining center in this section of the Donets Basin. It has a 90,000 kw. power station in its eastern suburb of Artemovskiy, textile, leather and food industries. Its southern suburb, Kamenolomni, has stone quarries (for which it is named) and metalworks. Another coal-mining center, Novoshakhtinsk (until 1939, Komintern), lies west of Shakhty.

Krasnodar Kray
Capital, Krasnodar; area, 32,800, population, 3,000,000

Krasnodar Kray occupies the western section of the Northern Caucasus adjoining the Sea of Azov and includes a short section of Transcaucasia along the Black Sea littoral. The presence within a relatively restricted area of maritime and high-altitude influences bring about a great variety of natural conditions and economic activities. Thus, the forested slopes of the Greater Caucasus are in sharp contrast to the treeless level steppes beyond the Kuban' River, and the subtropical Black Sea coast, protected from the northerly winter winds, is opposed to the continental climate of the remainder of the region.

The entire kray, with the exception of the mountains in the south and the dry steppes in the east, is covered with black earth of the highest grade. The soil conditions and the warm, humid summer climate combine to make the Kuban' region one of the most fertile agricultural regions of the USSR, able to provide a large number of products. In the southwest, along the Black Sea littoral, the subtropical, winterless climate favors the growth of citrus fruits, tea, and similar warm-weather crops. The mountainous portion of the region also presents factors favorable to the development of the economy. The left affluents of the Kuban', the Belaya, the Laba, and the Urup rivers, as well as the upper course of the Kuban' itself are potential sources of hydroelectric power. A rich petroleum-bearing area extends from the Taman' peninsula to the Belaya River along the northern foothills of the Greater Caucasus. Along the Black Sea, southeast of Novorossiysk, extensive marl deposits furnish an important basis for the cement industry. The region also includes the forested slopes of the Caucasus that are covered with oak and chestnut, two valuable types of wood. The Sea of Azov, finally, is rich in fish along the shallow northwest coast of Krasnodar Kray.

The population of the region is predominantly Russian. It includes also large numbers of Ukrainians and Adyge (Cherkess or Circassians), the latter being organized into an autonomous oblast. The Cossacks are concentrated in large villages along the Kuban' River.

The Russian settlement and consequent economic development received their most vigorous impetus from the construction of the Rostov-Baku railroad in the 1870's. During the twenty-five years following the completion of the line the population of the Kuban' district increased twice, and the area under cultivation fivefold. Mechanization was introduced early by the well-to-do peasants, who owned most of the land prior to collectivization. After the adoption of rationalized agriculture, spring wheat and sunflowers were assigned to the dry northern steppes, where the black-earth and chestnut soils suffer from drought in summer and are covered only by a thin snow cover in the winter months. The richest agricultural area lies along the Kuban' River. There, among vast expanses under winter wheat, barley, and corn, large areas are producing garden produce, melons and pumpkins, and fodder crops. The principal old industrial crops are sunflower and tobacco; during recent years cotton, *kenaf*, soy beans, castor beans, and essential-oil-bearing plants were introduced. Rice has been acclimatized in the swampy lowlands bordering on the Kuban', between Krasnodar and the delta. Livestock raising is more intensive here than it is along the Don and in the

Sal steppes, where because of the dry conditions only sheep and horses can be successfully reared.

The rich agricultural production of the Kuban' lowlands is processed at a number of centers, chiefly Krasnodar, Armavir, Kropotkin, and Labinsk. Of great importance are oil presses, canneries, flour mills, and tobacco factories.

The Black Sea littoral is characterized by a humid, maritime climate, luxuriant natural vegetation, mineral springs, and a picturesque location between the mountains and the sea. These factors combine to make the area provide garden crops and health resorts. Because of the limited land area under cultivation and the presence of resorts (Sochi, Matsesta, and Anapa), the growing of vegetables, fruits, vineyards, and dairy farming receive priority. Tobacco, southern hemp, oil-bearing plants are also cultivated. Flower gardens and decorative plants are common. Wine is made chiefly at Anapa, at Abrau-Dyurso near Novorossiysk, and at Solntsedar [gift of the sun], just west of Gelendzhik. Gelendzhik itself is an important dairying center. Tea is processed at Dagomys, northwest of Sochi.

The Kuban'-Black Sea petroleum region (near Maykop) is centered in Neftegorsk [oil mountain] and Apsheronsk (named for the oil-rich Apsheron peninsula). Near by are the oil towns of Khadyzhenskiy and recently-opened Kutais. Another field has been developed at Il'skiy, southwest of Krasnodar. Prior to the Second World War this region was one of the most rapidly developing petroleum areas of the USSR; it had a tenfold increase in production under the Soviet regime. Destruction caused by the war has, however, been responsible for a considerable setback in output.

The basic transportation routes are the Rostov-Baku and Novorossiysk-Stalingrad railroads, their junction being at Tikhoretsk, a major rail center with extensive yards and shops. Short branch lines serve most sections of the region. During the Second World War the opening of the Black Sea littoral railroad between Adler and Sukhumi (Georgian SSR) established another vital link across the Greater Caucasus to the Transcaucasian republics. Coastal steamers serve the Black Sea shore, stopping at Sochi, Tuapse, and Novorossiysk, the most important ports.

Krasnodar, formerly called Yekaterinodar, lies on the right bank of the Kuban', in the middle of the fertile black-earth agricultural area. Once the capital of the Kuban' Cossacks, it has oil-refining and metalworking industries. It is a major food-processing and rail center, having dairying, tobacco, distilling, canning, flour, and meat-packing plants. Steel tubing and telephone equipment are also manufactured. Surrounding the city are some of the principal jute-producing lands of the USSR.

Novorossiysk is a well-equipped Black Sea port on Tsemes Bay and the principal cement-milling center of the USSR. It ships the wheat of the Kuban' area and lies amidst such well-known resorts as Anapa, to the northwest, and Kabardinka and Gelendzhik, to the southeast. West of the city is the famous champagne center of Abrau-Dyurso. Novorossiysk produces agricultural machinery, bicycles, furniture, textiles, and flour. Grain elevators and oil tanks lie in the harbor area. The cement mills ("Krasnyy Oktyabr' " and "Krasnyy Proletariy") lie in the suburb Standart, north of the Tsemes Bay. Other mills lie in the towns of Verkhne-Bakanskaya and Gayduk, northwest of Novorossiysk.

Tuapse, another major port on the Black Sea, rivals Batumi in the shipping and refining of petroleum. Surrounded by orchards and vineyards, it is the terminus of an oil pipe line from Groznyy and Neftegorsk. It produces large amounts of fuel oil, which serves as the principal power source for electric stations throughout the region. Shipbuilding and the manufacture of machines for the petroleum industry are also important.

Sochi is the most popular health resort on the Black Sea coast. It is the site of numerous sanitariums and an experimental station for subtropical agriculture. To the southeast lie the satellite resorts of Matsesta (sulphur springs) and Khosta. It became a city of republic rank in 1948.

Other important centers of Krasnodar Kray are Armavir, with food (meat, flour, sunflower oil) and agricultural machinery industries, Yeysk, a fishing port having canning and meat-packing plants, and Kropotkin (food products).

ADYGE AUTONOMOUS OBLAST (capital, Maykop; area, 1,700, population, 300,000) is located on the middle Kuban' River, between its left affluents, the Laba and the Belaya. It was formed in 1922 and is one of the few remaining settlement areas of the Cherkess, or Circassian, ethnic group. The population, which is about 45 percent Cherkess or Adyge (the designation applied by the people to themselves), is for the remainder evenly divided among the Russian and the Ukrainian groups. The rural economy rests chiefly on the cultivation of winter wheat, sunflowers, and tobacco. Horse breeding is also engaged in.

Maykop, on the Belaya River, at the north foot of the Caucasus, is the center of the oil field of Neftegorsk and Apsheronsk, more than 30 miles southwest. The city has a small-scale metallurgical industry and produces machine tools, agricultural and lumbering machinery, furniture, tobacco, canned goods, and meat.

Stavropol' Kray
Capital, Stavropol'; area, 29,600, population, 1,500,000

Stavropol' Kray reaches to the crest of the Greater Caucasus only in its extreme southwestern portion along the upper Urup, a left affluent of the Kuban'. The basic portion of the region lies in the northern foothills of the Caucasus, the so-called Stavropol' upland, and in the dry steppes to the northeast. The watershed between the Caspian and the Black Sea basins passes roughly along the Stavropol' meridian, near the western border of the kray. Due to this circumstance, only a narrow strip of territory along the western boundary receives the benefit of the humid westerly winds blowing from the Black Sea. The rest of the area, east of the Stavropol' upland, is characterized by a dry climate. The yearly precipitation decreases from 16 inches in the west to 8 inches in the east; insolation and summer heat are very pronounced. Consequently, water courses are poorly developed, and trees are entirely absent. In the western and central portions fertile black-earth and chestnut soils predominate; only in the extreme east does the region have a semi-desert character.

The population of the region is predominantly Russian, with a strong Ukrainian admixture. In the southwest lives another section of the Cherkess, or Circassian, ethnic group, which is organized into the Cherkess Autonomous Oblast. This region, now known as Stavropol' Kray, was first organized within its present approximate limits in 1924, when it was called North Caucasus Kray. In 1937 it was renamed Ordzhonikidze Kray; it received its present designation in 1943. Prior to the Second World War, it also included the Karachay Autonomous Oblast, a division located in the southwest on the slopes of the Greater Caucasus. This autonomous unit, with an area of 3,800 square miles and a population of 150,000, had been constituted in 1926, when it was separated from the original Karachay-Cherkess Autonomous Oblast (formed in 1922). The Karachay, a Turkic people who constituted about one half of the population of the autonomous unit, were among those accused of collaboration with the Germans during the Second World War. In 1943 the nationality was abrogated, the people were dispersed and resettled, and the Karachay lost official recognition. The autonomous unit was abolished. Its major portion, including the capital, Mikoyan-Shakhar, now Klukhori, and the resort Teberda, and the village Uchkulan, now Madniskhevi, were ceded to the Georgian SSR, the strip along the upper Laba River passed to Krasnodar Kray; another portion, including the village Pregradnaya, was annexed to Cherkess Autonomous Oblast; the remainder became part of Stavropol' Kray proper.

The climatic and soil conditions of the region are favorable to the development of grain farming and the raising of livestock for wool and meat, activities which prevail for similar reasons in the dry steppes of the Lower Volga Region, in northern Kazakhstan, and in Western Siberia. The main crops are winter wheat, sunflowers in the west, and cotton in the east. In the section bordering on the upper and middle Kuma River, irrigated farming is devoted to the raising of orchards, garden crops, and vineyards, the latter particularly in the Budennovsk–Georgiyevsk area. With the construction of the Nevinnomyssk Canal, to be completed during the current Five-Year Plan, the glacier-fed Kuban' River will be linked with the Yegorlyk, an affluent of the Manych, and new areas will be put under irrigation in the western part of Stavropol' Kray. Truck produce is grown intensively in the relatively urban areas of the health resorts (Pyatigorsk, Kislovodsk, and others) in the south and in the southwestern mountain area garden and dairy farming is carried on. In the northern and eastern steppes the raising of sheep is most important. On specially organized state farms two major breeds predominate: the merino sheep for the production of fine wool and the *volosh* sheep, which furnishes meat and coarse wool. The Alpine pastures in the southwest support the so-called Karachay sheep, which also is used mainly for meat. Dairy cattle are raised in the health resort district, and hogs and horses on the mountains slopes.

The mineral resources of the region consist only of coal, which is worked in small amounts at Khumarinskoye and Ordzhonikidzevskiy, just north of Klukhori, of raw material for the chemical industry of Cherkess Autonomous Oblast, and of the mineral springs in the Pyatigorsk-Kislovodsk area. The products of agriculture and of the pastoral economy are partly processed within the region; some are exported in semi-processed form to other areas of the USSR. The principal export items are grain, vegetable oil, meat, tallow, dairy products, raw wool, fruits, and vegetables. The local industries are scattered throughout the region and are especially concentrated at Stavropol', Georgiyevsk, Nevinnomyssk, and Budennovsk, where flour milling, oil pressing, canning, dairying, wool washing, cotton ginning, and wine making are the principal activities.

Of special importance in the economy of the region are the health and tourist resorts. One of the most important resort areas of the USSR lies in the foothills of the Greater Caucasus. There the resort cities of Zheleznovodsk (ferruginous springs), Pyatigorsk, Yessentuki, and Kislovodsk are linked by an electrified branch with the main Rostov-Baku railroad at Mineral'nyye Vody. The bottling of mineral waters is a major export industry.

For communications the region relies chiefly on the Rostov-Baku trunk line, from which branches penetrate into the remote sections to Divnoye, Blagodarnoye, Budennovsk, and into the foothills of the Caucasus to Ust'-Dzhegutinskaya and Kislovodsk. The Sukhumi military road, one of the three pass roads through the mountains, continues from the Nevinnomyssk-Cherkessk-Ust'-Dzhegutinskaya rail branch through the valley of the Kuban' and the Teberda rivers, and enters the territory of the Georgian SSR at Klukhori. Of extreme importance for the future development of the region will be the final realization of the Manych Canal project linking the Caspian and the Black seas. Prior to the Second World War, the waterway had been canalized for a distance of over 150 miles eastward to the area of Divnoye. Due to destruction caused by the war, several reservoirs were emptied, and the canal installations fell into disuse. Small-scale reconstruction has been undertaken since the war; however, the completion of the project will have to await a future Plan.

Stavropol', the center of the kray, was known as Voroshilovsk from c. 1935 until 1943. It lies in the chief grain area of the region and has flour mills, a meat-packing plant, wool and leather industries, and produces chemicals and lumbering machinery. The vicinity of the city will benefit immeasurably from the new Nevinnomyssk Canal which will provide irrigation to this drought-ridden section.

Pyatigorsk, in the midst of five mountains (whence its name), of which the Besh-Tau and the Mashuk are best known, is the center of the four resort cities of the Northern Caucasus. Its warm sulphur springs and mud baths are much frequented. Next in size is Kislovodsk, at an elevation of 2,695 feet, with carbonated springs. Yessentuki, west of Pyatigorsk, has salt and alkaline springs, and Zheleznovodsk, to the north, ferruginous springs. In addition to their importance as health resorts, these four cities are centers of light industry, producing radio apparatus (Pyatigorsk), bottled mineral water (Yessentuki), and food products.

THE CHERKESS AUTONOMOUS OBLAST (capital, Cherkessk; area, 1,540; population, 100,000) lies along the upper Kuban' River and extends southwestward to the Urup, an affluent of the Kuban'. It was formed in 1926 as a national okrug, following the dissolution of the Karachay-Cherkess Autonomous Oblast (formed originally in 1922), and reached the status of autonomous oblast in 1928. Its population includes several related elements of the Cherkess, or Circassian, ethnic group, including the Kabardinians (who comprise one third of the total population), the Abaza (30 percent), and the Adyge branch of the Cherkess (7 percent). There are also Nogay Tatars (over 15 percent), Russians, and Ukrainians.

In the northern steppe the economy is based on grain farming, and in the southern foothills on livestock raising. Lumbering is carried on in the mountains in the south. Most of the industry is concentrated in the capital, Cherkessk.

Cherkessk was formerly known as Batalpashinsk; during the late 1930's it was called briefly Sulimov, and, after 1937, Yezhovo-Cherkessk, until the purge of Yezhov, in 1939. It has motor repair shops and chemical works (ammonium sulphate), and produces shoes, furniture, and clothing.

Kabardinian Autonomous Soviet Socialist Republic
Capital, Nal'chik; area, 4,600, population, 300,000

The Kabardinian Autonomous SSR includes the basins of the left affluents of the Terek River, notably the Malka and its branch, the Baksan, and extends from the upper courses of these mountain torrents to the Terek proper in the area where it makes its sharp turn toward the east. From the standpoint of physical geography, the republic includes three separate sections. In the south lies the highest part of the Greater Caucasus, with its glaciated peaks extending eastward from the area of Mount El'brus and including the peaks of Dykh-Tau, Koshtan-Tau, and Shchara, an unsettled, roadless mountain wilderness. The central portion comprises the slopes of the Caucasus, where the population is concentrated in the narrow gorges of the mountain streams flowing to the

Terek River. To the north lies the Kabardinian lowland, characterized by black earth, well watered and marked by a temperate climate. This plain is the most highly developed and relatively densely settled section of the republic.

The Kabardinian Autonomous Oblast was established originally in 1921 on the basis of the Kabardinian section of the Cherkess, or Circassian, ethnic group. The Kabardinians, whose language is closely related to that of the Adyge, represent the easternmost branch of the vast Circassian national area that once existed through the entire western Caucasus zone. In 1922 the territory inhabited by the Balkars was joined to the Kabardinian Autonomous Oblast to form the Kabardino-Balkar Autonomous Oblast, which was raised to the status of autonomous republic in 1936. The Balkars, a Turkic group closely related to the Karachay, were also accused of collaboration with the enemy during the Second World War. They lost their national identity in 1943, and the upper Baksan valley, the principal Balkar district of the Kabardino-Balkar Autonomous SSR, was ceded to the Georgian SSR. Following the abrogation of the Balkar national group, the name of the republic was changed to Kabardinian. Prior to the Second World War the Balkars constituted 12 percent of the total population of nearly 360,000, the Kabardinians nearly 50 percent, while Russians and Ukrainians made up the remaining 38 percent. As a result of the disappearance of the Balkar population, at least as far as demographic statistics are concerned, the Kabardinians now comprise about 60 percent of the total population of the republic. Because of the expansion of the North Ossetian Autonomous SSR northward to the Mozdok area, the Kabardinian republic ceded its extreme eastern portion to its neighbor in 1944.

The favorable agricultural conditions which prevail in the lowland make it possible to obtain excellent crops of wheat, corn, and sunflowers in the north and the northeast and of southern hemp and *kenaf* mainly in the east. The cultivation of orchard and garden crops is also highly developed. On the mountain slopes and the Alpine pastures at higher altitudes livestock is raised. Poultry farming is important on the plain.

Industry consists predominantly of the processing of the agricultural products. Flour mills, oil presses, jam, and starch factories are the most common enterprises. At Mayskiy, a rail junction northeast of Nal'chik, fiber plants are processed, and at Dokshukino, on the rail branch to Nal'chik, there are fruit-canning and wine-distilling plants. Other industries are based on the deposits of nickel, gold, and molybdenum in the high Caucasus, of which only molybdenum is systematically mined, at Tyrny-Auz, just east of Mount El'brus and overlooking the Baksan valley. On the Baksan River, at the village of Kyzburun 3, northwest of Nal'chik, is the important Baksan hydroelectric station which furnishes power to local industries and the electrified Mineral'nyye Vody–Kislovodsk rail spur. Lumbering in the mountains is associated with a number of woodworking plants. An important role in the economy of the republic is played by tourism and mountain climbing, which attracts thousands of alpinists yearly.

Nal'chik is situated at the end of a rail spur of the Rostov-Baku trunk line in an outlier of the Greater Caucasus. A noted summer resort, it produces food products (meat, flour, vegetable oil, and canned fruits), clothing, and wood articles.

Prokhladnyy, a rail junction on the main trunk line for branches to Groznyy and Mozdok, has extensive freight yards, metalworks, cement mill, and an oil press.

North Ossetian Autonomous Soviet Socialist Republic
Capital, Dzaudzhikau; area, 3,500, population, 450,000

The North Ossetian Autonomous SSR lies between the Kabardinian Republic, in the west, and Groznyy Oblast, in the east, along the upper Terek and its left affluents, including the Ardon and the Gizel'don. Since its territorial expansion after the Second World War, it extends northward to the middle course of the Terek River. The most highly developed section is the shallow basin between the foothills of the Caucasus in the south and an outlier of the main range to the north. This lowland, which is drained by the Terek River and crossed from west to east by the Rostov-Groznyy-Baku line, is a densely populated agricultural district.

The population of the republic is more than 80 percent Ossetian and has Russian and Ukrainian minorities. The area was first constituted as an autonomous oblast in 1924 and became an autonomous republic in 1936. After the Second World War its territory experienced a considerable expansion, which increased its area by nearly one-half. It annexed the easternmost portion of the Kabardinian Autonomous SSR, including the wine-making village of Gnadenburg (since renamed Vinogradnoye), a section of Stavropol' Kray (including the city of Mozdok), and the western strip of the abrogated Chechen-Ingush Autonomous

SSR (including the villages of Nazran', now Kosta-Khetagurovo, and Psedakh, now Alanskoye).

The chief crop of the republic is corn, which is processed in the giant corn *kombinat* of Beslan into numerous products, including starches, molasses, forage, glucose, and a nutritive medium of the penicillin mold. Other agricultural products are *kenaf*, the new fiber plant, and garden crops, which prosper especially in irrigated areas. In recent years, an important food industry has developed in the republic in addition to the corn processing at Beslan. Canning and the manufacturing of starches and molasses are the principal activities.

Within the agricultural zone two rail spurs leave the main trunk line —at Beslan for Dzaudzhikau and at Darg-Kokh for Alagir. South of the Alagir-Dzaudzhikau district begins the mountainous section of the republic. Here agriculture is possible only on a small scale in the river valleys. The principal economic assets of the region are mineral resources, the hydroelectric potential of mountain streams, lumber, and Alpine pastures.

The major mineral site is Sadon, south of Alagir, where there are lead and zinc mines. Just east of the mines, on the Ossetian Military Road, is the town of Mizur, with an ore-concentrating plant. The ore is smelted in the new metallurgical works at Dzaudzhikau. The nonferrous metallurgy of the republic is of Union-wide importance and is one of the mainstays of the local economy. A series of power stations on the Terek River and its affluents are intended to supply the demands of the local industries and those of neighboring areas. Among the main hydroelectric plants are the Gizel'don (southwest of Dzaudzhikau), Ardon (south of Sadon), and Dzaudzhikau installations. In addition to the development of hydroelectricity and nonferrous metallurgy, residents in the mountainous sections of the republic engage in lumbering and Alpine livestock raising. As in the Kabardinian Republic, mountain tourism is popular in North Ossetia.

Two major highways lead from here across the Greater Caucasus to the Georgian SSR. The Ossetian Military Road leaves the railroad at Alagir, passes along the Ardon valley, through Mamison Pass, and on toward Kutaisi. The Georgian Military Road, west of this, has its northern terminus at Dzaudzhikau and passes through the picturesque Dar'yal Gorge, past Mount Kazbek, and through Krestovyy Pass to Tbilisi. Unlike the Sukhumi and the Ossetian roads, the Georgian Military Road not only has tourist importance but also supports regular highway transportation lines between the two sides of the Greater Caucasus.

Dzaudzhikau, on the right bank of the Terek River at its exit from the mountain gorges, was originally called Vladikavkaz [ruler of the Caucasus]; from 1933 until 1944 it bore the name Ordzhonikidze, for the Bolshevik leader who ruled here during the Civil War. A cultural center of some distinction, it is the site of educational, agricultural, and ethnographic institutes and several museums. Its population consists of Russians (50 percent), Armenians, Georgians, Persians, Greeks, and Jews. At the end of a rail spur from the main Northern Caucasus railroad, it is also the northern end of the Georgian Military Road. There are lead and zinc works, metalworking industries, and glass and porcelain factories. It makes food products (canned fruits, wines, and starches), clothing, and wood articles. During the Second World War, the German Caucasus advance was halted just northwest of the city.

Malgobek is a petroleum center at the western wing of the Groznyy oil fields.

Mozdok, which passed in 1944 from Stavropol' Kray to the North Ossetian Republic, lies on the nothern bank of the middle Terek River, amid vineyards. It has a metalworking industry and produces wine, flour, and other foods, as well as building materials.

Alagir, on a rail spur and at the northern end of the Ossetian Military Road, is a resort town, having a lead and zinc smelter and lumber mills.

Groznyy Oblast
Capital, Groznyy; area, 12,700, population, 600,000

Groznyy Oblast was formed in 1944 on the site of the former Chechen-Ingush Autonomous SSR and includes the territory of the former Kizlyar Okrug, which was originally part of the Dagestan Autonomous SSR, and from 1938 until 1944 in Ordzhonikidze Kray. The oblast, which is bordered by North Ossetia in the west and by Dagestan in the east, includes four distinct regions: the southern mountainous section dissected by the wooded gorges of mountain torrents, the fertile central steppe extending from the foothills of the Caucasus to the low outlying range between the Sunzha and the Terek rivers, the irrigated Terek valley, and the vast dry steppes in the north.

The territorial-autonomous history of the region begins in 1922, when the Chechen ethnic group, one of the Japhetic Caucasian tribes, was constituted an autonomous oblast in the east in the vicinity of Groznyy. In 1924 the Ingush, a closely related group in the west, were also organized into an autonomous oblast. The two divisions combined in 1934 to form the Chechen-Ingush Autonomous Oblast, which was raised to the level of autonomous republic in 1936. During the Second World War both groups allegedly carried on fifth-column activities behind the Russian lines. As a result, the Chechen, who numbered 408,000 in 1939, and the 92,000 Ingush lost their identity as autonomous national units and were dispersed or resettled in other parts of the USSR. The territory of the Chechen-Ingush Autonomous SSR was distributed in 1944; the southern mountain strip passed to the Georgian SSR, the western-most section to the North Ossetian Autonomous SSR, an eastern zone to the Dagestan Autonomous SSR, while the bulk of the territory made up part of the newly constituted Groznyy Oblast. A considerable in-flux of Russians, and presumably also Ukrainians, took place after the war in order to resettle the depopulated areas left in the wake of the departure of all or part of the Chechen and Ingush nationalities. In very approximate terms, an immigration of about 200,000 brought the population of the oblast to its present 600,000.

For the economic importance of the oblast the Groznyy oil field is mainly responsible. This region was the second largest producer of oil in the USSR on the eve of the Second World War. The wells are con-centrated in the metropolitan area of Groznyy and in the hill ranges along the Terek-Sunzha watershed. The principal centers are Novo-groznenskiy (to 1944, Oysungur), southeast of Gudermes, Cherno-rech'ye near Groznyy, and Goragorskiy (formerly Gorskiy), east of Malgobek. A 45-mile gas and oil pipe line connects Goragorskiy and Groznyy. Unlike the Baku petroleum, the Groznyy product furnishes high-octane aviation gasoline, much paraffin, but no heavy oils.

The chief agricultural area of the oblast is the plain drained by the Sundzha River, an affluent of the Terek. Among the cereal crops, corn predominates; large areas are under winter wheat and fodder grasses. Garden crops and vineyards also show good results. Hogs and dairy cattle are raised. While agriculture relegates pastoral occupations to the background in the Terek valley, in the mountains and in the dry steppe to the north livestock breeding predominates. In the high alti-tudes Alpine pastures support cattle and goats, while in the poor steppe lands close to the Caspian shores sheep raising is most important. Among the newly introduced crops that have been adapted to the region are cotton and soy beans. Cotton plantations extend along the middle Terek

River to the delta at Kizlyar, where rice has been successfully cultivated in the lower sections and orchards and vineyards can be found in the higher parts of the valley.

The oblast is well served by the eastern sections of the Rostov-Baku main line. The two branches which follow the Terek and Sunzha rivers join at Gudermes. The spur which extended along the lower Terek to Kizlyar has been converted into an important trunk line by the construction during the Second World War of the Kizlyar-Astrakhan' railroad. This line which parallels the northwest coast of the Caspian Sea and passes through semi-desert areas represents the only direct link between Transcaucasia and the Lower Volga Region.

Groznyy, the former capital of the Chechen-Ingush Autonomous SSR and administrative center of the present oblast, is the center of the Groznyy oil fields, of which two sections lie a few miles northwest and southeast of the city, respectively. Pipe lines for crude oil and petroleum products, such as kerosene, lead to Makhach-Kala, Tuapse, and Trudovaya in the Donets Basin. The city has cracking plants and refineries, produces machinery for the petroleum industry, chemicals (sulphuric acid), lumber, and leather goods. There are meat-packing and canning establishments.

Kizlyar, the former center of Kizlyar Okrug, lies on the Terek River at the edge of the Caspian lowland, 46 feet below sea level. It has a large Armenian population. Surrounded by orchards and vineyards, it is known as an important wine-producing community. It is the southern terminus of the new railroad to Astrakhan'.

Gudermes, an important junction on the main Rostov-Baku railroad, has metalworking and fruit and vegetable-processing industries. It was raised to the status of city in 1941, which may be accounted for by the recent development of near-by oil fields.

Dagestan Autonomous Soviet Socialist Republic
Capital, Makhach-Kala ; area, 14,700, population, 900,000

The Dagestan Autonomous SSR lies in the triangle formed by the Greater Caucasus in the south, a spur of the main range in the west, and the Caspian Sea in the east. With the exception of a narrow lowland along the Caspian shore, the region is a complicated system of wild denuded mountain ranges, difficult of access. The name Dagestan itself, a Turkic term meaning mountain country, clearly describes the local relief. Agricultural development in restricted to the foothills and the valleys of the mountain streams flowing toward the Caspian Sea. Although the acreage under cultivation is small because of the physical factors, the warm climate and irrigation render possible the growth of intensive crops, such as subtropical fruits, vineyards, and cotton. Among the chief mineral resources, the republic counts petroleum, natural gas, sulphur, and nonferrous metals. The mountain torrents are potential sources of hydroelectric power and irrigation; the potential of the Sulak River alone has been estimated at 500,000 horsepower.

The national composition of the republic, unlike that of the other autonomous units of the USSR, is exceedingly complex. From antiquity the Dagestan littoral of the Caspian Sea has furnished invasion routes for successive waves of migration from Asia to Europe. Segments of each migration generally remained within the region and moved into the inaccessible mountains to escape the ravages of subsequent migration. As a result of this type of settlement, the mountains have a denser population pattern than the coastal plain. The mountain population of Dagestan includes about thirty different ethnic groups, speaking different, though sometimes related, languages. The principal groups are Avars, Lesghians, Darghins, Laks, and Andi. The Russians, who represent about 15 percent of the population, live mainly in the urban centers and along the shore.

The mountaineers engage chiefly in the raising of livestock, rug weaving, and metal handicrafts. Orchards and vineyards play an important role in the irrigated foothills. Recently cotton has also been introduced and is grown, with the help of irrigation, in the lowlands. Of the grain crops, corn and winter wheat are grown in the irrigated sections, while spring wheat and barley are raised by dry-farming methods. The main channel of the irrigation system, the October Revolution Canal, leads from the Sulak River along the railroad to Makhach-Kala and forms the trunk for countless branches and ramifications. Fisheries are important along the coast, especially north of Makhach-Kala on a long, narrow peninsula; at its tip is Lopatin, the main fishing center.

In addition to the fishing industry, the canning of fruits (mainly apples and cherries) plays an important role in the economy, especially in the mountains. In the lowlands cotton ginning, wine distilling, and flour milling are the main agricultural industries. There are cotton mills at Makhach-Kala and Derbent, and a large glassworks of national renown at Dagestanskiye Ogni [Dagestan fires], just northwest of Derbent. This plant operates on the basis of local quartz deposits and uses near-by methane gas wells as fuel; Glauber salt, another raw material, is brought across the Caspian Sea from Kara-Bogaz-Gol.

In recent years the exploitation of petroleum deposits has made considerable progress. Oil wells have been drilled between Makhach-Kala and Derbent, along the seashore; the main center is the city of Izberbash; other wells are at Kayakent, Achi-Su, and Ulubiyevo. Drilling has also been begun at Talgi, just south of Makhach-Kala. Among the hydroelectric plants that have been developed is the 45,000 kilowatt station at Gergebil', south of Buynaksk.

Makhach-Kala, formerly called Petrovsk-Port, is an important commercial port of the Caspian Sea, trading mainly with Iran and Central Asia in rice, silk, grain, cotton, and petroleum products. At the end of two pipe lines from the Groznyy fields and one from Izberbash, the city is an important petroleum-refining center. It has an aircraft plant, chemical works, and cotton and lumber mills, and produces wine and canned goods (fruits and fish). Many of the heavy industries are located in the adjacent new city of Kaspiysk (in the southeast), so named in 1947, which had been since 1936 a workers' settlement called Dvigatel'stroy [engine construction].

Buynaksk, formerly called Temir-Khan-Shura, lies on a rail branch southwest of Makhach-Kala. A former fortress, it is now a major wine and fruit-canning center and health resort.

Derbent, on the main railroad to Baku, is a center for the oil fields to the northwest. It has metalworks, a nitrogen-fixation plant, cotton and woolen mills, produces wines and canned goods, and is the site of a viticultural research station.

Khasavyurt, on the Groznyy–Makhach-Kala railroad and oil pipe lines, is the center of the cotton-growing area. It has ginning, canning, and wine-making industries and manufactures building materials.

CHAPTER 12

Urals

THE URAL REGION lies astride the Ural Mountains, which form along their watershed the natural frontier between Europe and Asia. It is the most important mining district of the USSR, rich especially in metallic ores, which form the base for a spectacular industrial development. The intensive industrialization of the Urals, which began with the first Five-Year Plan, paid off during the Second World War, when this region became the arsenal of the USSR, supplying the front with tanks, airplanes, arms, and other war materiel. The region covers an area of more than 290,000 square miles.

The Urals are an old range extending about fifteen hundred miles from the Arctic Ocean in the north to the Mugodzhar mountains in the south. The system is formed of a number of parallel ranges, which do not exceed 6,200 feet in height and have an average elevation of 1,600 feet. The formation of the mountains was accompanied by extensive folding and thrusting. Volcanic intrusions accompanied the deformation on the eastern slopes and are responsible for the rich mineralization in that portion of the range. Among the eroding factors, which wore down the range from its original elevation, thought to have once exceeded twelve thousand feet, are the vast body of water which once covered the West Siberian lowland to the east and the continental glacier which scoured the northern section of the range. From north to south the Urals are divided into the northern Urals, north of 61° N lat., the middle Urals, between 61° and 55° N lat., and the southern Urals, south to the Ural River at about 51° N. Farther south are the Mugodzhar mountains, a low outlier of the Urals, rising to 2,125 feet. The highest portion of the northern Urals lies outside the present region in the European North of the Russian SFSR. Its southern section consists of a series of relatively low parallel ranges. This type of structure continues south into the middle Urals, where a greater degree of erosion can, however, be observed in the extreme fragmentation of the ranges. The highest point of the middle Urals is the Konzhakovskiy Kamen', which rises to 5,155 feet and lies at about 60° N. The remainder of this section of the system consists of mere hills, and it is here that all rail lines cross the Urals from west to east. South of 55° N, in the southern Urals, the ranges are again longer and higher and oriented generally south and southwest. They are frequently cut by deep river valleys. Numerous limestone outcrops are associated with the formation of karst relief. The highest elevation in this part of the range is Yaman-Tau (5,375 feet).

Iron ore is the principal mineral resource. The richest deposits are in the middle and southern Urals, on the eastern slopes. The mountains Blagodat' and Vysokaya, in the middle Urals, and Magnitnaya, in the southern Urals, consist entirely of magnetite formations. Side by side with iron ore, important alloys such as manganese, nickel, and tungsten are also mined. On the western and eastern slopes are extensive copper deposits, with combinations of zinc, lead, silver, and gold. Platinum and gold are found mainly in placers and, to a much lesser extent, in lode deposits. Also of importance are bauxite, asbestos, and large potash deposits, the latter an important chemical raw material mined near Solikamsk. Industrial salt is available in abundance in the south at Sol'-Iletsk. The Urals have long been known for their rich supplies of precious and semiprecious stones, chiefly emerald, chrysoberyl, topaz, and amethyst. Coal is mined on the western slope at Kizel and on the eastern at Yegorshino and Chelyabinsk. In recent years oil fields have been developed in the western foothills along the Chusovaya River in the north and near Ishimbay in the south.

To the west of the Ural Mountains is a hilly plain which rises gradually toward the east and forms the Ufa Plateau east of the Kama and the Belaya rivers. The surface of this area is deeply dissected by wide river valleys and ravines. In the south lies the upland Obshchiy Syrt, which ends in cliff-like formations on the Caspian lowland. The Kama River, which traverses the region west of the Urals from north to south, receives the Chusovaya and the Belaya (with its affluent, the Ufa). Other important rivers on the west slopes of the Urals are the Pechora, in the north, and the Ural River, in the south. In the east, the Urals give rise to numerous left affluents of the Tobol River, including the Iset' and its tributary the Miass, the Tura, and the Tavda. Most of these rivers have a rapid course and are navigable in their upper reaches only at high water. Some rivers on the western slopes have cut a course through resistant rock formations, forming high, overhanging cliffs along their

URALS

(Central Urals are shown in detail on p. 241.)

banks. The level plain east of the Urals abounds in lakes, deep fresh-water lakes in the immediate vicinity of the Ural Mountains and shallow salt lakes farther east, all of which are vestiges of the vast sea which once washed the eastern slopes of the mountains.

The climate of the Urals is the most continental of the European USSR. The winters are severe and of long duration (six months in the north, five months in the south); the average January temperature is like that in the lower Pechora basin or on Novaya Zemlya. In spite of the great latitudinal extent of the Urals, the winters are generally severe throughout the region; only in the middle section do prevailing westerly winds have a tempering influence. Frosts of 0° F are common throughout the entire range, and even descend to —20° F in the north-east. The extremely low temperatures are relatively bearable, thanks to calm air conditions; strong winds accompanied by severe blizzards occur only in the Chkalov steppes to the south. True to the continental climate pattern, the summers are hot. Even in the north, average July temperatures approximate those of the southern Ukraine. In the windy southern steppes stifling southeasterlies often cause droughts and burn the grain crops. Except for the middle Urals, the region receives little precipitation, least of all in the southwestern section, influenced by the dry Central Asian climate.

The two main vegetation zones, forested podsols in the north and black-earth steppes in the south, are separated by a narrow wooded steppe belt. Dense forests, interrupted here and there by meadows and cultivated land, cover the entire north and extend far to the south along the Ural Mountains and their foothills. Coniferous types, such as pine, fir, and larch, prevail throughout this section; in the extreme north, cedar predominates. In the middle Urals, the forests have been con-siderably cleared, and birch and aspen replace the evergreen types. In the southwestern foothills are mixed forests, where conifers mingle with deciduous types, including elm, oak, maple, and linden. In the wooded steppe only deciduous trees are found. The southern zone represented a virgin feathergrass steppe until recently; now cultivated land covers vast stretches between the numerous lakes and salt flats, which increase in numbers toward Siberia in the east.

The Urals are sparsely populated. Of all the geographical regions of the European USSR, its density (45 per square mile) surpasses only that of the European North. Although the northern mining areas of the Urals were settled at an earlier time, the southern agricultural section now shows a larger population. Of the indigenous national groups of the Urals, the Bashkirs (most numerous group), the Tatars, the Udmurts, and the Komi-Permyaks constitute now only one fourth of the total population. The remainder is largely made up of Russians, with a small number of Ukrainians. Administratively, the Urals include the oblasts of Sverdlovsk in the northeast, Molotov in the northwest, Chelyabinsk in the east, and Chkalov in the south. The Bashkir and Udmurt Autonomous SSR's lie on the western slopes and foothills of the Ural Mountains.

Under the Soviet regime, great metallurgical plants have provided the base for heavy industry. The largest works operate at Nizhniy Tagil, Sverdlovsk, and Magnitogorsk. Old plants at Zlatoust, Beloretsk, and elsewhere have been modernized and expanded. Among the new industries are nonferrous metal smelters, machinery plants, car-building works (Nizhniy Tagil), locomotive works (Orsk), a tractor plant (Chelyabinsk), shipyards (Molotov), and so forth. In addition to the metalworking industries, there is in the Urals a large chemical plant at Berezniki, based on the Solikamsk potash deposits. For its power resources, the region has to rely on its own meager coal (Kizel) and lignite (in the area of Chelyabinsk) deposits and on good coking coal brought from the Karaganda fields and, to a lesser extent, from the Kuzbas.

Agriculture is important in Chelyabinsk Oblast, where grains are the main crops, and in the Bashkir Autonomous SSR, where such industrial crops as flax, hemp, and sunflowers are grown in addition to the basic grains. Spring wheat and melon crops prevail in dry Chkalov Oblast, which is also the main sheep-raising and horse-raising area. Apiculture is an important rural occupation.

Rail lines are the most important means of transportation of the Ural Mountains. The majority of the lines link the European USSR with Siberia and cross the Urals from west to east. The trunk routes come from Leningrad to Sverdlovsk, and from Moscow to Sverdlovsk and Chelyabinsk. On the Siberian side, two lines, from Sverdlovsk and Chelyabinsk, join at Omsk to form the Trans-Siberian Railroad. Of much less importance are the few navigable rivers on both sides of the range. The Kama River is the main navigation route and joins the region with the Volga and the central part of the European USSR. On the eastern slopes, the river network drains into the Irtysh-Ob' system in Western Siberia.

Sverdlovsk Oblast
Capital, Sverdlovsk ; area, 74,600, population, 3,000,000

Sverdlovsk Oblast is situated in the forested zone on the eastern (Siberian) slopes of the middle Urals. It is drained by the nonnavigable left affluents of the Tobol—the Iset', the Tura, and the Tavda rivers.

While Molotov Oblast has the distinction of having been the earliest industrialized section of the Urals, Sverdlovsk Oblast is noted for its remarkably rapid development. In this respect, it is one of the most progressive regions of the USSR. The trend was still further emphasized during the Second World War, when the population increased by 20 percent and new cities and workers' settlements sprang up throughout the area.

The mineral resources are one of the chief assets of the oblast and constitute a major factor in its development. They are notable not only for their abundance but also for the great variety ; all types of minerals found within the Urals are available in this one region. There are ferrous and nonferrous metals, gold and platinum, precious stones, and a variety of building materials.

Iron ore is found in four main locations. Foremost is the Nizhniy-Tagil and Kushva district, where magnetite and hematite are mined at the foot of Vysokaya Mountain, west of Nizhniy Tagil, at Lebyazh'ye Mountain, near by, and at Blagodat' Mountain, east of Kushva. Other iron deposits are in the areas of Alapayevsk (mine at Zyryanovskiy, south of the city), Serov, and Ivdel'. Iron is mined at Rudnichnyy, west of Serov, at Sama, north of Serov, at Ivdel', and in the far north at the headwaters of the Sos'va River, in the Severnyy Rudnik [northern mine] No. 3. Manganese also occurs in the Serov-Ivdel' district and is obtained at Polunochnoye, north of Ivdel', the northernmost rail terminus of the oblast, and at Marsyaty, north of Serov.

Nonferrous metals are represented mainly by copper and its associated zinc ores. The chief ore veins run from north to south and are located near Krasnoural'sk and at the important Kirovgrad site ; copper is mined at Levikha and Karpushikha, northwest of Kirovgrad, and at Belorechka in the south. On the northern outskirts of Sverdlovsk, copper is mined at Verkhnyaya Pyshma ; other mines are at Degtyarka, southeast of Revda.

During the Second World War the most extensive bauxite deposits of the USSR were opened for development on a large scale northwest of Serov. The major mines are located in the vicinity of the new city of Severoural'sk, at Pokrovsk-Ural'skiy, Cheremukhovo, and Kal'ya, and are known as the Krasnaya Shapochka [red cap] mines. Bauxite is also mined at Kamensk-Ural'skiy, and there are deposits near Alapayevsk and in the far north at Severnyy Rudnik No. 3.

In addition to the lignite mines of Karpinsk, new deposits were developed during the Second World War at Volchanka, between Severoural'sk and Krasnotur'insk. Anthracite is mined in the Yegorshino deposits at the city of Artemovskiy, northeast of Sverdlovsk, and in a belt extending southward past Altynay to the Sukhoy Log-Bogdanovich district.

Platinum production of the USSR is derived largely from ultrabasic rocks found in the upper reaches of the Tura River, north of Nizhniy Tagil. The metal is closely associated with gold in this area, which centers on Is; the principal mines are Artel'nyy, northwest of Is, Valerianovsk (southwest), Kos'ya (west), Malomal'sk (southeast), and Kytlym (north). Another gold and platinum area is at Visim and Uralets, southwest of Nizhniy Tagil.

Asbestos is produced in a number of localities, including the city of Asbest, east of Sverdlovsk, where exploitation began about 1890 in serpentinized peridotite formations. Smaller production centers are Novoasbest, southeast of Nizhniy Tagil, and Asbestovskiy, southwest of Alapayevsk. Gems and semiprecious stones, including emerald, beryl, amethyst, topaz, and malachite, occur in deposits of world-wide importance. Emerald mines gave their name to the center of Izumrud, northwest of Asbest.

Ferrous and nonferrous metallurgy and the associated machinery industry are the chief branches of the heavy industry in this region. The major metallurgical center is Nizhniy Tagil, which is becoming as important a producer as Magnitogorsk. There are numerous smaller metallurgical centers operating on a charcoal basis, including Serov, Alapayevsk, Pervoural'sk, Verkhnyaya Salda, Nizhnyaya Salda, Kushva, Nizhniye Sergi, and Krasnogvardeyskiy, east of Artemovskiy. These plants produce the full cycle of metallurgical products or specialize in the output of pig iron or rolled steel.

The principal copper-smelting centers are Krasnoural'sk, Kirovgrad, and Revda, the latter for the Degtyarka mines. Copper is refined electrolytically at Verkhnyaya Pyshma. A new nickel refinery was established at Rezh during the Second World War, and an aluminum works at Krasnotur'insk.

The main machinery-construction center is Sverdlovsk, which specializes in the output of mining and metallurgical machines. Railway rolling stock is manufactured at Nizhniy Tagil, and steel bridges at Verkhnyaya Salda. The production of refractory materials and silicate bricks is associated with most of the iron and steel centers, and cement is milled at Sukhoy Log and Tsementnyy, between Nev'yansk and Krasnoural'sk.

One of the main branches of the economy is the lumber industry. Novaya Lyalya is a major paper-making center, near which there are woodworking plants, at Lobva (north), and sawmills, at Verkhotur'ye (south). Other major lumber centers engaged in the processing industries are located in the eastern portion of the oblast. Tavda, at the end of a long rail branch from Sverdlovsk, produces veneers, furniture, skis, and has shipyards and railroad repair works. Turinsk, on the railroad west of Tavda, is one of the oldest cities of the Urals, dating from 1600, it acquired new match and paper industries during the postwar period. Small centers in the vicinity of the metallurgical plants specialize in the distillation of wood and the production of charcoal.

The oblast is well served by a rail network connecting all the major centers. The main north-south Sverdlovsk-Kushva-Serov line was extended during the Second World War to the newly developed Ivdel'-Polunochnoye district. In order to ease the heavy load of this main trunk, the Sos'va-Alapayevsk section was constructed at the end of the war, which provides a second rail link between the northern and the southern sections of the oblast. The main export items are heavy machinery, railway cars, asbestos, gold, platinum, and nonferrous metals.

In the mining districts agriculture is restricted to the raising of truck produce and dairy cattle. It is developed to the greatest extent in the southeast, near Irbit, where the main crops are grains, including some wheat, and potatoes. The northern areas are densely forested, and agriculture is possible only in isolated tracts.

Sverdlovsk (formerly Yekaterinburg) is a seven-way railway center on the Iset' River, near the southern limits of the oblast. Its population increased from 425,000 in 1939 to 600,000 in 1945. It forms the economic and cultural hub of the entire Urals Region, and the headquarters of the metallurgical and nonferrous industries. Its heavy machinery industry (*Uralmash*) produces mining, chemical, drilling, and

CENTRAL URALS

metallurgical machinery for the region. Electrical equipment is manufactured from metal produced at the local Verkh-Iset' mill, which produces transformer steels, the copper works of Verkhnyaya Pyshma, the Sredneural'sk copper works at Revda. It produces radio and television apparatus, aircraft motors, machine tools, ball bearings, chemicals, wood pulp and paper, clothing, and food products.

Among the principal satellite cities located in the vicinity of Sverdlovsk are Berezovskiy (northeast), the site of gold and tungsten mines, the electrolytic copper-refining center Verkhnyaya Pyshma (north), and the power center Sredneural'sk (northwest), site of a 100,000 kilowatt station. In an outer ring, within thirty miles of the center of Sverdlovsk, are the asbestos mines of Asbest (northeast), the steel-milling and chemical (chromite basis) plants of Pervoural'sk and the Sredneural'sk copper works of Revda (for the Degtyarka mines) in the west, and the new metallurgical and chemical works of Polevskoy (southwest), which are based on local cryolite and copper deposits and produce tinplate metal in the Severskiy steel mill.

Nizhniy Tagil, the second largest industrial center of the oblast, lies in the center of an important iron-mining district. Its population was 250,000 in 1948. It has an old metallurgical plant and a new steel mill, completed during the Second World War, which is said to be approaching the size of Magnitogorsk. The railway-car works lie in the eastern outskirts. There are coking and chemical plants, woodworking, ceramic, and food industries. Iron is mined at the foot of Vysokaya Mountain, in the southwestern suburbs. Eastward lies the metallurgical and steel-construction city of Verkhnyaya Salda, and to the north, the satellite iron center of Kushva. The copper cities of Kirovgrad and Krasnoural'sk are south and north of Nizhniy Tagil.

A new major industrial region is developing in the northern part of the oblast, in the area of Serov, Karpinsk, and Ivdel'. Serov, called Nadezhdinsk until 1939, and briefly Kabakovsk, is a steel-milling center, operating with charcoal and coke. It produces steel rails and other steel products, lumber, and typewriters. Northwest of Serov lies the lignite mining center of Karpinsk, formerly called Bogoslovsk and, until 1941, Ugol'nyy. Near by are the new aluminum works of Krasnotur'insk (until 1944, Tur'inskiy), which operate on the basis of the bauxite mines of Severoural'sk (until 1944, Petropavlovskiy) to the north and the newly discovered coal of Volchanka, halfway between the two cities. Typical war-time developments, Krasnotur'insk has a population of 45,000, and Severoural'sk, 30,000.

Far north of Serov, halfway to the northern limits of Sverdlovsk Oblast, is the new city Ivdel', the northernmost industrial center of the oblast. It produces lumber and motorcycles and is the center for an important manganese-mining region, having mines at Polunochnoye (north).

Alapayevsk, a steel-milling center based on charcoal, is also developing into a major industrial city. Near-by bauxite deposits and the recent completion of a hydroelectric plant may lay the basis for an aluminum industry. Asbestos works are at Asbestovskiy in the southwest. Hematite and copper ores are mined near by. The construction of the Sos'va-Alapayevsk railroad opened a direct route to the new industrial centers of the northern Urals.

Other important cities are the southern agricultural centers of Krasnoufimsk (southwest), Kamyshlov and Irbit (southeast), which have flour, leather, and metalworking industries, and the aluminum center Kamensk-Ural'skiy, with pipe foundry and cement mill, which was transferred from Chelyabinsk Oblast in 1943.

Molotov Oblast
Capital, Molotov; area, 65,900, population, 2,250,000

Molotov Oblast is located on the western slopes of the middle Urals and is drained by the Kama and its affluents, the Vishera and the Chusovaya rivers. Coniferous forests cover the northern section, fir and pine stands predominating, while in the southern foothills deciduous types, such as oak, linden, and maple, are encountered, trees which do not occur on the Siberian side of the mountains. Russians form the major part of the population. The Komi-Permyaks, who are a Finno-Ugric ethnic group related to the Komi people adjoining in the north, are constituted into a national okrug in the northwestern portion of the oblast. Bashkirs, Tatars, and Udmurts form minorities in the southern and the southwestern boundary belts.

The coal reserves of the region have been estimated at 4.8 billion tons. The strata are 5–7 feet thick and lie at a depth of 1,600–2,000 feet. This is the only coal found in the Urals that is suitable for coking. However, because of a high sulphur and ash content, it is usually mixed with high-grade coking coal from the Kuznetsk Basin or from Karaganda.

It is also extensively used alone as a fuel and in the chemical and ferroalloy industries. The deposits extend north and south along the foothills of the Urals for a distance of 70 miles and reappear again east and
southeast of Chusovoy. The chief mining centers is Kizel, with its satellite towns, which developed during the Second World War: Kospash,
Rudnichnyy, and Shakhta. South of Kizel lies the coal center of Polovinka, which became a city in 1946 and incorporated the southwestern
mining suburb Voroshilovskiy. Further on is Gubakha, the second largest coal city of the oblast, which became a city in 1941, when it absorbed the workers' settlement Krzhizhanovsk, on the bank of Kos'va
River. Gubakha has a 100,000 kilowatt power plant and extensive coking installations. South of Gubakha, along the railroad to Chusovoy,
lie the coal towns Nagornskiy (which developed during the Second
World War), Us'va (an older mine), and the city of Gremyachinsk (at
Baskaya station; another war-time development). Prospecting for new
coal-mining sites is actively being pursued. The search is not restricted
to the seams of the Kizel-Gubakha district only, but is carried on also
in the deposits east of Chusovoy, where on the railroad, a mine was
opened in 1943, at Skal'nyy station.

Petroleum is a local fuel resource of more recent date than coal. The
first strike took place accidentally in 1929 while geologists were drilling for potash salts at Verkhne-Chusovskiye Gorodki, on the Chusovaya,
between Molotov and Chusovoy. The field did not become a high producer, and although oil continues to be recovered and refined at a local
cracking plant, the operations at Verkhne-Chusovskiye Gorodki remain at a small scale. During the 1930's, oil-bearing strata were also
reached at Krasnokamsk, on the Kama River, west of Molotov, at the
northern edge of what was to be called the "Second Baku." Persistent
drilling for high-grade Devonian was crowned with success during the
Second World War, when oil was discovered at Severokamsk, some ten
miles northwest of Krasnokamsk.

Among the most important mineral assets of the oblast are the
vast deposits of common salt and potash and magnesium salts in the
Solikamsk-Berezniki area, on the Kama River. The common salt deposits had been known and exploited in the fifteenth century by the
Stroganov family, a rich trading group that financed the raids of
Yermak into Siberia. The far more valuable potassium and magnesium
salts, however, were not found until 1925. They are associated with
bromine and such rare earths as cesium and rubidium. The potassium

salt deposits are estimated at 18 billion tons. About 1.5 million tons are secured yearly at Solikamsk and sent south to Berezniki, where a large-scale chemical industry has been developed recently.

Metallurgical industry is represented in Molotov Oblast by the two mills of Chusovoy and Lys'va, which date from the eighteenth century and have been modernized in the Soviet regime. Chusovoy has a full production cycle, while Lys'va, just south of Chusovoy, produces only steel. A number of smaller metallurgical plants, engaging in the milling of pig iron or steel on a charcoal basis, include Pashiya and Teplaya Gora (iron), east of Chusovoy, Nytva (steel), southwest of Krasnokamsk, and Dobryanka and Chermoz (steel), on the Kama north of Molotov. Chromite is mined and used in a chemical plant at Sarany, on the railroad east of Chusovoy. The products of the metallurgical industry are exported in the form of sheet metal or supply the many machinery industries at Molotov and the smaller centers of Kungur (cement mixers), Ocher, and Pavlovskiy, south of Vereshchagino, and Yugo-Kamskiy (agricultural implements), east of Okhansk.

Lumber plays an important role in the economy and furnishes raw material for the paper mills of Krasnovishersk, the northernmost industrial town of the oblast, which supplies the Moscow newspaper Izvestia with newsprint, and the paper and pulp mills of Krasnokamsk and Severnyy Kommunar, northwest of Vereshchagino. Other important lumber-processing centers are Lyamino, near Chusovoy, and Vsevolodo-Vil'va, north of Kizel, which specialize in the production of charcoal, and Levshino, a northeastern suburb of Molotov, which produces prefabricated houses. Cement is milled at Pashiya, and there are glassworks at Sylva, east of Molotov, and at Sars, in the extreme southeast of the oblast.

Agriculture is important mainly in the southwest, which has been largely cleared of forests. The chief crops are grains (wheat, rye, and oats), flax, potatoes, and forage plants, including large areas under clover in the vicinity of Kungur, where clover seed is produced. In the mountainous sections truck and dairy farming are the main activities. In addition to dairy cattle, hogs are also raised in the suburban zones.

Of the two rail lines which pass through the oblast from west to east, the Kirov-Molotov-Kushva line is of greatest importance. From it a branch leads north to the Kizel-Gubakha coal district and the Solikamsk-Berezniki potash area, while other lines connect it directly with Sverdlovsk. For the northern part of the oblast, which abounds in unworked timber and mineral deposits, two rail projects are of the greatest significance. One involves a link between Solikamsk, the present northern terminus, and the North Pechora Railroad, completed in 1942. Such a rail connection would render possible the shipment of Vorkuta coking coal to the Ural metallurgical centers, thus reducing by as much as one half the distance over which coal is hauled at present from the Kuzbas or the Karaganda fields. A related project contemplates the construction of a northern Trans-Ural railroad, which would cross the mountains in the area of the upper Vishera River. Such a line would establish a connection between the opposite slopes of the northern Urals, of which the eastern slope in the Serov-Ivdel' area of Sverdlovsk Oblast is already making great strides in its economic development. The northern Trans-Ural line would, furthermore, favor the establishment of a new metallurgical base on the titanium-vanadium deposits of the upper Vishera River. The output of the Krasnovishersk paper mill, which is limited at the present time, due to its lack of proper transportation facilities, would also be greatly enhanced. Both rail projects, which according to all indications should be realized in a future Five-Year Plan, would lay the foundation of a great new industrial area in the untouched wilderness of the northern Urals.

It is also in the northern section of Molotov Oblast that the tapping of the waters of the Pechora River is due to take place in the near future. This project, which plays a vital role in the Great Volga scheme, involves the damming of the Pechora River in its upper reaches, the formation of a vast reservoir, and the consequent diversion of the northern waters to the Volga via the Kama River. The principal export products of the oblast are chemical fertilizers, lumber, paper, iron and steel, metal goods, and river vessels.

Molotov, called Perm' until 1940, was formed on the right bank of the Kama River by the union of the old city Perm' with the industrial suburb Motovilikha, later called Molotovo. The city now extends about fifteen miles along the banks of the river. At the junction of rail lines, it is an important transfer center for rail and river traffic. Its important machine construction industries produce machine tools, floating cranes, telephone apparatus, and motors. There are large shipyards and an aircraft factory. The chemical industry produces superphosphates, on the basis of phosphate brought on the Kama River from the Rudnichnyy (Kirov Oblast) mines, sulphuric acid, and electrolytic copper. Its lumber mills (prefabricated houses at Levshino, a northeastern suburb) and food industries are important. On the Kama River, just above the city, the Kama hydroelectric plant is under construction as part of the Great Volga scheme. It will have the second largest reservoir of the USSR, an area of 600 square miles.

Berezniki, in the salt district on the Kama River, produces salt from brine pumped from a depth of 250–650 feet. It has a great chemical industry, powered by a 100,000 kilowatt station, producing nitrate, potassium, and phosphate fertilizers, sulphuric acid, and explosives. At the site of the saltworks on the opposite side of the Kama River, Usol'ye, formerly part of Berezniki, was constituted as a separate city in 1940.

Solikamsk, north of Berezniki, has shipyards and paper and pulp mills in addition to its important salt, potash, and magnesium salt mines. Many of its industries are located at Borovsk, a northwestern suburban city, constituted in 1949.

Krasnokamsk, the paper-milling center in the oil fields west of Molotov, also produces agricultural machines and chemicals (ethyl alcohol). Its oil refinery receives the crude product via an 11-mile pipe line from Severokamsk in the northwest. Other near-by oil fields are at Strelka and Mayskiy. The industries are supplied by a 100,000 kilowatt power plant.

Kungur is a leather center on the Molotov-Sverdlovsk railroad. It has sawmills, a clothing industry, and produces cement mixers.

Other industrial centers are the coal cities, Kizel, Kospash, Gubakha, Gremyachinsk, and Polovinka, and the two major metallurgical sites, Chusovoy and Lys'va.

THE KOMI-PERMYAK NATIONAL OKRUG (capital, Kudymkar; area, 12,-000, population, 200,000) lies in the northwestern section of Molotov Oblast. With the exception of the Nenets National Okrug, it is the only such unit in the European USSR. It was formed as an ordinary administrative okrug in 1925 and was reorganized as a national okrug in 1929. The titular ethnic group is of Finno-Ugric stock and related to the Komi people in the north. It represents 70 percent of the total population.

Agriculture is important in the southern part of the okrug, where grains (mainly rye and oats), flax, vegetables, and potatoes are raised. Cattle is bred for meat and milk production. In the northern forests, which cover 75 percent of the total area, lumbering is the chief activity.

Industries, such as flax retting and flour milling, depend upon the agricultural production.

Kudymkar has linen and food industries. It is linked by a highway with Mendeleyevo station on the Molotov-Kirov railroad, which is the only route of access to the okrug.

Chelyabinsk Oblast
Capital, Chelyabinsk; area, 33,900, population, 2,100,000

Chelyabinsk Oblast is situated on the eastern (Siberian) slopes of the southern Urals, between Chkalov Oblast in the south and Sverdlovsk Oblast in the north. With the exception of a winding panhandle that crosses the crest of the mountains to the basin of the Ufa River, the region is drained in the southwest, near Magnitogorsk and Verkhne-Ural'sk, by the Ural River and in the remaining portion by affluents of the Tobol, the Miass and the Uy rivers being the most important. The highest precipitation (up to 28 inches annually) occurs on the western slopes of the Urals, in the area of Zlatoust. The eastern slope, which is on the leeward of the humid westerly winds, receives much less precipitation, especially south of Verkhne-Ural'sk where trees are almost totally absent.

Iron ore is the chief mineral resource of the region. The principal sites are Magnitnaya Mountain, at Magnitogorsk, with reserves of more than 450 million tons, Bakal and the mining town of Rudnichnyy to the south, which produce some of the purest high-grade ore of the USSR, and the titaniferous iron mines of Magnitka, east of Kusa. The total reserves of iron ore in Chelyabinsk Oblast amount to about one half the Ural iron resources. Most of the ore is of high quality and is concentrated in compact deposits. With the near-by ferroalloy deposits (manganese, chrome, nickel, tungsten), they are an excellent combination for specialization in high-grade steel production.

Copper-zinc ores are smelted at Karabash and Kyshtym, nickel at Verkhniy Ufaley, bauxite is mined at Balkany, east of Magnitogorsk, and there are gold mines and placers near Miass and Plast. Of great value for the metallurgical industries of the region are flux materials (dolomite and limestone) and refractory clays and magnesite; the latter is mined chiefly at Satka.

The oblast lacks coking coal, but is amply supplied with peat and lignite, suitable as fuel. The main lignite mining centers are Kopeysk, Korkino, and Yemanzhelinka. Anthracite is mined at Kartaly and Bredy, along the railroad to Orsk. These coal deposits represent an important fuel base not only for Chelyabinsk Oblast itself but also for adjoining Sverdlovsk Oblast, which is deficient in coal resources in its southern part.

The enterprises engaged in heavy industry, the principal economic activity of the region, include small steel mills of pre-Soviet origin, which have since been reconstructed and modernized, a number of machine construction and metalworking centers gravitating around these metallurgical plants, and finally the modern large-scale metallurgy and machine construction of such centers as Chelyabinsk and Magnitogorsk. Most of the small steel mills and associated industrial centers lie in the crooked arm of land jutting westward into the Bashkir Autonomous SSR. There is Asha, whose charcoal-fed steel mill supplies metal to the satellite cities Min'yar, in the northeast, and Sim (agricultural implements), in the southeast. The metalworks of Kropachevo, farther east, are also supplied by the Asha steel foundry. In the southern section of the panhandle lies the metallurgical plant of Katav-Ivanovsk, with cement and quartzite works, which supplies the tramway-construction plant of Ust'-Katav, to the north, and the metalworks of Yuryuzan', to the northeast. At the base of the western bulge lies the major metallurgical center Zlatoust. Northwest of Zlatoust is the machinery-building city Kusa, with the titanium and vanadium-bearing iron ore mines of Magnitka, east of Zlatoust. Southwest of Zlatoust are the ironworks, chemical industry, and magnesite plant of Satka, and the Bakal iron mines are a few miles beyond. In the extreme northwestern section of the oblast is the machine-construction city Nyazepetrovsk, and in the north, the metalworking center Kasli, which produces agricultural machinery and specializes in the production of artistic iron casting. Most of these metalworks are not entirely dependent on the production of near-by metallurgical centers, but frequently supply an important part of their steel needs in their own blast furnaces and foundries.

In addition to the large metallurgical and machinery centers of Magnitogorsk and Chelyabinsk, the copper smelters of Karabash and Kyshtym, the nickel refinery of Verkhniy Ufaley, and the zinc works of Chelyabinsk amply provide the oblast with nonferrous metallurgy.

As part of the Ural-Kuzbas exchange, the region supplies iron ore to the Kuznetsk Basin metallurgical mills, sends high-grade steels and ferroalloys to the neighboring regions, as well as to the Volga Region and the European Center, exports tractors and other agricultural implements to Western Siberia and Kazakhstan, and refractory materials, mainly magnesite, to the entire Union.

Until 1943 Chelyabinsk Oblast had the most extensive arable area of any section of the Urals and the greatest acreage under cultivation. In that year, however, the easternmost portion, having the major grain and cattle surplus of the oblast, was separated from Chelyabinsk and formed the new, largely agricultural, Kurgan Oblast, which is included in the natural division of Western Siberia. In the present remnant agricultural production is important only in the eastern belt, in the vicinity of Troitsk. Elsewhere dairy farming and the growing of truck produce for the large urban population predominate.

Chelyabinsk, which increased from 273,000 in 1939 to nearly 400,000 in 1945, lies at an important rail hub on the Miass River. With the construction of the Trans-Siberian Railroad in the 1890's, Chelyabinsk replaced the older Tyumen' as the "gateway to Siberia." Thanks to its excellent location on major transportation routes, the level terrain, and the abundance of fuel (lignite) and water, the former town, which was mainly noted for its flour mills, developed into the second largest industrial center on the eastern slopes of the Urals. The creation of nonferrous and high-grade ferrous metallurgy, of a machinery and chemical industry during the prewar Five-Year Plans, by 1939 raised the population $4\frac{1}{2}$ times higher than the 1926 return. The role of the Urals in the Second World War gave the city added impetus. The principal enterprises are a giant tractor plant, ferroalloy works, machine-tool plants, zinc works, cement mill, chemical plants (varnishes, sulphuric acid), aircraft factories. In 1943 a new metallurgical plant was completed, on the basis of Bakal iron ore and Kuznetsk coke. In the same year Chelyabinsk became a city subordinated directly to the Russian SFSR administration. The 150,000 kilowatt power station, which not only moves the local industries but also supplies Zlatoust, Miass, and Sverdlovsk via high-voltage lines, is based on the important lignite deposits in the immediate vicinity of the city. The chief mining centers are the cities Kopeysk (including the suburb Gornyak), southeast of Chelyabinsk, and Korkino (with near-by Yemanzhelinka), south of Chelyabinsk.

Magnitogorsk is the prototype of the new Soviet industrial center. Founded in 1931, on the left bank of the Ural River, at the west foot of Magnitnaya Mountain, and named for its rich magnetite deposits, the city developed in a few years into the major metallurgical center of the USSR. Its population, which was 146,000 in 1939, is approaching 270,000 during the postwar period; its area has increased from 17 square miles to 28 square miles because of the expansion of its industries and the growth of its right-bank section to a population of 30,000. Its development will be speeded further when the completion of the western section of the South Siberian Railroad provides a direct western outlet for its products. The iron mines, which are located east of the city, provide the basis for the vast metallurgical complex of six blast furnaces (two more scheduled for completion by 1950), 22 open-hearth furnaces (with four more under construction), eight coke batteries (two more by 1950), steel rolling mills, sulphide works, and plants producing parts for the auto, tractor, and railway-car industries. A large reservoir on the Ural River provides the water supply and a lignite-fed 100,000 kilowatt plant is the main power source.

Zlatoust, the third industrial center of the oblast, lies at the point where the Ay River, an affluent of the Ufa, breaks through the Ural Mountains, on a highway and the Kuybyshev-Chelyabinsk railroad. An old metallurgical center, its modernized plant (based on Bakal iron ore) produces special steels for the automobile and ball-bearings industries. It has railway-car shops and metal construction works, and produces chemicals and instruments.

Miass, an old machinery center southeast of Zlatoust on the railroad to Chelyabinsk, gained prominence during the Second World War with the construction of an automobile plant (the first in the Urals) in the suburb of Oktyabr'skiy.

The copper-smelting and mining center of Karabash is linked by a rail spur with Kyshtym, which produces electrolytic copper, steel, dynamite, and nitrochemicals. Northwest of Kyshtym, on the railroad to Sverdlovsk, lies the nickel center of Verkhniy Ufaley, with ironworks and a wood-distillation industry.

Troitsk, a rail junction south of Chelyabinsk, is a typical steppe city with an important agricultural industry, including tanning, wool milling, flour milling, and meat packing.

Plast, a new city, formed in 1940, is a mining and metallurgical center southwest of Chelyabinsk on the site of gold and arsenic deposits.

Udmurt Autonomous Soviet Socialist Republic
Capital, Izhevsk; area, 16,200, population, 1,200,000

The Udmurt Autonomous SSR lies between the Kama River in the southeast and the Vyatka in the northwest. Only short stretches of the two river valleys, which are inhabited mainly by Russians, fall within the limits of the republic, the bulk of the territory lies along the watershed where the Udmurts sought refuge at the time of Russian colonization. The northeastern portion of the republic lies within the area of the Vyatka Uval, a low outlier of the Ural Mountains. The remainder is a lowland drained by the Cheptsa and Kil'mez' rivers, two affluents of the Vyatka. These rivers play an important role in the flotage of lumber, one of the main resources of the republic. Forests cover about 40 percent of the area, fir constituting the most extensive stands. With the exception of the southern portion, where the wooded steppe prevails, the Udmurt Autonomous SSR lies in the forest zone.

About 50 percent of the population belong to the Udmurt ethnic group of the Finno-Ugric stock. Of the remainder more than 40 percent are Russians and the rest mainly Tatars and Bashkirs. The Udmurts were formerly known as the Votyaks. They were first constituted into an autonomous oblast in 1920, and were raised to the status of autonomous republic in 1934.

Heavy industry is represented in the republic by the metallurgical works of Izhevsk, which is one of the oldest in the Urals. It was reconstructed after the Revolution, and operates on the basis of iron ore from the Ural Mountains, which is shipped mainly along the Kama River. The plant specializes in high-quality steels used in the manufacture of machine tools, motorcycles, and other machinery. Votkinsk is another machinery center which produces its own steel. Kambarka, in the extreme southeast of the republic, makes farm wagons and carts; northwest of the city, at Butysh, on the Kama River, ship repair yards are in operation. Other industrial raw materials are peat, which is worked at Uva, a town west of Izhevsk, with which it is linked by a narrow-gauge railroad, and quartz, which furnishes a basis for glass making at Sergiyevskiy, on the new north-south railroad, and Valamaz, to the west. Mozhga and Izhevsk are the main lumber-milling centers.

In the northern section of the republic, along the Cheptsa River, flax is the main agricultural crop; it supplies the linen mill of Glazov. The southern agricultural area specializes in the cultivation of potatoes, rye, and oats, and serves as the main grain-supply area of the republic. Truck produce is grown in the urban belt of Izhevsk and Votkinsk.

The republic is crossed by two major east-west railways: the Kirov-Molotov line in the north and the Kazan'-Sverdlovsk line in the south.

During the Second World War the two lines were connected by the Izhevsk-Balezino north-south railroad.

Izhevsk is an important industrial center on the new connecting railroad. The products of its steel mill and rolling mill are used in the manufacture of agricultural implements, small arms, lathes, and motorcycles. Its population increased from 175,000 in 1939 to over 200,000 in 1945.

Votkinsk, so named for the former designation of the Udmurts, is connected by a rail spur with Izhevsk. It is the second metallurgical and machinery center of the republic, with steel foundries, munition and metalworks, and an aircraft factory.

Sarapul, on the Kama River, is a leather-goods center, and the lumber-milling city Mozhga (formerly variously known as Syuginskiy and Krasnyy) produces wood-distillation products and glass.

Bashkir Autonomous Soviet Socialist Republic
Capital, Ufa; area, 55,400, population, 3,000,000

The Bashkir Autonomous SSR occupies nearly the entire basin of the Belaya River, a left affluent of the Kama. The south-north course of the Belaya River and the west-east Ul'yanovsk-Chelyabinsk railroad intersect at Ufa and divide the republic into four sections; the southeast section contains most of the important mineral resources of the southern Urals. In the northeast, along the Ufa River, lumbering is the principal industry. In sharp contrast to the wooded, mountainous eastern section of the republic is the rolling black-earth steppe in the west, on the left bank of the Belaya River, where agricultural development is most advanced.

Among the principal mineral resources of the southeast are the vast Komarovo-Zigazinskiy iron ore reserves (more than one hundred million tons) which rival the high-quality Bakal ores in metal content. These reserves, which are being exploited at the mines of Zigazinskiy, Komarovo (southeast), Tukan (east), and Inzer (north), supply chiefly the metallurgical industries of Beloretsk and Magnitogorsk, with which they are connected by rail. Next in importance are the rich copper deposits in the vicinity of Baymak and the copper-zinc deposits at Sibay, northeast of Baymak. Gold is mined at Tubinskiy, south of Baymak, and elsewhere in the extreme southeast of the Bashkir Autonomous SSR. Northeast of Beloretsk are more gold sites, as well as deposits of such important ferroalloys as manganese and chrome. Manganese is mined at Bakr-Uzyak, southwest of Magnitogorsk, and at Malo-Uchalinskiy, northeast of Beloretsk; a chromite mine is in operation at Verkhne-Avsyan, southwest of Beloretsk. In the same area, there is also a sufficient supply of refractory and flux materials for the metallurgical industry of Beloretsk. Alone coking coal is missing, as in most other parts of the Urals, and the supplies come largely from Karaganda. Among the deposits which were opened for production during the Second World War are the bauxite sites of Pervomayskiy (until 1943, Kukshik) on the railroad west of Zlatoust.

The Bashkir, a Turkic group which settled in the Urals in the early eighteenth century, comprise only one fourth of the population of the republic. About 40 percent are Russians, and the rest are Ukrainians and Tatars. The republic was formed in 1919, among the first autonomous units of the USSR.

At the beginning of the first Five-Year Plan, the Bashkir Republic had a well-developed wheat and livestock region in the west, lumbering in the northeast, and ferrous and nonferrous metallurgical plants in the mountains. With the introduction of the planned economy, the area given over to industrial crops, such as flax, hemp, and sunflowers, and fodder grasses, was considerably increased. Industries were developed with the establishment of flour mills (Davlekanovo, Kushnarenkovo, northwest of Ufa, and Meleuz, south of Ishimbay), meat packing plants (Rayevskiy and Chishmy, southwest of Ufa, and Tuymazy), distilling (Birsk, Belebey), dairying, tanning etc. Coarse wool is milled at Nizhne-Troitskiy, south of Tuymazy. In the northeastern lumber region the paper mill of Krasnyy Klyuch, on the Ufa River, northeast of Ufa, is most important. Glassworks are located at Karaidel'skiy, north of Krasnyy Klyuch, and at Krasnousol'skiy, northeast of Sterlitamak, near the Belaya River. A soda plant is under construction.

While the old metallurgical plants were modernized and enlarged, totally new industries were established in the form of machinery works at Ufa, agricultural machine works at Blagoveshchensk, and the extensive oil fields of Ishimbay and Tuymazy. Petroleum production showed spectacular advances, increasing nearly one hundred times during the second Five-Year Plan. By 1940 production was about one million tons annually. A fourfold increase over 1940 is to be achieved by 1950 under the current Plan.

The construction of the Magnitogorsk steel industry at the "backdoor" of the Bashkir Republic played an enormous role in opening up the many untouched resources in the ore-rich southeast section. This process will receive an additional impetus during the current Plan because of the construction of a number of vital rail links. In order to bring Magnitogorsk into direct connection with the west, the Magnitogorsk-Abdulino line will be built as part of the over-all South Siberian rail trunk. The first building stage involves the Magnitogorsk-Sterlitamak section. After this increase in transportation facilities, the Komarovo-Zigazinskiy iron ore deposits will be worked at a much faster rate. A railroad is scheduled to be built from Ishimbay south to the Kuyurgaz or Babay coal fields at Yermolayevo, near the border of Chkalov Oblast. The development of this coal field will considerably increase the local supply and make unnecessary the usual long-distance haulage. Another rail project of the current Plan involves a line linking Magnitogorsk and the Baymak copper smelter, with a possible future extension south to the Orsk-Khalilovo industrial complex. The chief export items of the Bashkir Autonomous SSR are grain, cattle, lumber, copper, steel, wire, nails, oil, and motors.

Ufa, the capital of Bashkiria, lies on the high, right bank of the Belaya River, at the mouth of the Ufa and the intersection of the Ul'yanovsk-Chelyabinsk railroad. A new railroad leads south to Sterlitamak and the Ishimbay oil fields. In addition to its importance as a transportation center, Ufa has recently developed into a major industrial city. It has locomotive and car repair shops, shipyards (at its suburban port of Kirzhak across the Ufa River), cellulose and match mills, food industries (meat, flour) and distilleries. A cotton mill is planned for 1950. The city limits include the rail junction and sawmilling center of Dema, on the opposite side of the Belaya River.

Chernikovsk is a new city, which was formed in 1944 out of the industrial Stalin rayon of the city of Ufa.* It is situated northeast of Ufa, with which there are interurban communications. Chernikovsk, which has a population in excess of 50,000, contains most of the major industries formerly in Ufa, including machinery works (agricultural and mining machines), lumber mills, oil refineries (linked by pipe lines with the Tuymazy and Ishimbay fields), aircraft-motor works, electric equipment, and chemical plants.

Beloretsk, the major metallurgical center of Bashkiria, has a steel mill

* The separation of Kotovsk from Tambov is another example of this typical Soviet administrative process, which involves the organization of a separate city in the newly industrialized outskirts of an old center.

(using charcoal) ; the metal is used in the manufacture of nails and wire. It produces canned foods and lumber distillation products, including charcoal. Beloretsk receives its iron ore from the Komarovo-Zigazinskiy site and chrome and manganese from near-by deposits. North of the city lies the old steel mill of Tirlyanskiy.

Baymak (until 1938, when it became a city, called Baymak–Tanalykovo) is a major copper-mining and smelting center in the southern Urals. Northeast of Baymak, the Sibay copper-zinc site is being developed. Gold is mined at Tubinskiy to the south.

Sterlitamak, an important agricultural center on the Belaya River, lies at the northern edge of the Ishimbay oil fields. After the construction of the Ufa-Ishimbay-Yermolayevo-Chkalov railroad and the completion of the Magnitogorsk-Abdulino line, it is destined to become a rail hub of considerable proportions. It has an oil-drilling industry and produces leather goods, lumber, flour, meat, and alcohol.

The two major petroleum centers of the Bashkir Republic are the older Ishimbay, which developed during the second Five-Year Plan and has a refinery producing high-octane aviation gasoline, and the new city of Oktyabr'skiy, the center of the Tuymazy fields. Oktyabr'skiy, which came into being as a workers' settlement in 1940 and became a city in 1946, lies southwest of Tuymazy, near the Ik River, an affluent of the Kama. Its city limits include the former villages of Mullino and Naryshevo; the latter is connected by a rail spur and a pipe line with Urussu (Tatar Autonomous SSR). A pipe line connects Oktyabr'skiy with Ufa via Tuymazy. By 1950 Oktyabr'skiy is expected to have a population of 60,000 and an area of 3 square miles.

Chkalov Oblast
Capital, Chkalov; area, 47,400, population, 1,800,000

The territory of Chkalov Oblast, the southernmost division of the Urals, represents a type of "Russian corridor" between the Bashkir Autonomous SSR in the north and Kazakhstan in the south. Its population was originally based on the series of fortified points which the tsars established in the area in defense against the steppe peoples. Only the extreme eastern portion can be considered to fall within the mountain zone of the Urals. The remainder of the oblast is a fertile, level steppe which rises only slightly in the west in the vicinity of the Obshchiy Syrt. Even the section in the Ural Mountains does not rise much above 1,500 feet. Its landscape differs greatly from that of the higher mountain areas in the north. However, the abundance of the mineral deposits which are found in this area of Orsk-Khalilovo leaves no doubt as to the role that the Ural Mountains play in the development of the oblast.

The climate is of the extremely dry continental type, with very cold winters and hot summers. Only the northwestern portion, near Buzuluk, which is somewhat protected by the Ural Mountains from the dry southeasterly winds, receives an annual precipitation of 16–18 inches. The east and southeast receive only 10 inches yearly. In accordance with the precipitation, the soils vary from the high-grade black earth in the northwest to chestnut soils intermingled with salt flats in the south and the southeast. The dryness of the climate favored the establishment of a number of sanatoriums for dry-air and kumiss cures. The only forests of any consequence are the pine woods of Buzuluk, known for their 200-year-old trees. The rivers are of the steppe type and are subject to a brief spring freshet, followed by a gradual reduction in level during the summer months. They are not navigable and offer no hydroelectric potentialities. The principal stream is the Ural, which crosses the oblast from east to west and receives the Or' at Orsk and the Sakmara at Chkalov; the western section of the region is drained by the Samara.

Of mineral fuels are to be noted the recently discovered petroleum and natural gas near Buguruslan, the oil-shale deposits of the Obshchiy Syrt, adjoining Kuybyshev Oblast, and the coal of Dombarovskiy, southeast of Orsk. The Orsk-Khalilovo district is one of the most richly mineralized areas of the Urals. It contains, above all, the Khalilovo hematite site with reserves of over 100 million tons of iron ore, having valuable admixtures of chrome, nickel, and titanium. To the north of Khalilovo are rich nickel deposits, and to the west, near Blyava station and the city of Mednogorsk, important copper resources, where the ores contain iron, sulphur, gold, and silver. Also found in the district are cryolite at Kuvandyk (for the Orsk aluminum works), chromite, gold in veins and placers, and various construction materials. Sol'-Iletsk, in the southern section of the oblast, has extensive salt and gypsum mines. Near by are potash deposits, and west and south of Chkalov there is phosphate rock.

Two thirds of the territory is under cultivation. Because of the dry winters, spring wheat is the predominant grain crop. Sunflowers, melon, and squash are also important. Livestock raising is mainly for meat and wool production; sheep greatly exceed the number of hogs. While these traits are typical of the over-all agricultural economy, a considerable difference develops between the extremes. The northwest, which has a greater precipitation, contains most extensive meadows and forests. A higher percentage of crops are planted before the winter. The harvests are better than average; dairy farming is of some importance, and the rural population density is higher than the average, or more than 50 per square mile. In the dry southeast, on the contrary, pastures are far more extensive, millet is extensively grown as a dry-climate crop, sheep raising prevails, and the population density is less than 20 per square mile. On the Kazakhstan border camels are raised in large herds. Flour mills, oil presses, and meat-packing plants are the chief industrial enterprises based on the agricultural production. The principal centers are Chkalov, Orsk, Buguruslan, Buzuluk, Abdulino, and Sorochinsk.

The remarkable industrial development of the Orsk-Khalilovo district has sharply altered the economic balance of the oblast. From a primarily agricultural region, it has changed into one in which industry has rapidly come into the foreground. Most of the development occurred shortly before and during the Second World War. The principal enterprises are the metallurgical works of Novo-Troitsk, the copper and sulphur works of Mednogorsk, and the metallurgical and machinery plants of Orsk. In addition, Orsk produces heavy machinery and petroleum products. The industries of the district are supplied with coal from the local Dombarovskiy mines, but mainly from Karaganda via the South Siberian Railroad. Kumak, just northeast of Orsk, produces refractory clays for the blast furnaces. Gold is mined in the extreme eastern portion of the Oblast at Aydyrlinskiy and Siniy Shikhan. Among other mining industries of the region are the gypsum works of Dubenskiy on the railroad between Chkalov and Orsk, the asphalt and oil deposits of Saraktash, near by, and the salt and gypsum mines of Sol'-Iletsk (formerly called Iletskaya Zashchita), which form the basis of a chemical industry. Koltubanovskiy near Buzuluk, on the western limits of the oblast, has one of the few sawmills in the southern Urals.

Recent and future railroad construction plays an important role in the development of the economy. The building of the Sol'-Iletsk–Ural'sk line in 1937 established a direct link with the Lower Volga Region and the Ukraine. During the Second World War, Orsk was connected directly with Kandagach and the Emba oil fields at Gur'yev. Future projects involve the construction of the Chkalov-Ishimbay-Ufa and Sara (near Orsk)-Baymak-Magnitogorsk lines northward into the Bashkir Autonomous SSR.

Chkalov, called Orenburg until 1938 and renamed for the long-distance flier Valeriy Chkalov, lies in the open steppe on the right bank of the Ural River. The city was originally a fortified post established in the early eighteenth century in the Russian advance to the southern Urals and into Kazakhstan. It developed into a major commercial and caravan center, and the construction of the Trans-Caspian Railroad gave it additional significance. It produces airplane motors and parts and has locomotive and railway-car repair works. Leather, clothing, chemical, flour, and meat industries are important.

Buguruslan, on the Ufa-Kuybyshev railroad, is an agricultural center, with flour mills. Recently petroleum and natural gas deposits were developed at Sultangulovo (southeast) and Sadki (south), near the city. Pipe lines carry the products to Kuybyshev.

Buzuluk is an agricultural center on the Samara River. It produces agricultural implements, sheepskins, flour, and alcohol.

Orsk, on the Ural, at the mouth of the Or' River, is the center of the Orsk-Khalilovo industrial district. The end of an oil pipe line from Gur'yev, it has an oil-refining industry. Its metallurgical plant, with blast furnaces and a steel mill, supplies metal to the locomotive works and the heavy machine industry, which produces turbines, boilers, and power equipment. Nickel and aluminum works are in operation. Canned goods, meat (in a large packing plant), flour, and alcohol are also produced. Water supply of the Orsk industrial area will be assured after the completion of a reservoir ("Orsk Sea") of 140 square miles on the Ural River, 35 miles above Orsk.

Mednogorsk, founded in 1939, smelts the local copper deposits of Blyava and produces sulphuric acid as a by-product. Electric motors are also manufactured. The mining town of Rakityanka lies just northeast.

Novo-Troitsk is a new city, formed in 1945 by the union of the mining towns Akkermanovka (nickel) and Novo-Troitsk. Located halfway between the Khalilovo iron and nickel mines and the city of Orsk, Novo-Troitsk is the site of a new metallurgical development of the current Five-Year Plan. Construction on the site began in 1942, and the population reached 20,000 in 1946. Chromium and nickel steels are to be produced.

CHAPTER 13

Western Siberia

WESTERN SIBERIA occupies the huge expanse between the Urals and the Yenisey River and extends from the dry steppes of Kazakhstan in the south to the cold shores of the Arctic Ocean in the north. With an area of 936,000 square miles, it is one of the largest natural regions of the USSR.

Nine tenths of Western Siberia consists of an extremely level plain sloping almost imperceptibly toward the Arctic Ocean. This plain, the West Siberian lowland, was formed as a result of geologic faulting and the subsequent depositing of marine sediments. The valleys of the Ob' and the Irtysh rivers, the two chief streams of Western Siberia, are flat depressions, which become progressively swampy toward the north. South of the West Siberian lowland, several shallow depressions are occupied by lakes. The banks of the rivers occasionally rise in steep bluffs, up to 130 feet high, above the river bed. Because of the extreme flatness of the surrounding territory, the local inhabitants apply the term "mountain" to these precipitous cliffs. In the southern part of the lowland the relief is characterized by a series of low ridges extending in parallel in a general northeasterly direction for several miles. Such ridges are also distributed in a less noticeable and irregular fashion in other parts of Western Siberia. In the marshy sections they emerge in the form of dry islands, and in the north they give a hilly character to the prevailingly flat tundra.

In direct contrast to this flat lowland, the Altay mountain system rises in the extreme southeast of Western Siberia. The Kuznetsk Ala-Tau and the Salair Ridge adjoin the Altay in the northeast and enclose the important Kuznetsk Basin. This mountainous area gives rise to the most important rivers of the region and is the site of the richest mineral resources; its foothills include fertile farmlands. The Altay is lower than the ranges of Central Asia or the Caucasus, but is not easily accessible, due to an abrupt shelf formation, up to 1,500 feet in height, which bars

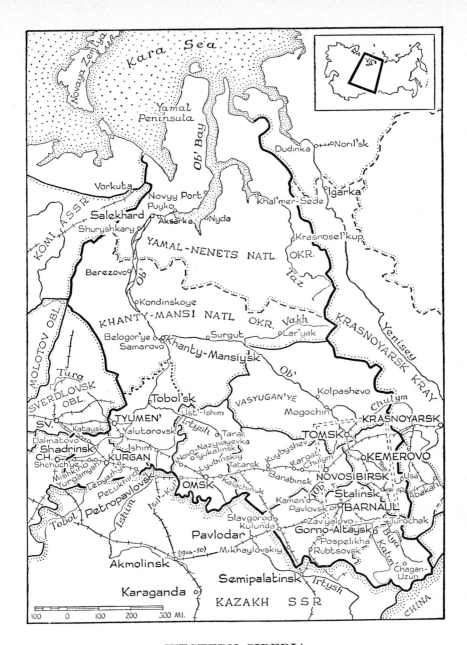

WESTERN SIBERIA

(Novosibirsk and Kuznetsk Basin are shown in detail on p. 279.)

the way from the direction of the West Siberian lowland. The highest portions of the Altay are the centrally located Katun' and Chuya ranges, having average elevations of 11,400 to 15,000 feet. The highest peak, Belukha, in the Katun' Range, rises to 15,157 feet. Traces of former glaciation are left in the form of picturesque, clear-water mountain lakes, scattered separately or in groups throughout the Altay. Characteristic relief forms for this mountain region are extensive, occasionally swampy, level highlands surrounded by dome-shaped heights or sharp rocky glaciated crests. The mountain streams rising in these areas cut narrow, deep gorges into the slopes; in their lower reaches they form relatively wide valleys, with steppe vegetation. The snow line in the Altay passes at an elevation of 8,500 feet in the west, and at 10,500 feet on the drier east and southeast slopes.

The numerous large and slow-flowing rivers of Western Siberia are all part of the huge Ob'-Irtysh drainage basin formed by the Ob', one of the principal streams of Siberia, and its chief affluent, the Irtysh. This basin, which is almost co-extensive with the West Siberian lowland, is marked by characteristically low, marshy divides, such as the Vasyugan'ye region on the middle Ob', which is subject to frequent floods.

The Ob' rises in two branches in the Altay Mountains. The Katun', the larger of the two headstreams, rises on the southern slope of the peak Belukha and joins the Biya, which flows out of Teletskoye Lake. Emerging onto the West Siberian lowland, the Ob' turns into a great navigable stream. Its valley widens considerably (up to 20 miles), and the river forms a large number of islands in its course. In its middle reaches the Ob' flows through a swampy region (the Vasyugan'ye), where it receives many important affluents. After joining the Irtysh, the river turns north toward the Arctic Ocean, which it enters through the large Ob' Gulf, a wide arm of the Kara Sea; here it cuts deep into the Siberian mainland and is free of ice from the middle of summer to the early autumn. A branch of the Ob' Gulf is Taz Bay, which constitutes now the mouth of the Taz River, but is believed to have received the waters of the Yenisey in an earlier geologic period. The very slow rate at which the Ob' flows to the sea is partially responsible for stagnation of the water in its lower reaches during the winter months. The water assumes a reddish color, has an unpleasant taste, and begins to emit gas bubbles. Fish which are placed in such water die or flee to the upper reaches of the affluents. The stagnation is thought to be caused by a lack of oxygen, which is absorbed by decaying organic materials.

The Irtysh rises in the Mongolian Altay and flows through the Kazakh SSR in its upper course. It enters Western Siberia above Omsk, and receives the Ishim and Tobol rivers, which also rise in Kazakhstan. Its left bank is generally low, while the higher right bank is formed of brittle clay formations, which are subject to frequent cave-ins. After receiving the Tobol, the Irtysh assumes the same characteristics as those of the lower Ob'.

The climate of Western Siberia, due to the great latitudinal extent of the region, varies considerably from place to place. However, the following common characteristics can be determined: extreme continentality, a severe winter, rarely broken by thaws, with temperatures as low as —40° F in the south; a short summer, which tends to become hot in the south; a cold spring; a warm, though short, autumn. While there are many clear days, in the steppe zone the frequent strong winds sometimes turn into dust storms. During the warm months there are wide diurnal temperature variations.

The climate of the Altay is somewhat more moderate. The winters are warmer, and the summers cooler and more humid; it receives more precipitation, especially in the central and eastern sections.

The various soil and vegetation zones of the USSR are clearly expressed in Western Siberia. North of 65° N. latitude reigns the tundra, partly hilly, but leveling out toward the Kara Sea. South of the tundra the taiga extends to 56° N. Due to the characteristic marshiness of the West Siberian taiga, large trees are generally concentrated near the streams, while in the marshy divides low-tree vegetation prevails. The banks of the streams gradually become lower in their upper reaches, until they merge with the surrounding swampy landscape, where only the steady inclination of the marsh grass provides a clue to the current of the river. The Vasyugan'ye region, on the divide between the middle Ob' and the Irtysh, is a typical example of this type of land form. South of 56° N. begins the wooded steppe, which turns gradually into a grassy steppe at about 54–53° N. This is the most important agricultural belt of Western Siberia. It has black earth as a dominant soil type, an average yearly temperature of slightly more than 32° F, a five-month winter, and a yearly rainfall of about 13 inches. Small birch and aspen clusters on leached gray forest soils interrupt the open black-earth expanses covered with fescue, feathergrass, and occasional saltwort and wormwood types. The transition from wooded to grassy steppe is delimited more sharply in Western Siberia than it is west of the Urals.

The Western Siberian wooded steppe has no broadleafed tree types, such as the oak or the maple, and is generally barer and bleaker than its East European equivalent. In the grassy steppe, feathergrass, wild oats, and wormwood are the prevailing vegetation types. In the bare depressions there are many shallow salt lakes, which sometimes turn into dry salt flats. The most important steppe areas are the Ishim Steppe, west of the Irtysh, the Baraba Steppe between the Irtysh and the Ob', and the Kulunda Steppe to the south. Wooded areas are most common in the Baraba Steppe.

In the Altay Mountains the forest zone rises to an elevation of about 6,500 feet. The predominant tree types are larch, pine, fir, and cedar, with an admixture of aspen and birch. The original area of the forests has been considerably reduced through lumbering and fires. Above the forest zone are the Alpine meadows, and in the extensive highlands there is a high mountain tundra.

Aside from some brown coal deposits in the area of Ishim, the Western Siberian lowland is very deficient in mineral resources. The Altay mountain system, on the contrary, abounds in such resources, especially nonferrous ores (silver, lead, zinc, and occasionally copper), which is mined principally on its Kazakh slopes. There gold mines and precious stones, such as jasper, are found. Between the Salair Ridge and the Kuznetsk Ala-Tau lies the Kuznetsk Basin, with the largest known coal reserves of the USSR, estimated at 450 billion tons. In addition to the ordinary coal types, the deposits include the sapropelite variety, which can be converted directly into fuel oil. In the southern Kuznetsk Ala-Tau there are large iron deposits, and zinc is mined in the Salair Ridge.

Western Siberia is still rather sparsely populated. It has a population of over 10 million people, which for an area of 936,000 square miles gives an average density of 11 per square mile. Among the most deserted regions are the north and the northeast and the higher portions of the Altay Mountains. The greatest population density is found in the agricultural steppe regions adjacent to the middle Urals and the Altay Mountains.

The Russians form the predominant element of the population (about 92 percent). Among the native inhabitants of Western Siberia, the Finno-Ugric group is most important; it includes the Khanty (Ostyaks), Mansi (Voguls), Komi (Zyryans), and the Nentsy (Samoyeds). All live in the north: the Nentsy in the tundra, the Khanty along the banks of the lower Ob' and its affluents, the Mansi along the Northern Sos'va River, and the Komi near the Ural Mountains. In the Altay Mountains, live Altaic tribes, such as the Oyrot people (part of the Turkic group), which are constituted into an autonomous oblast. The Tatars, with the exception of the Russians the most numerous national group, are settled along the middle Irtysh River, along the Ob', and along its upper affluents near the Altay Mountains. Near the border of Kazakhstan are Kazakh minorities. In addition, the population of Western Siberia includes Ukrainians, Poles, and Estonians on the farms and in the cities on the Trans-Siberian Railroad.

Until 1937 Western Siberia formed two large administrative units, the West Siberian Kray and Omsk Oblast. Because of the increase of population and the steady economic progress of the region, these two areas began to be split up into individual oblasts. This process continued until 1944. At present there are six oblasts and one kray: in the southwest, the Kurgan and the Tyumen' oblasts, the latter with the Khanty-Mansi and Yamal-Nenets national okrugs; in the south, Omsk Oblast; in the southeast, Tomsk, Novosibirsk, and Kemerovo oblasts, and Altay Kray, which includes the Gorno-Altay Autonomous Oblast.

In recent years the economy of Western Siberia has undergone a decisive shift from an agricultural basis to an industrial one. The metallurgical and chemical industries which have arisen in and near the Kuznetsk Basin have turned that section of the USSR into one of its major industrial areas. Although its water-power reserves are among the largest in the USSR, it is the coal of the Kuznetsk Basin which has given the impetus to this development. This important fuel base furnishes good coking coal not only to the gigantic local steel mills of Stalinsk but also to the metallurgy of the Urals, which have no high-grade coal supplies of their own. In return for the coal, the Urals send iron ore to the Kuznetsk Basin to feed the local steel industry. This exchange of iron and coal between the Urals and the Kuzbas was responsible for the creation of the so-called Ural-Kuznetsk *kombinat* in the early Five-Year Plans. However, with the subsequent development of the Karaganda coal basin nearer to the Urals and the increasing exploitation of Kuznetsk Basin iron ore, each industrial area is becoming more self-sufficient, and the once vital Ural-Kuznetsk link is gradually losing its importance.

In addition to heavy metallurgy, nonferrous (zinc and aluminum) metallurgy has also been developed. On the basis of the coking process, a large chemical industry has been created at Kemerovo. By means of the local iron and steel, machinery is manufactured at Novosibirsk, and locomotives and rolling stock at Stalinsk.

The development of large-scale agriculture has provided an impetus to the erection of agricultural machinery works at Omsk. There are numerous dairy and sugar refining plants, as well as a young textile industry. An active lumbering industry, with sawmilling and woodworking plants, supplies the Urals and the grassy-steppe zone with lumber and construction materials. In the far north the population engages in reindeer breeding, fishing, and fur trapping.

The growing of grain crops, especially spring wheat, prevails in the wooded steppe zone; sugar beets and hemp are cultivated only incidentally. The agricultural areas include large stretches of meadows and pasture land, which support herds of dairy cattle. During the Second World War the importance of the West Siberian farmlands increased considerably because of the loss of the rich agricultural regions occupied by the Germans in the west. The area sown to grain was extended, and Western Siberia supplied the army and large sections of the population with grain, butter, and other dairy products. Gradually, new agricultural areas are being extended into the northern forests, and vegetables are grown in hothouses beyond the Arctic circle.

The chief cities (Novosibirsk and Omsk) have risen at the intersection of the basic west-east line, the Trans-Siberian Railroad, with the two important rivers, the Irtysh and the Ob'. In addition, Novosibirsk is the northern terminus of the Turksib Railroad, one of the most important railway lines of the USSR, which links Siberia with the republics of Central Asia. At the crossing of the Turksib over the Ob' lies Barnaul, one of the oldest cities of Western Siberia and now an industrial center. A third important railway connects Novosibirsk with the Kuznetsk Basin, which also has another direct link with the Trans-Siberian line. The water routes of the Ob', the Irtysh, and the Tom' rivers serve for north-south transportation. The lower course of the Ob' forms part of the Northern Sea Route.

Kurgan Oblast
Capital, Kurgan; area, 27,500, population, 900,000

Kurgan Oblast is a wedge-shaped region lying in the extreme southwest of Western Siberia and on the border of the Kazakh SSR. In 1943 it was separated from Chelyabinsk Oblast and forms an independent unit with a predominantly agricultural economy. The generally uniform flatness of the oblast is interrupted by the valleys of the Tobol River, which passes through the region from south to north, and of the Iset' and Miass rivers in the west. It has a continental climate, with mean temperatures of 0° F in January and 68° F in July. The average yearly rainfall is 13 inches; periodic droughts are not unusual. Black soils prevail throughout the area, which is inhabited almost entirely by Russians, with Ukrainian and Tatar minorities.

Agricultural production consists essentially of various grain crops (mainly wheat) and the raising of livestock for dairy products and meat. The wheat belt extends along the Chelyabinsk-Kurgan-Petropavlovsk section of the Trans-Siberian Railroad and includes a large number of flour-milling towns and villages. The dairy cattle zone lies in the northern section of the oblast and is marked by numerous cheese factories and butter plants. In the south, along the Kazakh border, sheep raising is important. In the northwest, hemp and flax form a considerable part of the agricultural production. They are processed by mills located in and north of Shadrinsk.

In addition to the flour milling industry, centered at Dalmatovo, Shchuch'ye, and Mishkino, and the dairy industry, concentrated at Kataysk, Yurgamysh, Lebyazh'ye, and other towns, the oblast has meat-packing plants, tanneries, distilleries, and various other food-processing plants. There is some lumbering in the northern forested clusters of the wooded steppe zone; the principal sawmill is at Krasnyy Oktyabr', west of Kurgan. North of Kurgan, the mills at Ikovskoye and Borovlyanka produce wood pulp; Borovlyanka also has a glass factory. In the extreme east, Petukhovo (until 1944 known as Yudino) manufactures agricultural machinery.

Kurgan Oblast is served by two branches of the Trans-Siberian Railroad: the Petropavlosvk-Kurgan-Chelyabinsk line and the branch linking Kurgan with Sverdlovsk via Shadrinsk. The latter branch is used by the Moscow-Vladivostok express.

Kurgan, the capital, is the center of a wheat and dairy region in the Tobol valley. After the completion of the Kurgan-Shadrinsk line it became an important railroad junction on the western section of the Trans-Siberian. Its industries are based essentially on the local farm products, flour mills, meat-packing plants, tanneries, but they produce also agricultural machinery for local use.

Shadrinsk, the second city of the oblast, is a food-processing center, producing flour, dairy products, leather, hemp, and flax.

Tyumen' Oblast
Capital, Tyumen'; area, 526,300, population, 900,000

Tyumen' Oblast is one of the newest oblasts of Western Siberia, having been created in 1944 out of Omsk Oblast. The northern Yamal-Nenets and Khanty-Mansi national okrugs, formerly part of Omsk Oblast, were incorporated into Tyumen' Oblast at the time of its formation. Because of the latitudinal zonal differentiation within Tyumen' Oblast, which extends nearly 1,300 miles from north to south through the tundra, taiga and wooded steppe belts of Western Siberia, the oblast proper, in the south, and the two northern national okrugs shall be considered in turn.

TYUMEN' OBLAST PROPER (area, 52,000, population, 750,000), the extreme southern section of Tyumen' Oblast, is drained by the Irtysh and the lower reaches of its two affluents, the Ishim and the Tobol. It is in the northern part of the wooded steppe zone and has mean temperatures of —2° F in January and 65° in July. The average yearly rainfall is a little more than 16 inches.

This region is basically a dairy cattle and wheat-growing area in the south and in the river valleys of the north. Butter, milk, and cheese are produced along the Omsk-Tyumen'-Sverdlovsk branch of the Trans-Siberian. Along the railroad are also industries such as flour mills, meat-packing plants, and canneries. Flax is grown extensively along the Irtysh and the Tobol rivers.

Lumbering is an important section of the local economy. The timber is brought to sawmills at Yalutorovsk and Tyumen' along the railroad, and also to Tobol'sk, where it is employed in the shipbuilding and wood-working industries. Lumber is exported to the Urals and up the Irtysh to Omsk and the Kazakh SSR.

With the exception of some predominantly Tatar areas in the south, the population is chiefly Russian. The main cities, except Tobol'sk, at the confluence of the Irtysh and the Tobol, are located on the Trans-Siberian Railroad (Omsk-Tyumen'-Sverdlovsk branch). They are Ishim, Yalutorovsk, with the two neighboring industrial towns of Zavodo-ukovskiy and Zavodo-Petrovskiy, and the capital Tyumen'.

Tyumen', the oldest city of Siberia (founded in 1585), lies on the northernmost branch of the Trans-Siberian and on the Tura River, an affluent of the Tobol. It has shipyards, lumber mills (sawmilling, veneering, wood distilling) and food industries, producing flour, meat, and dairy products. Woolen and felt goods are also manufactured here. Tyumen' is the western navigation head in the Ob'-Irtysh waterway system. The eastern terminus of the old Perm'-Tyumen' railroad, the city was the principal entry gate of Siberia until the construction of the Trans-Siberian. It has since become an important river-rail transfer point for grain and lumber.

Tobol'sk, once a mighty fur-collecting city and, until 1824, the administrative center of Western Siberia, lies on the Irtysh at the mouth of the Tobol. It has declined since it was by-passed by the construction of the Trans-Siberian Railroad in the south, and it is now important as a supply point for the northern sections of Tyumen' Oblast, and receives the northern taiga products (furs, game, fish, lumber). Tobol'sk has shipyards, woodworking and metalworking, and light industries.

Ishim, at the intersection of the northern branch of the Trans-Siberian and the Ishim River (a left affluent of the Irtysh), is the center of a grain-growing and dairy-farming district.

THE KHANTY-MANSI NATIONAL OKRUG (capital, Khanty-Mansiysk; area, 215,500, population, 110,000) was known until 1940 as the Ostyak-Vogul National Okrug, for the former conventional names of the two chief national groups, the Khanty (Ostyaks) and Mansi (Voguls). It occupies the center of the West Siberian lowland, along the lower Ob' River and its affluents. The taiga covers most of the region, with the exception of the many swampy areas at the headwaters of the streams and along the watersheds.

The Russians, who live along the main streams, engage in agriculture, chiefly the cultivation of wheat and barley, and form the majority of the urban population. The Khanty (Ostyaks), the more important of the two basic national groups, live east of the Ob' and the Irtysh rivers, while the Mansi (Voguls) are established in the western section on the slopes of the Urals. The native population is engaged principally in hunting, fur trapping, fishing, and reindeer raising. The main fisheries are along the Ob' at Surgut, Khanty-Mansiysk, Kondinskoye, and Berezovo, and at Lar'yak, on the Vakh, a tributary of the Ob'. Khanty-Mansiysk and the neighboring village of Samarovo have fish canneries and sawmills. In the western section of the okrug at the headwaters of the Konda River, an affluent of the Irtysh, there is a large game reserve for beaver and sable. On the slopes of the northern Urals, rock crystal, Iceland spar, and platinum are found.

The capital, Khanty-Mansiysk (until 1940, Ostyako-Vogul'sk), lies at the confluence of the Ob' and the Irtysh rivers. It was constructed in the 1930's next to the old village of Samarovo. It produces fish, lumber, matches, and dairy goods. Air lines radiate from it to the remote corners of the okrug.

THE YAMAL-NENETS NATIONAL OKRUG (capital, Salekhard; area, 258,-800, population, 40,000) lies in the extreme north of Western Siberia on both sides of Ob' Gulf, this okrug includes the large Yamal Peninsula. Most of the region is situated in the tundra zone and has a similar climate and vegetation.

The population consists mainly of Nentsy east to the Taz River. In 1943 the area of Krasnosel'kup, comprising the basin of the Taz River, was transferred from Krasnoyarsk Kray to the Yamal-Nenets National Okrug. The Selkups, which comprise the main element of the population of the transferred area, are a branch of the Nentsy (Samoyed) people. Russians live in isolated groups in the valley of the lower Ob' and form the staff of many trading posts, polar stations, and so forth, along the coast of the Kara Sea.

The chief industries are fishing, reindeer raising, and fur trapping. Fisheries are concentrated at the mouth of the Ob' River and in the lower portion of the gulf at Shuryshkary, Salekhard, Aksarka, Puyko, Nyda, and Novyy Port. Salekhard and Novyy Port have canning establishments. Reindeer herds predominate along the coast and the lower course of the rivers. The growing of grains, potatoes, flax, and hemp is in an experimental stage.

The capital, Salekhard, is the former town of Obdorsk and was previously spelled Salegard.* It has fish canneries and sawmills. Novyy Port, which is, as the name implies, a new port, is one of the regular supply points on the Northern Sea Route in Ob' Gulf.

Omsk Oblast
Capital, Omsk; area, 53,800, population, 1,500,000

Until 1944, the year of the creation of Tyumen' Oblast, Omsk Oblast included the major portion of Western Siberia and extended from the border of the Kazakh SSR in the south to the Kara Sea in the north. After

---

* Salegard and Salekhard are merely two variant transliterations of the original Nenets word, which would presumably be expressed in English as Salehard. In order to express the "h"-sound of non-Russian languages, the letters "g" or "kh" of the Cyrillic alphabet are generally used.

the territorial change, Omsk Oblast became restricted to a roughly rectangular area drained by the Irtysh River, which flows through the oblast from southeast to northwest.

From north to south three distinct physico-economic zones can be considered in Omsk Oblast. In the north, extending as far south as 57° N, is the transition belt between taiga and wooded steppe. There is lumbering in the forested areas, and flax is cultivated in the clearings. Fur trapping is also important. The timber is floated to the sawmills at Ust'-Ishim and Tara on the Irtysh River; it is used for ship construction at Tara, the chief town of this region. Further south, extending nearly to the area of Omsk, is a dairy-cattle region, in which wheat and flax are cultivated. Nearly every village has dairy plants, making butter, cheese, and other products. The chief center is Tyukalinsk, which has metalworks and flour mills. To the southwest on the Trans-Siberian is Novo-Nazyvayevka, a peat-producing town. In the southern part of the oblast, with its center at Omsk, is the fertile black-earth area, specializing in wheat and other grains, including rye and oats. Large areas are under sunflower cultivation. Livestock (cattle and sheep) is raised, with emphasis on meat and wool production. The area abounds in grain elevators, flour mills, tanneries, and other agricultural processing establishments. In addition to Omsk, the largest towns are Kalachinsk, Isil'-Kul', and Lyubinskiy (until 1947 called Novo-Lyubino). The industries include metalworks, flour mills, and tractor repair shops.

The Irtysh serves as the main north-south artery, while the south is well served by the Trans-Siberian Railroad, of which two main branches unite at Omsk; one comes from Tyumen' in the northwest, the other leads from Kurgan via Petropavlovsk in the west.

Omsk, the capital of the oblast, is the second largest city and one of the most important industrial centers of Western Siberia. It grew remarkably during the Second World War, and its population increased from 280,000 in 1939 to 450,000 in 1946. Due to its rapid development, it was constituted in 1947 into an independent administrative-economic unit, equivalent to an oblast. It has a large variety of industries based on the local agricultural production: flour mills, grain elevators, slaughterhouses, and tanneries. It manufactures agricultural machinery of all types for use in the surrounding wheat region. It has auto assembly and tire plants, locomotive works, and shipyards. Its left-bank suburb, Kulomzino, or Novo-Omsk, is a sawmilling center and rail junction of the two Trans-Siberian branches.

Novosibirsk Oblast
Capital, Novosibirsk; area, 69,000, population, 2,100,000

Until 1943 Novosibirsk Oblast included a considerable portion of the southeastern section of Western Siberia. In that year the Kuznetsk Basin was constituted into a separate oblast, Kemerovo Oblast, and in 1944 the wooded, swampy region on the middle Ob' was separated from Novosibirsk Oblast to form Tomsk Oblast. As a result of the dismemberment of the original area, Novosibirsk Oblast is now restricted to a zone along the Trans-Siberian between the cities of Novosibirsk, in the east, and Tatarsk, in the west.

Except for industrial Novosibirsk, the oblast is predominantly a dairy-cattle and wheat region. Dairy plants stud the Baraba Steppe on both sides of the railroad, among the inland lakes (Chany, Sartlan, and Ubinskoye) which constitute the chief water bodies of the oblast. In the large towns along the railroad, such as Tatarsk, Barabinsk, Kuybyshev, Kargat, and Chulym, are flour mills, meat plants, and distilleries. North of this agricultural region is a swampy forest belt with a small lumbering industry.

The oblast is well supplied with rail lines. From the Trans-Siberian, two railways lead southward: from Tatarsk, a lateral line goes to Kulunda and on to Semipalatinsk, thus connecting the main line with the South Siberian and with the Turksib; from Novosibirsk itself, the Turksib goes to Central Asia. In addition, the Ob' River forms the north-south artery in the eastern section of the oblast.

The city of Novosibirsk has frequently been dubbed the "Chicago of Siberia," a term which fully expresses the rapid growth and industrialization of this metropolis of Western Siberia. Like Omsk, it received a strong impetus during the Second World War, and its population rose from the 1939 census figure of 405,000 to 750,000 in 1946. One of the independent administrative-economic city units of the USSR, it developed rapidly from a small railroad construction town, founded in 1897, mainly because of its favorable location at the intersection of several transportation routes. It is the terminus of the Turksib Railroad and of another line leading to the Kuznetsk Basin. Its metallurgical plant produces cold-rolled steel for the auto and tractor industry. The city has shipyards, an auto-assembly plant, machinery works, smelters, and it produces cotton goods and knitwear, plastics, bicycles, and metal goods.

There are extensive stockyards and slaughterhouses, flour mills, sawmills, and soap and perfume factories.

Novosibirsk is surrounded by a large number of industrial satellite towns: Berdsk (radios, flour) in the southeast, on the Ob', Bolotnoye (metal goods) east on the Trans-Siberian, Cherepanovo (dairy products, hides, and meat) south, on the Turksib, about half-way to Barnaul, Iskitim (cement) on the Turksib, nearer to Novosibirsk, and Toguchin (dairy products, flour, coal) east, on the Kuzbas line.

Barabinsk and Tatarsk are important agricultural centers in the west, on the Trans-Siberian line. They are in the Baraba Steppe and produce dairy goods, meat, hides, and flour.

Tomsk Oblast
Capital, Tomsk; area, 121,400, population, 600,000

Tomsk Oblast, formed in 1944 out of Novosibirsk Oblast, is situated chiefly in the swampy, almost impenetrable forest region known as Vasyugan'ye. It includes the middle course of the Ob' River and its affluents and is one of the few administrative divisions of Siberia that do not extend to the Trans-Siberian Railroad in the south.

Russians inhabit only the southeastern section of the oblast; in the remainder, the Khanty (Ostyaks) are the dominant element. The most important industry is connected with lumbering. Timber which is cut along the affluents of the Ob' is floated down to the sawmills at Kolpashevo and adjacent Togur, to Mogochin on the Ob' River, and to Samus' (shipyards), Moryakovskiy Zaton and Timiryazevskiy on the Tom' River. In this region, where agriculture was hardly known until about a decade ago, the extension of the cultivated area has made considerable progress, and today wheat, oats, and barley are grown along the Ob' and its principal affluents, dairy cattle are raised, and a considerable acreage is under flax cultivation. In the neighborhood of Tomsk and extending southward along the Tomsk-Tayga rail spur, truck produce is emphasized.

The Ob' River and its chief affluents, which are being dragged and made suitable for navigation, constitute the main transportation routes. The only rail line, in addition to the Tomsk-Tayga spur, which joins Tomsk to the Trans-Siberian, is the lumber railroad from Tomsk northeast to Asino on the Chulym River.

Tomsk, the capital, is one of the principal education centers of Siberia and the site of the first Siberian university (founded in 1888). Situated on the main Siberian west-east road, it lost some of its former importance when the Trans-Siberian was constructed, by-passing it in the south. It produces electric motors, light bulbs, matches, and plastic shoes. Flour, sawmilling, distilling, and metalworking are other industries.

Kolpashevo is the chief lumber-milling center, on the Ob' River northwest of Tomsk.

Altay Kray
Capital, Barnaul; area, 101,000, population, 2,400,000

Altay Kray lies in the basin of the upper Ob' and includes a section of the Altay Mountains, with their foothills, and the Kulunda Steppe in the northwest. The Altay Mountains abound in good construction timber and have rich Alpine meadows on the upper slopes. The mineral resources, as yet not completely determined, include gold, mercury, and several other metals. The headwaters of the Ob' River, which rise in the Altay Mountains, are a rich potential source of hydroelectric energy.

The wooded steppe, which adjoins the mountainous zone in the north, has black soils, relatively high summer temperatures, and sufficient rainfall, making it one of the most important agricultural areas of Siberia. The Kulunda Steppe, which has a considerable Ukrainian population, is a wheat and dairy cattle region, suffering periodically from drought. Its villages abound in dairy plants and flour mills. The chief towns of the Kulunda Steppe are Slavgorod and Kamen'. Along the Turksib Railroad is a zone in which wheat and sugar beets constitute the main crops. The chief towns of this area are Aleysk, a sugar-refining center, and Pospelikha, with a large flour mill. The sugar-beet region extends eastward beyond Barnaul to the area between the Barnaul-Biysk rail branch and the Salair Ridge. Here the raising of flax is also important. On the foothills of the Altay Mountains the breeding of dairy cattle and a well-developed dairy industry prevails.

The mining industry in the Altay foothills includes the lead-zinc mine at Zmeinogorsk, the tungsten mine of Kolyvan' (producing also semiprecious stones and marble) to the northeast, and the gold mine of Gornyak to the west. In the Kulunda Steppe, mirabilite or Glauber salt is quarried at Kulunda, and soda is produced by the chemical works of Mikhaylovskiy. Lumber mills are at Tal'menka, north of Barnaul, and along the Barnaul-Biysk railroad, chiefly at Borovlyanka, and at

Altayskoye, south of Biysk. West of Biysk, at Akutikha, is a large glass factory.

Railroad construction to be completed during the current Plan will provide the Altay Kray with a good railway network. The present main artery, the Turksib, is to be supplemented by the South Siberian Railroad, which will cross the kray from west to east, past Kulunda, Zav'yalovo, Pavlovsk, Barnaul, and Sorokino to Stalinsk in the Kuznetsk Basin, and by the lateral Tatarsk-Kulunda-Semipalatinsk line, which will parallel the western border of the region. The Barnaul-Biysk branch of the Turksib provides a vital link between the two chief cities of the kray.

Barnaul, the capital and industrial center of the kray, has developed from an eighteenth century mining town into a modern city. It has important textile and food industries, including cotton mills which process Central Asian cotton, clothing mills, flour mills and a meat-packing plant. It lies on the left bank of the Ob' River, at its intersection with the Turksib Railroad. Its importance as a communications center should be considerably increased after the completion of the South Siberian line.

Biysk, situated on the Biya, the right headstream of the Ob' and connected by railroad with Barnaul, is in a rich agricultural region. It has varied food-processing industries, producing meat, flour, sugar, and alcohol, and linen mills.

Chesnokovka, on the opposite bank of the Ob' River from Barnaul, at Altayskaya station, is a new center which rose from a village in 1936 to a city under kray jurisdiction in 1944. It serves as a processing center for the farm products of the surrounding agricultural district and produces flour, meat, and other goods based on the local produce.

Kamen', or Kamen' on the Ob' (Russian *Kamen'-na-Obi*) and Slavgorod are the chief agricultural centers of the Kulunda Steppe, exporting dairy products, flour, meat, and other farm products and making farm implements for local use.

Rubtsovsk, the newest industrial city of the region, lies on the Turksib railroad, southwest of Barnaul. During the Second World War it became a major producer of tractors, farm machinery, and electrical equipment.

THE GORNO-ALTAY AUTONOMOUS OBLAST (capital, Gorno-Altaysk; area, 35,800, population, 150,000) lies in the Altay Mountains, in the mountainous southeastern section of Altay Kray. It is inhabited by several Altaic tribes, including the Oyrots (formerly Oyrats), Temut,

Telenget, and Kumand. These Turkic and Mongolian ethnic groups comprise about 36 percent of the population of the oblast. The Russians, who make up over one half of the population, live chiefly in the vicinity of the capital, where the only farming districts are found. Until 1948 the region was known as the Oyrot Autonomous Oblast, so called for the predominant non-Russian minority.

Livestock raising is the principal branch of the economy west of the Katun' River, the left headstream of the Ob'. Dairying is an important industry. In the same area maral deer are bred. East of the Katun' River, in the less accessible part of the Altay Mountains, where forests prevail, lumbering and fur trapping are the main occupations.

Manganese and gold are mined near Turochak, and rich mercury deposits occur at Chagan-Uzun, on the upper Chuya River.

The main traffic artery of the oblast, which relies only on road transport, is the Chuya highway, connecting Biysk with the Mongolian People's Republic. The highway leaves Biysk, passes Gorno-Altaysk, and continues through the Altay Mountains along the course of the Chuya River, an affluent of the Katun'. The development of road communications may open the region to tourists and further the establishment of health resorts at several mineral springs in the mountains.

Gorno-Altaysk was originally called Ulala and was later known as Oyrot-Tura from the early 1930's until the latest name change in 1948. It lies near the Katun' River in a predominantly Russian farming district, producing grains and dairy products. The city has flour and lumber mills and produces furniture, leather, and felt boots.

Kemerovo Oblast
Capital, Kemerovo; area, 36,900, population, 1,950,000

Kemerovo Oblast, which was created in 1943 out of Novosibirsk Oblast, includes the important Kuznetsk Basin, situated between the Kuznetsk Ala-Tau in the west and the Salair Ridge in the east. In the south, it comprises the higher region of Gornaya Shoriya.

The Kuznetsk coal basin, which is included entirely in the oblast, has reserves of more than 450 billion tons, making it the richest coal region in the world, with the exception of the Appalachians in the eastern United States. Although the Kuzbas, as the Kuznetsk Basin is usually called, has approximately the same area as the Donets Basin, or about 10,000 square miles, its reserves are about five times larger than those in the Donbas. This is due to the fact that the Kuzbas coal lies in especially thick seams, reaching a size of about 50 feet. In addition, the coal occurs close to the surface, thus reducing the cost of mining. The coal of the Kuznetsk Basin is generally of high quality, with a low sulphur content (0.5 percent). Much of the coal is of coking quality; some varieties can be used even in place of coke. There is the sapropelite type, which contains up to 60 percent of volatile products and is very valuable for gas and chemical industries. In addition to the coal, which makes Kemerovo Oblast the major fuel base of the USSR after the Donbas, there are extensive iron ore deposits, manganese, polymetallic ores (mainly zinc and lead), and gold.

The creation of the huge industrial region, which now extends through the Kuznetsk Basin, dates back to 1930, when the Soviet Government decided to develop a second major coal and metallurgical combine (in addition to the one in the Ukraine) based on the resources of the Urals and the Kuzbas. This project led to the establishment of the Ural-Kuznetsk *kombinat*, a major industrial program involving basically the shipment of Kuzbas coking coal to the Urals and of Urals iron ore in the opposite direction. Recently the link between the Urals and the Kuzbas has begun to weaken. This gradual loosening of the once vital connection is due to the development of the Karaganda coal basin and the increasing exploitation of the Kuzbas iron ore resources.

The first gigantic plant constructed in the Kuznetsk Basin following the decision taken in 1930 was the Stalinsk iron and steel works which rose in 1932 on the banks of the Tom' River, opposite the old town of Kuznetsk. Today the Stalinsk mills produce more than 2 million tons of pig iron and steel annually. At Gur'yevsk is a modernized old iron and steel plant, which was created during the nineteenth century. Together with heavy metallurgy, the plan evolved in 1930 envisaged the establishment of large-scale nonferrous and chemical industries. Zinc and lead works at Belovo process polymetallic ores from the Salair site, as well as from the mines at Zyryanovsk and other locations in the Kazakh portion of the Altay Mountains.

Coal is supplied to these industries, as well as to users throughout Western Siberia, by large mines, partially electrified and mechanized, which cluster around Anzhero-Sudzhensk, Kemerovo, Leninsk-Kuznetskiy, Kiselevsk, Prokop'yevsk, and Osinniki. In recent years mines producing the high quality sapropelite type of coal have been developed in the area of Barzas, between Anzhero-Sudzhensk and Kemerovo. During the Second World War another rich coal field was reconnoitered on the

Usa River, an affluent of the Tom'. The exploitation of this field awaits the completion of the Stalinsk-Abakan section of the South Siberian Railroad. The Shushtulep coal district on the Kondoma River, south of Osinniki, was developed after the Second World War. In it is the southern Kuzbas power plant, a new large installation feeding power to Stalinsk, Osinniki, and the Tom'-Usa coal-field.

On the basis of the coal production at Kemerovo, an important coking and chemical industry has been developed in that city. Gas products stemming from the coking process and sulphuric acid, produced by the nonferrous metallurgical works, have laid the foundation for a fertilizer industry.

The iron ore, which is gradually making the Kuzbas steel mills independent of the Ural ore,* is being obtained in Gornaya Shoriya in the southern part of Kemerovo Oblast. The exploitation of these deposits received a great impetus during the Second World War. The mining center is the new town of Tashtagol, with a population of nearly 20,000, situated at the terminus of the longitudinal railway and on the upper Kondoma River. Subsidiary mines are at Shalym, to the north, and at Kochura, to the southwest. Other iron mines, closer to Stalinsk, are at Tel'bes, Odrabash, and Temir-Tau [iron mountain], and there is a concentrating plant at Mundybash. Manganese is obtained near Leninsk-Kuznetskiy, and new deposits have been discovered on the upper Usa River. With the completion of the Stalinsk-Abakan line, important iron ore deposits in the Khakass Autonomous Oblast will be made available for the Kuzbas and will contribute still more to the weakening of the link with the Urals.

Gold is mined mainly along the affluents of the Kiya River south of Mariinsk. The most important mining towns are Berikul'skiy, Pervomayskiy, Tsentral'nyy, and Makarakskiy. The Novyy placer lies southeast of Barzas. Other gold mines are in the Salair Ridge, including the placers at Ursk.

Agriculture is oriented principally toward the production of fresh milk, fruits, and vegetables for the many urban agglomerations of the oblast. There is a wide zone of truck-produce farms between the cities. Elsewhere in the lowlands wheat and other grains are grown. In the hilly, forested zones in the east and the south the emphasis is on livestock rais-

* In 1941, 32 percent of iron ore used in the Kuznets basin was of local origin. By 1945 the proportion had risen to 61 percent and by 1947 to 75 percent.

NOVOSIBIRSK AND KUZNETSK BASIN

ing for production of meat and wool, as well as dairy products. Lumbering is also important in the surrounding mountains.

The oblast is well supplied with a rail network connecting it with the Trans-Siberian at Novosibirsk and at Yurga. All major industrial centers are linked by the railroad, which extends south as far as Tashtagol. The South Siberian Railroad, now under construction, will provide an additional east-west route through the oblast.

The capital, Kemerovo, was formerly called Shcheglovsk. It has developed into an important coal and chemical center, with one of the largest coking plants of the USSR.

Stalinsk, the major metallurgical center of the basin, was developed in the first Five-Year Plan, on the Tom' River, opposite the old city of Kuznetsk, which was subsequently absorbed by the new industrial city. The second largest steel center of the USSR, rivaling Magnitogorsk, it has extensive milling installations, ferroalloy and aluminum plants, and produces locomotives and rolling stock.

Other coal-mining centers are (from north to south): Anzhero-Sudzhensk, Leninsk-Kuznetskiy, Kiselevsk, Prokop'yevsk, and Osinniki.

The metallurgical centers Belovo (zinc) and Gur'yevsk (iron), the rail junction of Tayga, and Mariinsk, supply point for the gold mines of the Kuznetsk Ala-Tau, are other important cities of the oblast.

CHAPTER 14

Eastern Siberia

EASTERN SIBERIA extends from west of the Yenisey River to the eastern mountain ranges which form the divide between the basins draining into the Arctic Ocean and into the Pacific. In the south, its border coincides with the frontiers of China and the Mongolian People's Republic; in the north, its shores are washed by the cold seas of the Arctic Ocean, covered with ice the greater part of the year. Two archipelagoes, the New Siberian Islands and Severnaya Zemlya [north land], which lie off the mainland in the Arctic Ocean, are included in Eastern Siberia. It is a huge area, extending about 2,000 miles from west to east, and nearly as much from north to south, but it is very sparsely settled. Its 2,800,000 square miles include a population of only 5,550,000, only somewhat over one half as many as are credited to Western Siberia.

As opposed to lower Western Siberia, Eastern Siberia is a region of plateaus and mountains. With respect to relief and to a lesser extent other physical factors, it can be divided into three basic parts: (1) the Central Siberian uplands, (2) the southern (Sayan-Baykal-Stanovoy) highlands, (3) the northeastern (Verkhoyansk-Yana-Kolyma) highlands.

The Central Siberian uplands occupy the greater portion of Eastern Siberia. The average elevation is 1,000 to 1,500 feet, but it rises occasionally to 3,000 feet in the center formed by the Anabar hills. Faulting played an important role in the geologic formation of this area, and there was an ensuing effusion of magmatic masses, which now extend over huge areas and in some places are as much as 1,000 feet deep. Wherever streams traverse these lava beds, they form deeply-cut gorges with overhanging walls and hazardous rapids. The plateau descends to the main river valleys in several terraces, and even forms plains in such low areas as the valley of the middle Lena River and its two affluents, the Aldan and the Vilyuy. Secondary formations within the Central

Siberian uplands comprise the Patom plateau, the Aldan plateau, and the Yenisey ridge, all of which are important gold regions.

Southern highlands. The Central Siberian uplands are bordered in the south by a series of ranges and high plateaus extending along the southern frontier of the Asiatic USSR. The westernmost section of these highlands are called the Sayan Mountains, an extensive complex rising to 11,500 feet at Munku-Sardyk, a glaciated peak located just west of Mondy (Buryat-Mongol Autonomous SSR). The average elevation of the Sayan system reaches 8,000 feet; it comprises the Western Sayan, which extends northeastward along the border between Krasnoyarsk Kray and Tuva Autonomous Oblast, and the Eastern Sayan, which reaches from the neighborhood of Krasnoyarsk southeastward to Munku-Sardyk.

Farther east lies Transbaykalia (called in Russian *Zabaykal'ye*), a large region extending from Lake Baykal to the Amur and consisting of plateaus and mountain ranges of various elevations, separated by wide, deep river valleys. The ranges generally extend northeastward; the longest continuous range is the Yablonovyy (formerly known as Yablonoy), which forms a divide between the Vitim River, an affluent of the Lena, flowing north to the Arctic Ocean, and the Shilka, a headstream of the Amur, flowing east to the Pacific. North of the Yablonovyy range lies the Vitim plateau, a gold-mining area. Important minor ranges are the Primor'ye and Baykal ranges along the western shore of Lake Baykal, Khamar-Daban, south of the lake, and several short parallel ranges in the Nerchinsk mining region. East of the Olekma River rises the Stanovoy range, stretching along the boundary of the Yakut Autonomous SSR and Amur Oblast. It reaches an elevation of more than 8,000 feet and is continued by the Dzhugdzhur range in the Far East. Its northern slope descends gradually onto the Aldan plateau, while the southern slopes, oriented toward the Amur River, are more abrupt.

Northeastern highlands. This mountain complex penetrates into the Far East, where it includes the Kolyma (or Gydan) range, the Anadyr range in the Chukchi peninsula, the Koryak range, and the volcanic crests of the Kamchatka peninsula. In Eastern Siberia the main land forms are the arc-shaped Verkhoyansk range and the high Cherskiy range, which enclose the Yana lowlands and the Oymyakon plateau, two of the coldest areas of the world. The two ranges have definite Alpine characteristics, such as rocky pointed crests, steep slopes, and traces of former glaciation. In the coastal lowlands along the Arctic Ocean and

EASTERN SIBERIA

(1) Khakass Autonomous Oblast; (2) Ust'-Orda Buryat-Mongol National Okrug;
(3) Aga Buryat-Mongol National Okrug

B-M ASSR: Buryat-Mongol Autonomous SSR

also on the New Siberian Islands there are deposits of fossilized ice, up to 50 feet thick, which are remains of the ice age. In many instances sediments of more recent periods enclose skeletons of mammoths; occasionally parts of bodies and even entire well-preserved bodies of the animals are found.

Eastern Siberia has a very extensive water network, including such great streams as the Yenisey and Lena rivers and Lake Baykal, the deepest and one of the most unusual lakes of the world.

The Yenisey, the most important river of Siberia, is formed by two headstreams, the Great (Bol'shoy) and the Little (Malyy) Yenisey, rising on the southern slopes of the Eastern Sayan, in Tuva Autonomous Oblast. The Yenisey is a turbulent mountain stream in its upper course, with many rapids and large potential hydroelectric power resources, but it becomes navigable in its middle course. Among its chief affluents are the three Tunguskas, flowing into the Yenisey from the Central Siberian uplands: the Verkhnyaya [upper] Tunguska, better known as the Angara, which is longer and has a greater volume than the Yenisey above their confluence, the Srednyaya [middle] or Podkamennaya [stony] Tunguska, and the Nizhnyaya [lower] Tunguska. Below the Nizhnyaya Tunguska, the Yenisey flows through the taiga, which thins out gradually toward the north and soon makes way for the tundra. The river widens considerably, attaining a width of more than 10 miles in its lower course. At Ust'-Yeniseysk it enters the island-filled Yenisey Bay, which connects through a narrow channel with Yenisey Gulf, an arm of the Kara Sea.

The Angara River is called Verkhnyaya Tunguska in its lower course. It is a powerful and abundant stream, with a fast current, interrupted by many rapids and falls, offering great potentialities with respect to water-power development. Its great volume of water, the absence of spring floods, and the low water temperature are due the fact that the Angara is fed by the waters of Lake Baykal. This lake is one of the most unusual bodies of water in the world. It is distinguished by its great depth (5,710 feet), its huge volume, and its extraordinary transparency. The geologic formation of the graben occupied by the lake is still continuing and accompanied by frequent earthquakes. It is surrounded by picturesque ranges consisting of crystalline rocks, which are the site of many hot springs. Another interesting aspect is offered by the original fauna and flora of Lake Baykal. Many species, including water plants, worms, mollusks, and fish, are found in no habitat other than Lake Baykal. Among them are the viviparous fish *golomyanka,* living at a considerable depth, and the *nerpa* seal.

The third largest river of Siberia, the Lena, rises near the northwestern shore of Lake Baykal, on the northern slope of the Baykal Range. In its upper course it cuts a deep valley through the Central Siberian uplands, and in places it forms gorges up to 1,000 feet deep; there are numerous rapids obstructing navigation. As it receives its main affluents, beginning with the Vitim and the Olekma rivers, the Lena gradually widens its course, becomes quieter, and forms many river islands. After receiving its largest affluents, the Aldan and the Vilyuy, the Lena becomes a majestic stream, truly a fresh-water sea flowing towards the Arctic Ocean. In its lower course, the Lena lacks any significant affluents and enters the Laptev Sea of the Arctic Ocean through a huge delta of about 7,000 square miles consisting of a multitude of islands and waterways of various sizes. In addition to the Yenisey and the Lena, a number of lesser, but still very large, streams flow into the Arctic Ocean. Until recently very little was known about them, but since the establishment of the Northern Sea Route they are also being opened to navigation. They comprise, between the Yenisey and the Lena, the Khatanga, the Anabar, and the Olenek rivers, and east of the Lena River, the Yana, the Indigirka, and the Kolyma rivers.

The climate of Eastern Siberia is still more continental and more severe than that of Western Siberia. The yearly isotherms no longer adhere to the parallels and slope toward the south. For example, the yearly freezing isotherm (32° F), which in the European USSR passes through Arkhangel'sk (at 64° N latitude) and in Western Siberia through Tobol'sk and Tomsk (at 56° N latitude), passes still farther south in Eastern Siberia to the vicinity of Krasnoyarsk and Irkutsk. Almost everywhere in Eastern Siberia about 180 days of the year have average daily temperatures below freezing.

Although Eastern Siberia covers a very large area, extending over 30 degrees of latitude, the climatic conditions are rather uniform. Winter is the longest and the most significant season throughout the region, even in the south, where the average elevation above sea-level is rather high. In general, winter temperatures are 15–20° lower in Eastern Siberia than they are in the west. Spring arrives late, but the temperature rises rapidly. In the southern Central Siberian uplands, daytime temperatures are rarely below freezing in the second half of May. During the same period midday temperatures often reach 55–60°, although they may drop to a few degrees above 0° F during the night. Toward the end of May, snow is left only in deep and protected crevasses and in the mountains. In the north, spring arrives two or three weeks later than in the south, and its arrival is accompanied by strong winds, called *purga*, which blow a cloud of tiny ice crystals off the snow-covered land.

Typically for the continental type of climate, temperature differences between winter and summer are excessive, and in Eastern Siberia summer highs reach 85° F. Before July, precipitation is negligible in the lowlands, a fact which hampers vegetation growth, especially in southern Transbaykalia. After the dry spell, rains usually occur in short, but heavy downpours. One month, September, can be called autumn, when the average daily temperature is still above freezing, but snow falls occasionally, and night temperatures hover again in the neighborhood of 10–15° F.

Temperature inversions caused by air drainage down the mountain slopes are very common. On clear nights the valley temperatures are much lower than those of the surrounding mountains. Spring and autumn frosts occur more often in the valley, and trees even bud on the slopes before they do in the valley. It is to these circumstances that a section of Eastern Siberia owes the title "pole of cold." Verkhoyansk is well known to have a January average of —59° F and a minimum of —90° F. The station at Oymyakon (formerly Oymekon), which was opened more recently, reports even lower temperatures.

The length of the winter, the low temperatures, and the thin snow cover in Eastern Siberia all combine to produce the maximum extent of permanently frozen subsoil. It is encountered at various depths, depending on the exposure to the sun, the nature of the soil, and other factors. It is the frozen subsoil which prevents ground-water drainage and produces the great, if inconstant, volume of the Siberian streams. It slows the production of decayed vegetation and humus, resulting in a meager plant cover. It presents no obstacle to agriculture, with the exception of necessity for special treatment of the acid soil, but does render difficult any construction or road-building work. A slow, gradual regression of the frozen subsoil has been noted in areas inhabited and developed by man to a large extent.

The greater part of Eastern Siberia lies in the taiga zone, the remainder in the north is tundra, and only a narrow, interrupted belt in the south has wooded and grassy steppes.

The steppes of southern Transbaykalia represent a penetration into the USSR of the extensive Mongolian steppes and deserts. Here, near the border of the Mongolian People's Republic, steppe vegetation even covers the crest of low ranges; farther north, it appears only as separate "islands" in the lower areas and gradually becomes wooded. Birch clusters are most common, with occasional pine or larch. Amid the prevailing black earth appear some salt flats and even small salt lakes.

North of 50° N latitude, the taiga is most common in the higher areas, and farther north it covers the entire Central Siberian uplands, thinning out gradually toward the north. In the south, the taiga includes larch and pine, with a sprinkling of birch, poplar, alder, and aspen. In the north, it is all larch, the Daurian variety being dominant. In low, moist spots spruce and fir form the so-called "black" taiga. Forest fires are common, and in many areas ashes cover huge expanses.

North of the Arctic Circle the taiga gradually disappears, the trees decrease in size, and the hilly tundra assumes command. Here and there, along protected river valleys, narrow taiga belts brave the rigorous climate and penetrate as far north as 72° N latitude, the northernmost limit of forest vegetation anywhere in the world.

The most important single resource is coal, which appears in the Cheremkhovo, the Kansk, the Yenisey, the Tunguska, and the Yakut basins. Most of the deposits are still unexploited, due to their isolation and remoteness from transportation routes. Coal has also been located in the Taymyr Peninsula, along the Laptev Sea, and in the Cherskiy Range—huge reserves that will probably not be touched for many years hence. Gold is mined in many areas in the south. Other deposits include nonferrous and rare metals: nickel, platinum, tin, tungsten, molybdenum, and polymetallic ores.

With a total population of 5,550,000, spread over an area of about 2.8 million square miles, Eastern Siberia has an average density of 2 per square mile. Only the Irkutsk and the Chita oblasts and the Buryat-Mongol Autonomous SSR have a density of population much above this average. In the Yakut Autonomous SSR it is 0.4, and in the northern areas there is one person for every 30 square miles. Nowhere else in the USSR, with the exception of the northern Urals and the deserts of Central Asia, does the population density sink so low. Huge areas are almost uninhabited, the population being concentrated along the river valleys and in the south along the Trans-Siberian Railroad.

The dominant Russian element of the population lives generally south of 60° N latitude in the west, and further south in the east, that is, along the Trans-Siberian and in the economically more developed areas. The main non-Russian groups are the Tuvinians and the Khakass in the southwest, the Buryat-Mongols in the southeast, and the Yakuts in the northeast. Except for the Buryat-Mongols, these nationalities belong to the Turkic group. Among the northern peoples, the Evenki (Tungus), the most numerous, live throughout the central section of Eastern Siberia. Smaller nationalities belong to the Finno-Ugric group (Nentsy), to the Tungus-Manchurian group (Dolgany, Eveny, and Evenki), and to the Paleoasiatic group (Kety and Oduly).

The natural limits of Eastern Siberia do not correspond exactly with the political-administrative boundaries of the units included within that region. Thus, Krasnoyarsk Kray comprises a portion of Western Siberia, west of the Yenisey, and the Kolyma (Gydan) and Anadyr' ranges in the extreme northeast of the natural region of Eastern Siberia are included within Khabarovsk Kray in the Far East.

Beside Krasnoyarsk Kray, the purely administrative (Russian) units include Irkutsk and Chita oblasts. The non-Russian nationalities are organized into autonomous units of varied importance. The Yakuts and Buryat-Mongols each have an autonomous SSR, the Tuvinians and the Khakass have autonomous oblasts, and the Evenki, the Dolgany, and the Nentsy have national okrugs.

In the national economy of the USSR, Eastern Siberia serves mainly as a supplier of lumber, furs, and gold. In the future, however, due to the extensive and only partially surveyed mineral resources, this region is bound to become one of the industrial bases of the country. For the present, most of the mining and manufacturing industries serve only local needs.

Coal basins have been developed in the areas of Cheremkhovo, Kansk, and Minusinsk, and a large portion of the tungsten and tin of the USSR is produced in the Buryat-Mongol Autonomous SSR and in Chita Oblast. Machine-building industries have been established in the larger cities along the Trans-Siberian, which is also the site of most of the sawmills and the food-processing plants engaged in flour milling, meat packing, and dairying.

The possibilities for the development of agriculture are less than they are in Western Siberia. The suitable steppe areas, with their black-earth and chestnut soils, form only small islands in the taiga, with the exception of the Minusinsk basin, which includes extensive farm lands. In spite of the handicaps, such as the mountainous relief, the severe climate, the light summer rainfall, frozen subsoil conditions, and the swampiness of many areas, agriculture penetrates surprisingly far northward. Hardy grains, including barley, spring rye and wheat grow on the Arctic Circle; potatoes and vegetables thrive even farther north, thanks to the warm summer and especially to the length of the summer days and consequent intensive insolation. For example, the period of growth and ripening of grain in the north of Yakutia is eighty to ninety days, or fifteen days less than in the Irkutsk area. Although the sown area has been increased considerably in recent years, Eastern Siberia is still dependent on grain import. The non-Russian population, Yakuts in the north and Buryats in the south, engage chiefly in livestock raising. The Evenki breed reindeer, but have also partly adopted a settled mode of life.

The chief, and often the only, means of transportation in most parts of Eastern Siberia are the rivers, and their importance has increased immeasurably since the organization of the Northern Sea Route. The Yenisey, the Lena, their affluents, and many of the smaller rivers are part of this gigantic water transportation system. The Trans-Siberian Railroad serves only the extreme southern part of the region. A few branch lines link it with the frontier or with important economic areas. The South Siberian trunk line, which is to be completed after 1950, will serve the extreme southwest of Eastern Siberia through Abakan to Tayshet. A few important highways connect the railroad trunk with areas to the north, and isolated points are served by air.

Krasnoyarsk Kray
Capital, Krasnoyarsk; area, 928,000, population, 2,100,000

Krasnoyarsk Kray extends from the Arctic Ocean in the north to the Sayan Mountains in the south over an area of 928,000 square miles. In the extreme south it comprises the Minusinsk basin, a plateau at an average elevation of 1,500 feet, which is surrounded by the Eastern and the Western Sayans and the Kuznetsk Ala-Tau. This area enjoys a dry climate, with snowless winters and steppe vegetation, making it one of the best agricultural regions of Eastern Siberia. Summer averages of over 70° F are sufficient not only for wheat but also for sugar beets; unfortunately, there is sometimes too little precipitation.

About 100 miles north of the Trans-Siberian Railroad, which passes through the wooded steppe zone, begins the taiga which stretches almost without interruption to the Arctic Circle. The left bank of the Yenisey, which forms the axial artery of the kray, is part of the West Siberian lowland and rises to an elevation of only 150 to 180 feet. The marshiness and the slow flowing of the rivers of the left bank present a sharp contrast to the higher right bank with its abundant streams studded with rapids. Beyond the Arctic Circle, the taiga makes way for the wooded tundra, followed by the tundra. At about 70° N latitude, the right-bank plateau ends, and both banks of the Yenisey form an extensive lowland near the mouth. In the far north, the great Taymyr Peninsula presents a typical Arctic desert.

The population of about 2,100,000 consists mainly of Russians in the south, below 59° N latitude; in the north are the Evenki (Tungus), the Kety, along the middle Yenisey, and the Dolgany and the Nganasany (Tavgiytsy), a branch of the Nentsy (Samoyed) people, in the Taymyr Peninsula. In the extreme southwest are the Khakass, a Turkic group.

Krasnoyarsk Kray was formed in 1934 and includes the Khakass Autonomous Oblast and the Taymyr (Dolgan-Nenets) and Evenki national okrugs, all formed in 1930.

KRASNOYARSK KRAY PROPER (area, 301,400, population, 1,750,000) maintains industries of national importance—gold-mining and lumbering. The chief gold-bearing areas are on the southern slopes of the Eastern Sayan, in the vicinity of Artemovsk (formerly Olkhovskiy), and the near-by town of Chibizhek, as well as in the Yenisey Ridge, north of the Yenisey-Angara confluence, where the main sites are Severo-Yeniseyskiy, Yuzhno-Yeniseyskiy, Ayakhta, Novo-Yerudinskiy, and Pit-Gorodok. Near Razdolinsk, in the same area, there are deposits of antimony, gold, magnesite, and mica. Bauxite is mined along the Tatarka River, just to the west, and graphite at Kureyka, near Igarka.

Other mining industries include the brown coal mines in the Kansk basin, with the chief mine at Irsha, and the Chulym basin (centered on Nazarovo), the manganese mine at Mazul'skiy, a southwestern suburb of Achinsk, kaolin clay quarries at Uyar, and mica quarries at Barga, to the north.

The chief sawmilling centers are located along the Trans-Siberian (Krasnoyarsk, Kansk) and along the Yenisey River (Predivinsk, Yeniseysk with its southern suburb of Maklakovo, and Igarka).

Machine-building industry, including the manufacture of mining machinery, and locomotive works are located at Krasnoyarsk. Other large towns of the kray, Achinsk, Kansk, and Minusinsk, have light manufacturing and food-processing industries (dairying, flour milling, meat packing, and clothing manufacturing). A large glass works is at Pamyati 13 Bortsov, a town northwest of Krasnoyarsk named in the "memory of 13 fighters" who died in the revolutionary struggles. Predivinsk is a shipbuilding town north of Krasnoyarsk.

In the steppe regions around Kansk, Achinsk, and Minusinsk are primarily wheat-growing and dairy-farming areas. Many small towns and villages specialize in dairy products. Flax, northern hemp, and sunflowers are also raised. The farms in the vicinity of Krasnoyarsk send truck produce into the urban area. In the forest clearings north of the Trans-Siberian, corn and potatoes form the chief crops.

In the higher areas, sheep are raised for meat and wool, and there are also horse-breeding farms.

The Trans-Siberian Railroad passes through the southern and most developed section of the kray. On it lie most of the large towns: Bogotol, Achinsk, Krasnoyarsk, Uyar, Kansk, and Ilanskiy. At Achinsk a branch railway goes south through the Khakass Autonomous Oblast to its capital, Abakan, where it will connect with the South Siberian trunk line. The Abakan-Tayshet section of this new railway leads through difficult mountain country of the Sayan ranges and is to be completed after 1950.

The Yenisey is navigable for steamers below Minusinsk for five months of the year in the upper and the middle course, and for only about three months in the lower course. The navigation season is the busiest time of the year for Igarka, for all the lumber which has been processed during the year must be loaded onto ships which have to be out of Arctic waters by October or run the risk of being frozen in.

Krasnoyarsk, capital and metropolis of Krasnoyarsk Kray, is a former military outpost founded on the left bank of the Yenisey River early in the seventeenth century. Having grown rapidly under the Soviets, it now has a population of about 300,000 and important industries such as locomotive works, paper and cellulose mills, a gold-mining machinery plant, sawmills, refrigerating plants, and flour mills. It also produces farm combines, drilling machinery, and cement. Owing to the expansion of its industries, the city now occupies both banks of the river at the intersection of the Trans-Siberian Railroad.

Achinsk, an agricultural center on the Chulym River and on the Trans-Siberian at the junction of the branch to Abakan, has dairying, meatpacking, and flour-milling industries. Near by are the Mazul'skiy manganese mines.

Kansk on the Kan River (a right affluent of the Yenisey), is the center of a rich farming district and of the Kansk lignite basin. It has the first large cotton mill of Eastern Siberia, built during the Second World War.

Minusinsk, the hub of the Minusinsk coal-mining and farming region lies on the right bank of the Yenisey River, opposite Abakan, the capital of the Khakass Autonomous Oblast. On the opposite bank of the river are also the Chernogorsk coal mines. Minusinsk is the point of origin of the Usa highway which crosses the Western Sayan Mountains into Tuva Autonomous Oblast.

Igarka, the major sawmilling center of the kray, lies on the right bank of the lower Yenisey, 425 miles from the mouth. It was founded in the late 1920's and rapidly developed into an important lumber port. It is the largest Siberian city (population, 25,000) north of the Arctic Circle.

THE KHAKASS AUTONOMOUS OBLAST (capital, Abakan; area, 24,000, population, 300,000) is situated in the mountainous country bordered by the Abakan range in the west and the Sayans in the south, in the extreme southwest of Krasnoyarsk Kray, this oblast has an industry based primarily on the rich mineral resources and livestock breeding. The population is half Russian and half Khakass.

Important coal mines are operating at Chernogorsk [black mountain], just northwest of Abakan and on a short spur of the Achinsk-Abakan rail line. At Askiz, barite, one of the basic materials for the paint industry, is quarried in large quantities. West of Abakan, in the mountains, large iron deposits have been surveyed. They are destined to feed the steel mills of Stalinsk in the Kuzbas, and their exploitation awaits only the completion of the South Siberian railway. The most important single mining industry is devoted to gold. The main mines lie all along the Abakan range and bear strange-sounding Khakass names or Eldorado-type denominations: in the north, Znamenityy [famous], Zolotogorskiy [gold mountain], Kommunar, Ordzhonikidzevskiy, Priiskovyy [placer], Tuim, and Balakhchin; in the south, Balyksa, and Kyzas.

The Khakass engage in lumbering and livestock raising. The timber is brought to sawmills at Sonskiy (on the Achinsk-Abakan Railroad) and Sarala, the site of a hydroelectric station. Cattle and sheep are raised mainly for hides, wool, and meat.

Abakan, the capital of the oblast, near the confluence of the Abakar and the Yenisey rivers, is a town of about 40,000 inhabitants. Its meat-packing plant processes most of the cattle products of the mountain zone. It also has sawmills and various light industries. When the South Siberian Railroad is completed, Abakan is bound to increase considerably in importance.

Chernogorsk, the coal-mining center near Abakan, supplies Krasnoyarsk with fuel.

THE EVENKI NATIONAL OKRUG (capital, Tura; area, 285,900, population, 25,000) occupies the entire central section of Krasnoyarsk Kray, with the exception of the middle Yenisey valley. The Evenki (Tungus) outnumber the other inhabitants, which include also some Yakuts in the Yessey area in the northeast. The economy is typical of that of all northern areas, fishing, reindeer raising, and fur trapping being the principal occupations. Among the mineral resources, graphite is being mined at Noginsk, on the Nizhnyaya Tunguska, and Iceland spar (a variety of calcite) is available in the vicinity of Tura. Many trading posts and cultural bases line the banks of the main rivers.

Tura, formerly called Turinskaya Kul'tbaza, is the administrative and cultural center of the okrug. It is the site of a polar station; some vegetables and other hardy crops are grown near by. Other important settlements are Baykit and Vanavara.

THE TAYMYR NATIONAL OKRUG (capital, Dudinka; area, 316,700, population, 25,000) was formerly known as the Dolgan-Nenets National Okrug, so named for its two most numerous nationalities, the Dolgany, of the Tungus family, and the Nganasany, a branch of the Nentsy (Samoyeds). The Dolgany are settled along the lower Khatanga and the upper Pyasina rivers. Russians inhabit the shores of the Yenisey, while the Nganasany roam the frozen wastes of the Taymyr peninsula.

In addition to the basic northern industries, the Taymyr National Okrug has several important mining establishments. Noril'sk, a mining town of several thousand inhabitants, has deposits of nickel, platinum, copper, and coal. It is linked by a sixty-mile narrow-gauge line with the port of Dudinka on the Yenisey. The ores are refined at the polymetallic works near the mines. It is planned to render the Pyasina River navigable in order to transport the ores directly by water from the Noril'sk mines. Extensive petroleum deposits have been surveyed in the Nordvik area (formerly part of the Yakut Autonomous SSR). Salt for the fishing industry is also obtained there. Other petroleum fields are springing up along the Malaya Kheta River, a short left affluent of the Yenisey, near its mouth. A fish cannery is operating at Ust-Yeniseysk.

A narrow belt extending from Dudinka northwest to Khatanga and Nordvik includes most of the sedentary population, the majority of the reindeer herds, as well as many trading and cultural posts. Polar stations dot the coast of the Arctic Ocean. The major ports and supply points of the Great Northern Sea Route are Dikson (Dickson), on a small island at the base of Yenisey Gulf, site of a polar station and coal depot, and Nordvik, the oil supply base and salt-producing center on Khatanga Gulf. Cape Chelyuskin, at the tip of the Taymyr peninsula, has a polar station and an air base. Most of the polar stations, ports, and important settlements are linked by air services, which are the only means of transportation during a good part of the year.

The archipelago of Severnaya Zemlya, lying north of the Taymyr peninsula, and several smaller islands in the Kara Sea, are attached to the Taymyr National Okrug. They are the site of several polar stations.

Dudinka, the capital, serves as Yenisey river port for the Noril'sk mines.

Tuva Autonomous Oblast
Capital, Kyzyl; area, 66,100, population, 150,000

Tuva Autonomous Oblast is the only administrative division of this type in the USSR, which is not part of an oblast or a kray. Its status, within the Russian SFSR, is equal to that of an autonomous SSR, an oblast, or a kray.

The area now included in Tuva Autonomous Oblast was formerly known as Uryankhay. In 1914 it was incorporated into the Russian Empire, after having been a Russian protectorate for two years. Following the disorders connected with the civil war in Russia, the Tuva People's Republic, better known as Tannu-Tuva until 1934, became an independent state under the tutelage of the USSR. In 1944 the Tuva People's Republic, on the occasion of the twenty-third anniversary of its independence, petitioned the USSR for admission into the Soviet Union. On October 11, 1944, the petition was accepted by the Supreme Soviet of the USSR, and the area was incorporated into Soviet territory with the status of autonomous oblast. The population includes about 90,000 Tuvinians, a national group related to the Kirghiz.

This region lies nearly at the geographical center of the Asiatic con-

tinent in a mountain basin about 2,000 feet high and circled by ranges
rising to 9,000 feet. It is drained by the headwaters of the Yenisey
River (the Bol'shoy [great] Yenisey or Biy-Khem, the Malyy [little]
Yenisey or Kaa-Khem, and the Khemchik) and is bounded by the Sayan
Mountains on the north and northeast and the range Tannu-Ula on
the south. According to the climatic conditions, which are generally
of the dry continental type, Tuva is divided into a forested, elevated
region in the east, with a sparse population engaged in reindeer breeding and fur trapping, and a drier lowland section in the west, where
a denser population engages in agriculture, chiefly the cultivation of
wheat and other grains, with the help of some irrigation, and raises
dairy cattle.

Tuva is rich in mineral resources; however, due to transportation
difficulties, their exploitation is still in the primary stages. The construction of a narrow-gauge railway from the coal mines at Irbek to Kyzyl
will improve considerably the supply of coal. Other important deposits
include salt (north of lake Ubsu-Nur), gold (in placers along the
upper course of its rivers), and iron, copper, and asbestos (near
Chadan).

The capital, Kyzyl, was formerly known variously as Belotsarsk
(until 1921), Krasny, Khem-Belder, and Kyzyl-Khoto. It is connected
by a good highway across the Sayan Mountains with Minusinsk and
lies at the union of the two headstreams of the Yenisey, the Biy-Khem
and the Kaa-Khem. It has developed into a modern town, with several
stone buildings, including the administration headquarters, and is linked
by roads and air services with the remote parts of the oblast.

Other important towns are Turan, northwest of Kyzyl, on the highway to Minusinsk, Shagonar, on the Yenisey below Kyzyl, and Chadan
and Kyzyl-Mazhalyk, in the Khemchik valley, the chief agricultural
area of the oblast.

Irkutsk Oblast
Capital, Irkutsk; area, 301,900, population, 1,200,000

Irkutsk Oblast lies in the southeastern section of the Central Siberian
uplands, west and north of Lake Baykal, and is drained by the upper
courses of the Angara, the Nizhnyaya Tunguska, and the Lena rivers.
Its average altitude is 1,300 to 2,000 feet; the highest points (over
7,000 feet) are in the Eastern Sayan, in the extreme southwest of the
oblast, and in the northern part of the Baykal range. The greater por-

tion of the oblast is covered with pine taiga, which turns into a larch forest in the northeast. The best agricultural areas (wooded and grassy steppe) lie along the Trans-Siberian Railroad in the south and the southwest, where gray forest soil and leached black earth are most common.

The population consists mainly of Russians in the southern part and along the Lena and the Vitim rivers and of Evenki (Tungus) in the north. A sizable group of Buryat-Mongols is organized into a national okrug.

Irkutsk Oblast presents the rare combination of three important power resources: lumber, coal, and water-power. The forested area is larger than that of the richest lumber region in the European USSR, Arkhangel'sk Oblast; the coal reserves exceed those of the Donbas, and the water-power which can be harnessed from the Angara River alone is equal to the output of ten Dneproges stations.

The coal mines are concentrated in the area of Cheremkhovo, on the Trans-Siberian and northwest of Irkutsk, and at Golovinskaya, farther northwest along the railroad and in the Ust'-Orda Buryat-Mongol National Okrug, but the Cheremkhovo coal basin extends over 150 miles along the Trans-Siberian from Lake Baykal to Nizhneudinsk.

Here also gold is the chief product; it is obtained chiefly in the Bodaybo region, where the gold-bearing area spreads over the Patom plateau, between the Vitim and the Lena rivers. The main operating mines are Andreyevsk, Aprel'sk, Artemovskiy, Kropotkin, and Svetlyy. A mining railway connects them with Bodaybo, the supply base on the Vitim River. Gold is also mined on a lesser scale along the upper Biryusa River in the southwest of the oblast. The mineral mica is produced in large quantities along the Mama River, an affluent of the Vitim, northwest of Bodaybo, at Slyudyanka (from *slyuda*, the Russian word for mica), at the southwestern end of Lake Baykal, and also on the upper Biryusa. At Usol'ye-Sibirskoye, a city between Irkutsk and Cheremkhovo, salt mines and oil wells are located near each other. Other deposits include manganese on Ol'khon Island of Lake Baykal and very rich iron deposits (which have not yet been worked to any great degree) along the Ilim and the Angara rivers.

The existing natural resources form the basis for engineering industries (Irkutsk), shipbuilding (Kirensk, Zhigalovo, Osetrovo on the Lena River, and Listvyanka on Lake Baykal), lumbering, woodworking, and match industries (mostly along the Trans-Siberian, notably at

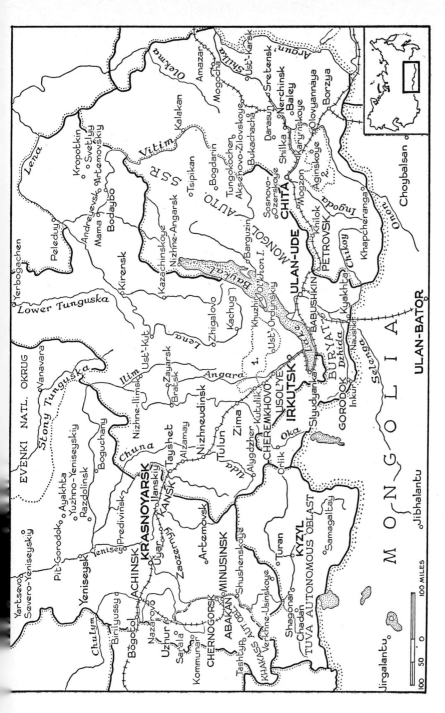

EASTERN SIBERIA (SOUTHERN PORTION)

(1) Ust'-Orda Buryat-Mongol National Okrug; (2) Aga Buryat-Mongol National Okrug

Suyetikha near Tayshet, Nizhneudinsk, Tulun, Zima, Usol'ye-Sibir-skoye, Kitoy, and Tal'tsy), and glass and ceramic industries (Tal'tsy and Mishelevka), based on local clay and quartz. The agricultural products are processed in flour mills and meat-packing plants.

The chief agricultural areas extend from Irkutsk northeastward into the Ust'-Orda Buryat-Mongol National Okrug, and from Usol'ye-Sibirskoye and Cheremkhovo northward along the Angara River to the vicinity of Ust'-Uda. The chief crops comprise wheat and other grains. Truck produce is grown around the larger cities. Cattle raising with emphasis on meat and dairy products is also chiefly along the Trans-Siberian.

Ol'khon Island in Lake Baykal is the hub of the fishing industry. The principal types are sturgeon, salmon, and umbra.

As in the case of the other sections of Eastern Siberia, the Trans-Siberian constitutes also here the basic transportation route, but it serves only the southernmost sections of the oblast. Improved highways connect important cities on the railroad (Irkutsk, Zima, Tulun) with the ports on the upper Lena River (Kachug, Zhigalovo, and Ust'-Kut).

Tayshet, a city on the Trans-Siberian near the border of Krasno-yarsk Kray, will be the eastern terminus of the South Siberian trunk line. It was from this station that construction on the Baykal-Amur *magistral* [trunk line], commonly known as BAM, was begun, in 1938. This railroad was intended to pass north of Lake Baykal and parallel to the existing line as far as Komsomol'sk in the Far East. The purpose was admittedly to construct a line which was less vulnerable to attack than the exposed Trans-Siberian which hugs the frontier of the USSR. By 1939, according to Soviet publications, the line had been pushed from Tayshet past Bratsk and on to Ust'-Kut on the upper Lena River. During the Second World War conflicting reports reached the United States with respect to the progress of construction. Maps were published showing the railroad as completed, unequivocally and without any reservations. Still Soviet publications do not acknowledge or even discuss the construction of the line to this day. Soviet maps published since 1944 do show feeder lines such as those leading from the Trans-Siberian north to Tyndynskiy and Ust'-Niman as completed, but the Baykal-Amur *magistral* itself is reduced to the short section Tayshet-Bratsk (shown as under construction in 1944). This is only part of the section which was acknowledged as completed in 1939. In view of the official Soviet silence, one can only surmise the present status of the railway. Some authorities see it as nearing completion, with a huge war-prisoner and slave labor force at work on the final sections; others believe that the entire project is no longer being pressed, because of the absence of the Japanese threat, and that materials and labor are being applied to the construction of the South Siberian trunk line and other immediate projects. Based on the available evidence, the latter explanation seems to carry more weight.

Navigation routes have been established on Lake Baykal, on the upper Lena below Kachug, Zhigalovo, or Ust'-Kut (depending on the water level and the draft of the vessel), and on the upper Angara between Lake Baykal and the rapids which begin at Bratsk. These rapids are to be used to create one of the most powerful systems of hydroelectric stations of the USSR. Other hydroelectric installations are projected for the Lake Baykal-Irkutsk section of the Angara River. This project, one of several of the 1938–42 Plan that were not realized, due to the war, is still in the planning stage, but may become part of a future Five-Year Plan.

Irkutsk lies on the right bank of the Angara River, opposite the mouth of the Irkut, about forty miles below Lake Baykal. Since the construction of the Trans-Siberian along the left bank of the Angara and the development of industrial suburbs (linked by a bridge with Irkutsk proper), the city has expanded considerably onto the opposite Angara bank. Long a supply point for the Bodaybo gold fields, it now manufactures gold-dredging machinery. It also produces machine tools and plywood; mica from the Mama district is processed here. Typical of the industrial development of Irkutsk is the left-bank suburb Zhilkino. A village of 400 inhabitants in 1920, it developed into a town of 9,000 by 1947, producing meat, flour, soap, and cattle feed. Irkutsk is the seat of a university and is considered the educational center of Eastern Siberia.

Cheremkhovo is the center of the Cheremkhovo coal basin extending northwest of Irkutsk along the Trans-Siberian Railroad.

Usol'ye, or Usol'ye-Sibirskoye, is another industrial center between Irkutsk and Cheremkhovo, having a chemical industry based on the local salt deposits.

THE UST'-ORDA BURYAT-MONGOL NATIONAL OKRUG (capital, Ust'-Ordynskiy; area, 8,000, population, 100,000) was formerly part of the Buryat-Mongol Autonomous SSR. At the time of the formation of

Irkutsk Oblast, in 1937, this okrug was organized in order to provide local autonomy for about 50,000 Buryat-Mongols who live in the predominantly Russian oblast.

The population is engaged primarily in agriculture (wheat) and livestock raising (dairy products and meat). The largest settlements are Kutulik, on the Trans-Siberian, and Ust-Ordynskiy, a food-processing center on the Irkutsk-Kachug highway.

Buryat-Mongol Autonomous Soviet Socialist Republic
Capital, Ulan-Ude; area, 135,700, population, 600,000

The Buryat-Mongol Autonomous SSR lies for the most part in Transbaykalia, between Lake Baykal and the Yablonovyy range, and only a narrow tongue extends southwest of the lake. Uplands and mountains are the prevailing land forms, including the Sayans and the range Khamar-Daban, south of Lake Baykal, and the Barguzin range, to the east. All the important rivers of Buryat-Mongolia, the Selenga, the Barguzin, and the Verkhnyaya [upper] Angara, flow into the lake.

About three fourths of the area of the republic is forested, chiefly with coniferous trees (larch, pine, and cedar). Treeless steppes are found only in certain lower regions, such as the Selenga valley, south of Ulan-Ude, where over one half the population is settled. The north and the northeast are sparsely inhabited. The Buryats, a Mongolian group, comprise about one half the total population, the remainder including chiefly Russians and some Evenki (Tungus) in the north.

The Buryat-Mongol Autonomous SSR was formed in 1923, out of the Buryat-Mongol and the Mongol-Buryat autonomous oblasts created two years earlier. Until 1937 the republic included two sections inhabited by Buryat-Mongols, which are now organized as national okrugs within the Irkutsk and the Chita oblasts.

One of the more important gold-mining areas lies in the Vitim Plateau, east of Lake Baykal; its chief mines are at Bogdarin, Tsipikan, and Baunt. Iron is mined in the Balbagar area along the Kurba River, an affluent of the Uda. Oil wells have been drilled at the mouth of the Selenga and southwest along the shore of Lake Baykal. Goose Lake, known in Russian as *Gusinoye Ozero*, is the site of extensive brown coal mines, where an underground coal-gas plant has been established in recent years. Important tungsten and molybdenum mines have been developed around the new city of Gorodok, on the upper Dzhida River.

Railway-car and locomotive works have been erected at Ulan-Ude during the second (1933–37) Five-Year Plan. Ulan-Ude also has a large meat-packing plant, glass factories, flour mills, and sawmills. Other lumber mills are along the Trans-Siberian Railroad at Il'inskoye and Babushkin. Fisheries and canning plants are located along Lake Baykal, the most important ones at Nizhne-Angarsk, Ust'-Barguzin, and Kabansk. A large tanning plant at Chikoy, east of Kyakhta, processes skins and hides from the entire southern section of the republic. To preserve and breed the sable, one of the more valuable fur animals, a reserve has been created on Lake Baykal, north of Barguzin.

Agricultural activity is restricted to the Selenga valley, south of Ulan-Ude, where wheat and other grains are grown. They are brought to flour mills in the vicinity of Ulan-Ude. In the vicinity of that city, truck produce is the chief farming product. Lesser agricultural areas have been developed near Sosnovo-Ozerskoye, in the Barguzin valley, and near the delta of the Selenga River. Further expansion in the drier regions would necessitate the creation of irrigation systems.

Most of the rural Buryat-Mongols engage in livestock raising, with emphasis on meat and wool production. Former nomadic herdsmen have adopted a settled mode of life, and have modernized and rationalized the raising and breeding of livestock, adopted the policy of preparing winter-hay, and so forth.

The Trans-Siberian Railroad crosses the republic in the south. From Ulan-Ude a branch runs to the Mongolian border at Naushki, just west of Kyakhta.* Two important automobile highways lead into the Mongolian People's Republic. The road from Irkutsk passes Kultuk, at the southwest end of Lake Baykal, crosses the western panhandle of the Buryat-Mongol Autonomous SSR, and passes into Mongolia at the frontier town of Mondy. Another highway leads from Ulan-Ude via Kyakhta to the Mongolian capital, Ulan-Bator. The tungsten mine of Gorodok is also supplied by a good highway from Ulan-Ude. There is navigation on the Selenga and on Lake Baykal.

Ulan-Ude, the capital, was formerly called Verkhneudinsk. It is situated at the confluence of the Uda and the Selenga rivers and the Trans-Siberian Railroad. It has developed rapidly since the 1930's in connection with the establishment of new industries (locomotive and car-building works and glass, lumber, and meat-packing plants) and has

---

* In 1949 this line was extended to Ulan-Bator, the capital of the Mongolian People's Republic.

now a population of about 150,000, one fourth that of the entire republic.

Babushkin (until 1941 called Mysovsk) is the chief lumber-milling center of the republic.

Gorodok, which developed in the late 1930's, has tungsten and molybdenum mines and a refinery on the upper Dzhida River.

Chita Oblast
Capital, Chita; area, 168,200, population, 1,050,000

Chita Oblast is located between the frontier of the USSR with Mongolia and China in the south and the Yablonovyy range in the north. Its relief is largely mountainous. In the south, several mountain ranges extend parallel to the Yablonovyy range, from southwest to northeast, the highest Borshchovochnyy range reaching altitudes of more than 8,000 feet. The southern and northeastern sections of the oblast are drained by the headstreams of the Amur River: the Shilka, which is formed by the union of the Onon and the Ingoda rivers, and the Argun', which rises in Manchuria and forms a long section of the USSR–China frontier. The Shilka joins the Argun' to form the Amur River, which flows along the frontier to the vicinity of Khabarovsk. The northern section falls within the Lena basin; it is drained by the Olekma and the Vitim, which forms the boundary between Chita Oblast and the Buryat-Mongol Autonomous SSR.

The climate is of the continental type, with little precipitation (12 to 18 inches yearly in the east) and very severe winters. The January average at Sretenskis —25° F. In large areas of the oblast the soil is permanently frozen. The forests are coniferous, pine prevailing in the west, and a combination of pine and larch in the east. Only the driest part, the extreme south, has steppe vegetation (Aga Steppe).

Russians form the majority of the population of the oblast and are concentrated in a wide belt along the Trans-Siberian Railroad. The north is inhabited by Evenki (Tungus), and a small Buryat-Mongol group is organized into the Aga Buryat-Mongol National Okrug.

Chita Oblast is very rich in mineral resources, chiefly lead-zinc ores, gold, and other rare metals, as well as coal and iron. Lead, zinc, and silver are mined at many sites along the Argun' River, extending from Ust'-Karsk in the north past Nerchinskiy Zavod to Aleksandrovskiy Zavod in the south. Refining works are located at Zapokrovskiy, northeast of Byrka.

Gold is mined at Darasun and Baley, two new cities east of Chita, along the upper Olekma River and its affluent, the Tungir, with the centers at Imeni 11 Oktyabrya and Itaka, northeast of Mogocha.

Chita Oblast is one of the most important tin-mining regions of the USSR. Tin ores are mined in the area of Khapcheranga, including Mangut, just east, and Sokhondo Peak, to the northwest, and in the Borzya-Olovyannaya (from *olovo*, the Russian word for tin) area, notably at Sherlovaya Gora. Other rare metals are molybdenum, produced at Gutay and Vershino-Shakhtaminskiy, and tungsten, which is obtained at Bukuka and Kolanguy, east of Olovyannaya.

The principal coal mines are at Chernovskiye Kopi, western suburb of Chita, and Bukachacha, on a short spur of the Trans-Siberian. Lesser locations are at Kholbon, west of Nerchinsk, and at Novo-Pavlovka, east of Petrovsk-Zabaykal'skiy. Except for Bukachacha, which produces good coking coal, the deposits include mainly brown coal. The iron ore is obtained at the Balyaginskiy mine, northwest of Petrovsk-Zabaykal'skiy, and at Berezovskoye, just south of Nerchinskiy Zavod, near the Argun' River.

An old iron foundry at Petrovsk-Zabaykal'skiy, working on the basis of the local coal and iron deposits, has been reconstructed and modernized into an up-to-date metallurgical plant. Other industries include machine building at Chita, shipbuilding at Kokuy, near Sretensk, and lumber mills and metalworks along the Trans-Siberian Railroad. Other towns have flour mills, tanneries, meat-packing plants based on the local agricultural production. There is a hot springs health resort at Yamarovka, south of Khilok.

Agriculture is developed only in the south, in the river valleys, and in the steppes on the USSR frontier. The chief crops are spring rye and wheat, the cold snowless winter prohibiting the cultivation of winter grain. Grain occupies about three fourths of the total sown area; the remainder is under flax and hay. Cattle breeding is very important, with emphasis on the production of butter and other dairy products.

The basic route is the Trans-Siberian Railroad, from which several important branch lines and highways lead to the frontier and into the northern areas. The Chinese Eastern Railway branches off near Karymskoye and enters Manchuria at Otpor station, having passed Olovyannaya and Borzya. From Borzya important narrow-gauge lines lead eastward to the Argun' River lead-zinc ore sites and southeastward to Choybalsan (formerly Bayan-Tumen) in the Mongolian People's

Republic. Short spurs connect the Trans-Siberian main line with Sretensk and Bukachacha.

Chita, the capital, is on the southern slope of the Yablonovyy range, near the Ingoda River, in a very picturesque valley surrounded by wooded hills. The coal-mining town of Chernovskiye Kopi was recently incorporated into the city. Chita has a locomotive works, sawmills, a meat-packing plant, and a well-developed sheepskin and leather industry.

Petrovsk-Zabaykal'skiy is another important industrial center.

AGA BURYAT-MONGOL NATIONAL OKRUG (capital, Aginskoye; area, 9,400, population, 30,000) was formerly part of the Buryat-Mongol Autonomous SSR and was created after the formation of Chita Oblast, in 1937, in order to give this nationality local autonomy. It is situated on the Aga River, in a livestock and agricultural area. The chief products are grain, butter, and lumber from the forested eastern part. The chief settlements comprise the administrative center, Aginskoye, Mogoytuy, on the Chinese Eastern branch of the Trans-Siberian, and Dul'durga, in the west.

Yakut Autonomous Soviet Socialist Republic
Capital, Yakutsk; area, 1,182,300, population, 450,000

The Yakuts are the most numerous of the native peoples of Siberia and inhabit a large region along the middle Lena River and its two main affluents, the Aldan and the Vilyuy, as well as smaller areas along the lower Lena and the Laptev Sea, the Yana River and the Indigirka.

While most of the other political-administrative units of Siberia have been delimited so as to include a portion of the economically developed and densely inhabited zone along the Trans-Siberian Railroad in addition to the sparsely populated areas of the north, the Yakut Autonomous SSR, which has been established on the basis of the dominant Yakut population, lies entirely within the tundra and taiga zones and does not extend as far south as the Trans-Siberian Railroad. The remoteness, lack of communications, and the sparsity of the population have been the chief obstacles to the development of the rich resources of this republic.

The Yakut Autonomous SSR is the largest single political-administrative unit of the Russian SFSR. Its area exceeds even that of any of the other fifteen union republics. It embraces the basins of the Lena; the Yana, and the Indigirka rivers, the Aldan plateau, and the Verkhoyansk and Cherskiy ranges. The distance across the republic is 1,250 miles from north to south and 900 miles from east to west. The winters are extremely cold, but the summers, though short, are warm and clear. The average July temperature at Yakutsk is 65° F, and the absolute maximum is as high as 90° F. As a result crops ripen even in the 90 to 110 frostless days. The lack of precipitation is partly made up by the presence of ground water resulting from the thawing of the upper soil layers.

In addition to the dominant Yakut element, the population includes Evenki (Tungus) in the south and Eveny (Lamuts) in the north. In the extreme northeast there are Oduly (Yukagirs) and Luoravetlany (Chukchi). There are Russians along the middle Lena, in the vicinity of Yakutsk, and at the mouth of the Yana, the Indigirka, and the Kolyma rivers.

The mineral resources of the Yakut Autonomous SSR form the main asset of the republic. Chief among them is gold, and among the gold-mining areas, the Aldan region is paramount. The mines, which have been mechanized to a large degree, furnish one fourth of the total gold production of the USSR. When this gold area began to be developed, in the early 1920's, the only route to the outside world led to Irkutsk via the Aldan River to the Lena and by highway from the upper course of the Lena to Irkutsk. This route was 2,500 miles long and was suitable only during the short summer. In order to improve the transportation of the gold, the important highway from Never, on the Trans-Siberian (near Skovorodino), to Aldan and from there to Yakutsk was constructed. The most important mining towns in the Aldan region are the city of Aldan (formerly Nezametnyy), Vtoroy-Orochen (formerly Sredne-Serebrovsk), Dzhekonda, Nizhne-Stalinsk, Orochen, Seligdar, Usmun, and more recently developed Verkhne-Stalinsk and Spokoynyy. Further south, along the highway and near the boundary of Amur Oblast, are Chul'man, Nagornyy, and Kabaktan.

In the years just preceding the Second World War another rich gold-bearing area was developed along the Allakh-Yun' River, an affluent of the Aldan, east of Yakutsk and on the western slopes of the Dzhugdzhur range. The center of the area is the town of Allakh-Yun', on the Okhotsk-Yakutsk highway. During 1940 the following mining towns were founded: Batylinskiy, Burkhalinskiy, Minorskiy, Yevkandzhinskiy, and Ynykchanskiy, and, in 1942, Yur. In 1948 the town of El'dikan was founded, southwest of Allakh-Yun'. Gold placers are also located along many other Yakut rivers, including the upper Anabar and the middle Vilyuy.

A huge coal-bearing basin is believed to exist along the middle and the lower Lena and its affluents. Mines are producing at present at Kangalasskiye Kopi, just north of Yakutsk, at Sangar, further downstream, and on the right bank of the Lena, at Bulun, near the Lena delta, at Verkhne-Vilyuysk, and at Zyryanka, on the Kolyma River.

Other important mines include the salt mines along the Kempendyay River, the iron mines along the lower Botoma River, an affluent of the Lena, the oil fields along the lower Tolba River, another Lena affluent, the lead-zinc and tin mines in the Verkhoyansk range, at Endybal'sk and Imtandzha, and the important tin mine at Ege-Khaya, on the Yana River below Verkhoyansk. Platinum, another important metal, occurs mainly along the upper Vilyuy River.

Lumbering has provided the basis for the shipbuilding industry at Peleduy, on the upper Lena. Other manufacturing industries include sawmills and woodworking plants at Peleduy and Yakutsk and clothing and shoe factories at Yakutsk.

During the war several important fishing establishments have been set up near and in the delta of the Lena River: Tumus, on Bykovskiy peninsula, north of Tiksi, Tit-Ara, on an island in the Lena River, and Trofimovsk, in the northeastern section of the delta.

Throughout the north, hunting and fur-trapping play an important role in the economy.

The agricultural region lies in the southwestern part of Yakutia, along the Lena and the Vilyuy rivers, in the lower course of the Aldan and along its affluent, the Amga. Here most of the Yakut population is concentrated, as well as the entire sown area and most of the livestock. It is the chief farming region in the northern section of Siberia. Wheat and other hardy grains are the basic crops.

In the north, reindeer raising furnishes most of the primary necessities of the population.

River fleets operate on the main rivers of the Yakut Autonomous SSR in conjunction with the Great Northern Sea Route. Beside the Lena, the Yana, the Indigirka, and the Kolyma have been opened to navigation.

Highways connect Yakutsk with Verkhoyansk, Okhotsk, Ayan, and the Amur River via the Aldan gold-bearing region. During the winter months air services bear the main transportation load throughout the Lena basin.

The chief ports along the Great Northern Sea Route are Tiksi, east of the Lena delta, and Ambarchik, east of the Kolyma mouth. The coast is supplied with many air bases, polar stations, and trading posts. One of the newest settlements combining all these functions is Chokurdakh, located on the lower Indigirka and just south of the old Yakut village of Allaykha.

Yakutsk, the capital, is the political and cultural center of the Yakut nation. It has become the center of the agricultural region and processes most of the farm products. It possesses sawmills, woodworking plants, and light manufacturing industries. The new town of Zhatay, on the Lena near by, has shipyards and construction industries.

Aldan, the center of the Aldan gold-mining district, was from 1939 to 1947 the seat of the Aldan administrative okrug, created especially to provide a separate administration for the gold fields.

Other important towns are Verkhoyansk, the center of the upper Yana valley, and Nizhne-Kolymsk, on the lower Kolyma River, both acting chiefly as fur-collection depots. On the Vilyuy is the large town of Vilyuysk, in a wheat and livestock-raising area. Olekminsk is a town on the Lena River near the mouth of the Olekma.

The islands north of the Yakut mainland, the New Siberian, Lyakhov, and De Long groups, form part of the Yakut Autonomous SSR. They have polar stations and deposits of mammoth ivory.

CHAPTER 15

Soviet Far East

THE SOVIET FAR EAST occupies the entire Pacific littoral of the Russian SFSR. This is the region farthest removed from the central European USSR and Moscow, which lies about 5,000 miles to the west. The vastness of the intervening country is best illustrated by the time difference of six hours between Moscow and Vladivostok.

The natural boundary of the Far East is formed in the west by the Stanovoy, Dzhugdzhur, Kolyma, and associated ranges, which separate the region from Eastern Siberia. In the south it extends to Pos'yet Gulf, near the intersection of the frontiers of the USSR, China, and Korea, and toward the north it spans 28 degrees of latitude to the Bering Strait, which separates the USSR from Alaska.

With an area of about 1,200,000 square miles, the Soviet Far East forms one of the largest natural regions of the USSR and at the same time one of the most variegated. All possible land forms are found here: from the steppes in the south to the foggy and inhospitable shores of Kamchatka and Sakhalin; from the pack ice near the Arctic islands to the deciduous woods of the southern Ussuri region. The Far East includes massive denuded mountain ranges, fertile grassy lowlands, and high volcanoes capped with eternal snows. All these diverse sections are united by one common geographic factor, the presence of the sea. The northwestern Pacific and its subsidiaries, the Bering Sea and the Sea of Okhotsk, not only contribute to the economic value of the Far East through the abundance of fish, seals, whales, and other marine animals, but they also form the major transportation route linking the scattered portions of the region.

From the point of view of relief conditions, the Far East may be divided into the following sections: the Amur region, the southern coastal area, Sakhalin and the Okhotsk littoral, Kamchatka and the Kurile Islands, and the Chukchi-Anadyr' region.

The Amur region, known in Russian as *Priamur'ye*, is the southwesternmost section of the Soviet Far East. It lies between the Stanovoy range in the north and the Amur River in the south and extends from Transbakalia to the Bureya range in the east. A secondary formation, consisting of the Yankan-Tukuringra-Dzhagdy ranges, lies south of the Stanovoy. The Bureya range, which rises to 14,000 feet in the north, slopes downward toward the south and passes into Manchuria as the Little Khingan range. The latter name is sometimes applied to the southern part of the Bureya range. Between the Stanovoy and Bureya ranges lies the Zeya-Bureya plateau, which slopes southward to the Amur River to form the Middle Amur lowland.

The southern coastal area, commonly called *Primor'ye* [maritime region] by the Russians, is limited by the Bureya range and the lower Amur in the north, the Ussuri River in the west, and the Sea of Japan and the Tatar Strait in the south and the east. It projects in the shape of a panhandle southward to the area of Vladivostok. The as yet little-explored Sikhote-Alin' range occupies the major portion of this area. The mountains extend in the shape of an arc along the coast, dropping abruptly into the sea and forming gentler slopes inland. Its highest points reach nearly 13,000 feet. The Ussuri valley and two plains, the Lower Amur lowland in the north and the lesser Khanka lowland in the south, form a continuous depression west of the Sikhote-Alin' range.

Sakhalin Island lies just off the southern coastal area across the Tatar Strait. It is featured by two parallel mountain ranges, of which the shorter eastern range rises to about 13,000 feet. The island extends more than 600 miles from north to south, having a low coast in the east and steep, rocky shores in the west.

The Okhotsk littoral, from the mouth of the Amur in the south to the Penzhina Gulf in the north, forms a narrow zone between the Sea of Okhotsk and the Dzhugdzhur and Kolyma ranges. The sea along this coast is stormy and distinguished by strong currents and high tides; during the winter the wind piles up chaotic ice floes along the shore.

The Kamchatka peninsula is extremely individualized geographically. It is surrounded by water and is attached to the mainland in the north by a narrow, marshy isthmus. East of the peninsula are the Commander Islands, and to the south, the Kurile Islands.

Two mountain ranges extend throughout the entire length of Kamchatka peninsula and enclose a wide valley along the Kamchatka River. Both ranges, but chiefly the eastern one, have considerable volcanic activity and show many outcrops of igneous rocks. Large expanses are covered with lava and volcanic ashes. More than one hundred volcanoes have been counted on Kamchatka, including nineteen active craters, which lie mainly in the eastern range. They are located in characteristically circular patterns around older eruption centers, which are now generally the sites of lakes. The most prominent volcanoes are the Avachinskaya Sopka (near Petropavlovsk) and the Klyuchevskaya Sopka, which rises to nearly 16,000 feet and for which up to thirty eruptions have been recorded. Above the 6,000-foot line, the cones are snow-covered all year round. In spite of their violence, the eruptions create little destruction, because the peninsula is so sparsely populated. Volcanic activity also manifests itself by the presence of numerous hot springs near the volcanoes.

The Kurile Islands form a festoon-shaped archipelago of thirty-six islands between the southern tip of the Kamchatka peninsula and the Japanese island of Hokkaido, separating the Sea of Okhotsk from the Pacific Ocean. On these high, rocky islands there are extinct and active volcanoes, as well as hot springs. Earthquakes are common occurrences.

The Chukchi-Anadyr' region is divided into two parts by the Anadyr' range, a divide rising to 19,000 feet. The southern portion forms the basin of the Anadyr' River, and the smaller northern part is oriented toward the Arctic Ocean. The Anadyr' basin is a partly hilly lowland, largely covered by tundra and extending southward to the Koryak range.

The Amur River is the most important river of the Soviet Far East. It is formed by the union of the Argun' and the Shilka rivers on the USSR–China border and connects the Amur region with the southern coastal area, forming a through route from Eastern Siberia to the Pacific Ocean. The run-off of precipitation over the permafrost soil of the north gives the Amur and its affluents great volume, especially in the late summer months. Where the Bureya and Little Khingan ranges hem in the course of the Amur, its banks assume a picturesque appearance. The Amur receives the Zeya (with its affluent, the Selemdzha) and the Bureya on the left and the Ussuri on the right. The former two flow in deep valleys through mountainous areas and have a precipitous flow until they reach the rich farm lands of the Middle Amur lowland. The Ussuri, in turn, flows northward from Lake Khanka, along the Manchurian border, to the Amur at Khabarovsk.

In the northern sections of the Soviet Far East the Kolyma River with its right affluents, and the Anadyr' and the Kamchatka rivers form the principal drainage basins.

SOVIET FAR EAST

The southern section of the Far East, the Maritime region, lies in the same latitudes as the Ukraine and the Caucasus, but the combined effect of the "cold pole" in neighboring Eastern Siberia and of the monsoons bring about a climate quite different from that in the European part of the USSR. The winters are dry, almost snowless, clear, and very cold; even in Vladivostok, which is exposed to the moderating influence of the sea and is located in the latitude of Sukhumi (Georgian SSR), the January temperatures approach those of Novaya Zemlya. Summers are hot, oppressive, and very humid. Heavy rains, amounting to more than one half the yearly precipitation, fall in July and August, resulting in overflowing rivers and occasionally destructive floods. The autumn is clear, very dry, and warm, while the spring is cool and windy. Toward the end of summer and in early autumn typhoons sometimes visit the southern part of the Ussuri valley. This basic monsoon climate type varies in accordance with the location of mountain ranges, the direction of the valleys, and the nearness of the sea. For example, winters in the upper Ussuri valley are warmer than those along the Amur, but they are harder to endure because of the strong winds and the dust-storms which are raised in areas thinly covered with snow.

Sakhalin Island, although quite close to the Maritime region, has a colder and a more severe climate. The Tatar Strait, along the west coast, freezes over in winter, and during the summer the Sea of Okhotsk, which maintains floating ice as late as June, cools the eastern half of the island. As a result, the climate of northern Sakhalin is similar to that of the European littoral of the Arctic Ocean, although it lies in the latitude of Tula. In the winter, mercury freezes in the thermometer, and only the summer months are devoid of freezing temperatures. The climate of southern Sakhalin is more hospitable. The Okhotsk littoral has again a severe climate. The Sea of Okhotsk cools the shore during the summer, but the temperatures become more extreme toward the interior. Cold, rain-bearing winds occur in the summer, and snow usually remains on the ground from early autumn till the beginning of summer.

The Kamchatka peninsula extends from the latitude of Leningrad in the north to that of Kiev in the south. Its climate is more moderate than that of the Okhotsk littoral to the west, but it is still more severe than that of the corresponding latitudes of the European USSR. Average yearly temperatures vary between 25° F in the north and 32° F in the south. Spring arrives late and is followed by a short summer. The western half of the peninsula, oriented toward the Sea of

Okhotsk, is colder than the eastern section. The central portion of the peninsula, the valley of the Kamchatka River, has a warmer and drier climate, while the eastern shore receives much more precipitation, with heavy snow and many foggy days. To the north, in the Chukchi-Anadyr' region, the climate assumes definite Arctic characteristics.

A great part of the Amur valley and the Maritime region is covered by mixed forests. In the north, coniferous woods prevail, while larch predominates in the west, and spruce in the east; other common types are pine and fir. In the south, coniferous types merge with the deciduous forests and gradually become immersed in the predominant Manchurian flora, distinguished by the Manchurian cedar, with bluish cones, the silver fir, maple, linden, oak, and other trees. Watersheds are covered by a very rich grass blanket and woods consisting mainly of the Mongolian oak, with an admixture of birch; in the river valleys the prevailing types are elm, ash, cork-oak, apple, and pear trees. In the southern Ussuri valley as many as 150 species of trees are encountered.

While deciduous forests form the dominant type of vegetation, considerable areas are covered by the so-called Amur steppes, located in the Amur region, along the lower Amur River, and around Lake Khanka. These moist lowlands have a luxurious grass cover, rising to a height of 6 feet and consisting of beach grass, thistles, lilies, feathergrass, accentuated by dog rose bushes and occasional clusters of oak, birch, and aspen. The soils are semi-marshy and very fertile. These grassy expanses developed as a result of the destruction of the forest.

Sakhalin Island has tundra along the low northern shores, but the rest of the island is densely forested. Deciduous types are found only in the valleys. Along the Okhotsk littoral the so-called Okhotsk vegetation type, consisting primarily of coniferous forests, predominates.

The isthmus connecting the Kamchatka peninsula to the mainland is covered with tundra to a line south of 60° N latitude; the center of the peninsula and part of the eastern littoral is forested. Along the shore the taiga degenerates into dense growths of small misshapen trees, and on the mountain slopes it clears up into tall cedar formations. In the Kamchatka valley the familiar tall grass vegetation prevails. The Chukchi-Anadyr' region in the north is entirely covered by tundra.

The mineral resources of the Soviet Far East are of a great variety and are only beginning to be exploited to their full extent. Gold is mined in the upper Zeya, Selemdzha, and Bureya valleys, along the Okhotsk littoral, and above all, in the Kolyma basin. Coal deposits occur in the Bureya valley, the southern Maritime region, on Sakhalin Island, and in the Chukchi-Anadyr' region. Oil fields exist on Kamchatka and Sakhalin. Other important deposits include iron, copper, lead-zinc ores, tungsten and molybdenum.

The Far East is a sparsely populated region. In an area of over 1 million square miles there are only about 3.5 million inhabitants. By far the greater part of the population lives in the Amur valley and the Maritime region, where the density of some districts reaches 5–6 per square mile. The remainder of the region is comparable to Eastern Siberia from the point of view of the population distribution.

At the present time Russians and Ukrainians make up four fifths of the total population, Chinese and Koreans, less than 10 percent; most of them live in the southern Maritime region. The Paleoasiatic and Tungus-Manchurian tribes which form the original inhabitants of this region comprise about 10 percent of the population. Part of them appear to be related to the Indians of North America; this group includes the Eskimos in the extreme northeast, the Unangany (Aleuts) on the Commander Islands, the Luoravetlany (Chukchi), the principal group, located on the Chukchi peninsula, the Nymylany (Koryaks), north of the Kamchatka peninsula, and the Itel'meny (Kamchadals), farther south in Kamchatka. The Nivkhi (Gilyaks) constitute a separated group. The Tungus-Manchurian tribes include the Nanay (Golds) and the Ude (Udege or Udekheytsy). Yakuts and Jews also form sizable minorities in the Soviet Far East.

After the Bolshevik Revolution the Far East was first constituted into a Far Eastern Republic, which in 1922 joined the Russian SFSR and became the Far Eastern Oblast. In 1926 this oblast was reorganized into the Far Eastern Kray, which continued to exist as a single unit until 1938. In that year, on the basis of climatic and other geographic and economic factors, it was divided into Khabarovsk Kray, the larger northern section of the Far East, comprising about 80 percent of the total area, and Maritime Kray, in the southern panhandle. In 1947, as a consequence of the Soviet annexation of Japanese Karafuto (southern Sakhalin) and the Kurile Islands, the newly constituted Sakhalin Oblast was separated from Khabarovsk Kray and became an independent unit. Amur Oblast was separated from Khabarovsk Kray in 1948 and acquired the northeast portion of Chita Oblast.

Although many new industries are being created in the Far East, it continues to be basically an important exporting producer of gold, furs, fish, and lumber. Gold is mined in many areas, in placer sites or as native ore. Furs, fish, and lumber have undergone a thorough modernization and rationalization of production. The output of furs has been considerably increased and improved following the creation of game reserves. The production of canned fish products forms an important branch of the fishing industry, the second largest in the USSR.

On the basis of newly discovered mineral resources, new industries are being created, including the mining of a great variety of ores, heavy metallurgy, the refining of lead and zinc, cement milling, food processing, and various light manufacturing activities.

The chief agricultural areas are the Zeya-Bureya plateau, the middle Amur valley, and the Ussuri-Khanka lowland. These so-called steppes are rendered very fertile by semi-marshy soils (including the Amur black earth), but the danger of drought in the spring and of torrential rains during the harvesting season necessitates the employment of special farming methods and the sowing of special crops. In spite of the existing handicaps, the area under cultivation has been increased in recent years, and further expansion is envisaged. Spring grain crops prevail in the north, and in the south rice, soy beans, and various millet and sorghum types are raised by the ancient Chinese terrace system.

The chief routes are the Trans-Siberian Railroad and the Amur River, which serve only the extreme south of the Far East. They cross at Khabarovsk, one of the most important urban centers, whence the Amur flows northeast toward Nikolayevsk and the Sea of Okhotsk, while the Trans-Siberian makes a sharp turn southward along the Ussuri valley to Vladivostok. The territory lying north of 54° N, the Okhotsk littoral, the Chukchi peninsula and Kamchatka, are linked with the south only by means of the sea route and lately also by air. The Northern Sea Route serves Petropavlovsk, the ports to the north as far as the Bering Strait, and the Arctic coast of the Chukchi peninsula to the mouth of the Kolyma River. A number of improved roads penetrate inland from such points as Magadan, Okhotsk, and Ayan, while air services maintain connections with the more remote points.

Amur Oblast
Capital, Blagoveshchensk; area, 139,000, population, 575,000

In 1948 Amur Oblast (with the exception of the upper Bureya mining area) was detached from Khabarovsk Kray and constituted a separate oblast. Its territory was enlarged at the same time through the incorporation of the northeastern portion of Chita Oblast, which came within the natural geographical confines of the Soviet Far East.

The oblast coincides roughly with the Amur region and is bounded in the north by the Stanovoy range and in the south by the Amur. In the northeast it extends to the Dzhagdy range and in the southeast to the Bureya range. Between the bordering ranges in the north lies the Zeya-Bureya plateau, which merges toward the south with the Middle Amur lowland, a treeless steppe with very fertile soils similar to the black-earth type. The region is drained by the Zeya and its chief left affluent, the Selemdzha, and by the lower Bureya River.

The Middle Amur lowland is one of the major grain-growing districts of the Soviet Far East. The basic crops are wheat, oats, and rye. Associated with the grain farming is an intensive dairying economy. Both agricultural branches form the basis for the well-developed agricultural industries of the region: flour milling, distilling, butter making, tanning, and others. The rural population density of this district is high for the eastern part of the Asiatic USSR, and within the Far East it is second only to the population density of the Khanka lowland of Maritime Kray.

In contrast to the rich farm lands of the southwest, the northeastern mountainous section of the oblast is important for its gold-mining and lumbering activities. The principal gold-mining areas are on the upper Selemdzha River, with the chief centers at Zlatoustovsk, Lukachek, and Stoyba, on the upper Zeya River, near the city of Zeya (at Oktyabr'skiy and Yasnyy), and in the vicinity of Bomnak. Other mines lie farther west on right tributaries of the Zeya, in the area of Tyndynskiy and along the middle Nyukzha River at Srednyaya Nyukzha.

Amur Oblast is served by the Trans-Siberian Railroad, which traverses the oblast from west to east along the Amur River. From the main trunk line, spurs serve the Amur River ports of Dzhalinda (from Skovorodino) and Blagoveshchensk (from Kuybyshevka). In conjunction with the projected Baykal-Amur *magistral*, a rail branch has been built northward from the area of Skovorodino to Tyndynskiy in a gold-mining district. Parallel to this northern rail branch lies the important highway leading from the Trans-Siberian rail station of Never (just east of Skovorodino) into the Yakut Autonomous SSR beyond the Stanovoy range.

Blagoveshchensk, which had a population of 58,761 in 1939, is a major industrial center on the Amur River at the mouth of the Zeya, op-

AMUR OBLAST

posite the Manchurian city of Heiho. It is linked by a rail spur with the
main Trans-Siberian line at Kuybyshevka. Its industries represent a
cross-section of the economy of the region, producing flour, biscuits,
sunflower-seed oil, leather, felt boots, and agricultural and gold-mining
machinery. Its lumber mills process timber floated down the Zeya River
from the north and manufacture matches and other wood products.
The city's shipyards build large river ships and oil tankers for use along
the lower Amur.

Two lesser agricultural centers lie on the Trans-Siberian main line
northeast of Blagoveshchensk: Kuybyshevka or Kuybyshevka-Vostochnaya (formerly called Aleksandrovka and Bochkarevo), which is the
junction for Blagoveshchensk, and Svobodnyy (formerly called Alekseyevka) at the junction of the Zeya River and the Trans-Siberian.

Raychikhinsk, in the extreme southeast of the oblast is a major coal-
mining center. Kivdinskiy is an important eastern mining suburb.

Skovorodino (formerly called Rukhlovo) is a supply point for the
gold mines of the northwestern sections and for the important Aldan
gold-mining district in the Yakut Autonomous SSR.

Khabarovsk Kray
Capital, Khabarovsk; area, 965,400, population, 1,250,000

Khabarovsk Kray occupies nearly the entire Far East, with the exception of the extreme south and the islands included in Sakhalin Oblast,
and is one of the largest political-administrative units of the USSR. Because of its great extent and in order to facilitate the administration
of the individual sectors, Khabarovsk Kray is divided into internal, or
intra-kray, oblasts, the only instance of such a subdivision of a kray
in the political-administrative scheme of the USSR. The internal divisions include Jewish Autonomous Oblast, Lower Amur Oblast, and
Kamchatka Oblast, which in turn comprises the Chukchi and the Koryak
national okrugs. In addition to these divisions, there are two isolated
areas of oblast size, one centered at Khabarovsk, the other in the Kolyma
basin and centered at Magadan, in which the constituent rayons come
under the direct jurisdiction of the Khabarovsk Kray administration.

Of the present population of Khabarovsk Kray, about 900,000, or 75
percent, live south of 54° N latitude. This southern group includes
mainly Russians and Ukrainians, in addition to members of the Tungus-
Manchurian group (Ude, Nanay, and Evenki) and the Paleoasiatic
group (Nivkhi). In the north, Russians are found mainly in southern

Kamchatka and in the Magadan area, with Paleoasiatic and Tungus-Manchurian nationalities in the remaining sections.

The standing of Khabarovsk Kray in the USSR with respect to its main products illustrates the importance of the region in the national economy. It ranks first in reindeer raising and seal hunting, second in fish and fur production, and third in gold mining.

THE KHABAROVSK AREA

Main city, Khabarovsk; area, 111,500, population, 650,000

Until 1939 organized separately as Khabarovsk Oblast (a constituent portion of Khabarovsk Kray), this area now consists of rayons which are under the direct jurisdiction of the Khabarovsk Kray administration. In 1948 the original territory was enlarged more than one half by the annexation of the upper Bureya valley from Amur Oblast and the district of Sovetskaya Gavan' from Maritime Kray. The accompanying territorial changes, which placed the Bureya coking-coal basin, the Komsomol'sk steel mills, and the port of Sovetskaya Gavan' within a unified administrative area illustrate well the manner in which economic criteria dictate changes in the administrative geography of the USSR.

The Khabarovsk area occupies a central position in the Soviet Far East. It is situated at the junction of the Amur and the Ussuri rivers and of the Trans-Siberian Railroad at the crossroads of the main transportation routes. In this extensively forested area the Siberian taiga prevails in the north, and Manchurian-type and mixed forests in the south, along the Ussuri River. Cultivated areas occur only in the neighborhood of the two large industrial cities, Khabarovsk and Komsomol'sk, where truck produce and wheat are raised, as well as in the extreme south, where rice has been introduced along the Ussuri. Fisheries abound along the broad Amur River and the coast of the Tatar Strait, while in the mountainous districts of the Sikhote-Alin' range lumbering is important. There are several large sawmills at Khor and at Bikin, on the Trans-Siberian, south of Khabarovsk, at Bolon' and Litovko, on the railroad leading northeast to Komsomol'sk, and along the newly completed extension to Sovetskaya Gavan'. Fishing is the chief occupation of the Nanay (Gold) population along the Amur, while the Ude minority along the upper Khor River engages mainly in lumbering. Russians and Ukrainians constitute the bulk of the farmers and industrial workers.

The principal economic assets of the area are the mineral resources and the associated heavy metallurgy and engineering industries. The richest mining district is the upper Bureya River valley, which remained within the Khabarovsk area following the separation of Amur Oblast, in 1948. The coking coal of the Bureya basin, mined chiefly at Sredniy Urgal, on the Urgal River (a left affluent of the Bureya), and at Chekunda and Ust'-Niman on the Bureya itself, supplies the metallurgical industry of Komsomol'sk. A considerable expansion of the Bureya coal basin has been scheduled for the current Five-Year Plan. Although a rail spur already connects Ust'-Niman and Chekunda with the main Trans-Siberian Railroad at Izvestkovyy in the Jewish Autonomous Oblast, it is expected that new railroad construction will provide a less circuitous route from the Bureya mines directly to the Komsomol'sk mills. Other important mines produce molybdenum and tungsten at Umal'tinskiy (called Polovinka until 1942) and gold at Sofiysk.

Khabarovsk, the capital of Khabarovsk Kray, had a population of 199,364 in 1939 and about 300,000 in 1947. It lies on the Amur River, at its junction with the Ussuri River and the Trans-Siberian Railroad, and is the chief transportation and freight-transshipment center of the Soviet Far East. It receives lumber and grain from Siberia, manufactured goods from the European USSR, lumber, rice, soy beans and cement from the south, oil from Sakhalin, fish from the lower Amur, and steel products from Komsomol'sk. Its extensive industries include oil refining, shipbuilding, aircraft and auto assembly, the manufacture of agricultural and other types of machinery, woodworking, meat packing, and flour milling. Founded in 1858, the city developed rapidly after the Bolshevik Revolution.

About two hundred miles northeast of Khabarovsk, on the Amur River, lies the famed city of youth, Komsomol'sk, or Komsomol'sk-na-Amure [Komsomol'sk on the Amur]. Construction of the city was begun in 1932 by members of the Young Communist League (commonly known by the Russian initial syllables Komsomol) on the site of a small fishing village, Permskoye. The population was 70,746 in 1939, and it has reached 150,000 since the end of the Second World War. Komsomol'sk is the site of the Amurstal' steel mills, the only heavy metallurgical establishment in the Soviet Far East. Other industries include shipyards, aircraft assembly, sawmills, and woodworking and construction plants. Komsomol'sk is on the railroad from Volochayevka (near Kha-

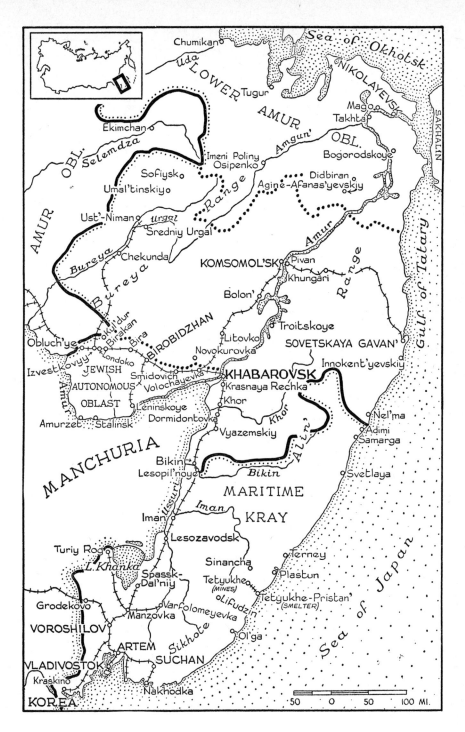

MARITIME KRAY AND KHABAROVSK

barovsk); the line has been extended during the Second World War southeast to the port of Sovetskaya Gavan'.

Sovetskaya Gavan' [Soviet haven] is a new fishing port and naval base on the Tatar Strait opposite Sakhalin. It was developed chiefly to provide a deep-water harbor in lieu of the sandbar-obstructed mouth of the Amur River. Important mainly as a naval base, it also has lumbering and fishing industries linked with the hinterland by the railroad to Komsomol'sk. North and south along the coast are fishing settlements and canneries, of which the largest are at Innokent'yevskiy and Nel'ma, Datta and Grossevichi.

JEWISH AUTONOMOUS OBLAST
Capital, Birobidzhan; area, 13,800, population, 150,000

The territory now comprised within the Jewish Autonomous Oblast was opened for colonization in 1928 in order to provide a national home for the Jews of the USSR. An autonomous administration was established in 1934. However, no mass migration developed, and Jews still constitute only about one half the total population of the region.

The oblast is situated in the large bend of the Amur, between the Bureya range (here also called the Little Khingan range) and Khabarovsk, and is drained by two left affluents of the Amur, the Bira and the Bidzhan. The arc formed by the Amur in the south is subtended by the Trans-Siberian as a chord in the north. An agricultural belt formed by a semi-marshy lowland next to the Amur produces wheat, rice, soy beans, and truck produce. In the northern and western sections, where a hilly, wooded terrain prevails, the chief activities concern lumbering, sawmilling, and the mining of gold and tin in the Little Khingan range. Limestone deposits along the Trans-Siberian Railroad in the area of Izvestkovyy furnish raw material for the cement mill at Londoko, and some coal is mined at Bira to the east. Also to be noted are iron ore, copper, and mercury deposits. Sawmills are concentrated in the eastern section of the oblast at Nikolayevka and in the area of Volochayevka, where the railroad to Komsomol'sk leaves the Trans-Siberian main line. Another rail branch leaves the main line at Izvestkovyy and goes north into the Bureya coal basin. The influx of Jews brought a large number of much-needed skilled artisans to the Far East, and as a consequence the Jewish Autonomous Oblast has become the center of the clothing, leather, and textile industries of the Soviet Far East.

Birobidzhan, which had a population of 29,654 in 1939, developed on the site of the small rail station of Tikhon'kaya and was named for the two main rivers of the oblast. In common usage the name Birobidzhan was applied also to the oblast as a whole. The city lies at the intersection of the Bira River and the Trans-Siberian. Its industries include lumber mills, producing plywood, furniture, and prefabricated housing, and clothing, shoe, and textile plants.

THE LOWER AMUR OBLAST
Capital, Nikolayevsk; area, 202,700, population, 150,000

This division extends from the lower Amur River along the Okhotsk littoral and the Dzhugdzhur range to the area of Okhotsk. Most of the population is concentrated in the extreme south, along the Amur River, where fisheries constitute the principal industry. Numerous fishing settlements and processing establishments (canneries, smoking sheds, refrigerators) dot the coast of the Tatar Strait, the estuary of the Amur, and the lakes amid the lower reaches of the river. Mago is a major fishing port and processing center on the Amur estuary below Nikolayevsk. Some wheat, vegetables, and potatoes are raised in a narrow zone along the Amur River. Gold is mined along the lower Kerbi and Amgun' rivers, while coal and iron deposits are worked near Nikolayevsk.

Along the Okhotsk littoral, the population (largely Eveny or Lamut) engages in reindeer raising, fishing, and gold mining. The chief settlements are the fishing ports of Okhotsk and Ayan; both are connected by trails with the hinterland of the Yakut Autonomous SSR.

Nikolayevsk, or Nikolayevsk-na-Amure [Nikolayevsk on the Amur], is the economic center of the Lower Amur Oblast. A former naval base, it has been largely replaced by Sovetskaya Gavan' to the south, but still remains the center for the fishing and gold-mining industries of the region. It has shipyards and petroleum refining installations, and manufactures cans for the fishing industry. It is also an important hub for airlines and a fur-collecting center.

THE MAGADAN-KOLYMA AREA
Main city, Magadan; area, 137,100, population, 150,000

Like the Khabarovsk area, this territory is not organized as a separate oblast within Khabarovsk Kray, but consists of rayons which are under the direct jurisdiction of the kray administration. The Magadan-Kolyma area, which has now become the center of activity of the Dal'stroy development project, is one of the most important gold-mining districts of the USSR. It began to be opened to exploitation in the early 1930's, when a good highway, usable all year round by heavy trucks, was built northward from Magadan to the Kolyma River. Numerous gold mines were developed, and concentration and refining mills were built. The principal industrial settlements lie along the highway or are connected to it by short spur roads. The main centers are Orotukan, Yagodnyy, Susuman, At-Uryakh, and Berelyakh. Other important settlements, somewhat outside the gold-mining district proper, are Srednikan and Seymchan. The native population, which includes mainly Eveny (Lamuts), Oduly (Yukagirs), and some Yakuts, engages in small-scale farming, reindeer raising, hunting, and fishing. The Russian element is employed in the mining and construction industries.

Magadan, the chief city of the region, was founded in 1932, near the little fishing village of Nagayevo. Since that time, Magadan has grown to a population of about 50,000, and Nagayevo has become its suburban port. The city is the chief supply center for the important mining district to the north and service a large truck fleet along the highway. It has auto repair shops and dockyards, assembles construction machines (bulldozers, excavators), and produces drilling machines, electric light bulbs, glasswork, and ceramics.

KAMCHATKA OBLAST
Capital, Petropavlovsk; area, 490,400, population, 150,000

Kamchatka Oblast proper, which has an area of 64,200 square miles and a population of about 110,000, includes only the southern section of the Kamchatka peninsula, which is inhabited chiefly by Russians. Attached to it in the north are territories with a predominant Paleo-asiatic population, which since 1930 have been organized into the Chukchi and the Koryak national okrugs.

The fishing industry is the main economic activity in Kamchatka Oblast proper. Most of the fish-processing and canning establishments extend along the western shore of the peninsula, the largest plants being at Kirovskiy, Kolpakovskiy, Mitoginskiy, Imeni Mikoyana, Kikhchik, and Ozernovskiy. The catch consists of salmon, cod, sardines, and herring. Off the northwest coast floating crab-canning installations produce nearly the entire USSR output of that commodity. Fur trapping and lumbering are common on the mountain slopes, while sawmills and small-scale truck farms are located along the central Kamchatka River valley. The Commander Islands, attached administratively to Kamchatka Oblast, are inhabited by the Unangany (Aleuts) and serve as a fishing base and a reserve for the fur seal and the sea otter. Between the islands and the peninsula lies one of the chief Soviet whaling grounds. Among the mineral resources, scattered gold placers and petroleum fields are to be mentioned. The petroleum deposits on the Bogachevka River, near the east coast, are of economic importance. The numerous hot springs related to the volcanism of the peninsula may be developed as health resorts.

Petropavlovsk, or Petropavlovsk-Kamchatskiy, lies on Avacha Bay, a good natural harbor on the southeastern coast. It is a fishing and whaling center and serves as an important port and naval base. Its principal industries are lumber milling, shipbuilding (in the suburb of Industrial'nyy), tin-can manufacturing, and brickworking.

KORYAK NATIONAL OKRUG (capital, Palana ; area, 151,700 square miles, population, 20,000) lies immediately north of Kamchatka Oblast proper. It includes the northern neck of the Kamchatka peninsula, which is partly inhabited by the Itel'meny (Kamchadals), the original inhabitants of Kamchatka. In the remainder of the okrug, except for some Eveny (Lamut) elements in the west, the Nymylany (Koryaks) constitute the basic stock of the population. The natives engage in fishing, fur trapping, and reindeer raising. Fish canning and other processing plants operate at Tilichiki, Olyutorskoye and adjoining Ust'-Apuka, Kichiga, and on Gizhiga Bay. Coal mined in the immediate vicinity of the main ports (Gizhiga, Kamenskoye, and Tilichiki) supplies local fuel needs. Extensive petroleum deposits are found at Voyampolka in the northern part of the Kamchatka peninsula.

Palana, to which the administrative seat of the okrug was moved in 1938 from Koryakskaya Kul'tbaza, is a fishing and reindeer-raising center on the northwest coast of the Kamchatka peninsula.

CHUKCHI NATIONAL OKRUG (capital, Anadyr' ; area, 274,500, population, 20,000) occupies the extreme northeast of the Asiatic continent, including the Chukchi peninsula. In the north it borders on the Chukchi Sea of the Arctic Ocean and is separated from Alaska by the Bering Strait. It is in the middle of this strait that Soviet territory on Big Diomede (or Ratmanov) Island comes within 3 miles of U.S. (Alaska) controlled Little Diomede Island. The Luoravetlany (Chukchi) form the basic elements of the population, and there are some Eveny (Lamuts) and Yakuts in the extreme west. The main activities are reindeer raising, hunting, and fishing. Coal for local use is mined at Anadyr' and Ugol'nyy, on the Gulf of Anadyr'. Lead-zinc ores exist near Cape Serdtse-Kamen' on the north coast. Whaling flotillas frequently visit the Gulf of Anadyr'. The coast and many sections of the interior are supplied with Russian-staffed trading posts, polar observation stations, and propaganda bases, which the Russians call *kul'tbaza* [cultural base]. The chief ports on the Northern Sea Route are Anadyr' and Provideniya.

Anadyr', formerly called Novo-Mariinsk, is the administrative and cultural center of the okrug. Small-scale agriculture is being developed near by. It has also a polar observation post.

Wrangel (or Vrangel') and Herald (or Geral'd) islands, north of the Chukchi peninsula in the Arctic Ocean, are attached administratively to Khabarovsk Kray and have polar observation stations.

Maritime Kray
Capital, Vladivostok; area, 64,900, population, 1,475,000

Maritime Kray lies in the extreme southern panhandle of the Soviet Far East, between Manchuria in the west and the Sea of Japan in the east. It represents only 6 percent of the total area of the Far East, but it includes nearly one half the total population.

The Sikhote-Alin' range, which hugs the arc-shaped coast of the Sea of Japan, separates the kray into two distinct sections: a narrow rocky littoral in the east and the fertile Ussuri-Khanka lowland in the west. The monsoon climate is clearly expressed here. The winter monsoon brings cold, dry air masses from the northwest and the summer winds bring warm, humid air from the sea. Although the winters in the plain are colder than those of Arkhangel'sk in the European North, the summer heat and greater precipitation are sufficient to produce rice and other subtropical crops.

When the kray was formed, in 1938, it included two former subdivisions of the Far Eastern Kray, the Maritime and the Ussuri oblasts. Soon, however, in order to obtain a more unified administration, the two internal oblasts were abolished in 1939 and 1943, respectively.*

---

* In theory and in order to be consistent with the nomenclature of the Soviet political-administrative system, Maritime Kray should have become an oblast following the liquidation of its internal divisions. However, this change in nomenclature was not effected, and Maritime Kray remains the only kray of the Russian SFSR which lacks an autonomous or other type of internal oblast.

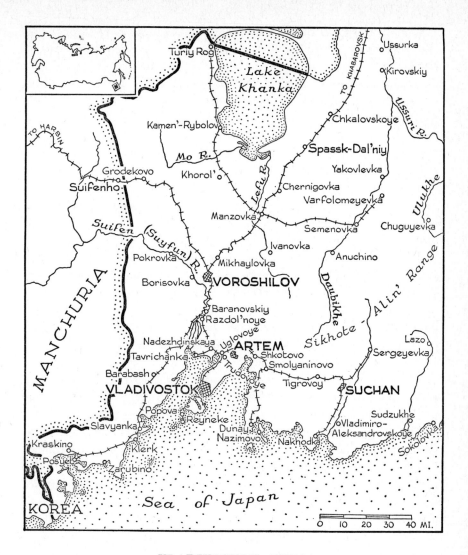

VLADIVOSTOK AREA

Economically one of the most important regions of the Soviet Far East, Maritime Kray has an extensive coal-mining industry centered chiefly on Suchan and Artem. Lesser mines at Tavrichanka and Kraskino produce mainly lignite. The Sikhote-Alin' range has a number of metallic deposits, which are exploited at the iron mine of Ol'ga, the lead, zinc, and silver mines near Tetyukhe, and the tin workings at Sinancha and Lifudzin. The nonferrous metals are smelted in the Tetyukhe works, which are located in the port of Tetyukhe, Tetyukhe-Pristan'. Iodine is processed on the Sea of Japan coast, at Veselyy Yar.

The major manufacturing and heavy industries of Maritime Kray are concentrated at Vladivostok, while Voroshilov is the center for the agricultural and food-processing industries based on the production of the Khanka-Ussuri plain. The cement requirements of the entire Soviet Far East are largely filled by the mill of Spassk-Dal'niy, near Lake Khanka. Lumber cut in the Sikhote-Alin' range is floated down the mountain streams to the sawmills along the Trans-Siberian at Iman and Lesozavodsk. The extensive coastal fisheries specialize in the production of canned salmon, caviar, sardines, and smoked fish. The major canning and other processing establishments lie on the shores of Peter the Great Bay, at Pos'yet, Klerk, Zarubino, and Slavyanka (southwest of Vladivostok), Putyatin and Nakhodka (southeast of Vladivostok), and on the east coast at Valentin, Sokolovka, Terney, Svetlaya, Plastun, and Adimi.

The crops raised in the Khanka-Ussuri plain are adapted to the existing humid and warm climate. They include the so-called Chinese crops, the soy bean, the chumiza and kaoliang types of millet, and perilla, an oil-bearing seed plant which produces quick-drying oil used in the manufacture of printing inks and varnish. The abundance of moisture and the easy methods of local irrigation favor the cultivation of rice. Ukrainian crops which have been acclimatized include sugar beets, corn, watermelon, squash, and garden fruit. The Ussuri valley is one of the leading honey producers of the USSR. Dairy farming has been developed in the Lake Khanka area. Near Razdol'noye is a reserve for spotted reindeer and roe deer, which furnish chamois leather.

The main railway line is the Trans-Siberian, which here runs south along the Ussuri River to its terminus at Vladivostok. A number of short branch lines serve mining areas (Kraskino and Suchan) or lead to the USSR–Chinese border towns (Grodekovo and Turiy Rog). Communication between the coastal settlements is possible only by Sea. The best

ports, in addition to Vladivostok, are Tetyukhe, Ol'ga, Nakhodka, and
Pos'yet, a Soviet submarine base.

Vladivostok, the capital of Maritime Kray, is the most important
Soviet port on the Pacific, and the eastern terminus of the Trans-
Siberian Railroad and the Northern Sea Route. It lies on the Golden
Horn Bay (an inlet of Peter the Great Bay) in a very picturesque loca-
tion. Its excellently equipped port is kept open all year by ice-breakers.
Its major industries are shipbuilding, engineering, and food canning.
The chief Soviet Pacific base of fishing, crabbing, and whaling flotillas,
it also has refrigerating, fish canning, tin-can manufacturing, and asso-
ciated enterprises.

Voroshilov, formerly called Nikol'sk-Ussuriyskiy, is the center of
the rich agricultural Khanka-Ussuri plan. Its industries are based on
the local production with specialization in the processing of soy beans,
sugar beets, and rice. A vast plant produces oil, oilcake, glycerine, soap,
and other products from the soy-bean yield. The city is the junction of
the Trans-Siberian and the former Chinese Eastern railways.

Suchan, the older of the two large coal-mining centers of the area,
lies on a rail branch east of Vladivostok. Its jurisdiction extends over
its northern coal-mining suburb of Severnyy Suchan and the lumber-
milling town of Tigrovoy, to the northwest.

Artem, which in 1928 had a production of coal equal to that of Suchan, surpassed the latter in its development during the Five-Year
Plans. In 1938 it produced three times as much coal as did Suchan,
and its 1947 population exceeded 50,000. Its two major coal-mining
suburbs are Uglovoye and Trudovoye.

Sakhalin Oblast
Capital, Yuzhno-Sakhalinsk ; area, 35,400, population, 300,000

Sakhalin Oblast was created in 1947 out of two internal oblasts of
Khabarovsk Kray: Sakhalin Oblast, which corresponded to the northern part of Sakhalin Island that remained Russian during the period
1905–45, and Southern Sakhalin Oblast, formed in 1946 out of the
Japanese possessions of Karafuto (Southern Sakhalin) and the Kurile
Islands that were occupied by the Soviet army in 1945. Southern
Sakhalin Oblast had been a provisional unit created for the duration
of the assimilation of the former Japanese territories to the Soviet way
of life. Once this process had been completed, it was considered more
efficient economically to separate all of Sakhalin from Khabarovsk Kray

and to constitute it into an independent oblast, including the Kurile Islands.

As an integral part of the sovietization of the former Japanese territories, all localities were renamed. A list of the major name changes follows.

PRESENT SOVIET NAME   FORMER JAPANESE NAME

Sakhalin Island

Present Soviet Name	Former Japanese Name
Aniva	Rutaka
Chekhov	Noda
Dolinsk	Ochiai
Gornozavodsk	Naihoro
Il'inskiy	Kushunnai
Kholmsk	Maoka
Korsakov	Otomari
Krasnogorsk	Chinnai
Lesogorsk	Nayoshi
Makarov	Shirutori
Nevel'sk	Honto
Poronaysk	Shikuka
Shakhtersk	Toro
Sinegorsk	Kawakami
Tomari	Tomarioru
Uglegorsk	Esutoru
Vostochnyy	Mototomari
Vzmor'ye	Shiraura
Yuzhno-Sakhalinsk	Toyohara

Kurile Islands

Present Soviet Name	Former Japanese Name
Kuril'sk (Iturup Island)	Shana
Severo-Kuril'sk (Paramushir Island)	Kashiwabara
Yuzhno-Kuril'sk (Kunashir Island)	Furukamappu

While some names (Makarov, Korsakov, Poronaysk) were of pre-1905 origin, other new denominations were adapted to the geographical location of the town: Yuzhno-Sakhalinsk (southern Sakhalin), Lesogorsk (wooded mountain), Shakhtersk (miner's town), Uglegorsk (coal mountain).

Situated off the mainland of the Soviet Far East and separated from it by the Tatar Strait, Sakhalin Island extends for more than 600 miles from the mouth of the Amur River southward to the Japanese island of Hokkaido, from which it is separated by the 25-mile-wide La

SAKHALIN

GLOSSARY

Soviet Name	Japanese Name
Aniva	Rutaka
Boshnyakovo	Nishi-Shakutan
Chekhov	Noda
Chkalovo	Kitose
Dolinsk	Ochiai
Gastello	Nairo
Gornozavodsk	Naihoro
Il'inskiy	Kushunnai
Kholmsk	Maoka
Korsakov	Otomari
Krasnogorsk	Chinnai
Leonidovo	Kami-shikuka
Lesogorsk	Nayoshi
Makarov	Shirutoru
Nevel'sk	Honto
Novikovo	Shiretoko
Novo-Aleksandrovsk	Konuma
Orlovo	Ushiro
Ozerskiy	Nagahama
Poronaysk	Shikuka
Pravda	Ohadomari
Pugachevo	Maguntanhama
Shakhtersk	Toro
Sinegorsk	Kawakami
Sokol	Otani
Starodubskoye	Sakaehama
Tomari	Tomarioru
Udarnyy	Taihei
Uglegorsk	Esutoru
Ugol'nyy	Okuzawa
Ul'yanovskoye	Dorokawa
Vakhrushev	Tomarikishi
Vostochnyy	Mototomari
Vzmor'ye	Shiraura
Yablochnyy	Rantomari
Yasnomorskiy	Oko
Yuzhno-Sakhalinsk	Tcyohara

Pérouse Strait. Two parallel mountain ranges extend throughout the length of the island and enclose a central agricultural valley.

The island has a varied native population, numbering about 5,000. These ethnic groups include Evenki (Tungus) and Ude (Orochon) in the north and Nivkhi (Gilyaks) and Ainu in the south. The prewar population of the island was about 450,000; 100,000 Russians inhabited the northern part, and 350,000 Japanese the southern part. As a result of the Second World War and the Soviet occupation, southern Sakhalin is being settled by Russians from densely populated areas of the European USSR. These new settlers are displacing or absorbing the Japanese population, which is being partly repatriated to Japan. In 1946 the hypothetical population of Sakhalin Oblast was 300,000; however, it can be expected to reach the prewar figure within a few years.

The main products of the island comprise coal, petroleum, lumber and paper products, and fish. Coal is mined in the vicinity of Aleksandrovsk, at Due, Mgachi, and Oktyabr'skiy, and in the south at Uglegorsk, Shakhtersk, Gornozavodsk, and Sinegorsk. The petroleum fields are producing some of the best-grade fuel of the USSR. They are centered in the northeast at Okha. During the Second World War, the yearly prewar productions of 500,000 tons was doubled, and new wells were developed south of Okha in the area of Ekhabi.

The fishing industry furnishes about one half the total catch of the Soviet Far East. Every city and many small fishing villages have canneries, refrigerating plants, and other installations connected with the processing of fish. Fisheries are concentrated especially on the west coast, near Rybnovsk, Shirokaya Pad', and Aleksandrovsk.

Lumber is floated down the short mountain streams to sawmills along the coast. In the south, the paper and pulp-milling industry is developed to a high degree. There are also shipbuilding, construction, woodworking, and fishing-equipment industries, especially in the south.

Agricultural production is as yet in its early stages. In the north, the central valley along the Tym' River produces fodder grasses, potatoes, and vegetables. Grains are of minor importance. Dairy farming plays an important part in the economy. In the south, where a milder climate prevails, sugar beets, leguminous crops, oats, barley, and some rice and wheat are also grown in the central valley.

The only railway in the north is the short line connecting Okha with its sheltered west-coast port Moskal'vo. The south has a well-developed rail network, consisting of two parallel coastal lines connected by a transverse. The southern termini are Korsakov and Nevel'sk. In the north, the railway reaches Il'insk on the west coat and Pobedino in the central Poronay River valley. Short spurs serve coal mines and ports along the coast. The current Plan envisages the extension of the east coast line from Pobedino to Aleksandrovsk, thus establishing a through route between the northern and the southern sections of Sakhalin.

Yuzhno-Sakhalinsk, the capital of the oblast since 1947, lies on the east coast railway in the center of an agricultural area. It has food-processing industries, including a sugar refinery, lumber and paper mills, and a fur plant.

Aleksandrovsk, or Aleksandrovsk-Sakhalinskiy, the former capital, is a fishing port on the west coast and the center of the northern coal basin.

Other centers, where lumber, paper, and fishing industries prevail, are Dolinsk, Kholmsk, Korsakov, Poronaysk, and Nevel'sk.

THE KURILE ISLANDS (area, 5,700, population, 15,000) are festooned from the southern tip of the Kamchatka peninsula southwest 430 miles to Hokkaido. The chain consists of thirty-six islands of volcanic origin, ranging from an area of less than 1 square mile to 930 square miles (Iturup or Etorofu Island). Besides the newly settled Russian population, there is a small Ainu element.

The chief economic activities are sulphur mining, whaling, and fishing (salmon, cod, and crabs). Horses are bred in the southern islands. The fish-canning industry has also been developed.

The principal settlements are Severo-Kuril'sk, on Paramushir Island, and Kuril'sk, on Iturup Island.

CHAPTER 16

Kazakh Soviet Socialist Republic (Kazakhstan)

Capital, Alma-Ata; area, 1,061,600, population, 6,000,000

THE KAZAKH SSR, or Kazakhstan ("land of the Kazakhs"), is the second largest union republic of the USSR. Its area equals about one third that of the United States and is larger than the total area of all the other union republics combined, except the RSFSR. Located deep in the Eurasian continent, Kazakhstan is nearly equidistant from the Atlantic and the Pacific oceans (along the same parallel) and extends between 40° and 55.5° N lat., thus occupying the southern and the central belt of the temperate zone. Its greatest dimension from the Caspian Sea in the west to the Altay Mountains in the east, is 1,855 miles, and 1,050 miles separate its northern boundary along the Trans-Siberian Railroad from its southern border in the northern ranges of the Tien Shan mountain system. Bounded on the north by the RSFSR, it stretches from the lower Volga in the west to the Sinkiang Province frontier of China, and on the south it touches its Central Asian neighbors, the Turkmen, the Uzbek, and the Kirghiz SSR's.

GENERAL SURVEY

THE KAZAKH SSR is essentially a vast flatland, lowest in the west and highest in the east, bordered by a high mountain belt in the southeast. It can be divided into three natural regions: the low Caspian depression and Turan lowland in the west and the southwest, the higher Kazakh upland and Bet-Pak Dala in the center, and the Altay and Tien Shan mountain belt in the east and the southeast.

The Caspian depression and Turan lowland rarely rise above the altitude of 600 feet, occupy the entire west and southwest of Kazakhstan and represent a region of subsidence in which marine and continental sediments have accumulated during recent geological eras. In the west, on the northern and the northeastern shores of the Caspian Sea, lies the Caspian depression, which descends at points along the shore to 92 feet below sea level. To the south, in the Mangyshlak peninsula, which projects into the Caspian Sea from the southeast, among several small deep depressions the Batyr' (or Karagiye) Sink reaches 426 feet below sea level. The Caspian depression, where the flat surface is interrupted only by the Kara-Tau range on the Mangyshlak peninsula, with an altitude of 1,742 feet, is separated from the Turan lowland by the Mugodzhar mountains, a southern spur of the Ural Mountains rising to 2,145 feet, and further south by the low plateau of Ust'-Urt. The latter barren, waterless region, composed of Tertiary and Cretaceous sediments, lies just west of the Aral Sea and reaches nearly 1,000 feet. It rises in characteristic cliff-like escarpments, called *chink*, above the surrounding plain, forming one of the most desolate desert regions of Kazakhstan.

The Turan lowland, east of the Mugodzhar mountains and the Aral Sea, includes the Turgay tableland in the north and the sandy deserts of the Aral Sea in the south. The Turgay tableland, which connects with the West Siberian lowland via the Turgay Gates, a long, narrow, lake-filled depression, shows a very characteristic land formation between the Aral Sea and the Irgiz River. Here, amid the surrounding lowland, separate, low, mesa-like plateaus rise like islands to altitudes of 300–600 feet. Among these table-top hills extend two elongated deserts, the Bolshiye (large) and Malyye (small) Barsuki, forerunners of the wide sandy expanses east of the Aral Sea. These deserts, including the smaller Aral Kara-Kum (not to be confused with its much more extensive namesake in the Turkmen SSR) and the larger Kyzyl-Kum, south of the Syr Darya, consist mainly of stationary sands covered by a sparse blanket of vegetation, interrupted by areas of moving sands and bare clay surfaces.

The Kazakh upland, called in Russian *Kazakhskaya Skladchataya Strana* ("Kazakh folded region"), occupies the entire east central section of Kazakhstan and is separated from the lower western section by Turgay Gates. The Kazakh upland forms part of the Upper Paleozoic (Hercynian) folded system and consists of a series of not very high, deeply eroded, short ranges and many separate hill formations of resistant rocks (granite, syenite, porphyry, etc.). It extends from the area of Kokchetav in the north, where it merges with the West Siberian lowland, to Lake Balkhash in the south and from the separate Ulu-Tau mountains in the west to the spurs of the Altay Mountains in the east. A number of higher central mountain ranges oriented northwest by southeast are scattered among the lower hills ; these are the Ulu-Tau (3,723 feet), Kyzyl-Ray (4,800 feet), the highest point in the Kazakh upland, and the Chingiz-Tau (4,274 feet), which merges into the Tarbagatay range, a spur of the Altay system.

South of the Kazakh upland and west of Lake Balkhash lies the Bet-Pak-Dala, known in Russian as *Golodnaya Step'* ("hungry steppe"),* a rather high plateau extending from the river Sary-Su in the north to the Chu River in the south, where its altitude is about 450 feet. It rises toward the north, reaching the height of about 1,500 feet and forming near the Sary-Su escarpments which are similar to those of the Ust'-Urt. Its surface consists mainly of cracked clay, with a sparse covering of scrub vegetation, alternating with salt flats in the north and with sands in the south. Outcrops of crystalline rocks occur in the east and are partially eroded and transformed into piles of rocky debris.

That section of the Altay mountain system which enters within the confines of the Kazakh SSR is commonly designated the Rudnyy Altay ("ore Altay"), because of its extensive lead, zinc, and copper deposits. The formation of the mountain ranges in this area dates back to the Upper Paleozoic period. The principal chain, which extends across the path of the Irtysh River, is called Narym range east of the Irtysh valley and Kalba range to the west. South of the Rudnyy Altay the depression of Lake Zaysan separates the Tarbagatay range, a system similar in structure to the Altay Mountains and rising to 9,500 feet, from the Altay proper.

Farther along the southeast frontier of Kazakhstan, several northern spurs of the Tien Shan mountain system penetrate into the Kazakh SSR, each separated from the other by Quaternary desert lowlands. The northernmost of these Tien Shan spurs, the Dzungarian Ala-Tau, is separated from the Tarbagatay range by the so-called Dzungarian Gates, a historic nomad invasion route from Central Asia into the Turan lowland. The Dzungarian Ala-Tau (16,550 feet), in turn, is separated from the Ketmen' range to the south by the valley of the Ili River, while, to the west, its foothills merge into the sandy desert of Sary-Ishik-

---

* This desert is frequently confused, even in Russian sources, with another smaller Golodnaya Step', an irrigated loess plain in the extreme south of the Kazakh SSR, bordering on the southeast section of the Kyzyl-Kum and located on the left bank of the Syr Darya.

Otrau, south of Lake Balkhash. The Ketmen' range (10,480 feet) is continued to the west by the Trans-Ili Ala-Tau (16,455 feet), which extends northwestward to the Bet-Pak-Dala as the Chu-Ili Mountains (3,470 feet). The important range Kara-Tau, rising to 5,700 feet, is the westernmost spur of the Tien Shan and extends northwestward into the Turan lowland parallel to the Syr Darya. Another sandy desert, the Muyun-Kum, extends along the northeastern slopes of the Kara-Tau northward to the Chu River.

The hydrography of the Kazakh SSR is characterized mainly by a poorly developed surface-water network and a very large number of closed inland drainage basins, resulting in fresh-water and salt lakes of various sizes. The most spectacular of these inland lakes or seas are the Caspian Sea, which is bordered by Kazakhstan in the west, the Aral Sea, in the southwest, on the border of the Uzbek SSR, and Lake Balkhash, in the southeast.

The Caspian Sea is the largest inland sea of the world, having an area of 163,825 square miles. Its bed has undergone considerable fluctuations of the earth's crust, resulting in corresponding changes in the water area during different geological periods. During the last 100 years the water level has been rising and falling with a maximum range of about 4 feet. Since 1929 it has been gradually falling, a phenomenon which has been ascribed by some to a subsidence of the sea bottom, and by others to a reduction in the discharge of the rivers. The northern section of the sea, which adjoins Kazakhstan, is relatively shallow and continues to grow shallow due to the large amount of sediments brought here by the such large inlets as the Volga and the Ural rivers. Due to these rivers, also, the salinity in this section is below the average of 13 percent. The shallowness and consequent high-water temperature of the northern portion of the Caspian Sea, coupled with the presence of a large amount of organic materials discharged by the Volga and other rivers, make it one of the richest fishing areas of the USSR, furnishing about 35 percent of the total catch. The most common fish types include sturgeon, salmon, herring, and carp.

To the east of the Caspian Sea lies the Aral Sea, the fourth largest inland lake of the world, with an area of 24,635 square miles. It is considerably shallower than the Caspian, having an average depth of 30 to 60 feet and a maximum depth of 223 feet near the high western shore. The slight salinity of the water (about 1 percent) is due to the relatively recent connection which existed between the Aral and the Caspian seas

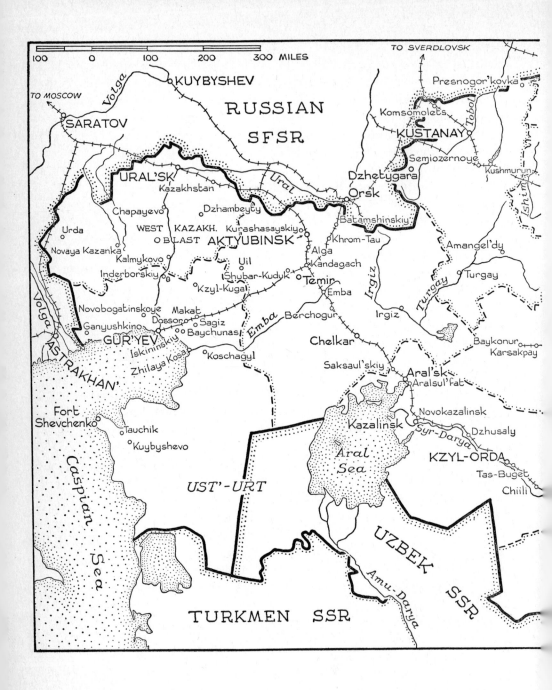

Scale (top): 100 0 100 200 300 MILES

TO SVERDLOVSK

TO MOSCOW

RUSSIAN SFSR

KUYBYSHEV

Volga

SARATOV

Presnogor'kovka

Komsomolets

Tobol

KUSTANAY

URAL'SK

Kazakhstan

Ural

Semiozernoye

Kushmurun

Dzhetygara

Orsk

Ishim

Chapayevo

Dzhambeyty

WEST KAZAKH.

OBLAST AKTYUBINSK

Kurashasayskiyo

Batamshinskiy

Amangel'dy

Urda

Khrom-Tau

Novaya Kazanka

Alga

Kalmykovo

Uil

Kandagach

Turgay

Inderborskiy

Shubar-Kuduk

Temir

Irgiz

Turgay

Kzyl-Kugal

Emba

Novobogatinskoye

Makat

Berchogur

Irgiz

Baykonur

Dossor

Sagiz

Emba

Karsakpay

Ganyushkino

Baychunas

GUR'YEV

Iskininskiy

Chelkar

Zhilaya Kosa

Koschagyl

Saksaul'skiy

Aral'sk

Volga

ASTRAKHAN'

Aralsul'fat

Novokazalinsk

Fort Shevchenko

Tauchik

Kazalinsk

Syr-Darya

Dzhusaly

KZYL-ORDA

Kuybyshevo

Caspian Sea

UST'-URT

Aral Sea

Tas-Buget

Chiili

UZBEK SSR

Amu-Darya

TURKMEN SSR

KAZAKH SOVIET SOCIALIST REPUBLIC

through an arm of the Amu Darya. The water is also remarkably transparent, and the lake bottom can be seen at a depth of 60 feet. Fish are present in large numbers, the most common types being the carp, the barbel, and the sturgeon.

The third largest inland basin is occupied by Lake Balkhash, which has an area of 6,680 square miles. It is located in the same latitude as the Aral Sea, but lies much higher than the latter, at about 1,100 feet. Although the lake is rather shallow (averaging 22 feet in depth), its water is of such low salinity that it can be used for irrigation and is consumed by Kazakh fishermen. This freshness of the water is due to the recent formation of the lake and the correspondingly short period of salification. Characteristic fish types are the white Balkhash perch and the carp-like *marinka* (Schizothorax), the latter having poisonous roe, but being otherwise edible.

With the exception of the Irtysh, all rivers of the Kazakh SSR drain into inland basins. Many of the large rivers, such as the Chu, the Sary-Su, and the Talas, lose so much water due to the intensive evaporation, their use for irrigation, and ground permeability that they do not reach any of the principal basins and empty into tiny salt lakes in the desert. In considering the rivers of Kazakhstan, one can distinguish two main types: those fed by melting snows and those fed by glaciers.

Most of the rivers draining the northern and the central parts of the Kazakh SSR belong to the first type. These are the Ural and the Emba, which empty into the Caspian Sea, the rivers of the Turgay tableland (the Irgiz and the Turgay), which flow into the large salt lake Chelkar-Tengiz, the left tributaries of the Irtysh (the Tobol and the Ishim), the Nura, which enters the saline lakes Kurgal'dzhin and Tengiz, and the Sary-Su, which loses itself in the sand and in small lakes. All these rivers in the steppe and desert sections of Kazakhstan have few tributaries. They are characterized by a short, turbulent high-water period in the spring thaw, while during the rest of the year, especially in the late summer, they become shallow and turgid, then even dry out altogether in the lower reaches. Among rivers of this type, only the Ural has any importance for navigation.

In the south and the southeast of Kazakhstan, rivers which rise in the high Tien Shan and Altay systems are chiefly glacier-fed. Among these are the Syr Darya, with its affluents, the Chirchik and the Arys', which empties into the Aral Sea, the Talas and the Chu, which flow into the desert, the inlets of Lake Balkhash (the Ili, the Karatal, the Ak-Su, and the Lepsa rivers), and the Irtysh, with its right tributaries (Kurchum, Narym, Bukhtarma, Ul'ba, and Uba rivers), which rise in the Altay Mountains. These rivers are of great economic importance for the Kazakh SSR. Their upper course, which generally runs through narrow, precipitous mountain valleys, is suitable for the establishment of hydroelectric power installations, while their lower reaches are used for irrigation. As opposed to the steppe rivers, these mountain streams have a fairly constant water level and reach their maximum volume at the very time (July–August) when they are most useful for irrigation of the areas under cultivation.

Of all the Kazakh rivers, only the Irtysh has any considerable importance from the point of view of navigation. It rises in Sinkiang Province of China as the Kara-Irtysh, or Chernyy Irtysh ("black Irtysh"), and enters Lake Zaysan, situated in a deep depression 60 miles inside the Kazakh SSR between the Altay Mountains and the Tarbagatay range. This lake acts as a natural reservoir, rendering the river navigable 200–220 days a year. The Irtysh is usually frozen from the second half of November to the second half of April.

The Kazakh SSR has a very dry, typically continental climate. The average yearly isotherms generally extend along the latitudes and vary from 33.3° F along the northern border to 56.3° F along the southern boundary. Average January temperatures are everywhere below freezing (except for a few isolated areas in the extreme south), reaching a low of 1.1° F in the north. In July the temperature difference is smaller, with average temperatures of 82.4° F in the south and 67.1° F in the north. In addition to these latitudal temperature differences, variations are observed along the same degree of latitude. For every degree of longitude, the average monthly temperature in January (the time of the maximum variation) decreases 0.54° F from west to east. The longitudinal temperature difference decreases toward the summer and disappears altogether during the hottest months.

These peculiarities of the temperature distribution (especially during the winter) are closely connected with the character of the existing air circulation. In the cold part of the year, the territory of Kazakhstan is under the preponderant influence of dry and very cold air masses which have their origin in the Arctic and in Siberia. These air masses exert their strongest influence in regions closest to their point of origin, that is, in northern and eastern Kazakhstan. Frontal movements occur seldom during the winter months and are then connected with the reduction of the Siberian High, a rare phenomenon which permits the northward flow of tropical air centered over Iran. The rare appearance of fronts is responsible for very little precipitation during the period November–March, an average of 2 to 3 inches. As a result, the snow cover is very thin and varies from an extreme of 12 inches in the north to 2 to 4 inches in the Aral Sea region, disappearing altogether near the Syr Darya.

Although a more developed air circulation occurs during the summer, the relative humidity of the air is so low that precipitation still appears only in small amounts. Up to 10 inches of rain falls in northern Kazakhstan in the April–October period. The Aral-Balkhash area, however, being the site of a summer high, receives only 1.2 to 3 inches during the same period. In the mountainous belt the situation is similar to that in the lowlands. The northernmost ranges in the Altay system have the greatest precipitation (12 to 16 inches in the winter, and 28 to 32 inches in the summer), while the southern mountains, in the western Tien Shan system, receives 20 to 24 inches in the winter and 16 to 20 inches in the summer. The precipitation in the Dzungarian Ala-Tau, in the same latitude as the Aral-Balkhash area, has a yearly rainfall of less than 18 inches.

The combination of the two main observed climatic factors—the decrease in rainfall from north to south and the rise in temperature in the same direction—leaves the greater part of Kazakhstan with insufficient humidity and produces conditions conducive to the creation of deserts. The evaporation of whatever little humidity does accumulate is helped considerably by strong winds which blow north and south from the high pressure area which generally occurs in the middle latitudes of the Kazakh SSR. The bare relief and the absence of wooded areas place no obstruction in the path of the winds which attain average monthly velocities of 11.3 miles per hour during the winter. These strong winds, beside contributing to evaporation, cause snowdrifts and soil erosion. However, they may become economically useful as a source of energy.

The seasons in Kazakhstan are typical of the existing continental climate. A short spring coupled with a rapid thaw is followed by a long, hot summer, with temperatures reaching 100° in the daytime and dropping to a few degrees above freezing during the night. A late, short autumn is followed in turn by a long, severe winter, during which there are frosts of —40° in the north and —10° in the south.

From the point of view of soil and vegetation zones, Kazakhstan can be divided into lowlands and uplands. While the zoning in the mountains depends on the altitude and proceeds from the semi-desert and steppe in the foothills up the slope through the forested zone to the Alpine meadows, the lowlands are divided according to latitude, from north to south, into steppe, semi-desert, and desert zones.

The wooded steppe of West Siberia penetrates as a narrow belt into the extreme northern section of the Kazakh SSR. Here ordinary black earth supports a preponderant meadow steppe interrupted by numerous birch groves, with occasional aspen and willow clusters. Toward the south, the humus content of the black earth decreases gradually, and the latter is replaced by chestnut-brown soils. At the same time, the forest clusters disappear entirely and make way for the typical steppe. While in the meadow steppe vegetation entirely covers the soil, here in the feathergrass steppe the plant cover is thinner and generally covers only 75 percent of the ground, leaving areas of bare soil. Narrow-leaved, drought-resistant feathergrass types predominate, together with fescue grass, an excellent fodder for sheep and horses.

The transition zone between the steppe and the dry steppe or semi-desert is marked by latitude 48° N. The chestnut soils are replaced by poorer brown soils, in which the humus content is only about 2 percent and which have a greater salt content leading to the formation of strongly alkaline soils in the depressions. Vegetation consists of a combination of feathergrass types (mainly in the northern sections) and wormwood grasses (in the south). In addition, saltwort and glasswort thistles predominate in salt depressions. For a short period during the spring the steppe assumes a fresh and flowery appearance. However, the short-lived plants have blossomed and withered by June, and the steppe takes on a uniform brownish color.

The low southern and southwestern sections of the Kazakh SSR fall within the desert zone. According to soil forms, deserts are divided into four types: sand, clay, salt, and stone deserts.

Sand deserts, which include most of the Turan lowland, are distinguished by sand dunes, which appear in form of parallel ridges and crescents. They may have a scarce vegetation cover, or they may be slowly moving with the predominant winds. The gray desert soil supports a few grass types (which immobilize the sands with their long, thin root systems), some bushes, and the characteristic *saksaul* (Arthrophytum or Haloxylon), an odd-shaped, gnarled, leafless desert tree, which may grow to a height of 20 feet and have a trunk diameter of 15 inches.

The Bet-Pak-Dala is a typical clay desert, with huge, cracked clay flats which give the appearance of flagstone-covered areas. During the spring, due to the impermeability of the soil, these flats become muddy and sticky, but they dry out to form an extremely hard surface in the summer. The only plant life consists of wormwood, tamarisk, and *saksaul*.

Salt deserts occur everywhere in depressions where water accumulates during the spring and leaves a saline deposit in the summer. The salt flats, which bear the local name *shor*, or *sor*, are nearly devoid of vegetation.

In the neighborhood of outcrops of crystalline rocks (remains of former mountains) amid the sand or clay deserts, stony gravel and debris accumulate to form the so-called stony desert area.

A special type of clay desert, a loess plain, occurs frequently in the foothills of the mountain belt. These areas, of which the *Golodnaya Step'* (west of the Syr Darya) is typical, normally support an ephemeral spring plant life. By means of irrigation, they have been transformed into cultivated areas and produce chiefly cotton.

In the steppe, along certain streams, a relatively dense belt of bush and tree vegetation develops, breaking the monotony of the landscape. These wooded portions, which occur in those sections of the river valley occasionally inundated by floods, are called *tugay*, a Kazakh word meaning forest. Ordinary forests, however, are found only in the mountains in the east and the southeast of the Kazakh SSR, especially in the Altay Mountains, the Tarbagatay range, and the Dzungarian Ala-Tau. Deciduous forests occur on the lower slopes and are succeeded by conifers at the height of 5,000 to 6,000 feet.

The Kazakh SSR represents one of the richest ore-bearing regions of the USSR. It occupies first place in reserves of nonferrous metals: copper, lead, zinc, silver, chrome, nickel, and molybdenum, and has also large reserves of petroleum, coal, salt, antimony, gold, tin, phosphorites, and bauxite.

Copper occurs in three large deposits in the Kazakh upland of central Kazakhstan: in the southwest at Dzhezkazgan, in the south on Lake Balkhash, at Kounradskiy, and in the northwest at Boshchekul'. Total reserves are estimated at 10 million tons.

So-called polymetallic deposits, including chiefly zinc, lead, and silver, with an admixture of copper and gold, have been located in the Altay Mountains, with emphasis on zinc, in the Dzungarian Ala-Tau and the Kara-Tau, with predominant lead ores, as well as in many areas of the Kazakh upland.

Chrome and nickel exist in the northern Mugodzhar Mountains, just south of the Orsk-Khalilovo deposits, of which they form a continuation. About 50 percent of the known nickel reserves of the USSR occur in this section of Kazakhstan.

Iron is also found in the Kazakh upland, southwest and southeast of Karaganda, while manganese appears chiefly in the Ulu-Tau and in the Mangyshlak peninsula.

The Kazakh SSR is the home of two large fuel bases of the USSR: the Ural-Emba petroleum fields and the Karaganda coal basin. The Emba oil region produces one of the highest-grade oils in the entire country. Reserves have been estimated at one billion tons. Beside the Karaganda basin, which is the third largest coal producer of the USSR, and has reserves of about 50 billion tons, local deposits exist in the Mugodzhar mountains, in southern Kazakhstan at Lenger, in the Ulu-Tau at Baykonur, and in several other areas.

Raw materials for chemical industries, such as phosphorites, borates, and salt, occur mainly in west and southwest Kazakhstan.

The Kazakh SSR, with an area of 1,061,600 square miles, supports a population of little more than 6 million people, giving an average density of 6 per square mile. Due to the natural factors the population is distributed very irregularly. It is densest in the eastern half of the republic, in a belt extending eastward from the Ural River, through the northern steppe, along the Irtysh through the Altay Mountains, and in the foothills of the southern mountain zone in the irrigated areas. In these regions the density varies from 50 to 100 persons per square mile. In sharp contrast, one person for every 10 square miles represents the distribution of the population in arid areas such as the Bet-Pak-Dala and the Ust'-Urt.

The basic portion of the population consists of Kazakhs (until 1925 called Kirghiz, and from 1925 to 1936, Kazaks), a people of the Turkic group, which include about 57 percent of the total population. Next in numbers are Russians (20 percent), Ukrainians (14 percent), and several other nationalities, including Uzbeks, Uygurs (Chinese Uzbeks), and Dungans (Chinese Moslems).

The territory of the present Kazakh SSR was first organized in 1920 as the Kirghiz Autonomous SSR, with its capital at Orenburg (since renamed Chkalov). In 1925 the Orenburg area was detached from the Kirghiz Autonomous SSR, and the capital was transferred to Ak-Mechet' (formerly Perovsk) which received thereupon the more ap-

propriate name Kzyl-Orda [red capital]. At the same time the name
of the Kirghiz Autonomous SSR was changed to Kazak, in accordance
with the change of name of the titular nationality. The Kara-Kalpak
Autonomous Oblast, which had been annexed in 1924 as a result of the
administrative reorganization of Central Asia, was transferred to the
Uzbek SSR in 1930. The capital had been moved to the present site,
Alma-Ata, in 1927–29. In 1936 the Kazak Autonomous SSR was raised
to the status of full union republic with the adoption of a modified spelling of the name: the Kazakh Soviet Socialist Republic.

After the old *guberniya* type of political-administrative organization
had been abolished, in 1928–29, oblasts were created in 1932, and their
number has increased from the original six to sixteen in 1947. While the
creation of new oblasts is often due to increases in population (this is
especially true of Siberia), this has not been a factor in the Kazakh SSR,
where the population increment has been negligible between the censuses
of 1926 (6,073,979) and 1939 (6,145,937); the population was still in
the neighborhood of 6 millions in 1947.

Kazakhstan is well supplied with power industries. Karaganda has
become the second largest coal producer of the Asiatic part of the USSR
(the Kuznetsk Basin is the largest) and the third largest in the entire
country. Production increased spectacularly during the Second World
War, from 4.2 million tons in 1937 to an estimated 15 million tons in
1947. Karaganda acts as the main coal base for the many metallurgical
industries of Kazakhstan; a very large portion of the production is also
shipped to Magnitogorsk via the new South Siberian Railroad, thus
cutting in half the distance over which coal was previously shipped to
the Urals from the Kuznetsk Basin.

Local coal deposits are exploited in the Kara-Tau range of the
Mangyshlak peninsula (Gur'yev Oblast), at Berchogur (Aktyubinsk
Oblast), at Baykonur (west Karaganda Oblast), near Makinsk and
northeast of Akmolinsk (Akmolinsk Oblast), at Ekibastuz (Pavlodar
Oblast), along the upper Kenderlyk River in the Saur range (East
Kazakhstan Oblast), and at Chokpak and Lenger (South Kazakhstan
Oblast). All these mines supply local metallurgical and other industries,
power plants, and so forth.

The Emba-Ural petroleum region northeast of the Caspian Sea occupies fourth place in the production of crude oil. Its leading fields are
at Dossor, Makat, Iskininskiy, Baychunas, and Koschagyl' (all in

Gur'yev Oblast) and at Shubar-Kuduk (Aktyubinsk Oblast). They are connected by pipe lines with refineries at Gur'yev and Orsk.

Water-power resources have been developed to a considerable degree in recent years. There are large hydroelectric plants on the Ul'ba River near Leninogorsk (East Kazakhstan Oblast), on the Nura River at Temir-Tau (Karaganda Oblast), and on the Irtysh near Ust'-Kamenogorsk (East Kazakhstan Oblast).

The first iron and steel plant was built at Temir-Tau, near Karaganda, during the Second World War. However, most important is the non-ferrous metallurgical industry, which includes copper refineries at Karsakpay, Dzhezkazgan, and Balkhash (all in Karaganda Oblast) and at Glubokoye (East Kazakhstan Oblast), lead and zinc works at Leninogorsk and Ust'-Kamenogorsk (East Kazakhstan Oblast), Tekeli (Taldy-Kurgan Oblast), and Chimkent (South Kazakhstan Oblast). A large ferroalloy plant has been established near Aktyubinsk during the Second World War, on the basis of the nickel and chrome mines to the northeast.

Machine-construction industries have been developed recently in several large cities of the Kazakh SSR. Alma-Ata has railroad-car repair works; Akmolinsk and Petropavlovsk produce agricultural machinery. Machinery is also made at Aktyubinsk.

Chemical industries on the basis of salt and phosphorite deposits have assumed great importance in the economy of Kazakhstan. Large phosphate fertilizer works are established near Aktyubinsk and near Dzhambul in the range Kara-Tau. At Inderborskiy (Gur'yev Oblast) rich borate deposits are exploited, and salt-extraction plants exist at Aral'sk and near Pavlodar.

Due to the scarcity of forests, lumbering plays a minor role in the industrial picture. Sawmills and wood-working industries are located near Semipalatinsk (in the Altay area) and near Alma-Ata (on the northern slope of the Trans-Ili Ala-Tau). Alma-Ata is also the main textile center of Kazakhstan; it has wool-spinning mills. Cotton mills have been established at Chimkent.

Industries based on agricultural and livestock products are widespread throughout the cultivated areas of the Kazakh SSR. Meat-packing plants, among the largest in the country, are at Ural'sk, Petropavlovsk, and Semipalatinsk. Beet sugar refineries are found in Alma-Ata, Merke, Taldy-Kurgan, Kara-Bulak, and Dzhambul. Fruit-preserving factories are in Chimkent, Dzhambul, and, especially, Alma-Ata,

the center of orchard gardening. Other industries are concerned with
flour milling (in the north and the southeast), tanning, leather products,
wool washing, cotton ginning, and cottonseed-oil extraction.

During the past twenty years Kazakhstan has undergone radical
changes from the point of view of agricultural economy. Previously the
basic Kazakh population was primarily engaged in nomadic livestock
raising, while its other elements tilled the soil. Russians and Ukrainians
sowed wheat and other grains in the northern steppe, and Uzbeks,
Uygurs, and Dungans irrigated the soil in the southern section of
Kazakhstan. As a result of the land reforms introduced by the Soviet
regime, the Kazakhs adopted a sedentary mode of life, created populated
places and farms, and developed a semi-nomadic type of livestock breeding, in which only the herdsmen accompany the stock from pasture to
pasture, no longer the entire community, as was customary. A considerable part of the stock is permanently stationed at the *aul*, the Kazakh
village, and only in summer is taken to the higher mountain grazing
grounds.

Three basic agricultural zones can be distinguished in Kazakhstan:
the north and the northeast, where the black-earth steppe supports
mainly grain crops (spring wheat and millet), as well as considerable
areas of sunflower cultivation, and dairy farming; the center and the
southwest, where the dry steppe and desert permit only semi-nomadic
sheep and cattle raising for meat and wool production; the south and
the southeast, where irrigated agriculture on rich loess soils and a warm
climate produce a great variety of crops: food crops, such as fruit,
grapes, wheat, rice, and chiefly industrial crops, including cotton, sugar
beets, tobacco, rubber-bearing plants (*koz-sagyz*, *tau-sagyz*, and chon-
drilla), and fiber-producing plants (*kenaf*, and *kendyr'*). Irrigated agriculture is located mainly along the banks of the Syr Darya, its affluent,
the Arys', and along the Talas, the Chu, the Ili, and the Kara-Tal rivers.

Fisheries form an important branch of the economy and are located
mainly on the northeast coast of the Caspian Sea. The centers of the
industry are at Gur'yev and Ganyushkino, on the Aral Sea (cannery
at Aral'sk), and on Lake Balkhash (at Burlyu-Tobe and Burlyu-
Baytal). Thirty-two fishing establishments were in operation in 1939.

The progress made by the Kazakh SSR in the industrial field would
have been unthinkable at an earlier date because of the lack of communications. The greater portion of Kazakhstan was without railroad lines,
and trade was effected mainly by means of camel caravans.

Until 1927 only the Trans-Caspian Railroad from Chkalov to Tashkent served for the whole of this vast area. During that year construction was started on the Turksib (Turkestan-Siberian) Railroad between Semipalatinsk (then the terminus of a branch of the Trans-Siberian leading from Novosibirsk) and Arys' on the Trans-Caspian line. This all-important link, nearly 1,000 miles long, provided a connection between the grain and the lumber areas of West Siberia and the cotton regions of Kazakhstan and Central Asia, thus supplying the cotton-growers, in particular, with wheat and freeing irrigated areas for more cotton cultivation. The Turksib Railroad has considerable importance also in the development of trade between the USSR and the Sinkiang Province of China.

Another vital link in the railway network of the Kazakh SSR was the line from Petropavlovsk south through Akmolinsk, Karaganda, and Mointy to Balkhash. This railroad is being converted into a Trans-Kazakhstan trunk line with the construction during the 1946–50 Five-Year Plan of the Mointy-Chu connection. The completion of this project will provide a north-south through route joining the Trans-Siberian at Petropavlovsk with the Turksib at Berlik, a station just northeast of Chu. From this north-south line a branch goes west from Zharyk station to the rich mining region of Dzhezkazgan-Karsakpay-Baykonur; this may be extended in the near future to a junction with the Trans-Caspian at Aral'sk.

The largest current railroad construction project, the South Siberian trunk line, which runs south of and parallel to the old Trans-Siberian between Tayshet and Kuybyshev and is scheduled for completion by 1950 (except for the Abakan-Tayshet section to be built after 1950); it passes through northern Kazakhstan along the line Pavlodar-Akmolinsk-Atbasar-Kartaly. The track between Akmolinsk and Kartaly, with a connection to Magnitogorsk, was completed in 1939. At present, work is in progress on the Pavlodar-Akmolinsk section. The South Siberian is at present providing a direct line from the Karaganda coal fields to the steel mills of Magnitogorsk and the south Ural Mountains in general.

Less spectacular lines, but nevertheless vital links in the Kazakh rail network, have been built in many sections of the republic. The Gur'yev-Kandagach line, which gives an exit from the Emba oil fields, has been extended from Kandagach north to Orsk, thus opening up the rich nickel and chrome deposits in the Mugodzhar mountains. The short Ural'sk–Sol'-Iletsk line provided a second northern exit to the overloaded Trans-

Caspian Railroad. The short branch from Lokot', on the Turksib, into the East Kazakhstan mining region to Leninogorsk gave access to the rich lead and zinc mines in the Altay.

As has been noted earlier, the river network of Kazakhstan provides no opportunities for the development of navigation. The only waterway of any importance is the Irtysh, which serves only the extreme eastern section of the republic. Steamship lines also operate on the lower Ural River and the Caspian Sea, between Aral'sk and Muynak (Kara-Kalpak Autonomous SSR) on the Aral Sea, and on Lake Balkhash. Several automobile roads have been built to supplement the transportation network, especially the Eastern Belt Highway, which connects the Altay mining areas in a region offering great physical obstacles to railroad construction.

OBLAST SURVEY: WESTERN KAZAKHSTAN

THE WESTERN SECTION of the Kazakh SSR includes the Caspian lowland, the Mugodzhar hills, and the western Ust'-Urt plateau. Except for the north, where sufficient precipitation permits the growing of millet, wheat, sunflowers, and mustard, the economy is characterized by extensive livestock raising. There are fisheries along the lower Ural River and in the Caspian Sea, where sealing is also important. The region contains the Emba oil area. Nickel, phosphorite, borates, and coal are other mineral resources. Communications are served by the Caspian Sea and by the Chkalov-Tashkent and Gur'yev-Kandagach-Orsk railroads.

West-Kazakhstan Oblast
Capital, Ural'sk; area, 60,900, population, 280,000

West-Kazakhstan Oblast lies in the extreme northwest of the republic and borders on Saratov and Chkalov oblasts of the Russian SFSR. It is bounded in the north by the Obshchiy Syrt hill formation. The dry steppe which makes up the entire oblast is traversed in the center by the south-flowing Ural River. The rest of the oblast contains only short intermittent streams and salt lakes. Agriculture is developed mainly in the north (millet and wheat), with a large acreage under mustard seed. Livestock (cattle, camels, and sheep) are raised in the south. There are salt deposits and natural-gas wells, as yet not exploited. Railroads touch the oblast only in the extreme north and west. The population consists of Russians in the agricultural areas and along the Ural River and Kazakhs in the drier districts.

Ural'sk, on the Ural River, is a meat-packing center and processes wool, skins, and grains. It was founded in the early seventeenth century and was called Yaitskiy Gorodok until 1775.

Gur'yev Oblast
Capital, Gur'yev ; area, 98,600, population, 240,000

With the exception of the Ust'-Urt plateau and the Mangyshlak peninsula in the south and a narrow eastern border strip, the entire Gur'yev Oblast lies in the Caspian depression below sea level. It has a very dry climate and is situated entirely within the dry steppe and the desert zones. Agriculture is negligible due to the lack of moisture, but goats, sheep, and camels are raised in large herds. The chief economic asset is the Emba oil district, which lies almost entirely within the confines of the oblast and produces high-grade crude oil. The major producing fields are Dossor and Makat (both opened before the Bolshevik Revolution), Baychunas and Iskininskiy (in the Gur'yev area), and Koschagyl' and Kul'sary (on the lower Emba River). An old pipe line connects Dossor with Rakusha on the Caspian Sea, while newer lines link Koschagyl' and Dossor with refineries at Gur'yev and Orsk. Natural-gas fields have been located northwest of Gur'yev. An important borate site is at Inderborskiy on Lake Inder, near the Ural River. In addition, potash, bromite, and common salt are found there. On the Mangyshlak peninsula, in the Kara-Tau range, coal is mined and there are manganese and petroleum deposits. Fisheries play a major part in the economy and are centered on Fort Shevchenko on the Mangyshlak peninsula and on Ganyushkino near the Volga delta. Bautino near Fort Shevchenko is a sealing base.

Gur'yev is on the right bank of the Ural River, near its mouth on the Caspian Sea. Terminus of pipe lines from the Emba oil fields, it was formerly merely an oil-shipping port, but acquired during the Second World War its own cracking plant and oil-refining installations on the left bank of the Ural River. A rail line links Gur'yev with Kandagach. The city, which dates from 1640, is the Kazakh center of the Caspian fishing industry.

Aktyubinsk Oblast

Capital, Aktyubinsk; area, 114,700, population, 300,000

Extending from the border of Chkalov Oblast (Russian SFSR) southward to the Aral Sea, Aktyubinsk Oblast includes brown-soil steppe in the north and desert in the south. The Mugodzhar hills separate the Caspian lowland (west) from the Turgay tableland (east). Because the oblast has little precipitation, varying from 10 inches in the south to 16 inches in the north, its river network is poorly developed. The only streams of any consequence are the Emba, which flows southwest toward the Caspian Sea and the Irgiz; it waters the eastern section and flows into the inland lake Chelkar-Tengiz.

Agriculture is restricted to a narrow belt in the north; the rest of the land is devoted to livestock raising (sheep, goats, camels). Rich nickel deposits near Batamshinskiy (formerly Kimpersayskiy) and chrome resources at Donskoye and Khrom-Tau [chrome mountain] are exploited in the northern Mugodzhars. Coal is mined at Berchogur and Kurashasayskiy. Extensive phosphorite deposits south of Aktyubinsk, notably near Kandagach, are processed into phosphate fertilizers at the Alga chemical works near Aktyubinsk. Another chemical plant at Chelkar is based on the salt deposits from the Aral Sea. The eastern wing of the Emba oil district, which penetrates into the oblast, has its chief field at Shubar-Kuduk. The Trans-Caspian Railroad intersects the oblast northwest by southeast, crossing the Orsk-Gur'yev line at Kandagach.

Aktyubinsk, situated on the Trans-Caspian Railroad and on the Ilek, a left affluent of the Ural River, has electrotechnical and engineering works, stockyards, and flour mills. During the Second World War a major ferroalloys plant was established near by, based on the nickel and chrome of the Mugodzhar hills and fueled by the Kurashasayskiy coal mines.

NORTHERN KAZAKHSTAN

THE NORTHERN SECTION of the Kazakh SSR lies basically in the West Siberian lowland, with an average yearly precipitation of 16 inches along the northern border of the republic, and is drained by the Tobol and the Ishim rivers, two left affluents of the Irtysh. The economy rests on wheat, dairy farming and sheep raising. It is the principal Kazakh grain-growing area and has large Russian and Ukrainian elements. Toward the drier south, the raising of sheep for meat and wool becomes dominant.

The region gravitates toward the Trans-Siberian Railroad and more recently toward the new South Siberian trunk line.

Kustanay Oblast
Capital, Kustanay; area, 76,700, population, 400,000

Kustanay Oblast contains the Turgay gates, which lie between the outliers of the Urals and the Kazakh upland and connect the West Siberian lowland in the north with the Turgay tableland in the south. The oblast has a wide, fertile black-earth belt in the north, changing into dry steppe toward the south. It is drained by the Tobol and its right affluent, the Ubagan, which flows through Kush-Murun salt lake. The south is watered by the Turgay River, which drains into the inland basin of the lake Chelkar-Tengiz. The oblast is bisected latitudinally by the Kartaly-Akmolinsk section of the South Siberian trunk railroad. North of the line, wheat, oats, and millet are grown, while, to the south, there is mainly cattle and sheep raising. An important gold-mining area lies in the upper reaches of the Tobol River at Dzhetygara.

Kustanay, situated on the Tobol and a branch of the South Siberian Railroad, processes agricultural products (meat, flour, skins, wool, and dairy products).

North-Kazakhstan Oblast
Capital, Petropavlovsk; area, 17,600, population, 360,000

This northernmost oblast of Kazakhstan lies in the Ishim Steppe, drained by the Ishim River, and forms part of the West Siberian lowland. The prevailing black earth supports a rich agricultural economy, producing wheat, oats, millet, and dairy goods. Crossed by the Trans-Siberian Railroad, the region resembles generally the oblasts of Kurgan, Tyumen', and Omsk of adjoining Western Siberia.

Petropavlovsk, a former caravan-trading center, lies at the junction of the Trans-Siberian and the Trans-Kazakhstan railroads. It processes the local farm products, has a large meat-packing plant, flour mills, tanneries, and since the Second World War it manufactures its own agricultural machinery.

Kokchetav Oblast
Capital, Kokchetav; area, 28,600, population, 320,000

Kokchetav Oblast lies in the wooded steppe zone (Ishim Steppe), which in the south rises into the picturesque hilly lake district of the Kokchetav upland. Sufficient precipitation and a black-earth soil form the basis for an essentially agricultural economy. The chief crops are wheat, oats, and millet, and, near Novo-Sukhotino, sunflowers. Dairying is of some importance. The oblast contains the Akmolinsk exclave of the Stepnyak gold-mining area, the well-known health resort of Borovoye in the lake district, and the city of Shchuchinsk. It is served by the Petropavlovsk-Balkhash railroad.

Kokchetav is an important agricultural center, with meat-packing, flour-milling, tanning, and distilling industries.

CENTRAL KAZAKHSTAN

THIS SECTION of Kazakhstan, situated in the Kazakh upland, is extremely rich in mineral resources. It contains the Karaganda coal basin, the Kounradskiy and Dzhezkazgan copper areas, and iron and manganese deposits. Its large-scale mining and metallurgical industries were developed almost entirely since the First Five-Year Plan. Irrigated truck and dairy farms supply the newly created urban centers.

Akmolinsk Oblast
Capital, Akmolinsk, area, 59,000, population, 440,000

Drained by the upper Ishim and the lower Nura rivers, Akmolinsk Oblast includes the black-earth and brown soil zones of the steppe region. The north is hilly and rises in the east into the Kazakh upland; the southwest is a rolling plain enclosing the inland Tengiz lake basin. The region has a rather dry continental climate, with precipitation averaging 12 inches. Its economy is chiefly agricultural, with emphasis on grain (wheats, oats, and millet) and dairy farming in the north and the east, dry farming in the west, and semi-nomadic sheep raising in the southwest. The mineral resources in course of exploitation include gold in the area of Stepnyak and Danilovka, antimony at Turgay, coal along the Petropavlovsk-Balkhash railroad north of Akmolinsk, and bauxite, also near Akmolinsk.

Akmolinsk lies on the upper Ishim River at the junction of the South-Siberian and Trans-Kazakhstan railroads. It is the center of a rich agricultural and grazing area, producing grains, dairy products, meat, and hides. It manufactures agricultural machines and has some lumber milling.

Other cities of the oblast are Atbasar, which processes livestock products and underwent considerable development since the completion of the

Akmolinsk-Kartaly section of the South-Siberian railroad, Makinsk (agricultural machinery), and Stepnyak, center of gold fields.

Karaganda Oblast
Capital, Karaganda ; area, 156,700, population, 460,000

The largest civil division of Kazakhstan, Karaganda Oblast, extends from Lake Balkhash 300 miles north to the area of Akmolinsk and more than 600 miles westward nearly to the Aral Sea. It is mainly in the desert and the dry steppe zones and includes a major portion of the Kazakh upland (north) and the Bet-Pak-Dala desert (south). Its main streams are the Nura and the Sary-Su, both flowing into inland lakes.

The oblast is the main mining and metallurgical section of the Kazakh SSR and includes the Karaganda coal basin, the large copper deposits of Kounradskiy and Dzhezkazgan, iron mines at Atasuskiy, and manganese mines at Dzhezdinskiy in the Ulu-Tau range (developed during 1942 to replace the German-occupied Nikopol' mines), tungsten and molybdenum at Akchatau (north of Balkhash), corundum at Semiz-Bugu (northeast of Karaganda), and scattered lead-zinc deposits. Copper smelting and refining installations are found at Uspenskiy (first plant to be erected in nineteenth century), at Balkhash (for the Kounradskiy mine), and at Karsakpay (old smelter) and Bol'shoy Dzhezkazgan (modern refining plant) for the Dzhezkazgan mine. Coal from the Baykonur mine is used in smelting the Dzhezkazgan ore. Near Karaganda lies Temir-Tau, the Kazakh steel-milling center.

Agriculture is carried on in the black-earth belt north of Karaganda, where wheat, vegetables, and dairy products are produced for the industrial areas. Elsewhere sheep, camels, and cattle are raised. The oblast is traversed by the Trans-Kazakhstan railroad, the Mointy-Chu section being scheduled for completion during the current Five-Year Plan. Branch railroads leave the main line at Zharyk station for the Dzhezkazgan copper-mining area and at Mointy for the Balkhash district.

Karaganda city is one of the youngest urban centers of the USSR. It developed from a tiny mining settlement of 150 inhabitants in 1926 to the present metropolis of about 220,000 people. During the Second World War alone its population increased 50,000 over the 1939 census figure of 165,937. The city is the center of the Karaganda coal basin with an average yearly production of about 15 million tons of coking coal, largely intended for the metallurgical industries of the Urals. The phenomenal development of the Karaganda industrial region has, since the end of the Second World War, been marked by the growth of the satellite coal-mining center of Saran', 12 miles south of the city, and the metallurgical center of Temir-Tau, to the northwest.

Temir-Tau [iron mountain] lies on a reservoir formed by the Nura River. Formerly a small sawmilling settlement named Samarkand (renamed Temir-Tau in 1945), the city developed rapidly during the Second World War after the establishment of a hydroelectric plant and the erection (in 1944) of the first steel mill of Kazakhstan, which is to have a yearly capacity of 120,000 tons of steel. Blast furnaces are projected to complete the cycle of the metallurgical production.

Balkhash, the second largest industrial center of the oblast, sprang into existence in 1928. In that year construction was begun on the copper-refining plant located on Bertys Bay, of Lake Balkhash, about 10 miles south of the Kounradskiy mines. As the industrial town grew, it was renamed successively Pribalkhash and Balkhash; it attained a population of 75,000 at the end of the Second World War. Irrigated farms in the vicinity supply the once arid city with truck produce.

The town of Bol'shoy [great] Dzhezkazgan, just south of the Dzhezkazgan copper mines, is the site of a recently constructed copper refinery which is rapidly outdistancing the older smelting center of Karsakpay farther west. Power for the electrolytic processes in the new refinery, said to have twice the capacity of the Balkhash plant, or 200,000 tons of refined copper per year, is furnished by a new hydroelectric plant at Kengir, just east, on the Kengir River, a tributary of the Sary-Su.

Eastern Kazakhstan

THE EASTERN SECTION of the Kazakh SSR includes the western Altay Mountains, rich in minerals, the Kazakh upland, and in the north a portion of the West Siberian lowland. The Irtysh River serves as the main waterway and separates the dry, sheep-raising area on the left bank from the wheat-growing Kulunda Steppe on the right bank. In the Altay, beekeeping, maral-deer raising, and lumbering are important activities. This area is also the richest part of the region from the point of view of mineral resources. The nonferrous metals (lead, zinc, and copper) which are mined here can be refined locally, thanks to an abundance of hydroelectric power.

Pavlodar Oblast
Capital, Pavlodar; area, 53,600, population, 260,000

Pavlodar Oblast bestrides the Irtysh River. The east (right) bank is a continuation of the Kulunda Steppe of the Altay Kray, while the west (left) bank is higher and drier, with rich mineral deposits. Here extensive coal deposits at Ekibastuz, a town of more than 10,000, are beginning to be exploited on the new Pavlodar-Akmolinsk section of the South Siberian Railroad. At the same time the large copper deposits of Maykain and Boshchekul' will also become accessible. At present only gold mining is carried on at the Maykain site. The salt brine lakes east of the Irtysh, near Pavlodar, have an extraction plant at Tavolzhan. Wheat and millet are grown in the Kulunda Steppe, and dairy cattle are raised. Forests occupy a considerable area along the border of the Altay Kray.

Pavlodar, at the junction of the Irtysh River and the South Siberian railroad, has meat and tanning industries, flour mills and sawmills. Chemicals are produced on the basis of the salt extracted east of the city.

Semipalatinsk Oblast
Capital, Semipalatinsk; area, 67,600, population, 360,000

Semipalatinsk Oblast lies just west of the Altay mountain system and is drained by the Irtysh River in the north and the Ayaguz in the south. The two drainage basins are separated by the Tarbagatay and the Chingiz-Tau ranges, which cross the oblast from east to west. The economy is mainly agricultural, with dry farming (wheat and millet) in the north and irrigation in the southeast; wheat and opium are produced. Cattle and sheep are raised extensively. A large portion of the cultivated area is devoted to the growing of sunflowers. Gold is the chief mineral resource of the oblast, and the mining area is centered on Zharma, Akzhal, and Zhangis-Tobe. Timber is cut in the northern forests and milled at Zhana-Semey, near Semipalatinsk. The oblast is served by the Turksib Railroad, from which an important highway branches off at Ayaguz for the Chinese border.

Semipalatinsk is a transportation hub at the junction of the Irtysh River and the Turksib Railroad. It has one of the largest meat-packing plants of the USSR, tanning and textile industries, and wool-processing and lumber mills. Railroad shops serve the Turksib main line and a recently completed branch railroad linking Semipalatinsk with the South Siberian at Kulunda and the Trans-Siberian at Tatarsk.

East-Kazakhstan Oblast
Capital, Ust'-Kamenogorsk; area, 37,300, population, 500,000

The East-Kazakhstan Oblast in the Altay Mountains is another important mining region of the Kazakh SSR. It is drained by the upper Irtysh River and its affluents, the Narym and the Bukhtarma. In the south lies Lake Zaysan in the middle of a large depression. The main deposits include zinc, lead, and silver ores, with an admixture of copper and gold. The principal mining centers are Leninogorsk, Zyryanovsk, and Belousovka. Tin and tungsten are mined in the Kalba range at Uba-redmet.* Coal deposits, as yet little exploited, are founded in the Saur range on the USSR-China border. Gold is mined in the neighborhood of Samarskoye, at Kuludzhunskiy and Palattsy and on the Kurchum River. The nonferrous metallurgical industries at Ust'-Kamenogorsk (zinc), Leninogorsk (lead and zinc), and Glubokoye (copper) are powered by hydroelectric plants at Ul'ba, on the Ul'ba River, near Leninogorsk, at Ablaketka, just south of Ust'-Kamenogorsk, on the Irtysh River, and at Glubokoye itself.

Ust'-Kamenogorsk was formerly sometimes known as Zashchita. It lies on the Irtysh River, at the mouth of the Ul'ba, and has a zinc-smelting plant, metalworks, and tanning and vegetable-oil industries. At Ablaketka, some 10 miles south, on the Irtysh River, is the Ust'-Kamenogorsk hydroelectric station, in process of construction during the postwar Five-Year Plan.

Leninogorsk, known as Ridder until 1940, is one of the foremost lead and zinc producers of the USSR. Discovered in 1834, the mines were originally exploited for silver. Since the Bolshevik Revolution the city has grown rapidly; it has now reached a population of 60,000.

SOUTHERN KAZAKHSTAN

THE SOUTHERN SECTION of the Kazakh SSR extends along the entire southern border of the republic from the Aral Sea in the west to the Chinese frontier in the east. Except for the Kyzyl-Kum desert lowland in the west, this portion of the republic lies at the foot of the Central Asian mountain ranges and is watered by short torrential streams which

* The toponymic Ubaredmet, seemingly unintelligible in any language, is a typical example of a class of Soviet place names. It consists of the telescoped initial syllables of the name of the Uba River and the Russian words *redkiye metally* (rare metals), a term including tin, tungsten, molybdenum, and similar metals.

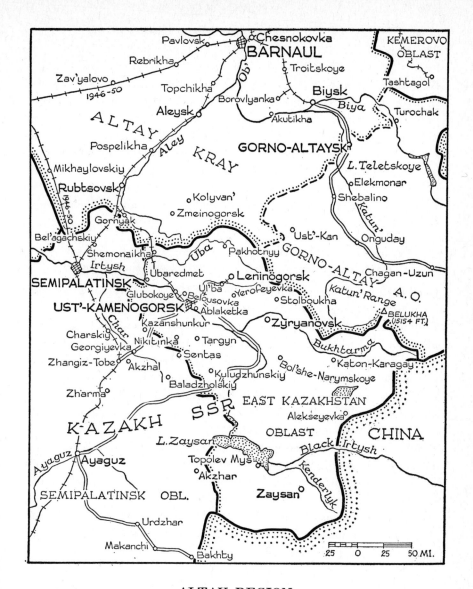

ALTAY REGION

disappear into the desert sands after having been used for irrigation. The principal branches of the rural economy include livestock raising, by using mountain pastures during the summer and the lowlands during the winter, irrigated agriculture (orchards, cotton, tobacco, *kok-sagyz*, sugar beets, and rice), and dry farming (wheat) on the mountain slopes. Sugar milling is one of the main agricultural industries. Lead-zinc ores and phosphorite are the chief mineral resources. Transportation is served by the Turksib and the Trans-Caspian railroads and to a small extent by the Ili River and Lake Balkhash. In addition to the basic Kazakh population and the usual Russian and Ukrainian element, there are Uzbeks (chiefly in the oases), Uygurs, and Dungans among the principal ethnic groups.

Taldy-Kurgan Oblast
Capital, Taldy-Kurgan; area, 46,200, population, 300,000

One of the most recently created oblasts (1944), Taldy-Kurgan Oblast includes the Dzungarian Ala-Tau and the desert area southeast of Lake Balkhash. It is drained by the Kara-Tal, the Ak-Su, and the Lepsa rivers, all flowing into Lake Balkhash. Irrigated agriculture is common on the mountain slopes and produces wheat, sugar beets, rice, opium, and to-bacco. Cotton is grown in the area of Panfilov (formerly Dzharkent), and cattle and sheep are raised in the drier areas. Tekeli, at the end of a spur of the Turksib Railroad, which passes through the oblast, has extensive lead-zinc mines and a refining plant. There are fisheries in Lake Balkhash, their center being at Burlyu-Tobe, at the east end of the lake. Food is processed in the area of Taldy-Kurgan; there are sugar mills at the oblast capital and at Kara-Bulak. Ush-Tobe is the center of a newly developed rice oasis and has a meat-packing plant.

Taldy-Kurgan has the appearance of a large village in the midst of a sugar beet region. Its industries are connected with sugar and flour milling and rice polishing.

Alma-Ata Oblast
Capital, Alma-Ata; area, 41,700, population, 520,000

Alma-Ata Oblast extends in the shape of an angular 80-mile wide strip along the Ili River from Lake Balkhash to the Chinese border. It is very mountainous in the south (Trans-Ili Ala-Tau and Ketmen' range) and has a sandy desert along the lower Ili in the northwest. The economy is entirely agricultural. On the southern mountain slopes irrigated farming produces a great variety of crops: basically wheat and sugar beets, but also tobacco, opium, rubber-bearing, fiber-producing, and medicinal plants. Garden fruits (apples and grapes) are very important. There is some lumbering in the mountain forest zone. In the desert near Lake Balkhash, sheep are raised and *saksaul* trees are processed for local fuel. On the lake shore are numerous fisheries. Industry consists mainly in food processing (sugar refining, flour milling, and fruit canning). The Turksib Railroad crosses from northeast to west. The Kazakhs form two thirds of the population, which includes also Russians, Ukrainians, and a considerable number of Uygurs.

Alma-Ata is the seat of government of the Kazakh SSR. Situated in the picturesque foothills of the Trans-Ili Ala-Tau, it is entirely surrounded by apple orchards, which gave the city its Kazakh name meaning "father of apples." Founded in 1854 as the Russian fortress of Vernyy, it became the capital of the Kazakh SSR in 1929. It has a heavy machine-building industry (including railroad shops), spinning mill, fruit-preserving and meat-packing plants, wine and tobacco factories, tanneries, and sawmills. It has a university (established 1928), a large library, Kazakh and Russian opera houses, theaters, and museums, and is the seat of the Kazakh Academy of Sciences.

Dzhambul Oblast
Capital, Dzhambul; area, 52,000, population, 320,000

Dzhambul Oblast consists of a narrow strip of fertile irrigated land along the foot of the Kirghiz range and the Kara-Tau and a wide forefield of desert, including the sandy Muyun-Kum south of the Chu River and the clay desert of Bet-Pak-Dala to the north. Agriculture is carried on in the irrigated area along the Chu, the Talas, and the Assa rivers; they grow a great variety of crops, including sugar beets, cotton, wheat, rice, tobacco, and fiber-producing plants. The raising of cattle, sheep, horses, and camels in the drier areas is important. Besides the new, large phosphate works, built in 1945, at Chulak-Tau, in the Kara-Tau range, and on a spur of the Turksib Railroad, the industry consists mainly of processing of agricultural and livestock products. Sugar refineries are at Dzhambul and Merke; both are on the Turksib Railroad, which skirts the foothills of the mountains to the south.

Dzhambul is one of the oldest cities of Kazakhstan. It stands at the site of Taraz, a fifth-century city, later called Yany (or Yangi), and followed by the modern Kazakh city of Auliye-Ata (Aulie-Ata). In 1933 this was renamed Mirzoyan (for a Kazakh Communist party chief), and in 1937 Dzhambul (for the well-known Kazakh bard). Dzhambul is the center of a sugar beet and orchard area; it has sugar-refining, fruit-canning, wool-washing, and distilling plants.

South-Kazakhstan Oblast
Capital, Chimkent; area, 61,500, population, 640,000

South-Kazakhstan Oblast, lies in the southwestern part of Kazakhstan. It is drained by the Syr Darya and its important affluent, the Arys', and includes the range Kara-Tau in the east and the desert Kyzyl-Kum in the west. The oblast is the main cotton region of the Kazakh SSR, with large ginning establishments at Chimkent, Sary-Agach, Turkestan, and Il'ich. The latter town, in the large Pakhta-Aral cotton plantation, is the center of the Golodnaya Step' ("hungry steppe"), a fertile loess plain, converted into an irrigated cotton area in recent years. In the range Kara-Tau there are extensive lead-zinc mines at Achisay and Kantagi, for which a large lead refinery is located at Chimkent. Fuel is furnished by coal mines at Lenger, Kel'temashat, and Chokpak. Sheep are raised in the deserts in the north and southwest. The Trans-Caspian and Turksib railroads join at Arys' station.

Chimkent lies in a rich cotton- and fruit-growing area. It has important lead works, a chemical plant for pharmaceutical products, cotton gins, flour mills, and fruit canneries. It is a former caravan center stormed by the Russians in 1864.

Lenger, a large coal-mining center, lies southeast of Chimkent and is connected by railroad.

Kzyl-Orda Oblast
Capital, Kzyl-Orda; area, 88,900, population, 300,000

Lying astride the lower Syr Darya, Kzyl-Orda Oblast includes one of the most arid regions of Kazakhstan just east of the Aral Sea. A major portion is covered by sandy deserts (the Aral Kara-Kum and the Kyzyl-Kum). Only irrigation with the water from the Syr Darya makes agriculture possible. The chief crop is rice. The construction of a large dam at Tas-Buget [stone dam] near Kzyl-Orda, a current project, will increase considerably the area under rice cultivation. Sheep and camel raising are important in the desert. There are extensive deposits of phosphorite and saltpeter, and along the Aral Sea shore, at Aralsul'fat, sodium and magnesium sulphate. Along the seashore also there are many fisheries, with a cannery at Aral'sk. The Trans-Caspian runs parallel to the Syr Darya.

Kzyl-Orda [red capital] lies on the site of the former Kokand fortress of Ak-Mechet', stormed by the Russians in 1853 and renamed Perovsk. Named Ak-Mechet' after the Revolution, it became the capital of the Kazak Autonomous SSR in 1925 and was called Kzyl-Orda, a name which remained, although the capital was transferred to Alma-Ata in 1929. The industry is chiefly connected with the local agricultural products: rice polishing, meat packing, and food canning.

CHAPTER 17

Central Asia

Soviet Central Asia extends from the Caspian Sea in the west to the Chinese frontier in the east, from Kazakhstan in the north to the borders of Iran and Afghanistan in the south. This region, which has some of the most unusual features of the natural divisions of the USSR, has an area of about 475,000 square miles. It is located farthest south and most removed from the tempering influence of the oceans.

The structure and relief of Central Asia can be divided into two parts: the northwestern section, comprising about two thirds of the total area, which includes extensive low, sandy deserts and irrigated oases in the foothills of the mountains, and the southeastern part, one third of the total area, a mountainous zone with some of the longest, highest, and most glaciated ranges of the world. The low region is part of the Turan lowland. It stretches from the Caspian Sea to the Syr Darya and the range Kara-Tau in the east and includes the southern portion of the Ust'-Urt plateau and the two largest deserts of Central Asia, the Kara-Kum and the Kyzyl-Kum, separated from each other by the Amu Darya. The Kara-Kum has the greater area, of which nine tenths are covered by sand. Here and there one encounters barren clay flats and salt-covered depressions. A number of dry river beds, similar to the *wadi* of the Sahara, run from the present river course toward the Caspian Sea. The largest of these dry valleys is the Uzboy, which is thought to have been a branch of the Amu Darya. Along the southern edge of the Kara-Kum, at the foot of the Kopet Dagh, are steppes and oases extending in a narrow belt along the USSR-Iran frontier. Other oases lie on the Tedzhen and Murgab rivers, as well as in the lower reaches of the Amu Darya (oasis of Khorezm). The Kyzyl-Kum lies somewhat higher than the Kara-Kum and has more rocky areas, devoid of sand cover. In its central section there are outcrops of Paleozoic rocks, rising to over 3,000 feet, which are the eroded and weathered remains of ancient mountain ranges. In the eastern part of the Kyzyl-Kum numerous steppe areas penetrate between the outspurs of the mountainous section. Such a steppe is the Fergana Valley, one of the densest populated areas of Central Asia.

The Tien Shan mountain system forms the most extensive portion of the mountainous section of Central Asia. It is composed of a number of separate ranges, all directed generally east and west; many of them bear the local name *ala-tau* [mottled mountains], because of the typical isolated patches of perpetual snow. The northern and the central ranges of the Tien Shan form part of the Lower and Upper Paleozoic (Hercynian) folded systems. The individual crests are separated by wide mountain valleys, constituting rich agricultural and pasture lands. On the frontier of the USSR and China, in the easternmost section of the central Tien Shan, several ranges merge into a powerful glaciated mountain hub, where the Pobeda [victory] Peak rises to 24,400 feet, the highest point in the Tien Shan. South of the Tien Shan lies the younger (tertiary) Pamir-Alay mountain system, distinguished by more compact and higher ranges, which includes the highest mountain of the USSR, Stalin Peak (24,595 feet). Near by is the greatest glacier of the world, the Fedchenko Glacier, about 50 miles long. The southernmost crest of the Tien Shan, the Alay range, is separated by the Alay valley from the northernmost range of the Pamir-Alay system, the Trans-Alay range, which rises to 23,377 feet at Lenin Peak. South of the Pamir-Alay system lies the Pamir, "the roof of the world." This is a high mountain mass of a plateau character in the east, but having high ranges separated by deep, precipitous river gorges in the west. Lesser ranges are the Kopet Dagh on the frontier between the USSR and Iran, and the Balkhan ranges near the Caspian Sea.

The entire territory of Central Asia drains into inland sea basins; not one drop of water reaches the open oceans. Most of the waterways of this region drain into the two most important rivers of Central Asia, the Syr Darya and the Amu Darya; both flow into the Aral Sea. The larger and more important of the two, the Amu Darya, is fed by the snows and glaciers of the Pamir-Alay mountain system and the Pamir plateau. It is formed by the junction of the Panj and the Vakhsh rivers, the former a boundary stream between the USSR and Afghanistan, the latter an important irrigation source in its lower reaches. The Amu Darya rapidly loses its mountain torrent characteristics and, turning northwest into the desert region, widens its course, but still maintains a strong eroding action. It enters the Aral Sea through a wide delta. Unfortunately, it is not very suitable for irrigation, because of its great water volume, its speed, and the variability of its course. The other river, the Syr Darya, rises in the Tien Shan system. It is formed by the Naryn, which flows through wide valleys south and southwest of lake Issyk-Kul', and the lesser Kara Darya, which rises in the Fergana range. As opposed to the Amu Darya, it has a smaller volume, width, and depth, but it is longer and very suitable for irrigation. It flows through the Fergana Valley and then turns northwest through the desert zone toward the Aral Sea, which it enters also through a delta. Its most important affluent is the Chirchik which waters the oasis of Tashkent.

Among the mountain lakes the most notable is Issyk-Kul' which has an area of 2,395 square miles and lies 5,193 feet above sea level. It is slightly saline and does not freeze in the winter. Lesser lakes are the Kara-Kul' and the Zor-Kul', in the Pamir plateau.

Due to its remoteness from the oceans, the climate of Central Asia is very continental in nature. The continental characteristics already noted in Kazakhstan are still more accentuated in this region. The internal seas, the Caspian and the Aral, which border on Central Asia are too small to exert any tempering influence. Average summer temperatures in the lowland rise as high as 90° F, and in a great part of the region frosts of a few degrees below 0° F are possible in the winter. Evergreen vegetation, such as that along the Batumi coast of the Black Sea, does not exist in Central Asia. There is very little precipitation, generally 4 to 5 inches a year over a great part of the territory; only in the foothills does the rainfall amount to 16 inches or more. These climatic extremes are especially notable in such high mountain areas as the Pamir. In the valleys, such as the Fergana and the Zeravshan valleys, the climate is milder. Winter conditions are unsettled. Snow generally falls in December and remains on the ground till February, although it may melt earlier. The transition from the cold of February to the warmth of May is very sudden. Toward the end of that summer month wheat ripens and apricots are ready for picking. This period is followed by a long, hot, dry summer, in which predominantly dry winds blow from the north and wither the vegetation. These winds create sandstorms in the desert and sometimes raise a fine dust which blots out the sun. In the foothills and the mountains the summer is more temperate: there is precipitation, and the vegetation does not dry out. Toward the end of August or the beginning of September the heat lets up and is followed by a warm autumn, the best season in Central Asia. The climate of the Pamir and of the higher ranges of the Tien Shan reminds one of the Far North. Frosts occur even in the early part of July; in the winter they fall to —49° F. During the summer the temperature rises to 60° F, and there is a great temperature difference between areas exposed to the sun and those in the shadow. The average yearly temperature in these mountain fastnesses approximates that on the shores of the White Sea.

The dry and extremely continental climate exerts a strong influence on the vegetation of Central Asia. Plants which adapt themselves to these conditions and are able to withstand drought periods are predominant in the desert and in the mountains. Steppe vegetation covers not only the plain but also the mountain slopes, reaching even to the area of permanent snows. In the high mountain valleys of the Tien Shan and the Pamir are salt steppes and salt lakes. Only a portion of the mountains is wooded, generally the northern and western slopes. Wooded belts (*tugay*) also occur along some rivers.

The desert vegetation consists of rather poor varieties. The plants are sometimes covered with thorns or fibers and are very sturdy. In the sandy desert the *saksaul* tree is the predominant type; of the other plants, umbrella-shaped plants, among which the Asafetida Giantfennel, exuding an ill-smelling resinous substance, and desert rhubarb, with large meaty leaves, are the most common. The long roots of the desert plants immobilize the sand, so that moving sand dunes are found only where no vegetation normally exists or where it has been destroyed by irrational grazing of livestock. Among the sands, occasional clay flats are covered sparsely by various types of wormwood and camelthorn, and saltwort is found in salt depressions. During spring and summer, the desert and steppe supports various bulbous plants, including wild onions. Along the rivers and the salt lakes there are thickets of *chiy*, a feather-grass often reaching a height of 12 feet, which is used by the local inhabitants for making mats and thatching roofs. The densely wooded clusters along streams include tamarisk, willow, poplar, and wild olive.

The mountain forests include deciduous trees on the lower slopes, with wild-growing walnut, pistachio, and apricot trees. Common European types, such as pine, oak, and linden, are completely lacking. In the eastern Tien Shan a type of fir is found. Above the forest zone there are rich mountain pastures, similar to Alpine meadows in the humid areas and to the Caspian steppe in the drier sections.

Central Asia has considerable reserves of mineral resources, but their exploitation has only recently been begun to any large extent. Along the mountain foothills there is a zone of petroleum deposits extending from the Caspian Sea (at Nebit-Dag), to the Fergana Valley and the lower Surkhan Darya, an affluent of the Amu Darya. Much importance is attached to the salt deposits in the Caspian gulf of Kara-Bogaz-Gol. This inlet, acting as a natural evaporating basin for the water of the Caspian Sea, has large deposits of Glauber salt (mirabilite). Sulphur deposits are found here to a greater extent than in any other part of the USSR, mainly in the center of the desert Kara-Kum, at Gaurdak, near the Amu Darya, and in the Fergana Valley. The ranges which surround this valley abound in nonferrous and rare metals: copper, lead, zinc, gold, silver, tungsten, mercury, and antimony. In the highlands of the Pamir, Iceland spar (a variety of calcite), precious stones, and gold are being mined at the present time. The combination of coal and iron deposits in and near the Fergana Valley have permitted the development of heavy industry.

The population of Soviet Central Asia amounts to 10.4 million people, with an average density of 22 per square mile. While in the desert area the average density falls as low as a few people per 100 square miles, the fertile and well-irrigated oases have a population density of about 1,000–1,500 per square mile, the highest rural population concentration in the USSR. The basic elements of the population belong to the Turkic and Iranian groups. The former, by far the more numerous, includes Uzbeks, Turkmen, Kirghiz, and Kara-Kalpaks, while the latter takes in the Tadzhiks, the remaining members of an ancient nationality of Central Asia, who speak a language akin to Iranian. The Uzbeks number more than one half the total population, besides Tadzhiks, Kirghiz, and Turkmen. Russians (above 6 percent), Bukhara Jews, Chinese Dungans, and others make up the remainder of this colorful ethnic mélange.

Until 1924 Soviet Central Asia was divided politically into the Turkestan Autonomous SSR (formed in 1922) and the Bukhara and the Khorezm Soviet People's republics (formed in 1920). Late in 1924 a reorganization of these territories and a redemarcation of boundaries along essentially ethnic lines led to the establishment of the Turkmen SSR, the Uzbek SSR (including the Tadzhik Autonomous SSR), and the Kara-Kirghiz (later Kirghiz) Autonomous SSR, which became part of the Russian SFSR. In 1929 and 1936, respectively, the Tadzhik and Kirghiz Autonomous SSR became full union republics.

Agricultural activities play the leading role in the economy of Central Asia. Depending upon the land form and the development of irrigation, the following branches of agriculture can be distinguished: (1) irrigated farming, with intensive crops adapted to land irrigation (mainly cotton); (2) dry farming, including chiefly grain crops on mountain slopes having sufficient rainfall; (3) lowland livestock raising, including sheep and camels, adapted to the dry steppe and the desert; (4) highland livestock raising of cattle, goats, and sheep, adapted to valley pastures. Of all these activities, irrigated farming is by far the most important; it employs the greater portion of the population and covers more than two thirds of the sown area. The main crop in the irrigated area is cotton, remarkably well suited to the fertile loess soil of the lower valleys and the warm, sunny climate of Central Asia. The chief cotton areas are the Fergana Valley, the oases of Tashkent, Samarkand, and Bukhara, and the Vakhsh valley. The cotton is processed in local ginning plants, the seeds are sent to oil-extracting presses, and the husks are used for fodder. Other irrigated crops are rice, alfalfa, wheat, corn, sesame, and melons. The irrigated fields are generally bordered by mulberry trees, on which the silkworm is cultivated. One of the most common fruit-trees is the apricot; widespread orchards also produce peaches, apples, pears, pomegranates, grapes. Dried fruits (apricots, peaches, and raisins) form important articles of export. Grain crops occupy a very small portion of the irrigated area and are grown mainly on the non-irrigated mountain slopes.

Livestock is raised all year round, generally in the high mountain valleys in the summer and the lowland steppe and desert in the winter. The most important herds are sheep (including the karakul sheep), camels, cattle, horses, and mountain goats and yak.

Beside the mining industry developed at the deposits of petroleum, coal, salt, sulphur, and nonferrous metals, the industry is concentrated in the region of Tashkent, where it is supplied with power by the two large hydroelectric installations, the Chirchik and the Farkhad power plants. Tashkent is the center of the heavy metallurgy, textile, machine-construction, and food industries. Plants which process agricultural products are located in many other parts of Central Asia; they include ginning plants, oil presses, tanneries, fruit canneries, sugar refineries, and cotton and silk mills.

The basic transportation route is the Trans-Caspian Railroad, which sends many branches into the chief economic regions of Central Asia: the spur from Mary to Kushka, on the Afghan border, and the branches from Chardzhou to Kungrad (now under construction), from Kagan to Termez and Stalinabad, and from Ursat'yevskaya to Andizhan–Kokand–Namangan. Water transport is rather unimportant, the only suitable route being the Amu Darya below Chardzhou. In the mountain regions transport has to rely on highways, the main routes linking Osh with Khorog, Tashkent and Leninabad with Stalinabad, and Stalinabad with Khorog. In the desert, camel caravans continue to be the main commercial link, supplying particularly the oasis of Khorezm.

CHAPTER 18

Kirghiz Soviet Socialist Republic

Capital, Frunze; area, 76,100, population, 1,490,000

THE KIRGHIZ SSR, also known as Kirghizia and Kirghizstan, is a high mountain country located chiefly in the Tien Shan and the Pamir-Alay systems. In the east, it borders on the Sinkiang Province of China, in the north on the Kazakh SSR, in the west on the Uzbek SSR, and in the southeast and south on the Tadzhik SSR. Its western section is split up into a northern and a southern portion in the shape of pincers embracing the Fergana Valley.

GENERAL SURVEY

The mountain ranges rise to an average elevation of 13,000 to 16,000 feet and are oriented from west to east, where they merge on the USSR-China frontier into a powerful glaciated mountain hub, dominated by the Khan-Tengri (22,945 feet) and the recently discovered Pobeda [victory] Peak (24,400 feet). The characteristically wide mountain valleys also lie at the relatively high elevation of 6,500 to 10,000 feet. Nearly the entire mountainous part of Kirghizstan is drained by the streams of the Syr Darya system, among which the Naryn is the longest river.

Only in two sections does Kirghizia have lowland characteristics; in the north, the steppe-like valleys of the Chu and the Talas rivers penetrate deep into the mountain zone, and in the west, the eastern periphery of the Fergana Valley lies in Kirghiz territory. These lowlands, which have an elevation of 1,300 to 1,600 feet, enjoy a relatively warm climate and receive considerable precipitation from the north and the west. The basin of the lake Issyk-Kul', although entirely surrounded by mountains, can also be considered a suitable agricultural area.

The mountainous section, which is least adaptable to agriculture due to the extreme land form and climate, abounds in potential water-power and mineral resources.

The Kirghiz SSR has a population of about one and one-half million people and an average density of 20 per square mile. The bulk of the population is concentrated in the lowlands, where the density is about 100 per square mile, while in the mountainous section the density drops to less than one person per square mile.

The basic element of the population consists of Kirghiz (until 1925 called Kara-Kirghiz *), which form two thirds of the total population. The remaining third consists principally of Russians (about 12 percent), Uzbeks (about 10 percent), and Ukrainians (6 percent).

Formerly the Kirghiz lived along the upper course of the Yenisey River, where a portion of their group still remains under the name Khakass. They migrated to their present territory in the sixteenth century, were subjugated by the Kokand khanate in the first half of the nineteenth century, and came under Russian rule in 1876.

Following the Bolshevik Revolution the territory of the present Kirghiz SSR first formed part of the provisional Turkestan Autonomous SSR. As a result of the administrative reorganization of Central Asia along national lines, the Kara-Kirghiz Autonomous Oblast was in 1924 constituted a part of the Russian SFSR. In 1925 the name Kara-Kirghiz was changed to Kirghiz, while the name of the Kirghiz Autonomous SSR, to the north, was changed to Kazak. As a result of these changes, these two national groups for the first time received officially their true designations which had been used by the Kirghiz and the Kazakhs (Kazaks) themselves for many centuries but had been ignored by outsiders. In 1926 the Kirghiz Autonomous Oblast became an Autonomous SSR, and in 1936, an SSR. The Kirghiz SSR is the only example to date of an autonomous oblast having attained the status of a full union republic.

After the okrug-kanton type of political-administrative division had been abolished, by the end of 1930, Kirghizia was divided directly into rayons. In 1939 oblasts began to be created, on the basis of economic factors; at present, the Kirghiz SSR is divided into six oblasts.

Of all the Central Asian republics, Kirghizia is best supplied with coal resources. The major sites exploited at the present time are at the periphery of the Fergana Valley: at Sulyukta and Kizyl-Kiya in the south, and at Kok-Yangak and Tashkumyr in the east. Minor deposits exist also at Kadzhisay at the southern shore of Issyk-Kul'. During the current

* Until 1925 the name Kirghiz was applied to the Kazakh national group.

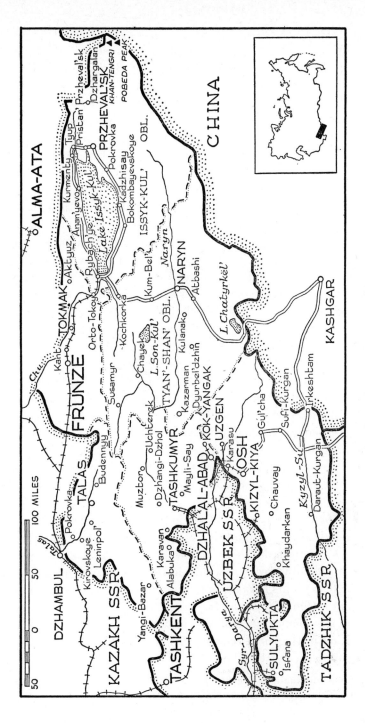

KIRGHIZ SOVIET SOCIALIST REPUBLIC

Five-Year Plan a new site of high-quality coking coal will be developed east of Uzgen, along the Yassy River; its main mines will be at Tuyuk and Kara-Tyube. Other deposits will be developed in the area of Dzhargalan, east of Przheval'sk. The current coal production reaches about 1.5 million tons; Kizyl-Kiya is the chief producer. Petroleum wells are located in the eastern Fergana Valley, at Changyrtash and Maylysay.

In addition to these power resources, nonferrous and rare metals are abundant in Kirghizia. On the southern edge of the Fergana Valley there are important mercury and antimony mines—at Khaydárkan, Frunze *, and Chauvay. A lead mine and a refinery are operating at Ak-Tyuz, on the south slopes of the Trans-Ili Ala-Tau. In addition, a tungsten and molybdenum mine is producing at Kum-Bel', north of Naryn. The lead mine at Ak-Tyuz is distinguished by a strong admixture of tin ore and the rare metal indium. Sulphur is quarried at Changyrtash, near the oil field. The post-war Five-Year Plan calls for the development of extensive arsenic deposits at Uchimchak, in the mountains southwest of Talas. Uranium is mined at Tyuya-Muyun and Maylysay.

During the Second World War the basis for a machine-building industry was laid in the form of an agricultural machinery works and an instruments plant. However, the essential industries are based on the local agricultural production: cotton, grain, sugar beets, tobacco, silk, wool, skins, meat, etc. Silk and cotton mills, cottonseed-oil presses, cotton ginning plants, and so forth are concentrated in the Fergana Valley; with the exception of tobacco processing in the Talas valley, the industries are all centered around Frunze, in the Chu valley. Five sugar refineries, a large meat-packing plant, flour mills, clothing and shoe plants, and fruit canneries are strung along the Lugovoy-Rybach'ye railroad in this area.

The chief food crop consists of grain, mainly wheat, which is grown in nonirrigated areas, on mountain slopes, and so forth. Of the industrial crops, which are raised chiefly in irrigated regions comprising over two thirds of the total sown area, cotton is grown in the Fergana Valley, sugar beets, fiber plants (*kendyr'* and *kenaf*), opium, tobacco, and southern hemp in the Chu, Talas, and Issyk-Kul' valleys.

In spite of the importance of agriculture, livestock raising occupies a top position in the rural economy. In the mountain zone 27 million acres are suitable as pasture land. Every spring, as soon as the grazing

---

* This mining town, until 1940 called Kadamdzhay, is not to be confused with the city of Frunze, capital of the Kirghiz SSR.

tracts in the lower valleys are burned by the sun, the herds are driven to the upper valleys, which throughout the summer abound in a rich, luxuriant Alpine vegetation. Goats and sheep outnumber by far the other herds.

Railroad lines penetrate only into the bordering lowlands of the Kirghiz SSR. One line, branching off from the Turksib Railroad at Lugovoy, traverses the Chu valley from west to east, through Frunze and Tokmak to Bystrovka. It is being extended during the post-war Five-Year Plan to Rybach'ye on Issyk-Kul'. This extension to the western end of the lake will provide a combined water-rail route from the important agricultural area around Przheval'sk and from the new Dzhargalan coal mines and further considerably the economic development of the Issyk-Kul' basin. Other rail lines penetrate in form of short spurs to the coal mines at the periphery of the Fergana Valley. In this manner Sulyukta, Kizyl-Kiya, Osh, Dzhalal-Abad, Kok-Yangak, and Tashkumyr are connected with the basic rail network of the Fergana Valley.

In the mountain zone, highways of various degrees of adequacy are the only means of communication. The best road links Frunze with Osh via Rybach'ye (which is developing into an important transportation hub), Naryn, and Uzgen. Roads joining Rybach'ye and Przheval'sk skirt the northern and southern shores of Issyk-Kul'. From Osh the famous Pamir highway leads southward over high plateau and mountain zones to Khorog, the capital of the Gorno-Badakhshan Autonomous Oblast of the Tadzhik SSR. Finally, Kirghizia serves as the starting point for two important trade routes converging at Kashgar, China.

The only water route is the shipping line connecting the port of Przheval'sk and Rybach'ye on Issyk-Kul'.

The Kirghiz SSR exports cotton into the European USSR, and coal, livestock, grain, and sugar into the neighboring Central Asian republics.

Oblast Survey

Frunze Oblast
Capital, Frunze; area, 6,000, population, 500,000

Located essentially in the Chu valley, at the foot of the Kirghiz range, Frunze Oblast forms the main economic region of the Kirghiz SSR. It is drained by the Chu River and its affluents, which form the basis of the Great Chu Canal project, intended to irrigate the entire valley. The construction of the Orto-Tokoy reservoir in Boom Gorge of the Chu

River, one of the highlights of the current Plan, will bring the project nearly to completion. A large number of hydroelectric stations are to be established in connection with the Chu project. The basic crops of the Chu valley are fiber plants (*kendyr'*, *kenaf*, and southern hemp), grown in the irrigated area near the Chu River, and sugar beets, raised in the zone traversed by the Lugovoy-Rybach'ye Railroad. The importance and extent of the sugar beet area is marked by the presence of five large sugar refineries at Karabalty, Pervomayskiy, Krasnooktyabr'skiy, Kant (a Kirghiz name meaning "sugar"), and at Oktyabr'skiy, a suburb of Tokmak. The Chu valley itself has been dubbed "sugar valley." Fruits and truck produce are grown in the Frunze-Tokmak zone. This region is the center of the light manufacturing industry of Kirghizstan. In addition to such food industries as meat packing, flour milling, fruit canning, there are plants engaged in the extraction of essential oils, fiber processing, machine construction, and the manufacture of clothing and shoes. In addition to the important lead-zinc mine of Ak-Tyuz in the east, the less valuable Buurdu lead deposits, southeast of Tokmak, are also being exploited. A number of health resorts, including Issyk-Ata and Ak-Su, are situated on the northern slopes of the Kirghiz range. The population is largely Russian and Ukrainian, with some Dungan elements in the east, near Tokmak.

Frunze, the capital of the Kirghiz SSR, lies in the center of the Chu valley on the Lugovoy-Rybach'ye branch of the Turksib Railroad. The city was built in 1873 as a Russian fortress and was named Pishpek. It developed rapidly after the construction of the railroad, in 1924, and in 1925 was renamed for the Bolshevik general, M. V. Frunze, born there in 1885. Its population rose from 36,610 in 1926 to 92,659 in 1939 and to about 140,000 by the end of the Second World War. It has a large, modern meat-packing plant and produces machinery, metalware, textiles, canned goods, flour, leather, and tobacco. Like other capitals of the Soviet union republics, it has several higher educational institutions and theaters (Russian and Kirghiz), and it is decorated by several parks.

Tokmak, the second city (population over 20,000) of the oblast, has an auto repair plant and engages in the processing of fiber plants and wool. A sugar refinery is situated in its suburb Oktyabr'skiy.

Issyk-Kul' Oblast
Capital, Przheval'sk ; area, 16,300, population, 180,000

This division comprises much of the high mountain country of Kirghizia, including the Kungey Ala-Tau and the Terskey Ala-Tau, which enclose

the lake Issyk-Kul' in the center. Wheat and opium poppies are cultivated along the eastern shore of the lake, while sheep and horses are
raised in the mountain valleys. Coal is mined on a small scale at Kadzhisay,
on the south shore of lake Issyk-Kul', and at Dzhargalan, on the Tyup
River, east of Przheval'sk. The latter site is scheduled for expansion
after the construction during the post-war Plan of a railroad from the
mine to the port of Przheval'sk. The current Plan provides also for the
erection of a cement plant at Kurmenty, on the northeastern shore,
with a yearly capacity of 30,000 tons. Processing industries are centered at Przheval'sk and Rybach'ye, which are connected by a lake shipping line. The mountains surrounding Issyk-Kul' contain numerous
health resorts, including Koysara and Dzhety-Oguz.

Przheval'sk (population over 20,000) was long known as Karakol
and was renamed in 1939 in honor of the Russian explorer Przheval'skiy,
who died here in 1888. It produces machinery, flour, sunflower oil, and
beverages (wine, beer, juices).

Rybach'ye, a town of more than 5,000, at the west end of Lake Issyk-
Kul', is a major communications center for northeast Kirghizia. The
terminus of the railroad from Lugovoy and Frunze, it acts as transfer
point for the lake steamers and as depot and supply point. A meat-
packing plant is to be constructed under the current Plan. Nearly 20
miles distant, on the Chu River, lies the recently completed Orto-Tokoy
reservoir (7 miles long), which will serve for the irrigation of the Chu
valley.

Tyan'-Shan' Oblast
Capital, Naryn; area, 21,200, population, 110,000

Situated in the middle of the Tien Shan (Russian *Tyan'-Shan'*) mountain system, where wide valleys separate the individual ranges, this oblast
is the most important livestock region of the Kirghiz SSR. It is traversed
from east to west by the Naryn River and is bounded in the north by
the Kirghiz range and the Terskey Ala-Tau, in the southwest by
the Kokshaal-Tau, on the USSR-China frontier, and in the west by the
Fergana range. Sheep, horses, and some cattle constitute the bulk of the
herds. Wheat and other grains are raised in the lower mountain valleys.
Several tungsten and molybdenum deposits are being worked, the major
ones being Kashka-Su and Kum-Bel' (called Kara-Unkurt until 1945),
north of Naryn. Gold placers are found in the upper river courses, and
salt is mined for local use. The main transportation artery is the Frunze-
Naryn-Osh auto road.

Naryn, a small city of 5,000 on the Naryn River, serves as supply point and trading center for the semi-nomadic local population, which during the summer months takes its herds into remote valleys such as the Dzhumgol and Susamyr areas, 100 to 150 miles northwest of Naryn. Local industries include sawmilling, brick-making, and tanning.

Osh Oblast
Capital, Osh ; area, 17,000, population, 390,000

This division, which forms the southern arm of the Kirghiz pincers gripping the Fergana Valley, lies on the northern slopes of the Turkestan and Alay ranges. In the southeast, it extends into the high mountain country of the Trans-Alay range and the Alay valley, outposts of the Pamir-Alay mountain system to the south. Intensive cotton cultivation takes place in the irrigated portions of the Fergana Valley (cotton ginning is centered at Karasu), while dry wheat farming is the common activity on the mountain slopes. Livestock is raised in the Alay valley. Osh Oblast contains the oldest two coal mines of Kirghizia: Sulyukta and Kizyl-Kiya, both connected by rail spurs with the main Fergana rail network. During the current Five-Year Plan a new coal-mining basin is being developed near Uzgen, to which a rail branch will be extended from Khanabad. The region also includes the mercury and antimony mines of Khaydarkan, Frunze (formerly Kadamdzhay), and Chauvay, which make the Kirghiz SSR the foremost producer of mercury in the USSR and the second with respect to antimony. A deposit of radioactive ore is found at Tuya-Muyun, west of Kizyl-Kiya. In addition to the basic Kirghiz population, there is a sizable Uzbek element living for the most part in the urban areas.

Osh, a city of about 50,000 inhabitants, has been an important silk center since the eighth century. Situated in a major sericultural district, it has silk-spinning and textile mills, cotton gins, and food-processing, tobacco, and metalworking industries. Near by are a health resort and Tash-Suleyman (Solomon's Throne), a rock which once attracted pilgrims from all Central Asia. Osh is the starting point of the Pamir automobile highway leading south to Khorog.

Kizyl-Kiya (population over 15,000) and Sulyukta (population over 10,000) are important coal-mining centers.

Dzhalal-Abad Oblast
Capital, Dzhalal-Abad; area, 9,200, population, 220,000

Adjoining Osh Oblast on the northeast and forming the northern arm of the pincers around the Fergana Valley, Dzhalal-Abad Oblast is bounded in the north by the Chatkal range and the Talas Ala-Tau, and in the east by the Fergana range. Cotton is grown in the irrigated edge of the Fergana Valley, while wheat and barley constitute the chief crops in the mountain valleys. Sericulture is a secondary activity in the cotton plantations. The oblast includes the Ketmen'-Tyube valley along the Naryn River, a district devoted to cotton planting (gin at Muztor) and livestock raising. The slope of the Fergana range is covered with nut and almond woods, including many wild fruit trees (apples, plums, and apricots) in the area of the River Orslanbob, or Arslanbob. The oblast includes the new coal-mining centers of Tashkumyr and Kok-Yangak. Changyrtash has oil fields and sulphur mines. Petroleum is also produced at Maylysay, where uranium is found. Uzbeks form a large element of the urban population.

Dzhalal-Abad, a city of about 30,000, is the manufacturing center of the oblast, with cotton gins, food-processing, metal, and tobacco industries, and a large vitamin and canning plant based on the near-by fruit and nut woods.

Kok-Yangak (founded in 1930) and Tashkumyr (dating from 1935) are the two major coal-mining centers of this section of Kirghizia, each counting 10,000 inhabitants.

Talas Oblast
Capital, Talas; area, 6,400, population, 90,000

This region is almost entirely cut off from the rest of the Kirghiz SSR by the Talas Ala-Tau and adjacent high mountain ranges. Its economic orientation is toward the Kazakh city of Dzhambul, on the Turksib Railroad. It is drained by the Talas River, along which the local crops (mainly tobacco, flax, and wheat) are raised. Cattle and sheep graze on the mountain slopes. The arsenic mine at Uchimchak is being developed during the present Plan. As in the Chu valley, Russians and Ukrainians form an important element of the population.

Talas (called Dmitriyevskoye until 1937) lies on the Talas River in the center of the oblast. It has agricultural industries based on the local products.

CHAPTER 19

Tadzhik Soviet Socialist Republic

Capital, Stalinabad; area, 54,900, population, 1,455,000

THE TADZHIK SSR, or Tadzhikistan, which adjoins the Kirghiz SSR in the south, lies in the extreme southeast of Soviet Central Asia. Its area of 54,900 square miles borders in the east on China, in the south on Afghanistan, and in the west on the Uzbek SSR. A narrow tongue of Afghan territory separates it from Pakistan. The frontiers of Tadzhikistan are quite irregular, especially in the north, where they include a section of the Fergana Valley and project a deep wedge into Uzbek territory. This area, until 1929 a part of the Uzbek SSR, was attached to the Tadzhik SSR on the basis of its dominant Tadzhik population.

GENERAL SURVEY

LIKE KIRGHIZIA, the Tadzhik SSR is a high mountain country. It has the highest average elevation of any union republic of the USSR. Its southeastern portion is formed by the Pamir highlands, called by the natives the "roof of the world," which is bordered in the northwest by a majestic mountain hub rising to 24,585 feet at Stalin Peak, the highest point of the USSR, and the site of the 50-mile-long Fedchenko Glacier, the longest continental ice stream of the world. In the center of the Tadzhik SSR, high ranges of the Pamir-Alay system generally extend east-west, rising toward the east. Lowlands are located in the northwest, along the Syr Darya, at the entrance to the Fergana Valley, and in the southwest, along the Kafirnigan (Gissar Valley) and the Vakhsh rivers.

With the exception of the northern part of Tadzhikistan, on the Syr Darya, the rivers of the republic drain into the Amu Darya system. The Panj River (Russian *Pyandzh*), which forms the border between the Tadzhik SSR and Afghanistan, joins the Vakhsh River (called Surkhab and Kyzyl-Su in its upper course) to form the Amu Darya, which in turn receives the Kafirnigan in the extreme southwest of the Tadzhik

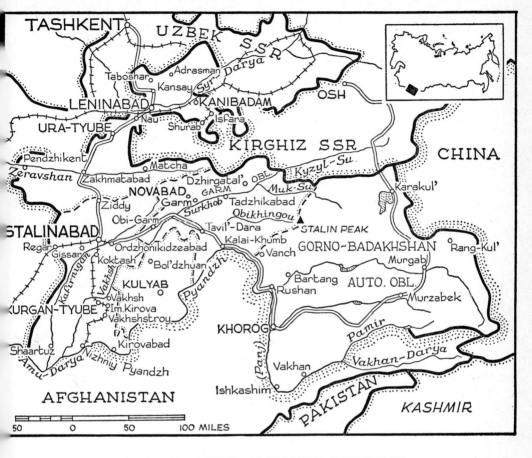

TADZHIK SOVIET SOCIALIST REPUBLIC

SSR. Several important canals form the basis of extensive irrigation systems in the Vakhsh and Gissar valleys.

The climate of the lowlands is distinctly of the desert type: hot, dry air, with average temperatures of over 88° F in July, and 38° F in January, and a yearly rainfall of about 10 inches. In the foothills and the lower ranges (to an elevation of about 5,500 feet), the climate becomes more humid and cooler, with average temperatures of 60–70° F in the summer and 15–25° F in the winter, and a yearly rainfall of 20 inches or more. Above 10,000 feet there are eternal snows and glaciers. In the Pamir unusual climatic conditions prevail. Due to the high mean elevation (10,000 to 15,000 feet), the average yearly temperature is below freezing. With high mountain ranges barring the way for humid air masses, the rainfall is even less than in the lowlands (about 3 inches a year).

Among the most common mineral resources are polymetallic and rare metal ores: lead, zinc, arsenic, bismuth (especially in the Kara-Mazar area in the north of the republic), coal, oil, fluorspar, optical minerals, salt, sulphur, and phosphorites. Gold, tin, and radioactive ores are also found.

The population of the Tadzhik SSR is about 1.5 million inhabitants. The average density is 30 per square mile, with sharp variations from a low of less than 2 in the Pamir highlands to a high of 150 in the Leninabad area.

The Tadzhiks comprise about three fourths of the total population. They are of Iranian origin and have lived in their present location since ancient times. Their language is akin to modern Persian. A large number of Tadzhiks are still living outside the confines of the USSR, in northern Pakistan and northeastern Afghanistan. The Uzbeks form the second largest element of the population (about 20 percent), settled mainly in the west and the northwest of the republic. About 15,000 Kirghiz are engaged in livestock raising in the eastern part of the Pamir.

The Tadzhiks were first constituted into an autonomous unit when the Tadzhik Autonomous SSR was created, in 1925, as part of the Uzbek SSR. Until then they had been subjugated by the Russians and the Bukhara khanate, and after the Bolshevik Revolution, had been incorporated into the provisional Turkestan Autonomous SSR. In 1929 the Tadzhik SSR was created as one of the union republics of the USSR. The Gorno-Badakhshan Autonomous Oblast had been erected in 1925 as an autonomous unit in the Pamir highlands. In 1939 the remainder of Tadzhikistan was divided into four oblasts. Since then two more oblasts have been established temporarily: Kurgan-Tyube (1943–47) and Ura-Tyube (1945–47).

Practically all branches of the industry have been developed only in recent years. The mining industry is centered in the northwest in the Fergana Valley and adjacent ranges. On the southern slopes of the Kurama range, northeast of Leninabad, are large deposits of lead-zinc ores, arsenic and bismuth, tungsten, vanadium, and radioactive ores. Across the Syr Darya and on the northern slopes of the Turkestan range, oil fields are producing at Nefteabad [oil town] and at Kim [for the initials of Russian words meaning Communist Youth International]; near by, coal is mined at Shurab. During the current Plan, coal is also beginning to be mined in the Gissar range at Ziddy. West of the Ziddy site, rich deposits of coal, rare metals, and so forth still await exploitation in the Takfan-Zauran-Kshtut region of the Zeravshan range. Gold is mined southeast of Garm and in the Pamir.

Among the manufacturing industries, the dominant ones are those based on the local agricultural production. There are many large cotton-ginning plants, a large cotton-mill (established in 1942 at Stalinabad), silk-spinning plants at Stalinabad and Leninabad, a tanning plant and smaller textile enterprises. The food industry is well represented by fruit canneries (of which the largest are at Leninabad and Kanibadam), cottonseed-oil presses (Kurgan-Tyube and Leninabad), a large meat-packing plant at Stalinabad, flour mills, rice-polishing plants, and wineries (at Leninabad, Ura-Tyube, and Pendzhikent). The metal working industry is engaged chiefly in producing spare parts for agricultural machinery and automobile parts. The machinery plant at Stalinabad also manufactures turbines and other equipment for hydroelectric installations. The first water-power plant was established in 1937 on the Varzob River, 8 miles north of Stalinabad. Since then, many smaller installations have been completed, and the current Plan foresees the completion of the second large power plant, the Lower Varzob hydroelectric station.

Like the other Central Asian republics, Tadzhikistan is an important cotton producer. Of the total sown area, 15 percent is under cotton. Formerly grown only in the northern Fergana Valley, the cotton plant has spread in recent years to the Kafirnigan and Vakhsh valleys. The newly developed areas, which have an exceptionally warm climate, specialize in the production of the long-staple Egyptian cotton, which occupies about one third of the total cotton area. Of great significance for the cotton cultivation are the gigantic new irrigation systems constructed in the Fergana Valley and in the Vakhsh and Gissar valleys; the Great Gissar Canal was completed at the time of the Second World War.

Orchards and vineyards occupy a significant place in the agricultural economy, especially in the northern valleys. Recently, subtropical fruits have been introduced into the Vakhsh valley. The mulberry tree, furnishing the basis for sericulture, grows side by side with the cotton plant, mainly in the areas of Leninabad and Stalinabad.

Grains, mainly wheat and barley, are raised in the unirrigated areas of the valleys and on the lower mountain slopes, and take in about three fourths of the total sown area.

Mountain pastures in the uplands of Tadzhikistan provide excellent fodder for numerous livestock herds. Livestock raising forms the basic branch of the economy in the eastern Pamir, where the yak serves as the all-utility animal. In the mountains of western Tadzhikistan the Gissar sheep is raised for meat and fat, and in the hot, dry lowlands of southwestern Tadzhikistan the karakul sheep is bred for its valuable fur. Some of the dairy cattle is fed on alfalfa in the irrigated cotton areas.

The only standard-gauge railway lines which penetrate into the Tadzhik SSR are the Fergana Valley line, which passes through the Leninabad wedge, and the railroad from Kagan (Uzbek SSR) via Termez to Stalinabad, with a short extention to Orzhonikidzeabad. A short rail spur connects the Shurab coal mines with the Fergana main line. Due to the difficult mountain terrain in the other parts of the republic, a narrow-gauge railroad has been built connecting Stalinabad with Kurgan-Tyube and extending beyond to Nizhniy Pyandzh on the Amu Darya; another leads from Stalinabad to the area of the new Ziddy coal fields. More narrow-gauge lines are projected to link the capital with Garm, Kulyab, Takfan, Pendzhikent, and Samarkand.

Among the main highways is the one connecting Leninabad and Stalinabad across the Turkestan, Zeravshan, and Gissar ranges, another linking Stalinabad and Khorog through the Darvaza Gorge and parallel to the Panj River, and the Pamir highway from Osh to Khorog.

Regular air services connect Stalinabad with Tashkent, Khorog, and other cities and towns of Tadzhikistan.

The Tadzhik SSR exports chiefly cotton, silk, dried and canned fruits, and among the metals, mainly lead and arsenic.

Oblast Survey

Leninabad Oblast
Capital, Leninabad; area, 9,400, population, 500,000

Located in the northwest of the republic, this oblast projects in the shape of a wedge into the Uzbek SSR, extending from the Zeravshan River across the Turkestan range and the Syr Darya to the Kurama range. It forms one of the most important economic areas of Central Asia, having extensive mining, manufacturing, and agricultural production. Along the Syr Darya cotton, mulberry trees (for sericulture), and fruits are important. Vineyards are centered here, as well as in the Zeravshan valley. In the unirrigated areas wheat is grown, and sheep and goats are raised. Leninabad, Kanibadam, Ura-Tyube, and Pendzhikent are the centers of the manufacturing industries: cotton and silk processing, silk weaving, fruit canning, cottonseed-oil extraction, and wine production. The southern slope of the Kurama range in the northern part of the oblast is the site of a great variety of mines: lead and zinc (Kansay and Kara-Mazar), uranium ores and vanadium (Taboshar), bismuth (Adrisman), arsenic (Takeli), tungsten and ozocerite (Chorukh-Dayron. Across the Syr Darya are the oil fields of Kim and Nefteabad and the coal mines of Shurab.

Leninabad was formerly called Khodzhent. It lies on the Syr Darya just off the Fergana Valley railroad and is important as a cotton and silk-processing center. Its industries include cotton ginning, silk spinning and milling, clothing and shoe manufacturing, food canning, cottonseed-oil extraction, and wine making.

Kanibadam, situated on the Tadzhik section of the Great Fergana Canal, produces canned goods and cottonseed oil.

Ura-Tyube, the capital of a separate oblast from 1945 to 1947, is a wine center in a grain and fruit-growing area.

Stalinabad Oblast *
Capital, Stalinabad; area, 9,700, population, 515,000

Lying south of Leninabad Oblast and extending to the Panj River (Afghanistan border) in the south, Stalinabad Oblast has an essentially agricultural economy. It includes the important cotton valleys along

* Stalinabad Oblast was abolished in 1951 and the territory formerly included in the oblast was placed directly under the Tadzhik SSR government.

the Vakhsh and Kafirnigan rivers, where subtropical fruits, jute, sugar cane, and yams have been recently introduced. On the low hill ranges there are extensive pistachio-nut woods and wheat fields. In the dry areas, near the Amu Darya, karakul sheep are raised. Sericulture is practiced near Stalinabad. Industry is centered at Stalinabad and Kurgan-Tyube (one of the largest cotton-ginning centers of the USSR) and includes cotton ginning, cotton and silk milling, meat packing, and fruit canning. Coal is mined at Ziddy, and there are extensive phosphorite deposits at Kara-Tag, north of the Gissar Valley. Northeast of Stalinabad a fluorspar works is being established; also, a cement plant northwest of the capital.

Stalinabad (population, 110,000) the capital of the Tadzhik SSR, lies on the Dyushambinka River (which still incorporates the old name of the city, Dyushambe), an affluent of the Kafirnigan River. A new city, created after 1929 out of the old village of Dyushambe, it lies on the railroad from Kagan (Uzbek SSR) and the highway from Leninabad. Being the political and cultural center of Tadzhikistan, it has also become the chief industrial center of the Gissar Valley. It has cotton and silk mills, meat-packing and tanning plants, wine and rum distilleries, and manufactures hydroelectric turbines, agricultural implements and hardware. It receives its power from the Varzob power plant, which will be supplemented by the Lower Varzob station (now under construction).

Kurgan-Tyube, situated in the Vakhsh valley, is one of the largest cotton-ginning centers of the USSR. It also produces cottonseed oil, meat, flour, and metal products. Narrow-gauge rail lines radiate from here through the southern section of the Tadzhik SSR. The city was the capital of a separate oblast from 1943 to 1947.

Kulyab Oblast
Capital, Kulyab; area, 4,600, population, 205,000

Bounded by the Panj River in the south and east, Kulyab Oblast has a mixed agricultural economy. Cotton is grown in the irrigated lower valleys, wheat and truck produce in the higher sections. Sheep, goats, and cattle are raised on the mountain slopes. There are extensive walnut forests in the north. The industry is restricted to cotton ginning and cottonseed-oil extraction. Gold placers are worked along the upper course of the rivers.

Kulyab is a small town engaged in cotton ginning and metal working. Salt deposits are mined near by.

Garm Oblast
Capital, Novabad; area, 7,600, population, 190,000

This oblast has an economy similar to that of Kulyab Oblast; how-ever, the emphasis is on livestock raising. It is more mountainous, and wheat forms the chief crop. Goats and sheep constitute the main herds. Gold placers occur along the rivers.

Garm, the former capital, lies on the Surkhab River, in a wheat and livestock area. Some silk is produced in the neighborhood. The oblast capital was transferred in 1950 to the village of Shulmak, which was renamed Novabad. This name, meaning "new city" (a hybrid combina-tion of the Russian *Nov-* and the Iranian *abad*), would indicate that considerable urban construction preceded the transfer of the adminis-trative center.

Gorno-Badakhshan Autonomous Oblast
Capital, Khorog; area, 23,600, population, 45,000

Located in the Pamir highlands, the Gorno-Badakhshan Autonomous Oblast forms the extreme southeastern portion of Tadzhikistan. It is bordered by China on the east and by Afghanistan on the south and the west, being separated by a ten-mile wide strip of Afghan territory from Pakistan and Kashmir. The eastern section has a high plateau character, with an elevation of 11,500 to 13,000 feet, while the western portion is dissected into high ranges and deep, narrow valleys oriented east-west. All the rivers flow into the Panj River (USSR-Afghanistan border). There are many lakes, including the Kara-Kul' in the north-east, Sarez Lake on the Murgab River, and the Zor-Kul', which gives rise to the Pamir River, one of the headwaters of the Panj. The eastern section of the oblast is inhabited by semi-nomadic Kirghiz, who engage in livestock raising based on yak, sheep, and goats. Gold is mined at Rang-Kul'; salt, limestone, and peat deposits are also being worked. The western valleys are inhabited by several Tadzhik tribes, who speak dif-ferent dialects and engage in agriculture and livestock raising. The chief crops are grains (wheat, barley, and rye) and beans. Vegetables and fruits have recently been introduced. The Osh-Khorog highway forms the main transportation route.

Khorog lies on the Gunt River near its confluence with the Panj. It has light manufacturing industries and is the terminus of highways from Stalinabad and Osh. There is regular air service to Stalinabad.

CHAPTER 20

Uzbek Soviet Socialist Republic

Capital, Tashkent; area, 157,400, population, 6,000,000

THE UZBEK SSR or Uzbekistan is the most populous and economically the most important Central Asian republic of the USSR. Its area amounts to only one third of the total area of Central Asia, but includes over one half the total population and sown area, two thirds of the railroads, four fifths of the cotton area and industry, and most of the large cities.

GENERAL SURVEY

IT IS LOCATED between the high ranges of the Tien Shan in the east and southeast and the sandy lowlands in the west and northwest. The Chatkal, Turkestan, and Gissar ranges, outspurs of the Tien Shan and Pamir-Alay mountain systems, penetrate into Uzbekistan from the east. The greater portion of the republic, however, forms a plain with huge waterless desert areas, which are frequently interrupted by oases, especially in the east. These oases are the economic and population centers of the Uzbek SSR.

The largest oasis is the Fergana Valley, of which the greater part lies in Uzbek territory, with the outer fringes in Kirghizia and Tadzhikistan. The Fergana Valley is irrigated by the Syr Darya and numerous streams descending from the surrounding mountain ranges. To the west, the Tashkent oasis is drained by the Chirchik and the Angren rivers, two of the main affluents of the Syr Darya. The Samarkand and Bukhara oases are drained by the Zeravshan River, a former affluent of the Amu Darya, which now disappears into the sands before reaching that river. The Syr Darya, after leaving the Fergana Valley, irrigates the Golodnaya Step', a formerly arid loess plain only recently transformed into a fertile agricultural region, part of which lies in the Kazakh SSR. Near

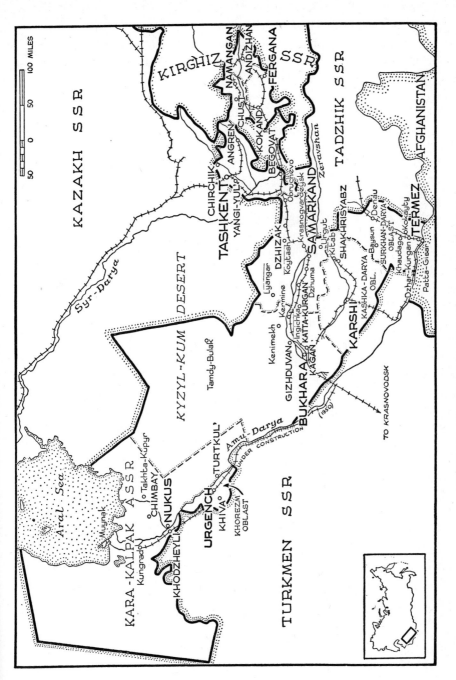

UZBEK SOVIET SOCIALIST REPUBLIC

its delta on the Aral Sea, the Amu Darya irrigates the historically important Khorezm (or Khiva) oasis.

The climate is sharply continental and dry, a factor which is responsible for the predominantly irrigated agriculture in Uzbekistan. The average temperatures are about 28° F in January and 77° to 86° F in July. The yearly rainfall varies considerably, from 3 inches in the driest lowland sections to 24 inches in the foothills.

Uzbekistan has fewer mineral resources than have the other republics of Central Asia, due to its predominantly lowland character; however, in view of the greater accessibility and population of the Uzbek SSR, the available resources have been explored and determined to a greater degree. Oil deposits occur in the Fergana Valley and in the southeast of the republic, coal in the Angren valley, and salt at Shorsu, also in the Fergana Valley. Other important deposits include copper, polymetallic ores, gold, marble, and tungsten-molybdenum ores.

The present population of the Uzbek SSR is about 6,000,000. The greatest part of the population is concentrated in the oases. One quarter of the inhabitants live in cities. In the Uzbek SSR proper, the Uzbeks constitute three quarters of the total population, while in the Kara-Kalpak Autonomous SSR, they form only one third of the population. The Uzbeks are members of the Turkic group and are expert in irrigation farming methods. They are among the best cotton and fruit growers and sericulturists of the USSR.

The Uzbek SSR was created in October, 1924, out of sections of the former Turkestan Autonomous SSR. Until 1929 it included the Tadzhik Autonomous SSR, which became a full union republic in that year. The present oblasts were created after 1938; the most recent formation was that of Kashka Darya Oblast in 1943. The Kara-Kalpak Autonomous SSR was joined to the Uzbek SSR in 1936.

Until the Bolshevik Revolution, Uzbekistan was an essentially agrarian region, with industries based exclusively on the local agricultural production: cotton ginning, cottonseed-oil extraction, silk spinning, fruit drying, and so forth. Under the Soviets, this area has become the largest industrial region of Central Asia and one of the most important of the Asiatic USSR.

Typical of the industrial development of the Uzbek SSR has been the introduction of heavy industry, centered generally in the Tashkent area. It includes agricultural machinery works at Tashkent, a large chemical and nitrate fertilizer *kombinat* at Chirchik, and, most important, the steel mills of Begovat, the only metallurgical works in Central Asia, which were constructed during the Second World War.

Petroleum wells have been developed especially in the Fergana Valley. Near Andizhan are oil and natural-gas fields. Other oil fields are at Chimion and Shorsu in the southern part of the valley. In the Surkhan-Darya Oblast, in the southeast of the republic, petroleum is produced at Khaudag. Coal is mined at the Angren site, southeast of Tashkent. These deposits were discovered on the eve of the Second World War, were developed during the war, and resulted in the creation of a new industrial area centered at the new city of Angren. Sulphur is mined at Shorsu in the Fergana Valley and furnishes the basis for a local chemical industry. During the current Plan a zinc plant and a copper refinery are to be established at the Almalyk mine. Tungsten and molybdenum are mined at Lyangar (Samarkand Oblast).

Light industry includes the large cotton mills at Tashkent and Fergana, more than fifty cotton gins, silk and karakul-processing plants, and so forth. On the basis of fruit growing, a well-developed canning and drying industry has been created. In addition there are eight cottonseed-oil presses, several rice-polishing plants, wineries, and tobacco factories.

During the Second World War, due to the impetus given to the Uzbek industry by the numerous enterprises evacuated to Uzbekistan from the areas overrun or threatened by the German armies, many new industries were established and old branches were further developed. These included heavy and medium machine construction, lathe manufacturing, electrical equipment, aviation industry, sugar refining, hydrolytic processes, glass industry, artificial fiber production, and so forth.

Since early in 1942 the republic has embarked upon an ambitious program for the construction of hydroelectric installations. By 1944 four power plants had been completed and ten more were under construction. The largest project involved the construction of the Farkhad hydroelectric station on the Syr Darya and opposite the steel mills of Begovat. The construction on this station was begun in 1943 and was completed during the current Plan.

Uzbekistan is the most important producer of cotton in the USSR. Due to the expertness of the Uzbeks, the productivity per acre is very high. Of the total acreage under cotton, about 44 percent is located in the Uzbek SSR, which contributes about 60 percent of the total cotton production. The Fergana Valley is the most important cotton region of the republic.

In addition to cotton, silk and wool are also important products of the Uzbek SSR. These textile raw materials, form the basis for an important section of the Uzbek industry. Uzbekistan also devotes large areas to sesame (nearly one half of the total USSR production), *kenaf*, tobacco, and flax.

The main grain areas are in central and southern Uzbekistan, where there is much dry farming. Rice, one of the oldest crops, is raised mainly east of Samarkand, in the Tashkent oasis, and in several sections of the Fergana Valley. The chief fodder crop, alfalfa, used mostly for dairy cattle, is grown side by side with the cotton plant.

The Uzbek SSR is also one of the main orchard and vineyard regions of the USSR, with a great variety of fruits. The production of dried fruits (apricots, peaches, raisins, and so forth) is one of the specialties.

The agricultural sections of the Uzbek SSR have been irrigated since ancient times. Under the Soviets, the existing irrigation systems were reconstructed and enlarged. The most noteworthy irrigation project, completed in 1939, is the 200-mile-long Great Fergana Canal.

The most important branch of livestock breeding is the raising of karakul sheep, chiefly in Bukhara Oblast and in the Kara-Kalpak Autonomous SSR, producing about two thirds of the karakul of the USSR.

The Trans-Caspian Railroad between the Amu Darya in the southwest and Tashkent in the northeast constitutes the chief transportation artery of the Uzbek SSR. It serves the oases of Bukhara, Samarkand, and Tashkent. Two important lines branch off the main trunk; the one from Kagan past Karshi and Termez and on to Stalinabad serves the oases of the Kashka Darya and Surkhan Darya oblasts; the other, branching off at Ursat'yevskaya, serves the Fergana Valley cities of Kokand, Andizhan, Margelan, Fergana, and Namangan, and many short spurs serve the coal and other mines at the periphery of the valley.

The only available water transportation is offered by the lower Amu Darya and by the Aral Sea.

Oblast Survey

Andizhan Oblast
Capital, Andizhan; area, 1,600, population, 600,000

Andizhan Oblast is in the eastern part of the Fergana Valley and is drained by the Kara Darya, one of the headstreams of the Syr Darya. The major part of the area is under cotton cultivation; there is some wheat in the unirrigated higher sections. Mulberry trees are planted in the cotton fields and form the basis for sericulture. Cattle and horses are raised where water is available, and sheep in the drier areas. The industry is based on the cotton and silk production and comprises ginning plants and silk mills. The oil fields (Andizhan, Palvantash, and Yuzhnyy Alamyshik) south of Andizhan and east of Leninsk produce petroleum and natural gas. The gas is piped to these two large cities for use as domestic fuel. The predominantly Uzbek population includes also some Kirghiz.

Andizhan is a center of railroads leading to Kokand, Namangan, Kokan-Kishlak, and Karasu (Kirghiz SSR). It has cotton-ginning and cottonseed-oil-extracting industries, food-processing plants, and metalworks. Many earthquakes have occurred here, the last one in 1902.

Leninsk, formerly called Assake, is a major cotton-ginning center.

Fergana Oblast
Capital, Fergana; area, 3,100, population, 720,000

This oblast takes in the southwestern portion of the Fergana Valley. Its large southern section is irrigated by numerous streams descending from the Alay range and fanning out into complex canal networks in the valley. The irrigated section has cotton cultivation and sericulture; sheep are raised in the northern desert section, next to the Syr Darya. The industry consists of cotton and silk mills at Fergana, Margelan, and Kokand, cement works at Kuvasay, and oil fields at Chimion, with a cracking plant at Vannovskiy. Important chemical works are operating at Shorsu, on the basis of the local sulphur and ozocerite deposits. The Fergana Valley railway passes through the oblast, with two branches leading to Namangan and to Kizyl-Kiya (Kirghiz SSR).

Fergana is an important cotton and silk textile center with cottonseed-oil presses, clothing mills, hydrolysis works, and a large power plant. It was founded by the Russians in 1876 and was called successively Novyy [new] Margelan and Skobelev.

Margelan is a large silk-spinning and weaving center, important since the tenth century.

Kokand, an ancient city and former capital of the Kokand khanate, developed as a modern industrial center in Soviet times. It has super-phosphate and machine plants and an active cotton and silk-processing industry. Beet sugar is refined here.

Namangan Oblast
Capital, Namangan ; area, 2,400, population, 450,000

Namangan Oblast occupies the entire northern part of the Fergana Valley, north of the Syr Darya and its headstream, the Naryn River. Here, also, there is extensive irrigation, especially in the east; cotton cultivation and sericulture predominate. Wheat is grown on the lower mountain slopes. Cattle, horses, and sheep are raised. The oblast has an extensive cotton-ginning industry and some silk milling. An antimony mine is operating at Kassansay ; near by the Urta-Tokoy reservoir is under construction on the river Kassan-Say.

Namangan, the capital, has a well-developed textile (cotton and silk) industry, as do all the other large cities of the Fergana Valley.

Chust is in the northern Fergana Valley in a cotton and silk-growing area.

Tashkent Oblast
Capital, Tashkent; area, 5,900, population, 1,350,000

Bounded by mountains in the northeast and the east (Kurama and Chatkal ranges), Tashkent Oblast is drained by the Syr Darya and its two principal affluents, the Chirchik and the Angren. In the lowlands, there is extensive irrigation for the cultivation of cotton, fiber-producing plants, rice, and orchards, and some dry farming (wheat). An important industrial area is centered at Tashkent. During the Second World War, a second industrial hub was created at Begovat by the construction of the Uzbek steel mills and the Farkhad hydroelectric station, and a new coal basin was developed at Angren, southeast of Tashkent. During the current Plan a large copper refinery is being built at Almalyk. The Trans-Caspian Railroad crosses the oblast from north to south.

Tashkent, the capital of the Uzbek SSR, is the largest and one of the oldest cities of Central Asia at the junction of many historic routes. Under the Soviet regime, it developed into a large industrial center with agricultural machinery works, railroad shops, cotton-textile and paper

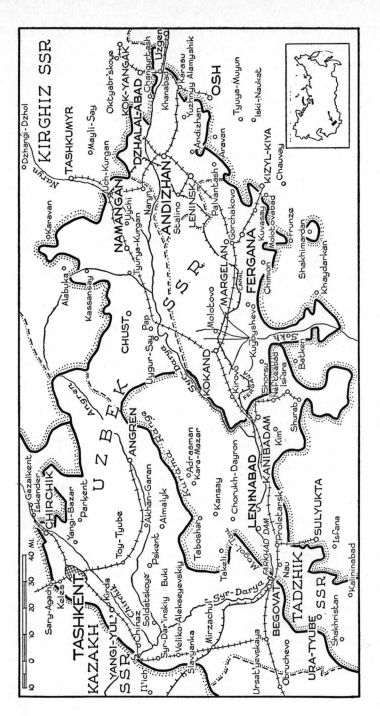

FERGANA VALLEY

mills, clothing factories, and shoe plants. The food industries include meat packing, flour milling, and fruit and vegetable canning. The city dates from the seventh century. It became the capital of the Uzbek SSR in 1930.

Angren, the newest and largest coal-mining center of Central Asia, developed during the Second World War and passed to large-scale industrial production in 1947. It is linked by rail and a coal-gas pipeline with Tashkent and furnishes coking coal to the Begovat steel mills.

Begovat, notable until the Second World War as a cement and cotton center, has become the site (since 1943) of a new Central Asian metallurgical industry, producing iron and steel products. Its industrial development has also been furthered by the construction near by, on the Syr Darya, of the Farkhad hydroelectric station. Work was begun in 1943, and its capacity is planned to reach 66,000 kilowatts.

Chirchik is a major electro-chemical center on the Chirchik River northeast of Tashkent. It produces nitrogen fertilizer and related chemicals and machinery for the chemical industry, and it is the site of a large hydroelectric station. A new city, it was developed largely in the 1930's.

Yangi-Yul' was formerly called Kaunchi and received a typical Soviet name meaning "new way" in the Uzbek language. It is an agricultural processing center, developed largely during the 1930's, and produces cotton, canned goods, and sugar.

Samarkand Oblast
Capital, Samarkand; area, 12,300, population, 960,000

Samarkand Oblast is drained by the Zeravshan River and includes the mountain ranges Nura-Tau and Ak-Tau in the north. The agriculture emphasizes cotton growing, sericulture, and orchards in the Zeravshan valley; elsewhere, there is dry farming (wheat). Karakul sheep and goats are raised. Industry is based on the farm products and includes cotton ginning, wine production, and food processing at Samarkand, Katta-Kurgan (site of a large new reservoir), and Dzhizak. A new tungsten and molybdenum mine is producing at Lyangar, in the Nura-Tau.

Samarkand is a cotton-ginning and silk-milling center; it has also clothing and shoe mills, wine and tea production, and fruit canneries. It is the oldest city of Central Asia; it dates from the third or fourth millennium B.C. The city was known to the Greeks as Maracanda. Samarkand was the capital of the Uzbek SSR from 1925 to 1930.

Dzhizak, an old city on the Trans-Caspian Railroad between Samarkand and Tashkent, produces metal and tobacco products and cotton.

Katta-Kurgan is an industrial center processing vegetable fats and oils, cotton, and meat products. Since the end of the Second World War, it is the site of a vast storage reservoir ("Uzbek Sea") fed by a canal from the Zeravshan River. The reservoir, situated south of the city, reached its full capacity of 660 million cubic meters in the spring of 1949.

Surkhan-Darya Oblast
Capital, Termez; area, 7,700, population, 300,000

It is bounded by the Amu Darya in the south and the range Baysun-Tau in the west; cotton is cultivated in the irrigated river valleys (the Surkhan Darya is the most important stream), and there is dry farming (wheat) on the hillsides. Karakul sheep and goats are raised in the dry lowlands. The larger towns have cotton-ginning plants, and there are oil fields at Khaudag and Uch-Kzyl.

Termez is one of the hottest cities of the USSR. It lies on the Amu Darya, near the mouth of the Surkhan Darya and on the Kagan-Stalinabad railroad. There cotton ginning, metalworking, and food processing are carried on.

Kashka-Darya Oblast
Capital, Karshi; area, 11,300, population, 405,000

This oblast lies west of Surkhan Darya Oblast and is drained by the Kashka Darya. Along the upper course of this river, in the Kitab-Shakhrisyabz region, cotton is cultivated and fruit is grown; farther downstream, along the Kashka Darya, in the area of Karshi, cotton and wheat are grown, and there is sericulture. Elsewhere, in the drier sections, wheat is grown and karakul sheep are bred. The Kagan-Stalinabad railroad passes through the oblast; there is also a branch line to Kitab.

At Karshi are food-processing, distilling, and metal-working industries. It was formerly known as Bek-Budi.

Shakhrizyabz is a minor industrial town near Kitab, with metal, silk, and food industries.

Bukhara Oblast
Capital, Bukhara; area, 49,600, population, 465,000

This oblast is the largest in the Uzbek SSR. In 1943 it acquired the Tamdy-Bulak district, an area of about 25,000 square miles, from the Kara-Kalpak Autonomous SSR. It includes the lower Zeravshan valley and a large section of the desert Kyzyl-Kum in the north. Beside the cultivation of cotton, sericulture and orchard farming are engaged in and the processing of karakul skins is a specialty of the region. The Trans-Caspian Railroad crosses the southern section of the oblast, and the line to Stalinabad branches off at Kagan.

Bukhara has karakul-processing, silk-spinning, and clothing-manufacturing industries. It is an old center of Islamic culture. After the construction of the Trans-Caspian Railroad, it was known until about 1930 as Staraya [old] Bukhara in contrast to the town which grew up around the station and became known as Novaya [new] Bukhara, now called Kagan.

Gizhduvan, northeast of Bukhara, produces cotton textiles, metal, and food products.

Kagan, a junction on the Trans-Caspian Railroad southeast of Bukhara, was originally named Novaya Bukhara when the line by-passed that ancient city. It has rail workshops and a cotton-processing industry.

Khorezm Oblast
Capital, Urgench; area, 1,900, population, 315,000

Khorezm Oblast lies in the Khorezm oasis, better known as Khiva oasis. It is bounded by the Turkmen SSR in the south and the Kara-Kalpak Autonomous SSR in the north. Primarily an irrigated cotton region, it also has sericulture, rice cultivation, and cattle raising. Cotton- and silk-processing industries are located in the towns. The Chardzhou-Kungrad rail line is being constructed through the oblast. Besides the capital, Urgench, formerly called Novo-Urgench, the chief city is Khiva.

Khiva, a historic city, was after the seventh century the capital of the Khorezm, or Khwarazm, kingdom, which became the Khiva khanate, conquered in 1873 by the Russians. It has a small cotton, carpet, and metalworking industry.

Kara-Kalpak Autonomous Soviet Socialist Republic
Capital, Nukus; area, 61,600, population, 435,000

The Kara-Kalpaks were first constituted into an autonomous oblast in 1925 and incorporated into the Kazak Autonomous SSR. In 1930 it was transferred to the Russian SFSR and raised to the status of autonomous SSR in 1932. In accordance with the provisions of the 1936 constitution, it was then made part of the Uzbek SSR.

The Kara-Kalpak Autonomous SSR is divided by the delta of the Amu Darya into an eastern section, which forms part of the Turan lowland, and a smaller western section in the Ust'-Urt plateau. Its average yearly temperature is 50–55° F, and the average yearly rainfall only 3–4 inches. The region undergoes very intensive insolation and evaporation. The Kyzyl-Kum desert, which occupies the major portion of the Turan lowland section, has shifting sand dunes, and only the Amu Darya valley and delta have loamy sediments suitable for irrigated agriculture.

The most important crop is cotton, which is cultivated mainly in the southern part of the Amu Darya valley, near Shabbaz and Turtkul', and in the delta, near Chimbay (east) and Kungrad (west). A secondary crop, cultivated throughout the cotton areas and used for fodder, is the lucerne variety of alfalfa. In addition, rice paddies are in the swampy delta section, and wheat is grown in the river valley. Camels and sheep (of which about three fourths are of the karakul breed) constitute the most important herds in the desert. Industries consist of cotton ginning, meat packing, and flour milling. There are several fisheries on the shore of the Aral Sea, and a large cannery at Muynak. Until the construction of the Chardzhou-Kungrad is completed, transportation will be restricted to the rather undependable Amu Darya and the Aral Sea. A ship route connects Muynak with Aral'sk (Kazakh SSR) on the northeast shore of the Aral Sea.

The population of the Kara-Kalpak Autonomous SSR consists chiefly of Kara-Kalpaks (38 percent), Kazakhs (30 percent), and Uzbeks (25 percent).

Nukus became the capital of the Kara-Kalpak Autonomous SSR after the former seat, Turtkul', had been repeatedly threatened by Amu Darya floods. Located in an irrigated cotton area, it produces shoes, clothing, cotton textiles, and leather.

The other large centers of the republic, Khodzheyli, Chimbay, and Turtkul', lie in the Amu Darya valley and produce cotton and its by-products.

CHAPTER 21

Turkmen Soviet Socialist Republic

Capital, Ashkhabad; area, 187,200, population, 1,170,000

THE TURKMEN SSR, or Turkmenistan, lies between the Caspian Sea and the Amu Darya in the southwest of Soviet Central Asia. It is bordered in the north by Kazakhstan and the Kara-Kalpak Autonomous SSR and in the south, along the Kopet Dagh and Paropamiz ranges, by the frontier between Iran and Afghanistan and the USSR.

GENERAL SURVEY

TURKMENISTAN is essentially a rolling desert lowland, sloping westward toward the Caspian Sea and the Sarykamysh depression. The greater portion is formed by the desert Kara-Kum, which takes in about 90 percent of the area of the republic. The desert is bordered by a number of oases watered by streams descending from the Kopet Dagh and other ranges in the south (Murgab and Tedzhen rivers) or located along the Amu Darya in the northeast of Turkmenistan.

The climate is of the continental type, very dry and warm. Average January temperatures vary from 36° F in the south to 25° F in the north, and July temperatures range from 90° F in the south to 83° F in the north. Rainfall averages 4 to 8 inches a year, but rises to 16 inches on the mountain slopes in the south. From the point of insolation, the Turkmen SSR occupies one of the first places in the USSR. Evaporation surpasses precipitation by several factors.

Due to the climatic conditions, vegetation is very poorly developed in this republic. The desert areas serve only as meager grazing grounds, and agriculture is possible only along the narrow loess plains in the river valleys and at the foot of the mountains. Of all the republics of Central Asia, Turkmenistan is the most arid and depends to the greatest degree on irrigation. Dry farming is possible only in a few separate sectors.

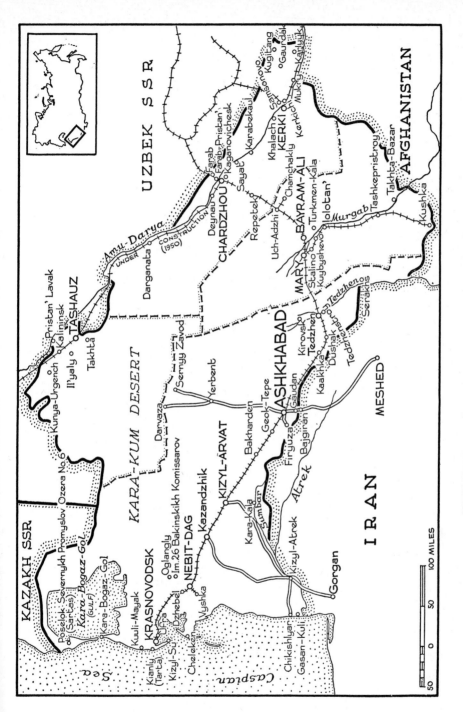

TURKMEN SOVIET SOCIALIST REPUBLIC

Among the mineral resources, petroleum occupies first place and occurs principally near the Caspian Sea. Other deposits include the extensive mirabilite (sodium sulphate) site on Kara-Bogaz-Gol, ozocerite,
sulphur, salt, polymetallic ores, and so forth.

The population of the Turkmen SSR is smaller than that of any other
Central Asian republic. Due to the small area under cultivation, one third
of the population lives in urban settlements. The greatest population
density exists in the oases and along the Trans-Caspian Railroad, while
the desert areas are very sparsely populated.

The chief element of the population consists of the Turkmen national
group, and there are minorities of Uzbeks and Persians. The Russians
are concenterated mainly in the areas of Ashkhabad, Mary, Chardzhou,
and Kushka.

The Turkmen SSR was created in the end of 1924 out of the former
Turkestan Autonomous SSR. The division into modern oblasts took
place in 1939, when the oblasts of Ashkhabad, Chardzhou, Krasnovodsk,
Mary, and Tashauz were created. In 1943 Kerki Oblast was separated
from Chardzhou Oblast. Following a reorganization of the administration in 1947, Krasnovodsk Oblast was incorporated into Ashkhabad
Oblast, and Kerki into Chardzhou, reducing the number of oblasts to
four.

The main branches of the mining industry deal with the production
of petroleum and mirabilite. Oil wells are located on the Cheleken peninsula (an island which became attached to the mainland due to the lowering of the level of the Caspian Sea), and in the area of Nebit-Dag.
An oil refinery was built at Krasnovodsk during the Second World War.
Mirabilite, or Glauber salt, is quarried at many points along the shore
of Kara-Bogaz-Gol, centered at the town of Kara-Bogaz-Gol. On the
Cheleken peninsula there are also plants for the processing of ozocerite,
iodine, and bromine. Sulphur is mined in the center of the Kara-Kum
(at Sernyy Zavod and Darvaza) and at Gaurdak, in the extreme southeast of the republic. Salt deposits are worked in many sections of the
republic, and bentonite is mined in the Balkhan range, north of Nebit-
Dag.

Among the manufacturing industries, the textile branch is the leading producer. On the eve of the Second World War, Turkmenistan
counted thirty-two small and six large cotton-ginning plants. Chardzhou
and Ashkhabad have silk-spinning works and cotton mills, while there
is a wool-washing installation at Mary.

Locomotive repair shops and a mechanized glass factory are located at Ashkhabad. Other plants are equipped for the repair of automobiles, trucks, tractors, and agricultural machines.

The food industry has been developed in recent years and includes flour milling, cottonsed-oil extraction, meat packing, refrigerating, fruit canning, and fruit drying. A specialized industry is carpet weaving, one of the oldest occupations of the Turkmen people.

Irrigated agriculture covers about 90 percent of the total sown area, thus placing the republic in first place in the USSR with regard to dependence on irrigation. Dry farming is possible only on the mountain slopes in the south. Among the recent irrigation projects are the reservoirs on the Murgab and Tedzhen rivers and the southern Kara-Kum Canal, which is to connect these two rivers with the Amu Darya near Kelif. The Great Turkmen Canal, linking the Amu Darya delta near Nukus with the Caspian Sea near Krasnovodsk and supplied with hydro-electric stations and branch canals, is scheduled for 1951-57.

Cotton is the chief crop of Turkmenistan, its cultivation being centered in the Murgab and the Tedzhen oases, as well as along the Amu Darya. Under the Soviets many new crops were introduced, including essential-oil-producing, rubber-bearing plants, sesame. Among the fruits, melons are most common. Vineyards are centered in the areas of Ashkhabad and Geok-Tepe. The production of silk amounts to about 10 percent of that of the USSR, and one fourth of that of Central Asia.

Sheep, mainly the karakul breed, form the basic herds of the Turkmen SSR. In addition, horses of many fine breeds and camels are raised. The fodder resources of the republic consist of the desert vegetation of the Kara-Kum, the foothill and mountain pastures in the south, and occasional alfalfa areas in the oases. Much effort has been made to rationalize livestock raising, maintain permanent wells in the desert, and so forth. According to recent estimates it would be possible to develop the Kara-Kum sufficiently so that it will provide fodder for 4 million head of livestock.

The Caspian Sea shore is the site of a number of fisheries, centered at Gasan-Kuli and in the area of Krasnovodsk.

The main artery of the republic is the Trans-Caspian Railroad between Krasnovodsk on the Caspian Sea and the Amu Darya. An important spur branches off at Mary and leads to the Afghan border at Kushka. During the current Plan the construction of the Chardzhou-Kungrad line is to be completed, marking the first step toward the realization of the long-projected Chardzhou–Aleksandrov-Gay trunk line, designed to ease the load of the Trans-Caspian Railroad and to provide a shorter link between the southwest of Central Asia and the European USSR.

Several highways traverse the desert areas and are usable in part for auto traffic. Air services connect the various isolated areas of the republic.

Oblast Survey

Ashkhabad Oblast
Capital, Ashkhabad; area, 87,600, population, 430,000

In 1947 Ashkhabad Oblast absorbed the former Krasnovodsk Oblast, and thus it now occupies the entire southwestern part of the Turkmen SSR. It is bordered in the south by the range Kopet Dagh along the USSR-Iran border and in the west by the Caspian Sea, and it includes a large section of the Kara-Kum, the Balkhan ranges, and the gulf of Kara-Bogaz-Gol. The agricultural areas extend along the northern slopes of the Kopet Dagh, where cotton, fruits, and vegetables are grown principally in the lower irrigated zone, and wheat and other grains in the dry sections. Sericulture and viticulture play an important role. Along the Tedzhen River, chiefly in the Tedzhen oasis, the emphasis is on grain, even in the irrigated sections, and the growing of cotton and the culture of sesame are secondary. On the Iranian border, in the region of Kara-Kala and Arpaklen, dry subtropical conditions prevail and date palms and sugar cane have been planted. In the extreme southwest, along the upper Tedzhen River, there are entensive pistachio-nut woods. The population is extensively engaged in livestock breeding; in the desert the emphasis is on sheep (mainly the karakul breed) and goats, and in the irrigated and elevated areas, on cattle and horses.

The Nebit-Dag area, in the western part of the oblast, is the chief petroleum region in Central Asia. The main oil wells are in the neighborhood of Vyshka (on a spur of the Trans-Caspian Railroad), at Imeni 28 Bakinskikh Kommissarov, and at Oglangly. Other petroleum wells are on the Cheleken Peninsula, together with ozocerite, bromine, and iodine deposits. On the coast of the Caspian Sea, northwest of Krasnovodsk, salt is quarried at Kuuli-Mayak. To the north is the rich Glauber salt region of Kara-Bogaz-Gol. The town of Kara-Bogaz-Gol, at the narrow inlet connecting the shallow basin of Kara-Bogaz-Gol with the Caspian Sea, is the chief producing center. On the basis of the sulphate deposits and the coal of Tuar-Kyr, west of the gulf, a large chemical plant is to be constructed here. The most important sulphate quarrying centers are at Sartas (connected by a narrow-gauge line with the port of Bek-Dash, on the Caspian side of the land-tongue), at Chagala, in the north, and at Kizyl-Kup, in the south. In addition to Tuar-Kyr, coal is also mined at Yagman, in the Balkhan range. North of Chikishlyar there are extensive natural gas fields along the coast of the Caspian Sea. Fishing is important along the coast. The chief fisheries and canning establishments are at Gasan-Kuli, near the Iranian border, on elongated Ogurchinskiy Island, at Kizyl-Su, south of Krasnovodsk, and Tarta, just west of Krasnovodsk. Beside Ashkhabad, Krasnovodsk, Kizyl-Arvat, and other towns along the railroad are devoted to industry. At Krasnovodsk is a large cracking plant, built during the Second World War; there are also metalworks, gypsum works, and clothing mills. Kizyl-Arvat is a locomotive and car repair center for the equipment of the Trans-Caspian line. Several small towns just west of Ashkhabad, such as Bezmein and Geok-Tepe, are famous for their wines. Bakharden has a woolen mill, and a new cement plant has been erected at Bezmein. Some of the richest barite and witherite deposits of the USSR are being exploited in the area of Arpaklen, on the Iranian frontier. The important sulphur mines of Darvaza and Sernyy Zavod [sulphur works] are part of Ashkhabad Oblast.

Ashkhabad, the capital of the Turkmen SSR, has cotton-ginning and milling, as well as silk-spinning plants. A large mechanized glass factory, a meat-packing plant, wineries, and so forth are also located there. Ashkhabad is one of the cities of the USSR with motion picture studios, and it has several scientific research and higher educational institutions, as well as a Turkmen museum. Firyuza, near the Iranian border, is its summer resort. It was founded by the Russians in 1881, and until the Revolution its name was spelled Askhabad. From approximately 1920 until 1927 it was called Poltoratsk. The city was badly damaged in an earthquake in 1948.

Kizyl-Arvat, on the Krasnovodsk-Ashkhabad railroad, is an engineering center, with locomotive and car-repair shops. Meat processing and rug weaving are other industries.

Krasnovodsk, a major Caspian port located in a desert area, is the terminus of the Trans-Caspian Railroad and of pipelines from the Nebit-Dag petroleum fields. Notable chiefly as a trans-shipment point for petroleum, cotton, salt, grain, and timber, it acquired during the Second World War its own petroleum-refining industry. It was founded in 1869 near the fortress of Mikhailovsk and served as base for the Russian conquest of Turkmenia. A separate Krasnovodsk Oblast existed from 1939 to 1947, with Krasnovodsk as its capital.

Nebit-Dag, on the Trans-Caspian Railroad, is the leading petroleum-producer of the Turkmen SSR, linked by pipelines to Krasnovodsk. A rail spur to Vyshka serves the oilfields.

Mary Oblast
Capital, Mary; area, 34,700, population, 265,000

Mary Oblast lies on both sides of the Murgab River and is bordered by Afghanistan in the south. All along the Murgab River cotton (the chief crop) is cultivated in a narrow irrigated belt which widens into a large area in the Murgab, or Mary, oasis, formed by multiple branches of the Murgab which disappear gradually into the sands of the Kara-Kum. In addition to cotton, wheat and alfalfa are grown here. Alfalfa is used as a fodder crop for cattle and horses. Along the upper Murgab River, on the border of Afghanistan, there are extensive pistachio woods. Goats and karakul sheep are raised in the desert areas. Iolotan' and Bayram-Ali are the chief cotton-ginning and cottonseed-oil-extraction centers. The oblast is crossed by the Trans-Caspian Railroad and the projected route of the Kara-Kum Canal, which passes north of and parallel to the railroad. From Mary a branch railway goes south to Kushka, on the Afghanistan border and at the southernmost point of the USSR.

Mary is a wool- and cotton-textile center in the middle of Murgab oasis and on the Trans-Caspian Railroad. Other important industries include metalworking, food processing, and carpet making. Mary was developed in the nineteenth century, at a point 18 miles west of the site of ancient Merv, or Margiana (modern Bayram-Ali), a center of Islamic culture in the Middle Ages. It was captured by the Russians in 1884.

Bayram-Ali, located in the Mary oasis on the Trans-Caspian Railroad, is a cotton center with gins, oil mills, and soap factory. It lies at the site of ancient Merv.

Chardzhou Oblast
Capital, Chardzhou; area, 35,900, population, 240,000

Chardzhou Oblast is a long, narrow region following the Amu Darya in the eastern part of the Turkmen SSR. In 1947 it absorbed Kerki Oblast (in the extreme southeast), which had been separated from it in 1943. The only sections of the oblast suitable for agriculture are the banks of the Amu Darya, where cotton is cultivated primarily, but some attention is given to wheat and sericulture. With the construction of the Kara-Kum Canal through an old arm of the Amu Darya, the Kelif Uzboy, large desert sections will be irrigated and opened to agriculture. Cotton and silk are processed at Chardzhou, Kerki, and Kerkichi. An entire industrial region is being created in the Gaurdak-Kugitang area on the right bank of the Amu Darya and in the extreme southeast of the oblast. Here a superphosphate plant has been erected on the basis of the local potash deposits; in addition, common salt, sulphur, copper, and coal are mined here, and the presence of petroleum is probable. The oblast is crossed by the Trans-Caspian Railroad, which crosses the Amu Darya at Chardzhou, and by a section of the Kagan-Stalinabad, which passes through the southeast. From Chardzhou a new railway is being constructed northward along the Amu Darya into the Uzbek SSR.

Chardzhou is a cotton and silk center. It has shipyards, metalworks, and fruit-canning plants. Due to its location at the intersection of the Amu Darya and the railroad, it acts as an important river-rail transportation hub. Its importance will be considerably enhanced by the completion of the railway to Kungrad, which will make Chardzhou the principal supply point for the region of the lower Amu Darya valley and the southern shore of the Aral Sea (Khorezm Oblast and the Kara-Kalpak Autonomous SSR of the Uzbek SSR). Chardzhou was formerly called, at various periods, Chardzhuy, Novyy Chardzhuy, and Leninsk-Turkmenskiy.

Kerki, in a cotton and livestock-raising area, engages in agricultural processing (cotton, meat) and light manufacturing (textiles and leather goods). It was the capital of a separate oblast from 1943 to 1947.

Tashauz Oblast
Capital, Tashauz; area, 29,000, population, 235,000

Tashauz Oblast is physically a part of the Khorezm, or Khiva, oasis, the eastern section of which is constituted into the Khorezm Oblast of the Uzbek SSR. This political division of the oasis was carried out on the basis of the distribution of the Uzbek and Turkmen majorities. The northern section of the oblast is drained by the numerous arms of the Amu Darya, while the southern part constitutes a portion of the desert Kara-Kum. The irrigated area is constantly being extended by the construction of new canals. American short-staple cotton is cultivated intensively, together with lucerne seed, and cattle and horses are raised. In the neighboring desert sections, camels, karakul, and fat-tail sheep are bred. There are also some saltpeter deposits near the Amu Darya. The Chardzhou-Kungrad line will pass through the extreme northeastern portion of the oblast.

Tashauz, the capital, has cotton-ginning plants and oilseed mills. Its port on the Amu Darya is Lavak-Pristan'.

CHAPTER 22

Transcaucasia

TRANSCAUCASIA is one of the southernmost regions of the USSR, extending over an area of 74,000 square miles south of the Greater Caucasus range. It is bordered by the Black Sea and the Caspian Sea and adjoins Turkey and Iran in the south. Besides being one of the warmest and richest areas of the Soviet Union, it presents a great variety of widely contrasting land forms, which occur in close proximity and range from luxuriant subtropical forests to dry desert-steppes and from the warm blue sea to the eternal snows of the high ranges, which are punctuated by the gigantic regular cones of extinct volcanoes. There are sections in which insufficient rainfall necessitates the use of irrigation for agriculture; in others precipitation is as plentiful as in humid subtropical countries, and the palm tree, the orange tree, and the tea bush are representative vegetation types.

Transcaucasia includes the steep southern slopes of the Greater Caucasus range * in the north and the mountain region commonly known as the Armenian plateau, in the south. These two folded sections are separated by a synclinal zone, which is formed by the basins of the Rion and the Kura rivers. In the center the Surami range, oriented north and south, forms a connection between the elevated areas of the region. Separated from the principal mountain systems and lying in the extreme southeast of Transcaucasia are the Talysh mountains, which constitute an extension of the Elburz mountains of Iran.

The Armenian plateau consists of a number of individual highlands rising from 5,000 to 6,800 feet and separated from each other by minor ranges. The highest section of the Armenian plateau, the Karabakh upland, lies southeast of the large Lake Sevan (or Gokcha) and reaches an altitude of 8,300 feet. The major portion of the bordering mountain ranges is commonly known as the Lesser Caucasus and extends from the Surami range. These crests nowhere reach the snow line, and they

* The Greater Caucasus range is discussed in Chapter 11.

rise above 10,000 feet only in the southern section. Volcanism plays an important role in this region. There are a number of extinct volcanoes, including the 13,500 feet high Mount Aragats (or Alagez). The greater part of the Armenian plateau is covered with extrusive volcanic rocks, including eroded basaltic formations. Mineral springs occur throughout the area, and destructive earthquakes often create great havoc; the most recent disaster was in 1926 at Leninakan.

The Rion River basin faces the Black Sea. Its lowest section along the coast is known as Kolkhida (ancient Colchis); it consists largely of marshes and lagoons. Recently this area has been the site of a large reclamation-drainage project. The Kura River basin, which includes the major part of eastern Transcaucasia, is a large alluvial plain drained by the Kura and the Aras (Russian *Araks*) rivers. It is essentially a sterile steppe in the central section, punctuated by occasional salt flats and changing into more fertile black earth on the lower slopes of the northern and southern highlands.

The Rion lowland has a humid subtropical climate, with a warm winter—the January average at Batumi is 43° F—a hot, humid summer, and a very heavy rainfall (100 inches a year at Batumi). Precipitation occurs chiefly in the summer, when moisture-laden winds blow from the Black Sea. This circumstance makes the local climate unlike the Mediterranean type, and classifies it rather with the monsoon climates of East Asia (Japan and southern China). The winters are extremely mild along the Black Sea coast; occasionally there are frosts in January, but they are not severe and are of short duration.

Eastern Transcaucasia, including the Kura lowland, has a more continental climate, due principally to the barrier of the Surami range, which bars the warm Black Sea winds from this area. The winters are rather warm, but frosts occur more often, and temperatures drop lower than in the west. Summer is hot, and there is much less precipitation (about 15 inches) than on the Black Sea. In the extreme southeast the Lenkoran' lowland at the foot of the Talysh range again has a humid subtropical climate. The Talysh range condenses the humid Caspian Sea air and produces considerable precipitation in the coastal plain.

The Armenian plateau, in the south, has a continental climate. The local winters are as cold there as in the northern half of the European USSR. At Yerevan (elevation: 3,300 feet), frosts are as low as —13° F, and in July temperatures rise to 104° F. The amount of rainfall varies in the various sections; generally it is less than 12 to 14 inches a year, necessitating irrigation methods in the low-lying Aras valley.

Vegetation types throughout Transcaucasia vary in accordance with the predominant climate. Along the Black Sea coast the high temperatures and humidity lead to the development of a very luxurious and dense vegetation, forming nearly inaccessible jungles in some sections. The trees, which are largely of Western and Central European origin, reach an exceptionally large size. In spite of the vegetation cover, there is much erosion in this area and the streams are very muddy. Among the most common garden plants are magnolia, cactus, eucalyptus, tangerine, orange, lemon, olive, tea, bamboo, and assorted palms. The dry steppe vegetation of eastern Transcaucasia, with its salt flats and a meager plant cover (consisting chiefly of wormwood, saltwort, and thorny bushes), is in sharp contrast to the small subtropical zone in the Lenkoran' lowland, where the very hard and dense ironwood is most important. The ranges and gorges in the Armenian plateau are covered with deciduous trees; the steppes on the plateau have a rather rich grass cover. In addition to animals commonly found in the Greater Caucasus, the fauna of Transcaucasia includes Mediterranean and Iranian species such as the porcupine and the dzheyran-antelope, and in the steppes, numerous rodents. In the Talysh range leopards and occasionally hyenas and tigers are encountered. Along the Lenkoran' littoral there are many aquatic birds for which a reserve has been created at Kizyl-Agach.

The population of Transcaucasia belongs to a large number of ethnic groups. The Georgian group includes the Georgians proper, and many smaller related nationalities, such as Svans, Khevsurs, Pshaves, Imeretians and Adzhars; the Iranian group comprises the Ossetians, the Kurds, and the Talysh people, and the Abkhaz form a branch of the Caucasian group. The Georgians and the Armenians are the most numerous. Eastern Transcaucasia is settled by the Azerbaijan people of the Turkic group, who migrated to this area from the northeast from beyond the Caspian Sea.

The total population of Transcaucasia (about 8,100,000 people) is distributed quite irregularly, due to relief and climatic factors. Most sparsely settled are the Greater and the Lesser Caucasus ranges and the dry steppes in the eastern sections, while the Black Sea littoral of the Georgian SSR and the Rion valley show the greatest population density.

Until 1936 Transcaucasia formed a single political unit: the Transcaucasian Soviet Federated Socialist Republic, then one of the union republics of the USSR. With the promulgation of the 1936 Constitution, this federated republic was split up into its primary components based on the three principal nationalities: Armenian, Azerbaijan, and Georgian SSR's. Minor nationalities, such as Abkhaz, Adzhars, and Ossetians, are organized into lesser autonomous units such as autonomous SSR's or autonomous oblasts.

Petroleum is the most important single asset of Transcaucasia. The Baku oil region of world-wide significance is the principal petroleum producer of the USSR, furnishing more than one half the total output. Pipe lines for crude oil, kerosene, and other petroleum products lead from Baku across the entire region to Batumi on the Black Sea, next to Baku, the principal oil port and refining center of Transcaucasia. Before the Second World War the petroleum industry accounted for two fifths of all factory workers, two thirds of the use of electric energy, more than one half the industrial production, and almost two thirds of the exports of Transcaucasia. Since then, however, the creation of new industries and the increase of electric power sources have reduced the relative importance of this branch of the economy. Among the other important power resources are the coal mines of Tkibuli and Tkvarcheli in Georgia, especially the reserves of hydroelectric power, which equal the reserves of the European part of the USSR. Among the most important metal deposits are the manganese mines of Chiatura (Georgia), the second largest in the world, copper in Armenia, and iron in Azerbaijan.

Manufacturing industries are mainly devoted to the processing of the local agricultural products: fruit canning, wine-making, distilling, and cotton ginning. Azerbaijan has a well-developed textile industry, and many of the precious woods are used in wood-working plants. Heavy metallurgy is represented by the steel mills of Rustavi (Georgia) and the ferro-manganese works of Zestafoni (Georgia), and there are machinery plants in many of the large cities. Chemicals and cement are also produced.

In connection with the varied natural conditions and under the influence of the vertical zoning in the mountains, all rural economy forms are represented—from orchard farming in the irrigated sections to nomadic livestock raising in the drier areas. The land is divided according to usability as follows: one fifth is arid, due to the presence of rocks, sands, or marshes; another fifth is forested; more than one third is pasture land, including the dry lowland steppe areas (used in the winter) and the mountain meadows (used in the summer). Only one fourth of the total area is under cultivation. The principal crops are garden fruits (apples, pears, apricots, peaches, plums, chestnuts, walnuts, and almonds) and subtropical products such as tea and citrus fruits along the Black Sea coast. Sericulture and viticulture are also important. Transcaucasia is the second most important cotton producer of the USSR; the principal cotton areas are in the dry, gray-soil lowlands of the Aras and the Kura, where the most extensive irrigation systems have been developed. In Abkhazia tobacco is grown, and the flooded lowlands of eastern and southern Transcaucasia are suitable for the cultivation of rice. Grains are subordinated in favor of the more specialized industrial and subtropical crops. Livestock is generally driven over great distances, from the winter pastures in the dry steppes to the mountains, where the Alpine meadows furnish excellent summer fodder. This nomadic type of livestock raising is gradually making way for more intensive, sedentary methods, since the dry steppes are gradually being irrigated, and large areas are coming under fodder crops. Sheep and cattle form the principal herds. Horses are few, and they are replaced partly by water buffaloes (for farm work) and partly by camels, mules, and donkeys (for transportation).

The basic railroads are the Batumi-Baku line, with a large number of branches and spurs, including the coastal railways along the Black and the Caspian seas, and the southern branch, which links Tbilisi and Baku via Dzhul'fa and the Aras valley. The Transcaucasian railway system provides connections with the Turkish rail network at Leninakan, and from Dzhul'fa a line goes south to Tabriz (Iran), with an ultimate extension to Tehran. Most of the lines have been electrified or are in process of electrification. Transportation in the higher sections has to rely on highways, among which the Sukhumi, the Ossetian, and the Georgian military roads across the Greater Caucasus range are most noteworthy. Due to the mountainous character of the river courses, inland navigation is negligible.

Azerbaijan Soviet Socialist Republic
Capital, Baku; area, 33,100, population, 3,100,000

The Azerbaijan (or Azerbaydzhan) SSR lies in the eastern section of Transcaucasia, on the Caspian Sea. It includes the southeastern spurs of the Greater Caucasus, which terminates in the Apsheron peninsula, the easternmost section of the Lesser Caucasus, and in the extreme south-east, the Talysh range and the adjacent Lenkoran' lowland. The basic central portion of the republic is formed by the extensive lowland drained by the Kura River and its chief affluent, the Aras.

Being isolated by the surrounding mountain belt from the moisture-laden winds blowing from the Black Sea, Azerbaijan has a dry, continental climate, varying considerably depending on elevation. Thus, the central lowland is a dry steppe, with a very hot climate of the Aral-Caspian type. Temperature averages are over 75° F in July and 32° F in January. The winters are nearly snowless, and the average yearly precipitation is 8 to 16 inches. Agriculture requires irrigation, and in the winter the unirrigated areas are used as pasture land. The mountainous areas enjoy lower average temperatures, and the southern slopes of the Greater Caucasus, as well as the Talysh range, receive considerable precipitation. In the foothills and the valleys dry farming is practiced, while the slopes serve as summer grazing grounds. Subtropical conditions prevail in the Lenkoran' lowland, which has an average yearly rainfall of up to 65 inches.

As elsewhere in Transcaucasia, most of the rivers are unsuitable for navigation. Only shallow-draught vessels go up the Kura, as far as Yevlakh. However, there are extensive hydroelectric power reserves, which are gradually being developed.

The principal mineral resource is petroleum, in the Baku region. Other deposits, which are being worked, include the iron mines at Dash-kesan, copper at Kedabek and Dostafyur, alunite at Zaglik, cement raw materials near Tauz, and so forth. There are extensive reserves of arsenic, molybdenum, and cobalt. Salt is mined near Nakhichevan', and obtained from the sea on the Apsheron peninsula. Azerbaijan has a number of mineral springs and healing mud sites, as well as a type of raw petroleum used for medicinal purposes at Naftalan, southeast of Kirovabad.

The basic Azerbaijan element, constituting about three fifths of the total population, lives chiefly in the central lowland along the Kura River. Among the minorities are Armenians (in the Nagorno-Karabakh Autonomous Oblast and in the cities), Georgians (in the west along the Georgian border), Russians (especially in Baku), Tats, and Talysh (in the Lenkoran' lowland). The total population is about 3,100,000, of which more than 35 percent is classified as urban.

The Azerbaijan SSR was created in April, 1920. From 1922 until

AZERBAIJAN SOVIET SOCIALIST REPUBLIC

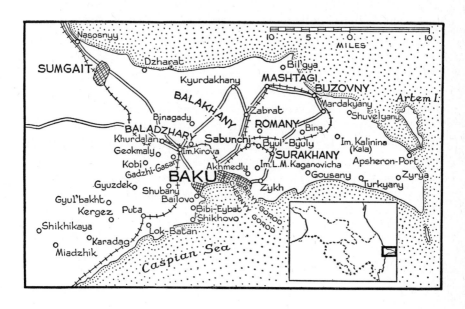

BAKU AREA

1936 it formed part of the Transcaucasian SFSR, and after the liquidation of the federation it became a union republic of the USSR in December, 1936. Azerbaijan includes two minor autonomous units: the Nakhichevan' Autonomous SSR, formed in February, 1924, and the Nagorno-Karabakh Autonomous Oblast, formed in July, 1923.

The most important branch of the economy is the petroleum industry. Azerbaijan is the principal oil region of the USSR and one of the richest in the world. Production is centered for the most part on the Apsheron peninsula; however, new wells are also producing along the coast in the south. Such old fields as Balakhany and Surakhany have been supplemented by new fields from deeper strata and from offshore deposits, such as Artem Island and Il'ich Bay. The fields south of the Apsheron peninsula extend through Alyaty, Pirsagat, and Byandovan to Nefte-Chala. Cracking plants are located at Baku. Petroleum from these fields is either pumped through pipe lines to Batumi, oil port and refining center on the Black Sea, or shipped in tankers via the Caspian Sea to Astrakhan' and up the Volga into the interior of the European USSR.

The region south and southwest of Kirovabad in the Lesser Caucasus is destined to become the second industrial base of Azerbaijan. Here, a large number of mineral deposits have been located, including magnetite at Dashkesan, alunite at Zaglik, and pyrite with other copper ores at Kedabek and Chiragidzor. Other deposits include manganese, cobalt, marble, limestone, and barite. At present, priority is being given to the development of the iron mines at Dashkesan, which are to supply the new iron and steel mills under construction at Rustavi (Georgia). An electric railway has been built from the main line to the Dashkesan area, which lies at an elevation of over 5,000 feet and where a mining town with a population of about six thousand has been established.

Manufacturing industries are based essentially on the local agricultural production and include cotton and silk milling, fruit canning, and fish processing. Machinery is manufactured at Baku, which also has chemical works, tanneries, and food industries. Northwest of Baku, where the Caspian coastal railway crosses the Sumgait River, a new industrial city is rising. This new urban center, Sumgait, will be the site of chemical works and pipe-rolling mills and will be supplied by a local power station.

Of great importance for the future development of the petroleum industry and the other mining and manufacturing industries of Azerbaijan will be the completion of the Mingechaur hydroelectric project.

This power development, the largest construction project of the current Five-Year Plan, involves the building of a dam and power plant on the Kura River, at a point 25 miles northwest of Yevlakh, and the creation of the second-largest artificial sea of the USSR (after the Rybinsk Sea, northeast of Moscow). The Mingechaur Sea will be about 10 miles wide, and is to extend 35 miles upstream, along the Kura, past the mouths of the Alazan' and the Iori rivers.

Outside of the Apsheron peninsula, agriculture constitutes the major branch of the activity. In the irrigated steppe areas, cotton is the major crop. The Mili and the Mugan' steppes, south of the Kura and on each side of the Aras River, are watered by a well-developed network of irrigation canals. The lowest portions of the Kura lowland specialize in the production of long-staple cotton, which is used in the milling of fine cloth. Two new towns have grown up in these new irrigated areas: Zhdanovsk, in the Mili steppe, and Karachala, on the lower Kura River. The cotton is processed in ginning establishments along the lower Kura (Sabirabad, Ali-Bayramli, and Sal'yany) and along the main rail trunk (at Yevlakh, Lyaki, and Udzhary). Alfalfa also furnishes an excellent fodder crop two to three times a year, and as a rotation crop it increases considerably the yield of the areas under cotton. Secondary crops in the irrigated lowlands include wheat, rice, sesame, and fruits and vegetables. The unirrigated areas serve as excellent winter grazing grounds. In the autumn, countless herds descend from the Greater and Lesser Caucasus ranges to the Kura steppes, where they are protected from severe cold and find fodder grass nearly all year round.

On the slopes of the Greater Caucasus the principal agricultural products are fruits, silk, and tobacco. Typical of the fruit-growing areas is the Kuba region, on the northern slopes of the eastern Greater Caucasus. Sericulture is practiced mainly along the southern slopes of the Caucasus; it is centered at Shemakha and the silk-milling city of Nukha. Tobacco is grown in the area of Zakataly. Through these foothill regions, wool and silk are processed by many home industries, and every sizable town has rug-weaving establishments. Vineyards form the basis for a wine-making and distilling industry.

The economy of the humid subtropical Lenkoran' lowland is based partially on long-established crops, such as rice and orchard products and also on newly introduced crops, including tea and citrus fruits. These plants prosper in a narrow zone along the low Caspian Sea coast.

The fishing industry plays an important role in the economy of Azerbaijan. The catch consists mainly of herring, carp, and sturgeon, which are processed into caviar and canned products. The fisheries are centered on the Caspian Sea coast at the mouth of the Kura River and north of the Apsheron peninsula.

Three main railway routes serve Azerbaijan. The central trunk line goes from Baku westward past Yevlakh and Kirovabad toward Tbilisi, passing through the cotton areas along the Kura River. Another line leaves Baku for the northwest and parallels the Caspian Sea coast toward Dagestan. The third railroad, of most recent construction, leaves the central trunk at Alyaty and follows the Aras River and USSR-Iran frontier to Dzhul'fa junction in the Nakhichevan' Autonomous SSR. Spur lines link the main routes with Lenkoran', Mingechaur (site of the power plant), and Dashkesan. The rail network is supplemented by roads which serve especially the slopes of the Greater Caucasus (Nukha and Zakataly) and the Lesser Caucasus system. The Kura River is navigable below Yevlakh for small vessels.

The chief export products of Azerbaijan include petroleum and petroleum products, cotton, rice, fruits, wines, silk, and fish.

Baku, the capital, is the fifth city of the USSR, having a population of about 800,000 inhabitants. Baku proper is situated on Il'ich Bay, on the south side of the Apsheron Peninsula; however, the entire peninsula is included within the city limits, which thus encompass nearly all the producing oil fields of the Azerbaijan SSR. The city proper includes the old Persian section, with many mosques and palaces and the new industrial and residential sections which rise in the shape of an amphitheater around the bay. Chernyy Gorod [black city] and Belyy Gorod [white city] are, respectively, the old and the new industrial sections of the city, where most of the cracking plants and other factories are located. The many towns and oil fields on the dry Apsheron peninsula are linked with Baku by electric railways and have to be supplied with water. Here and there on the peninsula orchards and vineyards are cultivated by means of irrigation. To ease the work of the port of Baku, a new oil-loading port, Port Apsheron, has been built on the east side of the peninsula.

Kirovabad, the second city of the Azerbaijan SSR, was formerly known as Gandzha and Yelizavetpol'. It is an important cotton- and wool-milling center, with numerous food industries.

NAKHICHEVAN' AUTONOMOUS SOVIET SOCIALIST REPUBLIC
Capital, Nakhichevan'; area, 2,100, population, 160,000

The Nakhichevan' Autonomous SSR, lies geographically within the limits of Armenia, but is included in the Azerbaijan SSR because of its predominant Azerbaijan population. Separated from Azerbaijan SSR proper by the southeastern part of the Armenian SSR, it is bordered in the north by the Daralagez and Zangezur ranges, and in the south by the Aras River, which forms the Iranian frontier. It is marked by a very dry climate, the absence of forests, and an essentially agricultural economy. The chief crops are cotton and grain, along the Aras River; in the foothills, orchards and vineyards prevail, together with tobacco and mulberry trees (the basis for sericulture). In the mountains sheep are raised.

The industry processes the agricultural products. There are cotton-ginning plants, wineries, tanneries, fruit canneries, and silk-spinning mills. Salt is the most important mineral resource. It is mined primarily northwest of Nakhichevan' and supplies all Transcaucasia. Construction materials, sulphur, copper, and polymetallic ores are also mined.

The capital is Nakhichevan', a food-processing and wine center. Other important towns are Ordubad, with fruit canneries and silk mills, and Dzhul'fa, a rail junction with lines to Tbilisi (Georgia), Baku, and Tabriz (Iran).

NAGORNO-KARABAKH AUTONOMOUS OBLAST
Capital, Stepanakert; area, 1,700, population, 130,000

The Nagorno-Karabakh Autonomous Oblast [Mountainous Karabakh] was constituted within the Azerbaijan SSR in 1923, on the basis of the local Armenian population, which forms an isolated ethnic island within the republic. The region lies on the eastern slopes of the Lesser Caucasus, where it is bounded in the west by the Karabakh range. It is watered by the Terter, an affluent of the Kura. Forests, which cover about 30 percent of the total area, predominate in the west on the mountain slopes. The inhabitants, of which 90 percent are Armenians, are engaged primarily in the raising of cattle, sheep, and mules and in the growing of cotton and sericulture. The towns produce silk goods and wines.

Stepanakert, the capital, was formerly called Khankendy and was renamed in honor of Stepan Shaumyan, a Baku revolutionary. Shusha is another important center near by.

Armenian Soviet Socialist Republic
Capital, Yerevan; area, 11,500, population, 1,345,000

The Armenian SSR, situated in the south-central section of Transcaucasia, is essentially a mountainous region consisting of a series of high plateaus surrounded by higher mountain crests. More than one half the total area lies at an elevation of more than 4,000 feet and less than 4 percent is below 2,000 feet. The lowest sections of Armenia are the Aras valley and the adjacent Yerevan basin, which have the greatest concentration of population and the basic industries of the republic. The Armenian SSR also includes the Sevan Lake basin and the Lori steppe in the north, and the Leninakan plateau in the west.

Due to the surrounding mountain barriers and the generally high average elevation, Armenia has a continental climate of the dry, cold, temperate type. There are local differences, such as a hot, dry summer in the Aras valley and a cooler and more humid summer in the elevated areas, but the basic characteristics are true of the entire region. Average January temperatures vary from 14° to 20° F, and August averages from 63° to 77° F. The average yearly rainfall is 12 to 28 inches. Due to the dry climate, the fertile soils, largely of volcanic origin, require irrigation for agriculture. The mountains abound in Alpine meadows, which serve as summer grazing grounds, not only for Armenian herds but also the livestock of neighboring republics.

Armenia is drained mainly by the Aras River, which forms its southern frontier, and to a lesser extent by affluents of the Kura River. The most important body of water is Lake Sevan, situated at about 6,250 feet above sea level. The lake has a large number of inlets, but only one outlet, the Zanga River, which joins the Aras after a course of about 65 miles and a drop of 3,300 feet. The steep slope of the river, together with the great volume of Lake Sevan, provide ideal conditions for the creation of an extensive system of hydroelectric stations along the Zanga River. The grandiose Sevan-Zanga hydroelectric project, now in course of execution, contemplates the reduction of the lake area to less than half its present size over a period of 50 years (in order to minimize the loss of water through evaporation) and the creation of a veritable "cascade" of power stations along the Zanga River. Stations at Kanaker and at Yerevan have already been completed; the current Five-Year Plan requires the construction of two others, the Ozernaya hydroelectric station, an underground installation at Sevan near the outlet of Lake

ARMENIAN SOVIET SOCIALIST REPUBLIC

Sevan, and the Gyumush hydroelectric station, downstream on the Zanga River. Several more stations are to be built subsequently. Water power is of especially great importance for the economy of the Armenian SSR, because of the lack of mineral fuel resources, such as coal, petroleum, or peat, and the absence of forests in the higher sections.

The major mineral deposits include copper (Alaverdi and Kafan), molybdenum (Kadzharan), zinc and chrome ores, construction stones (volcanic tuff, marble, pumice), lithographic stone, chemical raw materials, and other minerals.

The population of the Armenian SSR is more uniform than that of the other Transcaucasian republics. The Armenians, a people with an ancient culture, constitute about 85 percent of the population of the republic. They are also settled in the adjacent sections of Turkey and Iran, as well as elsewhere in the USSR, forming an important element of the city population in Georgia, Azerbaijan, and the Northern Caucasus. In order to assemble reserves of skilled labor for the industrialization of the Armenian SSR, the Soviet Government has in recent months invited Armenians from many areas outside the USSR, including the Near East and the United States, to return to their homeland. A small-scale immigration has thus developed (50,000 in 1946), which will contribute considerably to the further development of this small republic.

The Armenian was formed in November, 1920. From 1922 to 1936 it formed part of the Transcaucasian SFSR, and since December, 1936, it has been a union republic within the USSR.

The mining industries include primarily the mining of copper at Alaverdi, in the north of the republic, and at Kafan, in the Zangezur range in the extreme southeast. Alaverdi has copper refineries and chemical works which produce superphosphates. The copper mines are located at Alaverdi proper and at its satellite mining towns of Shamlug, Akhtala, and Dzagidzor. Kafan lies on a spur of the Alyaty-Dzhul'fa railroad and is one of the oldest mines of Armenia. Near by, to the northwest, lie the newly developed molybdenum mines of Kadzharan. Extensive limestone deposits at Amamlu ʹand along the Zanga River provide raw material for the production of calcium carbide, one of the elements used in the manufacture of synthetic rubber. Pumice is quarried at Ani-Pemza and at Akhuryan (former Duzkend), near Leninakan, while volcanic tuff, which is obtained chiefly at Artik, provides an excellent building stone. Other mineral products include obsidian, another volcanic rock, and fire-proof clays at Tumanyan, south of Alaverdi.

The abundance of hydroelectric power available in the Zanga valley, especially in the area of Yerevan, has brought about the creation of a number of industries requiring large amounts of cheap energy, including the production of aluminum and of synthetic rubber. Yerevan also has machinery works which produce lathes, agricultural implements, small hydro-turbines, as well as a cable manufacturing plant. Chemicals are produced at Kirovakan, and Leninakan has a dyeing industry working in connection with its textile mills. Large cement works have been built at Ararat, and there are lumber mills at Sevan and Idzhevan. Other industries are concerned with the production of glass and ceramic products, as well as with watch-making. The textile industry, one of the important branches of the economy, is centered at Leninakan, which has cotton and knitwear mills, and at Yerevan and the neighboring towns of Malatiya and Sebastiya, which are mainly concerned with the spinning and the weaving of silk.

The valley of the middle Aras River and the Yerevan basin form one of the principal agricultural areas of Armenia. The volcanic and alluvial soils are rendered fertile by means of irrigation methods and are very suitable for such crops as cotton, fruits, and wine, due to the intense insolation which this area receives in spite of its elevation of about 3,000 feet above sea level. The fruit is canned chiefly in Yerevan and Megri, in the extreme southeast of the republic; cotton is ginned in the mills of Oktemberyan, while the vineyards form the basis for an extensive wine and cognac industry, centered at Yerevan and the neighboring towns of Ashtarak, Echmiadzin, and Artashat (former Kamarlu). Tobacco is also grown in this area.

At higher altitudes, the emphasis in agriculture is on grain farming, notably wheat and barley, and the growing of sugar beets (a new local crop) and potatoes. By means of irrigation orchards are also cultivated at an altitude of 3,000 to 6,000 feet above sea level. The Leninakan steppe, in the west, and the Lori steppe, in the north, are the main farming areas on the Armenian plateau. Sugar refineries are located at Leninakan and at Amamlu. The chief potato-growing areas are near Kalinino, Stepanavan, and Krasnosel'sk, all in the north of Armenia near the Georgian frontier. Elsewhere in the higher sections of the republic, livestock (chiefly sheep and goats) is raised for the production of cheese (of the Swiss type), wool, meat, and skins. Fish abound in Lake Sevan, trout predominating.

One single railroad serves the Armenian SSR, entering the republic from Georgia in the north and skirting the western and southern borders via Alaverdi, Leninakan, and Zangibazar toward Dzhul'fa in the Nakhichevan' Autonomous SSR. From Leninakan the main trunk sends a line westward into Turkey and a short spur southeast toward Artik, the volcanic tuff center. From Zangibazar a branch goes north to Yerevan, with an extension beyond the capital to the sites of the new Zanga hydroelectric plant. A good network of highways serves the mountainous sections. The chief export products are copper, synthetic rubber, building stone, cotton, cognac, wool, and leather.

The capital of the Armenian SSR is Yerevan, which was formerly known as Erivan'. It is situated on the left bank of the Zanga River, at an elevation of about 3,000 feet. It is overlooked by mountains in the north and forms the center of the fertile Yerevan basin, which opens onto the Aras valley. A dense network of canals irrigates large areas of orchards and gardens around the city. Once a minor provincial town, important only for its cognac production, Yerevan has developed into an important industrial center, due mainly to the water power generated along the Zanga River. It is now host to important aluminum and synthetic rubber industries, and it produces machinery of various types, rubber tires, chemicals, leather, canned meats, textiles, tobacco products, canned fruits, and so forth.

Leninakan, the second city of Armenia, is a rail junction and industrial center near the Turkish border. It was formerly called Gumry and Aleksandropol'. Mainly cotton textiles, knitwear, beet sugar, meat, flour and other food products are produced there.

Georgian Soviet Socialist Republic
Capital, Tbilisi (Tiflis) ; area, 29,400, population, 3,555,000

In the western portion of Transcaucasia the Georgian SSR is divided by the Surami range into two distinct sections: Western Georgia, with a humid, temperate climate, and Eastern Georgia, with a drier, continental type of climate. In the north, the Georgian SSR is bounded by the Greater Caucasus and in the south, by the Lesser Caucasus system.

Western Georgia, which includes the Black Sea littoral and the Rion lowland, is characterized by humid subtropical conditions; the warmest winters and the greatest precipitation of the USSR are to be found here. Temperatures fluctuate between the winter averages of 37° to 44° F and the summer averages of 73° to 75° F. The yearly rainfall averages 50 to 100 inches. The red lateritic soil supports an extremely abundant and varied subtropical vegetation. In sharp contrast to this region is Eastern Georgia, where the temperatures vary from the January averages of 32°–36° F to the July mean of 82° F. The average yearly rainfall amounts only to about 20 inches. The best agricultural areas are the Kura valley, between Gori and Tbilisi, and Kakhetia. In the mountainous areas average temperatures diminish with relation to the elevation. The forest zone extends from 2,100 to 2,600 feet to 6,000 to 8,300 feet. Above this belt are Alpine meadows, and beyond there are snowy peaks partially covered with glaciers.

The most important mineral resources are manganese (at Chiatura, one of the richest deposits in the world), coal (at Tkibuli and Tkvarcheli), petroleum (in the Shiraki steppe and in the Black Sea littoral), barites (near Kutaisi), rare metals, including molybdenum, antimony, tungsten, and mercury, as well as various types of construction materials. Georgia has numerous mineral springs, with the principal sites at Borzhomi, Abastumani, and Tskhaltubo. The humid climate, together with the mountainous relief, and glaciers in the Greater Caucasus supply Georgia with a large amount of hydroelectric energy. The principal water-power sources are the Rion, the Kura and its affluent, and the Khram, as well as the Black Sea littoral streams the Kodor, the Ingur, and the Adzharis-Tskhali.

Georgians constitute about two thirds of the total population of the Georgian SSR. Among the minorities the Armenians are most numerous (12 percent of the total); they are settled mainly in Tbilisi. Russians, Ukrainians, Greeks, Jews, and Kurds follow with respect to numbers. Several isolated mountain tribes live in the valleys of the Greater Caucasus. Most important among them are the Pshaves, settled along the upper Aragva River, the Khevsurs, to the west, and the Svans, along the upper Ingur River. Georgia has the greatest population density among the Transcaucasian republics, the largest concentration being in Western Georgia and Kakhetia. Three minorities, the Adzhars and the Abkhaz on the Black Sea and the Ossetians on the southern slope of the Greater Caucasus, have been organized into autonomous units within the Georgian SSR.

As a result of the liquidation within the Russian SFSR of several autonomous units, which had been accused of collaboration with the Germans and of traitorous activities during the Second World War, the Georgian SSR gained about 2,500 square miles of territory on the northern slopes of the Greater Caucasus. It received the southern portion (1,200 square miles) of the abolished Karachay Autonomous Oblast, including the former capital of the oblast, Mikoyan-Shakhar (now renamed Klukhori), and the health resort of Teberda. It also gained the southwestern corner (300 square miles) of the former Balkar-Kabardinian (now Kabardinian) Autonomous SSR, including Mount El'brus, the highest peak of the Caucasus, as well as a 70-mile-long strip of about 1,000 square miles in the south of the former Chechen-Ingush Autonomous SSR. These transfers of territory from the Russian SFSR to the Georgian SSR took place in 1943.

The economic importance of the Georgian SSR lies chiefly in its manganese production, its petroleum-refining industry, and the growing of subtropical products, tobacco and vineyards.

Manganese ore is mined at Chiatura, site of the second largest manganese reserves in the world. Part of the production is utilized in the ferromanganese works of Zestafoni, the first heavy metallurgical installation of the republic, which was based on the power from the Rion hydroelectric station. The rest is exported to other parts of the USSR and abroad via the port of Poti, on the Black Sea. The old coal mines of Tkibuli, west of Chiatura, yield a kind of brown coal, while the Tkvarcheli mines, developed before the Second World War in the Abkhaz Autonomous SSR, supply the growing metallurgical industry of Georgia with good-quality coking coal. Recently other brown-coal mines have been developed near Akhaltsikhe. Petroleum deposits in the Shiraki steppe, in the eastern part of the republic, are being increasingly exploited. The raw fuel is processed in the cracking plant of Mirzaani, located near the fields. Barite deposits near Kutaisi form the basis of an important chemical industry in that city and make that section of Georgia one of the main producers of that mineral in the USSR.

Heavy industry in the Georgian SSR included previously the ferromanganese works of Zestafoni and machinery works in Tbilisi and Kutaisi. It is being developed to a considerable degree during the current Five-Year Plan by the construction of the first Transcaucasian iron and steel mills at Rustavi, on the Kura River, southeast of Tbilisi. Rustavi, now under construction, lies on the right bank of the river, and the plant, which will be supplied from the Dashkesan iron mines, on the opposite

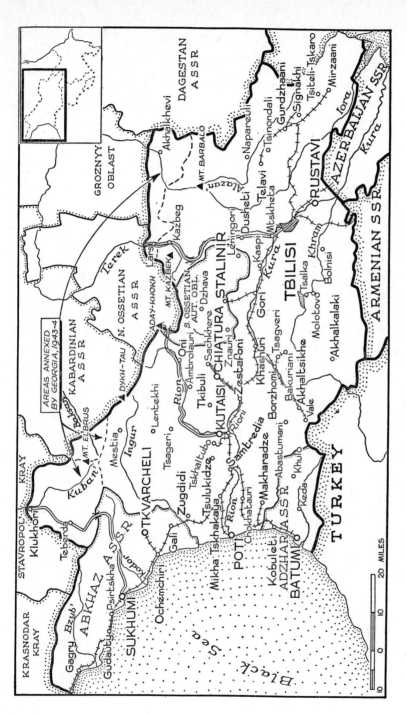

GEORGIAN SOVIET SOCIALIST REPUBLIC

bank. The city is scheduled to have a population of about 50,000 inhabitants. Kutaisi is the site of the first Transcaucasian automobile plant, under construction during the current Plan, the initial production to be restricted to 30,000 3½-ton trucks per year. There are cement works at Kaspi and lumber mills at Mtskheta, Borzhomi, and Marelisi. A large paper mill has been built on the Ingur River in the vicinity of Zugdidi.

The principal agricultural regions in the Georgian SSR are the Black Sea littoral and Imeretia, in the west, and Kakhetia, in the east. The Black Sea littoral includes the coastal zones of the Abkhaz and Adzhar Autonomous SSR and the Kolkhida (or Colchis) lowland along the lower course of the Rion River. Kolkhida was formerly a malaria-infested marshy region covered with dense jungle vegetation. In order to render this area suitable for agriculture, a huge drainage project was begun during the years before the Second World War, and is being continued during the present time. The Rion River and its arms were diked in, and the banks were planted with eucalyptus trees to absorb moisture from the ground. The importance of this subtropical region lies mainly in the fact that, with the exception of the small Lenkoran' lowland of Azerbaijan, this is the only area of the USSR where such crops as tea, citrus fruits (including oranges, lemons, tangerines, and recently grapefruit), tung trees, geranium, camphor, ramie, and so forth can be grown in industrial amounts. Tea and citrus fruit plantations cover the greatest acreage. In addition to the subtropical crops, tobacco, almond, and fruits are also important. The industry is based almost entirely on the agricultural production. There are tea-drying plants, tobacco factories, canneries, fruit driers, essential-oil plants, and other industries. Imeretia, which lies in the upper part of the Rion basin, is noted for its silk and wine production. Sericulture is practiced in the region west of Kutaisi, near Samtredia and Tsulukidze, and large silk mills are located in Kutaisi itself. Wines are made south of Kutaisi, with an important center at Zestafoni. Other important crops are corn, the most important grain type under cultivation, and sugar beets, which were introduced into Georgia during the second Five-Year Plan. Kakhetia, in northeastern Georgia, is the most important wine-producing area of the republic. Abundant heat and insolation, together with sufficient rainfall and a fertile soil, render this region most suitable for viticulture. The Kakhetian wines form one of the chief exports of the Georgian SSR. Other products include cotton, only recently introduced into Kakhetia, tobacco, and raw silk. Wine is also produced in the area south of Tbilisi, with the center at Bolnisi (formerly Lyuksemburgi).

The livestock herds of Georgia graze chiefly in mountain pastures. This is especially true of the sheep and goats. There is some dairy farming in the Kura valley.

The health resorts of the Georgian SSR play an important role in the economy of the country. They fall principally within the mineral springs and climatological varieties and are frequented by tourists and convalescents from the entire USSR. The best-known resorts are Abastumani, in the southwest, the high altitude resorts of Borzhomi (famous for its bottled mineral water) and near-by Bakuriani, and also Surami and Tskhaltubo.

For transportation facilities Georgia relies mainly on the Baku-Tbilisi-Batumi trunk railroad and its many branches. During the Second World War the Black Sea coastal line was completed; it is now used by direct Moscow-Tbilisi trains. Formerly the route led around the eastern end of the Greater Caucasus and via Baku. Short spurs connect the main trunk line with the port of Poti, the mines of Tkibuli and Chiatura, the resort of Borzhomi, and the lignite mines near Akhaltsikhe, as well as with Stalinir, the capital of the South Ossetian Autonomous Oblast. From Navtlug, an eastern suburb of Tbilisi, a branch goes northeast to Kakhetia, and the southern main line leads to the Armenian SSR and the Aras valley. Three important highways cross the central portion of the Greater Caucasus into Georgia. These are the Sukhumi military road, crossing at Klukhori Pass and terminating at Sukhumi on the Black Sea, the Ossetian military road, which leads through Mamison Pass to Kutaisi, and the Georgian military road, which starts at Dzaudzhikau (North Ossetian Autonomous SSR), winds through the picturesque Dar'yal gorge, overcomes the crest at Krestovyy Pass, and has its southern terminus at Mtskheta and Tbilisi.

The principal export products of the Georgian SSR include manganese, lumber, tobacco, fruits (mainly citrus fruits), wine, and tea.

Tbilisi (formerly Tiflis) is the capital of the Georgian SSR and the second largest city and industrial center of Transcaucasia. It is a very old city, which was founded on the historic route leading from Europe to Asia along the Kura valley. It lies at the junction of the Transcaucasian trunk railroad with the Georgian military road. The industry includes machine construction (primarily implements used in oil drilling and the processing of raw silk, wine, and tea), textile milling (silk and wool weaving), tanning, and the manufacturing of shoes and clothing. Food processing industries are also important. Tbilisi receives its power from the Zemo-Avchala hydroelectric station (commonly known as *Zages*), located a few miles upstream on the Kura River. It is the site of the Georgian Academy of Sciences, a university, and many technical and scientific institutions. The city extends north and south in the Kura valley. The oldest central part, with narrow, crooked alleys and a typically Asiatic appearance, lies near sulphur springs which have long been used in curative baths. To the north and the south of the central portion extend the modern industrial and residential sections of the capital, including the largest plants and marshaling yards.

Kutaisi, on the Rion River, just above the Rion hydroelectric station, is the largest city and industrial center of Western Georgia, served by a rail spur, highways, and airlines. It manufactures automobile trucks, coal-mining machinery, chemicals (sulphuric acid, lithopone), textiles, and leather goods. Its industrial development received considerable impetus during the post-war Five-Year Plan. The ancient capital of Imeretia, the city was officially called Kutais until 1936.

Rustavi, the newest city of the Georgian SSR and destined to become the fourth largest center of the republic, with an estimated population of 50,000, developed after 1943 and was made a city in 1948. It is the seat of the Transcaucasian steel industry, with a full metallurgical production cycle. Situated southeast of Tbilisi, it consists of a residential right-bank section and an industrial left-bank portion linked by a bridge of the Kura River.

Chiatura (formerly spelled Chiatury), on a rail spur northeast of Kutaisi, is one of the largest manganese-mining centers of the world. Having been exploited since 1879, the mines are now powered by the Rion hydroelectric plant. The manganese supplies the Zestafoni ferromanganese works and is shipped via the Black Sea ports of Poti and Batumi.

Poti, an important port on the Black Sea, in the Kolkhida lowland, acts chiefly as an outlet for the Chiatura manganese mines. It ships also lumber, corn, and wine.

Gori is a fruit-canning and cotton-milling town and the birthplace of Stalin.

ABKHAZ AUTONOMOUS SOVIET SOCIALIST REPUBLIC
Capital, Sukhumi; area, 3,300, population, 330,000

The Abkhaz Autonomous SSR or Abkhasia (Russian *Abkhaziya*) occupies the extreme northwestern portion of the Georgian SSR, on the
southwestern slope of the Greater Caucasus, oriented toward the Black
Sea. Nearly the entire population, including, in addition to the basic
Abkhaz national group, Georgians, Russians, Armenians, and Greeks,
is established in a narrow littoral zone between the town of Gagra and
the Ingur (or Enguri) River, which forms the southeastern border of
the republic. The mountain slopes are largely forested. The humid subtropical climate of the lowland makes possible the cultivation of such
important crops as citrus fruits (tangerines, lemons, oranges, and grapefruit), tea, tung-wood, geranium, and other subtropical plants. The
principal staple crops are corn and a high-quality tobacco, which is
partly exported abroad and makes the Abkhaz Autonomous SSR one of
the major tobacco-growing areas of the USSR. Lumbering is important
in the forested area, and there is a large paper mill on the Ingur River.
Other important power resources are the excellent coking coal of Tkvarcheli and the many mountain streams which furnish hydroelectric energy.
The industry consists chiefly of sawmilling, woodworking, wine making,
tobacco processing, and fruit canning and its centers are the capital,
Sukhumi, Gudauta, Ochamchire, and Gagra. The Black Sea littoral is a
popular climatic resort area, having numerous tourist resorts and sana-
toria. The principal transportation routes are the Black Sea shore railroad, which was completed during the Second World War, and the
Sukhumi military road, which leads across the Greater Caucasus at Klukhori Pass and has its terminus at Sukhumi, on the Black Sea coast.

Sukhumi, which was formerly called Sukhum, is one of the most important subtropical health resorts of the USSR. It is the center of the
tobacco-growing area and has tobacco factories, distilleries, metalworks, and food-processing plants. There are tropical botanical gardens
and a research institute devoted to subtropical agriculture. Near by on
the Gumista River is a hydroelectric station completed after the Second
World War.

Gali is an agricultural processing center in a tea and citrus-fruit
district.

Tkvarcheli, which developed in the 1930's, has overtaken the older

Tkibuli as the principal coal-mining center of the Georgian SSR and supplies coking coal to the Rustavi steel mills.

ADZHAR AUTONOMOUS SOVIET SOCIALIST REPUBLIC
Capital, Batumi; area, 1,100, population, 195,000

The Adzhar Autonomous SSR or Adzharistan lies in the southwestern corner of the Georgian SSR, between the Black Sea and the Turkey-USSR frontier. Its basic Adzhar population consists of Georgians who became Moslems under previous Turkish rule. The region is generally mountainous and has a humid subtropical climate and a yearly rainfall of about 100 inches. The inhabitants of the higher, forested inland section are engaged principally in livestock rearing, lumbering, and tobacco growing and are poorly supplied with transportation routes. The narrow littoral is the most important area of Adzharistan. Here the subtropical climate favors such important crops as tea, tangerines, lemons, oranges, grapefruit, tung and camphor woods, bamboo, and so forth. Adzharistan is the principal USSR producer of tea and citrus fruits. Many tourist and seaside resorts are scattered along the coast, which is served by the railroad from Tbilisi and Baku. Crude oil and kerosene pipe lines from Baku terminate at Batumi, the capital and industrial center of the republic. A hydroelectric station built on the Adzharis-Tskhali River, east of Batumi, supplies power for the industries.

Batumi is the terminus of the Transcaucasian Railroad and one of the principal petroleum-loading ports of the USSR. Crude oil, which is piped from Baku, is processed in several cracking plants. It has an iron foundry, a tea-picking-machinery plant, tobacco factories and clothing mills. North of the city are botanical gardens where flora of the humid subtropical zone are grown. Near by extend large plantations of tea, tobacco, and citrus fruits.

SOUTH OSSETIAN AUTONOMOUS OBLAST
Capital, Stalinir; area, 1,500, population, 120,000

The South Ossetian Autonomous Oblast (Russian, *Yugo-Osetinskaya Avtonomnaya Oblast'*) is the southern portion of the Ossetian domain, in the central Greater Caucasus, of which the northern section is constituted into the North Ossetian Autonomous SSR within the Russian SFSR. It is situated on the southern slopes of the Greater Caucasus and watered mainly by the Liakhvi River. The population is 69 percent

Ossetian and 20 percent Georgian, engaged primarily in raising goats and sheep. There is some orchard farming and growing of grain crops in the south. The industries, which are connected with lumbering and dairying, are centered at the capital, known by the Ossetian name Stalinir and the Georgian form Staliniri. The region has several health and tourist resorts, such as Dzhava, north of Stalinir.

Stalinir, which was called Tskhinvali until about 1935, has fruit canning, dairying, and sawmilling industries. It is linked to Gori by a rail line completed during the Second World War.

CHAPTER 23

Ukrainian Soviet Socialist Republic

Capital, Kiev (Kiyev) ; area, 222,600, population, 40,500,000

THE UKRAINIAN SSR, or Ukraine, is in second place among the union republics from the point of view of population and economic potentials. The Ukraine is situated in the southwestern portion of the East European lowland, on the shores of the Sea of Azov and the Black Sea, and extends westward beyond the Carpathian Mountains to the Tisza River.

GENERAL SURVEY

THE PREDOMINANT LOWLAND CHARACTER of the region is interrupted here and there by some low elevations, such as the Donets ridge in the southeast, the Volyn'-Podolian plateau in the west, and the intervening Dnieper ridge. The Carpathians, with their foothills to the north, constitute the only mountainous section of the Ukraine. Five distinct physical regions can be distinguished: (1) the Poles'ye, a forested zone in the north; (2) the wooded steppe in the center; (3) the steppe proper in the south; (4) the Carpathian foothills in the west; and (5) the Carpathians and the Transcarpathian Ukraine.

The Poles'ye in the north and the northwest forms a southern extension of the extensive Poles'ye lowland which constitutes the basic relief form of the adjoining Belorussian SSR. It is a low sandy and forested expanse, distinguished by considerable swampiness (Pripet Marshes). The woods are a mixture of deciduous and evergreen types. Podsols and marshy ground constitute the principal soil forms. The Poles'ye is drained by the lower course of two principal affluents of the Dnieper: the Pripet (or Pripyat'), on the right, and the Desna, on the left.

The wooded steppe on the right bank of the Dnieper is formed by the Volyn'-Podolian plateau. This upland is highest in the northwest and slopes gradually toward the east and the southeast. It has crystalline rock formations covered by recent sediments (sand, clay, and limestone) along the watersheds and a top layer of loess. The rivers in this area frequently flow through canyon-like gorges, and rapids are commonly obstacles to navigation. Ravines and gullies are typical relief features. In the northwest, broad-leaved trees abound. The remainder of the region has black-earth steppe. The southeastern edge of the upland, the so-called Dnieper ridge, continues beyond the Dnieper to form the Azov uplands, extending northeastward along the coast of the Sea of Azov.

The left bank portion of the wooded steppe zone is formed by the Dnieper lowland, which slopes from the Central Russian upland southwestward to the Dnieper River. It is drained by several important left affluents of the Dnieper, among them the Sula, the Psel, and the Vorskla rivers. The last outspurs of the Central Russian upland penetrate into this area from the northeast. The uniformity of the loess-covered plain is broken by a large number of small shallow depressions, which become filled with water during the spring thaw. The northern portion of the plain was once covered by glaciers, which left moraine sediments, now covered with loess, and large expanses of sand sediments. The rivers generally have a slow current and are used for lumber drives. They overflow in the spring, inundating large areas, but become shallow during the summer. Woods are found only in the river valleys, while cultivated steppes predominate along the watersheds.

The Black Sea lowland along the shores of the Black Sea and the Sea of Azov constitutes a true steppe form. It is drained by the lower courses of the Dnieper, the Southern Bug, and the Dniester, and a large number of smaller, partly intermittent, streams. The coast is characterized by cliffs, which are gradually being washed out by the action of the sea, and by the so-called limans, coastal lagoons which were formed in recent geologic times by the flooding of the lower river valleys and are separated by narrow sandspits, called *kosa*, from the open sea. The flatness of the plain is marred by many ravines, the remains of former river valleys, and by mound-like elevations which were erected by the ancient inhabitants of the steppe. The Donets ridge, which rises to 1,184 feet, also lies in the steppe zone, in the extreme east of the Ukrainian SSR. It consists of the remains of an old deeply eroded and weathered upland, which now appears only as a hilly plateau of sandstone, clayey schists, and limestone. The valleys of rivers and many ravines cut deeply into the surface of the area. Along its northern edge the plateau forms picturesque chalk cliffs on the Northern Donets River.

The Carpathian foothills extend from the Volyn'-Podolian upland in

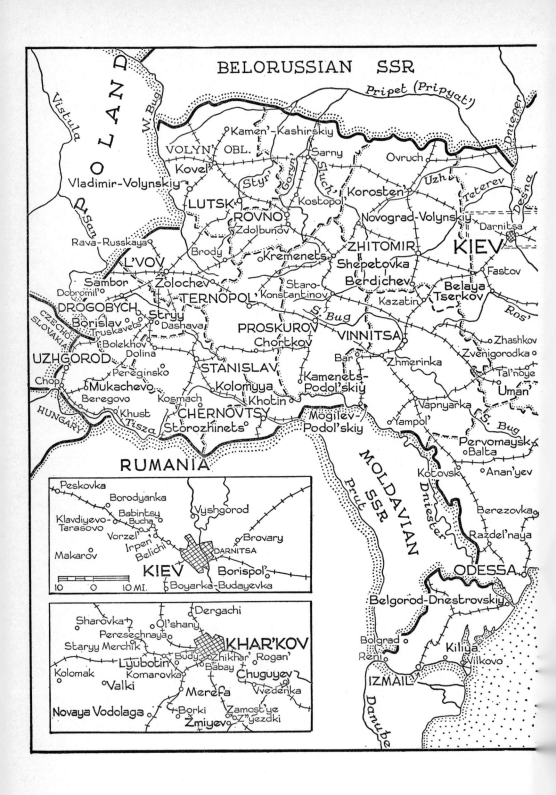

BELORUSSIAN SSR

POLAND

Vistula

W. Bug

Pripet (Pripyat')

Kamen'-Kashirskiy

VOLYN' OBL.

Kovel

Sarny

Ovruch

Uzh

Teterev

Desna

Dnieper

Vladimir-Volynskiy

Styr'

Goryn'

Sluch'

Korosten'

Darnitsa

LUTSK

Kostopol'

Novograd-Volynskiy

KIEV

ROVNO

Zdolbunov

ZHITOMIR

Fastov

Rava-Russkaya

San

Brody

Kremenets

Shepetovka

Berdichev

Belaya

L'VOV

Zolochev

Staro-

Tserkov

Sambor

Konstantinov

Ros'

Dobromil'

TERNOPOL'

Kazatin

CZECHO-

DROGOBYCH

S. Bug

SLOVAKIA

Borislav

Stryy

PROSKUROV

VINNITSA

Zhashkov

Truskavets

Dashava

Chortkov

Bar

Zhmerinka

Zvenigorodka

Bolekhov

Dolina

Tal'noye

UZHGOROD

Pereginsko

STANISLAV

Kamenets-

Vapnyarka

Uman'

Chop

Mukachevo

Kolomyya

Podol'skiy

S. Bug

Beregovo

Kosmach

Khotin

Yampol'

Pervomaysk

Khust

CHERNOVTSY

Mogilev-

Balta

HUNGARY

Tisza

Storozhinets'

Podol'skiy

Kotovsk

Anan'yev

RUMANIA

MOLDAVIAN SSR

Prut

Dniester

Berezovka

Razdel'naya

Peskovka

Borodyanka

Vyshgorod

Klavdiyevo-

Babintsy

Tarasovo

Bucha

Brovary

ODESSA

Vorzel'

Makarov

Irpen'

DARNITSA

Belichi

Belgorod-Dnestrovskiy

KIEV

Borispol'

Bolgrad

Kiliya

10   0   10 MI.

Boyarka-Budayevka

Reni

Vilkovo

Dergachi

IZMAIL

Sharovka

Ol'shany

Peresechnaya

KHAR'KOV

Danube

Staryy Merchik

Budy

Zhikhar'

Rogan'

Kolomak

Komarovka

Babay

Chuguyev

Lyubotin

Valki

Merefa

Vvedenka

Novaya Vodolaga

Borki

Zamost'ye

Zmiyev

Z"yezdki

UKRAINIAN SOVIET SOCIALIST REPUBLIC

(Donets Basin is shown in detail on p. 451.)

the east to the Carpathians in the west. They are drained by the Dniester River and its affluents, which flow in narrow, convoluted river valleys through picturesque wooded depressions. The watersheds, devoid of forests, constitute the basic cultivated areas; they are under wheat, corn, and tobacco. Black earth prevails in all these lowland sections of the Ukraine.

The Carpathians extend through the Ukrainian SSR over a distance of about 150 miles. They constitute a number of ranges, rising gradually toward the southeast, where they reach an elevation of more than 6,600 feet, with passes at points up to 3,000 feet above sea-level. The least accessible section of the mountains lies in Northern Bukovina (Chernovtsy Oblast). The Ukrainian Carpathians form a part of the wooded section of the mountain range. They are covered with deciduous trees on the lower slopes and with evergreens in the upper reaches. The chief rock formations are sandstone and schists with occasional volcanic intrusives. Above 5,000 feet, mountain meadow pastures prevail. There is no permanent snow cover. Isolated snow fields remain until June and reappear in September. Considerable rainfall (40 to 60 inches a year) feeds such important rivers as the Tisza, which flows southwestward, the Dniester, and the Prut, which descend the eastern slopes. In general, the Carpathians are easily accessible and are crossed by highways and rail lines.

The Transcarpathian Ukraine (until 1945 part of Czechoslovakia) lies on the southern slopes of the Carpathians and extends onto the Hungarian lowland, where it is bounded by the Tisza River in the south.

The Dnieper is the most important Ukrainian river. It rises in Smolensk Oblast, outside the Ukrainian SSR. Below Kiev it forms many islands and braided branches in its course. Until the construction of the Dnieper hydroelectric station (*Dneproges*), the rapids in the vicinity of Zaporozh'ye interfered with continuous navigation. Since the completion of the dam and the flooding of the rapids above the dam, the entire river has become navigable. The other important rivers of the Ukraine, the Dniester, the Southern Bug, and the Northern Donets (an affluent of the Don), are all less suitable for navigation.

Compared with the other regions of the European part of the USSR, the Ukraine has a rather temperate climate, although colder and more continental in the eastern part. Thaws occur frequently during the winter, summers are hot, especially in the south, while autumn is dry and continuously clear. Spring arrives early in the west and, together with

a long, warm autumn, provides excellent conditions for the development
of agriculture. Average January temperatures vary from 27° F in the
southwest to 14° F in the east, and July averages from 68° F in the
north to 73° F in the south. The northern section of the Ukraine receives adequate rainfall (about 20 inches a year), but the south is much
drier, having an average yearly rainfall of 9 inches. Most of the precipitation occurs in the first half of the year. During the summer, frequent
violent rainstorms occur in the eastern sections.

The greater portion of the Ukraine lies in the wooded steppe and
steppe zones, where black earth prevails. In the northern section, which
lies in the forested zone, grassy marshes occur in abundance. In the
wooded steppe zone the forest reserves have largely been depleted. Broad-
leaved types, such as oak, maple, ash, and elm, occur only along the
rivers and extend in green ribbons through gullies and ravines up to
the watersheds. Characteristic local vegetation types are the dense
growths of alder, willow, and poplar which border the inundated banks
of the rivers and the many ox-bows and lakes which remain after the
spring floods. The steppes on the watersheds have long been converted
into rich wheat fields, a typical feature of the Ukrainian landscape.

Among the mineral resources which abound in the Ukrainian SSR,
the primary raw materials for heavy metallurgy are most important.
Scarcely anywhere else in the USSR are coal, iron, and manganese found
within such proximity of each other as in the eastern Ukraine. The
Donets Basin, or Donbas, with reserves of more than 90 billion tons, is
the principal coal producer of the USSR. The Krivoy Rog iron mines
produce iron ore of a high quality and metal content. Between these
two sites are the rich manganese deposits in the area of Nikopol'. In the
Donbas are extensive salt and mercury deposits. Petroleum fields lie in
the foothills of the Carpathians, where salt, potash, and natural gas are
also found. Another petroleum site is in the area of Romny (Sumy
Oblast). The northern, marshy section of the Ukraine—Poles'ye—
abounds in peat. Other minerals include polymetallic ores (Donets
Basin), phosphorites, kaolin, limestone, marl, gypsum, and so forth.

The Ukraine is the most densely inhabited union republic of the USSR.
Its 40 million inhabitants represent about one fifth of the total population of the USSR. The average population density is 180 per square
mile; however, there is considerable variation throughout the region.
The greatest concentration exists in the western Ukraine, along the
foot of the Carpathians, where the density reaches 340 to 390 per square

mile. The Donbas shows a density of 260 to 390 per square mile, while the concentration of the population in certain industrial areas goes as high as 525 per square mile. In sharp contrast to these densely settled sections, the northern wooded area of the Poles'ye supports only 50 to 75 persons per square mile, and even less in the marshy portions. The southern steppes also show a density of only 95 to 130 per square mile.

Large villages form the most typical settlement pattern in the Ukraine. Rural population centers of as many as 15,000 or more inhabitants stretch along the river valleys or along dry ravines, where artificial ponds provide the water supply. In many instances villages merge into each other and form a continuous settlement many miles long. Surrounded by orchards and with white-washed, thatched mud huts scattered about in disorderly fashion, they often present a singularly charming appearance.

About one third of the population lives in urban centers. The Ukrainian SSR counts fifteen cities of over 100,000 inhabitants and more than forty cities with a population of over 50,000. The large centers lie mainly in the Donets Basin, along the Dnieper and the shores of the Black Sea, as well as in the western Ukraine.

The national composition of the population of the Ukraine is quite homogeneous. The Ukrainians constitute about 80 percent of the total. Among the more important minorities are the Russians, who live principally in the Donbas and in the northern section, the Belorussians in the northwest, Poles in the west, and Bulgarians in the southwest. Before the Second World War, Jews formed a considerable percentage of the urban population, especially in the right-bank towns and in the western Ukraine. A considerable number of Volga Tatars are also found in the Donets Basin.

The Ukrainians constitute the second most important national group in the USSR. Their language, their culture and their mode of life are closely related to those of the Russians. Long split among several powers, the Ukrainians were as late as the end of the eighteenth century under the rule of the Russians (left-bank Ukraine), of the Poles (right-bank Ukraine), and of the Turks (southern steppes). Shortly thereafter the major portion of the Ukrainian people came under Russian rule, but many still remained in the Austro-Hungarian Empire and in Rumania. In 1917 the Ukrainian SSR was created, but it was not until the final annexations of territory from Poland (1939), Rumania (1940), and Czechoslovakia (1945) that most Ukrainians of eastern Europe became united into one territorial entity.

The present administrative-territorial system was introduced into the Ukrainian SSR in 1932 by the creation of seven oblasts. By 1939 the number had increased to fifteen. Following the partition of Poland, in 1939, and the annexation of the Western Ukraine to the Ukrainian SSR, six more oblasts (Volyn', Rovno, L'vov, Drogobych, Ternopol', and Stanislav) were added. In 1940 Rumania ceded Bessarabia and Northern Bukovina to the USSR. The extreme northern and southern sections of the territory were incorporated into the Ukrainian SSR as the Chernovtsy and Izmail oblasts in view of their predominant Ukrainian population. However, the Ukraine lost the greater part of Moldavian Autonomous SSR (formed in 1924) when the Moldavian territory was joined to the central part of Bessarabia to form the newly constituted Moldavian SSR. Seven districts (rayons) of the Moldavian Autonomous SSR, including those of Balta and Kotovsk remained in the Ukrainian SSR as part of the Odessa Oblast, due to the predominance of a Ukrainian population. In 1945 the western frontier of the Ukrainian SSR was changed in favor of Poland with the adoption of the so-called "Curzon line," which left the city of Przemyśl (Russian *Peremyshl'*) and areas to the northeast and southwest, along the San River, to Poland. In June, 1945, the Carpatho-Ukraine, or Ruthenia, was transferred from Czechoslovakia and constituted into the Transcarpathian (*Zakarpatskaya*) Oblast. At present the Ukrainian SSR is divided into twenty-five oblasts.

The economy of the Ukrainian SSR combines a rich agricultural development with a powerful mining and metallurgical industry, based in particular on the coal of the Donets Basin and the iron ore of Krivoy Rog. As a result of the industrialization of the USSR, the Ukraine became not only a basic grain-exporting region of the USSR, as well as an area of intensive agriculture and agricultural industry, but also the major coal and metallurgical base and heavy-machine construction center of the USSR. The Ukraine has more than one fifth of the total sown area of the USSR and produces one quarter of the grain, two thirds of the sugar, three fifths of the coal and pig iron, one half of the salt and about one fifth of the machines and chemicals.

In 1940 the Donets Basin furnished 85 million tons of coal per year. It supplied not only all the industry of the Ukraine itself but also the metropolitan areas of Moscow, Leningrad, and other industrial centers, as well as the entire southern rail network of the USSR west of the Volga and south of the Moscow coal basin. During the period of the German occupation of the Ukraine (1941–43), the coal mines suffered greatly. At present, reconstruction work is in full swing, mines are being reestablished, and it is hoped to have reached prewar production by the end of the post-war Five-Year Plan. The major coal-mining centers are Stalino, Yenakiyevo, Gorlovka, Kadiyevka, Chistyakovo, Krasnyy Luch, and Sverdlovsk. Anthracite, used principally for fuel, is mined in the eastern and the southern sections, while coking coal is produced in the western and the northern parts of the Donets Basin.

The giant iron and steel mills of the Ukraine lie mainly in the western part of the Donbas, that is, in the coke-supplying area, in the Krivoy Rog iron basin, and along the Dnieper between these two raw-material sources. Among the mills producing over one million tons of pig iron per year are modernized prerevolutionary plants at Makeyevka (Donbas), and at Dnepropetrovsk and at Dneprodzerzhinsk on the Dnieper and new plants at Krivoy Rog, Zaporozh'ye, and Zhdanov. The Azovstal' mills at Zhdanov use Kerch' (Crimea) iron ore, which is shipped across the Sea of Azov.

Machine construction has been developed to a very large extent in the Ukraine in recent years. Due to the close proximity of the sources of metal and in view of the lack of skilled local labor, the Ukraine was designed to produce types of machinery requiring little precision work, but large amounts of metal. Plants located in the Donbas specialize in heavy machine construction; among them, Kramatorsk produces coal-mining and steel-milling machinery, and Voroshilovgrad has a large locomotive works. Agricultural machinery plants are located along the Dnieper and on the right bank. Khar'kov possesses a large tractor plant and locomotive works and produces hydro-turbines and electric motors. There are car-building works at Nikolayev and Dnepropetrovsk, shipyards at Nikolayev, Kherson, and Kiev, and oil-drilling machinery is made in L'vov.

The industrial picture of the Ukraine includes a number of factors suitable for the establishment of a strong chemical industry: the by-products of coking and metallurgical processes, the presence of such important raw materials as salt and phosphorites, the availability of cheap energy produced by coal-fed (*Zugres* and *Shtergres*) or hydroelectric (*Dneproges*) power stations, and finally the need for chemical products in agriculture (fertilizers) and in other branches of the economy. There are several superphosphate plants on the right bank, a large soda industry in the Artemovsk-Lisichansk area in the north of the Donets Basin, based on local salt deposits, chemical plants tied closely to the coking and the metallurgical establishments, and sulphuric acid and fertilizer plants connected with the metallurgy of zinc.

In addition to zinc, which is imported into the Donets Basin, nonferrous metallurgy includes that of aluminum, which is also imported and worked at Zaporozh'ye on the basis of *Dneproges* power, and of mercury, mined near Nikitovka in the Donbas.

The petroleum and natural-gas industry is of only local importance and is intended to supply the Ukraine with its gas and liquid fuel needs. The oil fields lie in the foothills of the Carpathians, near Borislav and Drogobych. During the current Plan, a natural gas pipe line was laid from Dashava (in the oil fields) to Kiev. The Ukraine also imports petroleum from Baku via the ports of Osipenko and Odessa, and the station of Trudovaya (Donbas) is the terminus of a kerosene pipe line from the Groznyy fields.

The textile industry (wool, cotton, and linen milling) supplies only local needs. The food industry, on the other hand, is of national importance. This is true especially of the sugar-refining industry, located mainly in the Vinnitsa and Kiev oblasts, on the right bank, and in the Poltava and Kiev oblasts, on the left bank.

The agriculture of the Ukrainian SSR, less important than heavy industry with respect to the value of production, occupies, nonetheless, a major position in the economy of the USSR. Arable land occupies 60 percent of the total area. Prior to the Second World War the Ukraine was one of the regions best equipped with machine-tractor stations and agricultural machinery. Among the cereals, winter wheat in the west, spring wheat in the east, and barley are most important. The sugar beet is by far the major industrial crop; sunflower, cotton, and tobacco are grown to a lesser extent. Orchard farming is popular and produces melons and pumpkins, garden fruits (apples, pears, plums, and cherries), and in the south, apricots and grapes. Horses, cattle, and pigs are raised throughout the region.

The right-bank Poles'ye is least developed agriculturally. Marshes and forests occupy most of the area. In the isolated patches of moist arable land, potatoes, buckwheat, flax, and hemp are the chief crops. The area abounds, however, in pasture land, and dairy farming is

strongly developed. In the left-bank Poles'ye, land has long been cultivated and drained. There are occasional marshy and forested sections,
mainly between the Dnieper and the Desna. The chief crops are hemp,
tobacco, buckwheat, and leguminous plants. Orchard farming is important. The right-bank wooded steppe is the principal agricultural
region of the Ukraine. It combines fertile black earth with a warm and
moist climate, and the ready availability of phosphate fertilizer. The
sugar beet is predominant and closely linked with the sugar industry.
Among the cereals, rye, winter wheat, and oats are most important;
potatoes and leguminous crops are also grown. The by-products of sugar
refining and fodder crops support large livestock herds raised for dairy
products and meat. The growing of fruit is of national importance.
Vineyards lie in protected valleys near the Dniester River. The left-bank
wooded steppe grows crops similar to those of the right bank. Sugar
beets decrease toward the east and are gradually replaced by sunflowers.
Similarly, winter wheat gradually makes way for spring wheat. In the
southern steppes, where a drier climate prevails, wheat is the most important crop. Rye, corn, and barley are also grown, the latter mainly
in the very dry districts. Along the Sea of Azov and westward to the
lower Dnieper cotton has been introduced in recent years and is grown
without irrigation. Ukrainian cotton is of rather poor quality and produces little fiber. Melons are grown to a great extent, and there are vineyards along the Sea of Azov coast and around Odessa. In the Carpathian
realm, the northern foothills abound in wheat and sugar beets. Up-slope
dairy farming is important. Agriculture is poorly developed in the
Transcarpathian Ukraine. Large areas are covered by forests and pasture land. In the vicinity of the large metropolitan centers, such as Kiev,
Khar'kov, L'vov, as well as in the densely inhabited sections of the
Donbas, around Krivoy Rog, and along the Dnieper, truck produce and
dairy farming are most important.

The intensely developed economy of the Ukraine requires a correspondingly well-developed transportation network. In view of the shallowness of most of the Ukrainian rivers, the railroads bear most of the
load. The Ukraine has the densest rail network of the USSR, the chief
centers being at L'vov, Kiev, and Khar'kov. Among recently completed
lines and spurs, the direct Donbas-Moscow trunk is of the greatest
significance. Only since 1932, when the construction of the *Dneproges*
dam was completed and an artificial lake was created at the site of the
rapids (a former obstacle to navigation), has the Dnieper become the

major navigable through route of the Ukraine. The major ports are Zhdanov and Osipenko on the Sea of Azov, and Kherson, Nikolayev, and Odessa on the Black Sea. Odessa is one of the major maritime trade centers of the USSR.

The Ukraine exports coal, iron and steel, grain, salt, and sugar, and imports cloth from Moscow and Ivanovo, precision tools from Moscow and Leningrad, lumber from Gor'kiy Oblast, along the Volga, or from the Belorussian SSR along the Dnieper, petroleum products from Groznyy (by rail and pipe line) and from Baku (by sea via Batumi-Odessa), and fish from the Lower Volga.

Oblast Survey

THE TWENTY-FIVE OBLASTS of the Ukrainian SSR can be grouped into seven geographic regions on the basis of physical, economic, and historical factors: the right-bank and the left-bank sections of the wooded steppe, the Donets Basin, the Dnieper bend, the Black Sea lowland, the Ukrainian Poles'ye, and the Western Ukraine.

THE RIGHT-BANK WOODED STEPPE

THE RIGHT-BANK WOODED STEPPE, which is the original settlement area of the Ukrainian people, includes the oblasts of Kamenets-Podol'skiy, Vinnitsa, and Kiev. Its fertile black-earth soils and the warm, humid climate have combined to turn the area into a region of intensive agriculture, a dense population, and a well-developed rail network. Sugar beets are the leading crop. Through careful tilling of the soil, the application of phosphate fertilizer, and the rotation with grains and forage grasses, high yields are obtained which furnish up to three tons of sugar per 2.5 acres. The principal grains are winter wheat, rye, barley, and oats. Leguminous crops (peas, lentils, beans) are extensively grown to restore soil fertility. In connection with the intensive crop cultivation, the raising of hogs and cattle for meat and milk production is also very important. Forage grasses and the by-products of the sugar-refining and associated distilling industries constitute an excellent feed supply. Also connected with the sugar economy of the area are the lignite and peat industries, which fuel the processing plants, the quarrying of limestone (used in the sugar-bleaching process), and the mining of phosphorite, which is converted into fertilizer.

Kiev Oblast
Area, 15,900, population, 3,500,000

Kiev Oblast lies in the Dnieper lowland (in the north) and in the Volyn'-Podolian upland (in the south). It is drained by the Dnieper and its right affluents, the Teterev and the Ros' rivers. In the northern section, which penetrates into the forested Poles'ye, the growing of flax, potatoes, and buckwheat are important. The rest of the oblast falls within the sugar economy. Truck produce in the Kiev metropolitan area and orchards in the south, near Uman', and the southeast, near Smela, are important. Peat is worked mainly northwest of Kiev and near Smela, while lignite comes from Yurkovka near Zvenigorodka. Sugar mills abound throughout the center and the south; flour milling and distilling are other rural industries.

Kiev, the capital of the Ukrainian SSR since 1934, was the third largest city of the USSR on the eve of the Second World War. Situated on the middle course of the Dnieper River, below the mouths of its two large affluents, the Pripet and the Desna, Kiev occupies a central location at the junction of the river, four rail trunk lines, and many highways. An ancient city and until the middle 13th century the capital of Kievan Russia, Kiev is the site of many historical relics and monuments. An early commercial and food-processing center, it developed into an industrial point of first rank under the Soviet regime. Its heavy industries produce machine tools, machines, motors, aircraft parts, boilers, agricultural implements, motorcycles, and bicycles, as well as equipment for chemical, sugar, and tanning industries. There are electrical (radios and telephones), textile, and food industries. A number of major enterprises, including lumber mills, a meat-packing plant, a rubber-goods factory, and railway-car works are located in the left-bank industrial suburb of Darnitsa. Shipyards produce vessels for the Dnieper River traffic. A natural-gas pipe line for industrial and domestic use was laid in the post-war period from Dashava.

Other major industrial centers of the oblast are Belaya Tserkov', south of Kiev, Uman' in the far south, and Smela and Cherkassy on the Dnieper in the southeast. They are primarily food-processing centers, with sugar and flour mills and metal, clothing, and leather industries.

Vinnitsa Oblast
Area, 10,600, population, 2,300,000

Vinnitsa Oblast lies in the Volyn'-Podolian upland, bounded in the south-west by the Dniester River and drained by the Southern Bug River. In addition to the basic sugar-beet and wheat crops, fruits, tobacco, and corn are raised near the Dniester River. Viticulture is possible in the deep, protected valleys of the southwest. The oblast is one of the fore-most sugar producers of the Ukraine.

Vinnitsa, on the Southern Bug, has an industry closely connected with the agricultural economy. It processes the local products (sugar, flour, meat, alcohol) and has machine repair shops and a superphosphate plant.

Mogilev-Podol'skiy, on the Dniester in the south, has food-canning, lumber, and metalworking industries.

Kamenets-Podol'skiy Oblast
Area, 8,000, population, 1,800,000

Kamenets-Podol'skiy Oblast is also located in the Volyn'-Podolian up-land, north of the Dniester River. It lies at the western end of the sugar region and also engages in the raising of fruits, tobacco, and corn near the Dniester River. Phosphorite and peat deposits are worked. In the northern forest belt, lumbering, paper milling, and ceramics are the chief occupations.

Proskurov, the capital, is a rail center on the upper Southern Bug River. It has food industries (flour milling and sugar refining), machine shops, and clothing and furniture plants.

Other industrial points are Kamenets-Podol'skiy near the Dniester, with fruit canneries, meat-packing and clothing industries, and She-petovka, a rail center in the forest area, with sawmills, and meat-packing and railroad shops.

THE LEFT-BANK WOODED STEPPE

THE LEFT-BANK WOODED STEPPE includes the oblasts of Poltava, Sumy, and Khar'kov and represents a transition region between the right-bank Ukraine in the west and the Central Black-Earth Region of the Russian SFSR in the east. Although sugar beets continue to form a major crop, the emphasis is placed to a greater extent on grain crops, among which winter and spring wheat are most important. Potatoes and tobacco, in the north, and sunflowers and melons, in the south, are also raised. Hog raising forms the basis of a major meat-packing industry. Machinery industries are located chiefly in Khar'kov.

Khar'kov Oblast
Area, 12,000, population, 2,500,000

Khar'kov Oblast lies in the southwestern outspurs of the Central Russian upland and is drained by the Northern Donets and the upper Orel' and the lower Oskol rivers. Sugar beets predominate in the north, wheat and sunflowers in the south, and truck produce and orchards in the Khar'kov metropolitan area. Rural industry is based chiefly on the processing of the agricultural products and engages in sugar refining, flour milling, sunflower-oil extraction, distilling, and dairying. The oblast possesses a good rail network on the route from the Donets Basin to Moscow.

Khar'kov, the capital of the Ukraine until 1934, is its second city and its foremost machine-construction center. Situated at the junction of six rail lines at the gates to the Donets Basin and Krivoy Rog industrial areas, it dates from the seventeenth century and developed rapidly after the industrialization of the southern Ukraine in the late nineteenth century. Its impressive array of products includes tractors, turbine generators, coal-mining and oil-drilling equipment, electrical goods, diesel motors, ball bearings, machine tools, harvester combines, locomotives, and bicycles. It also has light and food industries.

Izyum, on the Northern Donets, southeast of Khar'kov, has metalworking, ceramic, and sawmilling industries.

Kupyansk, a major rail center east of Khar'kov, engages in machine construction, metalworking, and lumber and sugar milling.

Poltava Oblast
Area, 13,200, population, 2,200,000

Poltava Oblast, in the Dnieper lowland, is bounded on the southwest by the Dnieper River and drained by its left affluents, the Sula, the Psel, and the Vorskla. It grows chiefly sugar beets and wheat, as well as other grains, hemp, mint, sunflowers, and corn. Sugar refining and flour milling are the main rural industries.

Poltava, a four-way rail junction on the Vorskla River, is a processing center for a rich sugar and wheat region. It has locomotive repair shops, flour mills, meat-packing plants, and oil presses. Just northeast is the site of the battle of Poltava (1709), which marked the decisive defeat of the Swedes under Charles XII by Peter the Great.

Kremenchug, a lumber- and grain-trading point on the Dnieper, has light and food industries and produces road-construction machines. Its right-bank suburb, Kryukov, has large railway-car works.

Sumy Oblast
Area, 9,400, population, 1,700,000

Sumy Oblast, lies in the western outliers of the Central Russian upland and is drained by the upper Vorskla, the Psel, the Sula, and the Seym rivers. Basic crop combinations are sugar beets and wheat in the south, and hemp and wheat in the north. Also grown in the north are potatoes and buckwheat; in the south, tobacco and mint. Sugar refining, flour milling, and hemp retting are the chief industries. An oil field is under development near Romny.

Sumy is a sugar-refining center on the Psel River; it produces also agricultural machines, chemical fertilizer, and woolens.

Other industrial cities are Konotop, a rail junction with machine shops and food industries, and Shostka, which produces chemicals and photographic film.

DONETS BASIN

THE DONETS BASIN, which includes the oblasts of Voroshilovgrad and Stalino, is the most heavily industrialized section of the Ukraine and one of the principal industrial bases of the USSR. The impressive industrial development of the district is the result of the combination of local coal production and the iron-ore imports from the Krivoy Rog area, which forms the basis of the large-scale metallurgical industry. Nearly all the major mills concentrated in the Donbas pass through a full cycle of metallurgical production; they had a prewar capacity of 6 million tons of pig iron, $5\frac{1}{2}$ million tons of ingot steel, and 3 million tons of rolled metal. The coking process, which is essential for the iron and steel industry, also feeds the basic chemical industries producing nitrate fertilizer and other chemicals. The use of iron and steel products in the heavy-machine industry completes the industrial scheme of the region. Associated with these principal activities are the quarrying of building and flux materials (dolomite, limestone, refractory clays, and cement rock), the mining of salt, mercury, and lead-zinc ores, as well as large glass and soda works. A dense rail network and a unified power-transmission system connect the various enterprises. The vast number of urban centers, cities and workers' settlements, which have grown up around the metallurgical and machinery works and the coal mines, represent a concentration of almost one third of the urban population of the republic within 1/20 of its area.

Stalino Oblast
Area, 10,200, population, 3,000,000

Stalino Oblast includes the western section of the Donets Basin, extending from the Sea to Azov in the south to the Northern Donets in the north. Agriculture (wheat, sunflowers, and cotton) is of importance only outside of the industrial section. Salt is mined near Artemovsk and mercury near Nikitovka. The principal coal-mining centers are Stalino, Makeyevka, Yenakiyevo, and Gorlovka.

Stalino, the largest city of the Donets Basin, had a population of 392,000 in 1948. It was originally called Yuzovo, or Yuzovka, for a Scottish industrialist, Hughes; it was called Stalin in the early part of the Soviet period. It has metallurgical, chemical, and coal-mining industries.

Makeyevka, a few miles northeast of Stalino, is the site of the Kirov metallurgical works, one of the largest of the Donbas, and coking installations. Coal mines operate in the suburban areas.

Yenakiyevo was called Rykovo from the 1920's until 1935, then Ordzhonikidze until 1943, when it again received its original name. It has a metallurgical industry, chemical works, and coal mines.

Gorlovka also has metallurgical, chemical, and coal-mining industries. Its northern suburb of Nikitovka has mercury mines and near-by Trudovaya is the terminus of an oil pipe line from the Groznyy fields in the Caucasus.

Konstantinovka has a metallurgical industry, zinc works, and produces ceramics, glass, and cement, as well as superphosphate fertilizer.

Kramatorsk is noted as a heavy-machine construction center which produces mining and metallurgical equipment. It also has railway-car repair shops and ceramics works. Druzhkovka, to the south, is another machinery center.

Slavyansk is a chemical center where there are salt mines and soda works, limestone quarries, and porcelain works. Artemovsk (formerly Bakhmut), to the southeast, is the center of an important salt-mining

DONETS BASIN

region, having 35 percent of the reserves of the USSR, and the site of soda works.

Debal'tsevo is one of the chief rail centers of the Donets Basin.

Chistyakovo, to the south, is a major coal-mining point.

Zhdanov, called Mariupol' until 1948, the principal port for the Donets Basin, on the Sea of Azov, is the seat of the new Azovstal' metallurgical works, one of the largest of the region. It also has the Il'ich works, which produce special steels, shipyards, and fish canneries.

Voroshilovgrad Oblast
Area, 10,300, population, 1,800,000

Voroshilovgrad Oblast is the easternmost division of the Ukrainian SSR. It includes the eastern portion of the Donets Basin and extends northward into a typical Ukrainian wheat and sunflower region. Most of its coal mines produce anthracite.

Voroshilovgrad, formerly called Lugansk, has large locomotive works and metallurgical and pipe-rolling mills and produces enameled goods and mining machinery.

Voroshilovsk (formerly Alchevsk) has metallurgical and coking industries. Just south is the coal-mining city of Parizhskaya Kommuna [Paris commune].

Kadiyevka, called Sergo from 1935 until 1943, and Krasnyy Luch are the two main coal-mining centers of the oblast, with many large satellite towns grouped near by. Almaznaya, southwest of Kadiyevka, produces special steel alloys. Lesser coal centers in the southeastern section of the region are Krasnodon, Sverdlovsk, and Roven'ki.

Rubezhnoye, in the northern coal district, on the Northern Donets, has large chemical (explosives) works, and produces paints and glass.

DNIEPER BEND

THE DNIEPER BEND, which includes Dnepropetrovsk Oblast and the adjacent section of Zaporozh'ye Oblast, is the second center of heavy industry in the Ukraine. Metallurgy, which is largely based on Krivoy Rog iron ore and Nikopol' manganese, is the principal branch of the industry. It receives its coal and flux materials from the Donets Basin. Unlike the Donbas, which frequently suffers from a shortage of water, it is amply supplied with water from the Dnieper River, which is also the source of most of its electric power. The main industrial centers lie either at the sources of raw materials (Krivoy Rog, Nikopol') or on the Dnieper River (Dneprodzerzhinsk, Dnepropetrovsk, and Zaporozh'ye). Agricultural production emphasizes wheat, barley, sunflowers, southern hemp, and soy beans. On the basis of the local grain production and grain brought along the Dnieper, a large flour-milling industry has developed.

Dnepropetrovsk Oblast
Area, 12,600, population, 2,200,000

Dnepropetrovsk Oblast extends from the Dnieper Bend to the Donets Basin and is divided into two equal sections by the course of the Dnieper River. Grains and sunflowers are the basic crops, with some hemp in the northeast and cotton in the southwest. The major rural industries are flour milling, meat packing, and dairying.

Dnepropetrovsk, on the Dnieper River, is a major industrial and transportation center formerly called Yekaterinoslav. It has large metallurgical works, pipe rolling mills, rail and sheet-metal mills, and steel-construction works. An automobile plant is to be established during the post-war Five-Year Plan. The city has clothing, leather, and food industries and is an important lumber-trade center.

Dneprodzerzhinsk, on the Dnieper, west of Dnepropetrovsk, has metallurgical and chemical works, producing rolled steel products, coke, and nitrate fertilizer, plastics, and cement. Metal construction and railway-car building are other important activities.

Krivoy Rog, the center of a rich iron-ore region, distinguished by reserves of more than one million tons and a high metal content (70 percent), has metallurgical works and iron foundries.

Nikopol', the center of one of the main manganese areas of the USSR, has concentrating plants, shipyards, and one of the largest pipe-rolling mills of the Union. The manganese mining areas lie northeast of Nikopol' in the district of Marganets [manganese] and in the northwest, near Ordzhonikidze.

Lesser industrial centers are Novo-Moskovsk, with sheet-metal mills, and Pavlograd, a pulp-milling and furniture city.

Zaporozh'ye Oblast
Area, 10,400, population, 1,300,000

Zaporozh'ye Oblast extends from the Dnieper River to the Sea of Azov. Agricultural emphasis is on wheat in the north and on cotton in the southern flat steppes. Other crops include castor beans, vineyards (near Osipenko), and fruits near Melitopol' and Kamenka-Dneprovskaya.

Zaporozh'ye (the former Aleksandrovsk) is a major industrial and hydroelectric-power center, the site of the Dnieper dam and power station (*Dneproges*). This largest water-power producer of Europe has a capacity of 550,000 kilowatts. Completed in 1932, the dam was blown up in 1941 by the retreating Russians in accordance with their scorched-earth policy. Reconstruction began shortly after its recapture in 1943, and in 1947 the first turbine went into operation. The power generated by *Dneproges* furnished the basis for the industrial development of Zaporozh'ye, supplying its new special steel works, aluminum, and magnesium plants. It produces harvester combines and chemicals.

Melitopol', an agricultural center in the southern steppe, has machine shops, producing diesel motors, grain-elevator equipment, and pumps. In addition to chemical and furniture industries, it also has flour mills, meat-packing plants, and cottonseed-oil presses.

Osipenko, until 1940 called Berdyansk, is an important port on the Sea of Azov. It has agricultural machinery works, an aircraft plant, shipyards, and railroad repair shops. Near by is a health and beach resort.

THE BLACK SEA LOWLAND

THE BLACK SEA LOWLAND, with its dry level steppes, includes the oblasts of Odessa, Nikolayev, Kherson, the southern part of Zaporozh'ye, as well as Kirovograd and Izmail. This area which was annexed by the Russian Empire only in the eighteenth century, is a region of relatively recent settlement. Only toward the end of the last century did extensive grain growing replace the previously predominant pastoral economy, and the region developed into the main grain producer of the Ukraine. In the Soviet period a vast cotton area was introduced in the lower Dnieper area and cultivated by dry-farming methods in rotation with fodder crops. Elsewhere sunflowers, soy beans, fruits, melons, and vineyards became important. The local industry is closely connected with the agricultural production and engages in processing and machine manufacturing. Shipbuilding is centered in the large coastal cities.

Kherson Oblast
Area, 10,600, population, 700,000

Kherson Oblast extends north of the Crimea from the Sea of Azov to the Black Sea. It is a typical flat, dry steppe, with cotton and wheat growing. Kakhovka, on the Dnieper River below Zaporozh'ye, is the site of the second great Dnieper dam, scheduled for 1951–57, with irrigation canals reaching into the Crimea. Skadovsk and Khorly, on the Black Sea, and Genichesk, on the Sea of Azov, are minor fishing ports.

Kherson is a major port at the mouth of the Dnieper River, where there are shipyards, repair docks, agricultural machinery works, and extensive food-canning industries. It is the terminus of a new railroad built during the Second World War from the Crimea.

Nikolayev Oblast
Area, 7,500, population, 800,000

Nikolayev Oblast lies on the Black Sea and is drained by the lower Southern Bug and the Ingul rivers. Cotton and wheat are the chief crops, with castor beans and sunflowers in the north, truck produce near Nikolayev, and dairy farming. In the rural areas flour milling, dairying, and sugar refining are the main industries.

Nikolayev lies at the head of the Bug Liman, over forty miles from the Black Sea. It is a major shipbuilding center and exports grain, sugar, iron, and manganese ore. It produces agricultural machines and has textile, food, and fish-canning industries.

Odessa Oblast
Area, 10,800, population, 1,800,000

Odessa Oblast lies in the western section of the Black Sea lowland and extends from the Black Sea to the Volyn'-Podolian upland in the north. It is bounded in the west by the Moldavian SSR. Numerous minor intermittent streams drain it in the south, and the Southern Bug in the north. Sugar beets are the main crop in the north, wheat and sunflowers in the center, and cotton in the south. Of lesser importance are corn, fruits, and castor beans. Sugar refining, flour milling, dairying, and wine making are the chief rural industries.

Odessa, the third city of the Ukraine and one of the major ports of the USSR, exports lumber and grains, and imports oil from the Caucasus, coal from the Donbas, cement from Novorossiysk, for local industries and for transshipment to the right-bank Ukraine, Belorussia, and as far as Leningrad. Its industries include machinery works, which produce agricultural implements, machine tools, grain-elevator and food-industry equipment, cranes, and printing machinery. Its food industries process mainly sugar, flour, and canned goods. There are clothing and shoe factories, chemicals plants (superphosphate, iodine, linoleum, petroleum refining), woodworking and jute industries. The city has shipyards and railroad shops; during the post-war Plan, an automobile assembly plant will go into operation. Situated on the picturesque hillside, Odessa descends in several terraces, including a famous stairway, to the sea. Northward and southward along the coast are well-known health resorts (Khadzhibey Liman, Kugal'nik Liman Arkadiya, and Fontan) with mineral springs and mud baths. Regular overseas connections are maintained from the port.

Pervomaysk (formerly Ol'viopol') is situated on the Southern Bug and produces agricultural machines, flour, and meat.

Kirovograd Oblast
Area, 9,600, population, 1,100,000

Kirovograd Oblast lies somewhat north of the level steppe in the Volyn'-Podolian upland. It is bounded on the northeast by the Dnieper River and drained by the Ingul and Ingulets rivers. Wheat is the basic crop; sugar beets are grown in the northwest and the east, sunflowers in the south, and potatoes and flax in the moist, wooded region of the north. There are deposits of lignite, kaolin, refractory clays, and granite. Sugar refining, flour milling, and dairying are the main rural industries.

Kirovograd was originally called Yelizavetgrad. In 1924 it was renamed Zinov'yevsk, then Kirovo in 1936, and Kirovograd in 1939. It lies on the upper Ingul River in a lignite-mining region and has important agricultural machine works and food-processing plants.

Znamenka is a rail center which has metalworking and food industries.

Aleksandriya, which has tanneries and flour mills, is also developing into the main lignite-mining center of the right-bank Ukraine.

Izmail Oblast
Area, 4,800, population, 700,000

Izmail Oblast was formed in 1940 out of the southernmost part of Bessarabia which had a predominant Ukrainian and Russian population. It lies between the Dniester River and the Kiliya arm of the Danube delta and has Moldavian minorities in the northwest and Bulgarian elements in the west, near Bolgrad. The main crops are wheat, barley, and corn in the northwest, where sheep are also extensively raised. Near the Black Sea there are large vineyards and orchards. The oblast is one of the most important wine-producing districts of the USSR. Along the coast there are fisheries and saltworks. Building materials constitute the only mineral resources.

Izmail (Rumanian *Ismail*) is a port and a fishing center on the Kiliya arm of the Danube delta. It produces caviar and has an active grain and lumber trade.

Kiliya (Rumanian *Chilia Nouă*) is a fishing port on the Danube delta, east of Izmail.

Belgorod-Dnestrovskiy (Rumanian *Cetatea Albă*) was known as Akkerman until 1944. It is a port on the Dniester Liman, trading in wine, fish, and wool. It has fisheries and saltworks and is surrounded by vineyards and orchards.

POLES'YE

THE UKRAINIAN POLES'YE, which includes the oblasts of Zhitomir and Chernigov and the northern sections of Kiev and Sumy oblasts, is distinguished by a relatively high humidity, wooded terrain (especially in the west), and podsolic soils, similar to its Belorussian counterpart, which adjoins it in the north. Among the sparsely settled population, industries are poorly developed. Intensive crops are grown in the forest clearings, including flax, hemp, potatoes, and forage crops, which support some dairy-cattle herds. In the south, along the border of the wooded steppe zone, sugar beets and tobacco are cultivated. The Poles'ye is the only Ukrainian region (not counting the western oblasts, which have not been long exposed to the Soviet planned economy) where rye acreage exceeds that of wheat. Buckwheat is also grown as a local food staple. Industry is largely based on agricultural and lumber resources. Among the food industries, starch processing and distilling are the chief activities. There are woodworking and furniture plants, porcelain works, tanneries, and hemp and flax retting installations. Among the mineral resources, one should note granite, sandstone, used in the making of refractory bricks, and labradorite. Peat extraction is important as a fuel basis.

Zhitomir Oblast
Area, 11,600, population, 1,800,000

Zhitomir Oblast lies on the northern edge of the Volyn'-Podolian up-land and extends northward into the Poles'ye. Sugar beets and wheat penetrate into the southern section, but in the remainder, potatoes, flax, buckwheat, and hops are grown. The forested area in the north yields lumber, clays, kaolin, and granite, and quartzite and has ceramic and paper-milling industries. In the southern rural areas sugar refining, distilling, and flour milling are the main industries.

Zhitomir, on the Teterev River, is a rail center, with lumber and grain trade. It has large furniture factories.

Berdichev, an active trading center, has important sugar and leather industries and clothing and dyeing plants, and flour and tobacco products are produced there.

Korosten', a rail junction in the northern part of the oblast, has various chemical plants, glass and porcelain works, and lumber and paper mills.

Novograd-Volynskiy, in the southwest, has machine shops and distilling and furniture industries.

Chernigov Oblast
Area, 12,200, population, 1,700,000

Chernigov Oblast is bounded on the west by the Dnieper and is drained by its chief left affluent, the Desna River. In addition to the basic rye, oats, and buckwheat crops, hemp and flax are grown in the north, potatoes in the center, and sugar beets, tobacco, and mint in the southeast. Lumbering is carried on in the wooded areas of the north and the west, and peat cutting in the marshy river valleys. Sugar refining, flour milling, meat packing, and flax and hemp retting are the main rural industries.

Chernigov, on the right bank of the Desna River, is one of the oldest cities of the Ukraine, having lumber and food-processing industries (canned goods, alcohol, and flour) and chemical works.

Nezhin is an agricultural center in a grain, potato, and sugar-beet district, while Priluki, the other industrial center of the oblast, processes sugar, tobacco, and flour and engages in the manufacture of clothing, leather goods, and furniture.

WESTERN UKRAINE

THE WESTERN UKRAINE includes those areas (except for Izmail Oblast) which were incorporated into the Ukrainian SSR after 1939 and later. Six oblasts (Rovno, Volyn', Ternopol', L'vov, Stanislav, and Drogobych) were annexed in the autumn of 1939 following the partition of Poland and the Soviet occupation of its eastern section. Chernovtsy Oblast was formed in the Northern Bukovina and the extreme northern section of Bessarabia after the acquisition of these territories from Rumania, in the summer of 1940. The Transcarpathian Oblast was ceded to the Ukraine according to an agreement with Czechoslovakia in 1945. The Western Ukraine can be roughly considered in four geographical sections: the Carpathian section in the south, on the slopes and in the foothills of the Carpathian Mountains, the Poles'ye, a northern lowland along the right affluents of the Pripet River, the hilly central section in the Volyn'-Podolian upland, and the Transcarpathian section.

The Carpathian section of the Western Ukraine includes the oblasts of Chernovtsy, Stanislav, and Drogobych. Its economy is based essentially on the mineral resources of the area: petroleum, natural gas, salt, and potash, and on the lumber resources on the slopes. There are a number of health resorts in the valleys.

Chernovtsy Oblast
Area, 3,200, population, 900,000

Chernovtsy Oblast lies along the upper Prut and the Dniester rivers. The forests (mainly beech), building materials, salt, and petroleum are found in the higher foothills. Agriculture puts the emphasis on grains (wheat, corn, and barley), potatoes and sugar beets in the south and on fruit growing along the Dniester, in the northeast. Sheep raising and lumbering are the main activities in the mountains. Sawmilling, woodworking, sugar refining, flour milling, and wine making are the chief rural industries.

Chernovtsy (Rumanian *Cernăuţi*) called Chernovitsy until 1944, lies on a terrace above the Prut River. It has large textile and machine industries and produces chemicals, lumber, and food products.

Storozhinets (Rumanian *Storojineţ*) is a road center in the agricultural region southwest of Chernovtsy.

Khotin (Rumanian *Hotin*) lies in an orchard and vineyard area on the Dniester River. There is a noted leather industry.

Stanislav Oblast
Area, 5,400, population, 1,300,000

Stanislav Oblast is drained by the upper Dniester and its right affluents descending from the Carpathian Mountains. It has important petroleum, salt, natural-gas, and potash deposits in the areas of Dolina and Bolekhov, with petroleum fields extending along the foothills in a southeasterly direction to Kosmach, southwest of Kolomyya. The principal oil towns are Bolekhov, Dolina, Pereginsko, Bogorodchany (where ozocerite is also secured), Solotvin, Nadvornaya, Pechenezhin, and Kosmach. Petroleum is refined at Bolekhov, Stanislav, and Kolomyya. The main lumber centers are Delyatin and Kuty, which has a large wood-distillation industry. On the right bank of the Dniester River lies the agricultural zone of the oblast, where grains, tobacco, and sugar beets are raised. Tobacco is processed at Zabolotov and sugar at Gorodenka.

Stanislav (Polish *Stanisławów*, German *Stanislau*) has railroad and machine shops, an oil refinery, and textile and leather industries and produces asphalt, ceramics, lumber, and food products.

Kolomyya (Polish *Kołomyja*, German *Kolomea*), on the upper Prut River, has machine works and oil-refining and chemical plants. Textiles and cement are also produced.

Drogobych Oblast
Area, 4,000, population, 1,200,000

Drogobych Oblast lies on the northern slopes of the Carpathian Mountains and is bordered by Poland in the west. It is the chief petroleum region of the Western Ukraine, with the chief oil fields in the area of Drogobych and Borislav. Near by are potassium and magnesium salt mines and natural-gas wells. Salt is mined at Dobromil'. Agriculture is important along the Dniester River.

Drogobych (Polish *Drohobycz*) is the center of the Western Ukrainian petroleum region, with important refining and chemical installations and potash and magnesium salt mines. It trades in petroleum, livestock, and agricultural products and produces rubber goods, lumber, and food products.

Borislav (Polish *Borysław*) is another petroleum center southwest of Drogobych. It has petroleum and natural-gas wells and engages in the manufacture of drilling equipment and the processing of ozocerite. The health resort of Truskavets, with mineral springs, lies just to the east.

Sambor is an agricultural center, with sawmilling, flour-milling, and distilling industries.

Stryy (Polish *Stryj*) is a rail center where there are machine and metalworking industries, producing mainly drilling equipment, and chemical and lumber (matches and furniture) plants. Petroleum and natural gas are secured near by. From the gas wells of Dashava, just northeast of the city, a pipe line has been laid to Kiev during the post-war Five-Year Plan for industrial and domestic consumption.

The Poles'ye, which is wooded in the north, close to the Pripet River, also contains extensive marshy areas. It is the most backward section of the Western Ukraine. Its subsistence crops are rye and potatoes. Industry is poorly developed and is restricted to flour milling, sawmilling, and brickworking in the rural areas.

Rovno Oblast
Area, 8,000, population, 1,200,000

Rovno Oblast is drained by the Goryn and its affluent, the Sluch'. In the south, on the higher ground of the Volyn'-Podolian upland, agriculture produces grains, hops, tobacco, and sugar beets; in the northern section lumbering is the main industry. Granite, cement rock, and slate are quarried.

Rovno (Polish *Równe*) is a rail center having railroad shops, agricultural machinery works, and chemical and lumber industries.

Volyn' Oblast
Area, 7,700, population, 1,100,000

Volyn' Oblast which borders on Poland along the Western Bug River in the west, has some agriculture (grains and tobacco) in the south, but mainly lumbering industries in the north, along the Pripet River and its affluents.

Lutsk (Polish *Łuck*), the capital, lies on a minor rail branch, at the southern edge of the Pripet Marshes. It is an agricultural center and produces agricultural implements, clothing, leather, lumber, and flour.

Vladimir-Volynskiy (Polish *Włodzimierz*) is a rail junction and grain-trading point near the Polish border.

Kovel' (Polish *Kowel*) is a rail center with knitting and hosiery mills, sawmills, tobacco, and flour mills.

The central section of the Western Ukraine lies in the fertile Volyn'-Podolian upland and includes the oblasts of Ternopol' and L'vov, as well as the adjoining zones of the oblasts to the north and the south. It is drained by the Dniester River and its left affluents, which cut deep ravines into the plateau. Its black-earth soils and the moderate climate favor an agricultural economy. The section is very similar to the right-bank wooded steppe of the old Soviet Ukraine in its dense rail network, its concentrated population, and the large number of urban centers. Grains (wheat, rye, and barley), potatoes, and sugar beets are the basic crops for the large food-processing industry, with flour mills and distilleries.

Ternopol' Oblast
Area, 5,300, population, 1,500,000

Ternopol' Oblast lies in the watershed area between the Pripet and the Dniester rivers. Grains (mainly winter wheat) and sunflowers are the principal crops throughout the larger portion of the oblast. Sugar beets are cultivated in the extreme north, and fruits in the south along the Dniester River. Building stone is quarried in several places.

Ternopol' (until 1944, Tarnopol') is a rail center with an active grain and egg trade. It produces agricultural implements, cement, lumber, and food products.

Kremenets (Polish *Krzemieniec*), on a rail spur north of Ternopol', produces flour-milling equipment, ceramics, and cement. There are peat bogs and chalk quarries.

Chortkov (Polish *Czortków*) is a rail center south of Ternopol', producing rubber goods, cement, and tile.

L'vov Oblast
Area, 4,300, population, 1,500,000

L'vov Oblast lies on the Polish border on the upper Western Bug. East of L'vov grains, potatoes, and fruits are the chief crops. Extensive quarrying industries form the basis for the manufacture of cement, glass, bricks, and tiles.

L'vov (Polish *Lwów*), the largest city of the Western Ukraine, is a nine-way rail hub and major industrial center trading in agricultural products, petroleum, and lumber. It produces precision instruments, radio and telegraph equipment, and light bulbs. Its machinery plants produce agricultural implements, gas equipment, and bicycles. Other industries are connected with oil refining, textile milling, glassworking, and the manufacture of furniture, shoes, and lumber and food products. During the post-war Five-Year Plan, which schedules further industrialization of the city, an automobile assembly plant will go into operation.

Zolochev (Polish *Złoczów*), on the L'vov-Ternopol' railroad, is a center for newly developed lignite mines. It has metalworking, tanning, lumber, and distilling industries.

Transcarpathian Oblast
Area, 5,000, population, 900,000

The Transcarpathian (Russian *Zakarpatskaya*) Oblast lies on the southwest slopes of the eastern Carpathians and is watered by mountain streams flowing southward to the Tisza River, an affluent of the Danube. The mountain slopes, which extend throughout the major part of the territory, are covered with excellent beech and oak stands. Fertile soils, suitable for the growing of grains (corn, wheat, oats, and rye) and potatoes, are found only in the mountain valleys and in the southern zone along the Tisza River. On the southern hill slopes grapes and tobacco are grown. Among the mineral resources salt is mined at Solotvin and there are petroleum, lignite, and low-quality iron deposits. Several mineral springs have bottling industries. Wood distillation and woodworking industries are found at Svalyava, Perechin, and Velikiy Bychkov. A paper mill has been constructed at Rakhovo during the post-war period. The region, which was formerly known as Carpatho-Ukraine, or Ruthenia, and in Czech as *Podkarpatska Rus*, was ceded by Czechoslovakia in September, 1945 and organized as a separate oblast within the Ukrainian SSR.

Uzhgorod (Czech *Užhorod*, Hungarian *Ungvár*), near the Czech border, is the capital of the oblast. It has food-processing and lumber industries.

Mukachevo (Czech *Mukačevo*, Hungarian *Munkács*), southeast of Uzhgorod, is another industrial center of the region.

CHAPTER 24

Moldavian Soviet Socialist Republic

Capital, Kishinev; area, 13,100, population, 2,660,000

THE MOLDAVIAN SRR lies in the extreme southwest of the European USSR, between the Dniester River in the east and the Prut in the west. It consists of the central section of Bessarabia, which represents 90 percent of the total area, and a small district on the left bank of the Dniester in what was the former Moldavian Autonomous SSR.

The basic central portion of the republic is a plateau known as the Bessarabian-Moldavian upland, which rises to 1,410 feet and extends westward beyond the Prut River. The upland is composed of young sedimentary rock, mainly limestone, covered with a layer of loess. Its higher, wooded portions, known as the Kodry, have podsolic soils which support deciduous forests of oak, ash, and maple. North of the plateau lies the level, treeless Bel'tsy steppe, and to the south, the dry Budzhak steppe. Both are covered with rich black-earth soils. In the south, tree vegetation is found only in the flood plains of the lower Dniester and the Prut rivers.

The republic is one of the warmest regions of the European USSR, having a mean annual temperature of 50° F. Precipitation varies between 16 and 20 inches yearly. Temperatures increase from north to south, while the rainfall decreases in the same direction. Most of the rains occur in June and July in the form of heavy downpours and summer storms. The warmest and the best-watered parts are the river valleys and the central plateau district. As in other parts of the southern European USSR, dry northeasterly winds prevail.

Construction materials constitute the chief mineral resources. Vast gypsum deposits lie in the vicinity of Lipkany, in the extreme north of the republic. Granite, chalk, and cement rock are found in the Dniester valley, northwest of Rybnitsa. During the current Five-Year Plan, surveys of possible coal and oil fields are to be effected.

The Moldavians, who represent about 65 percent of the total popula-

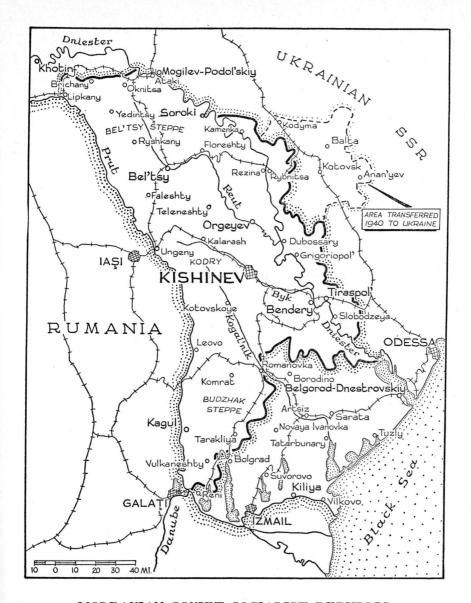

MOLDAVIAN SOVIET SOCIALIST REPUBLIC

tion, speak a Rumanian dialect and use the Cyrillic alphabet. They constitute the major part of the rural population and a considerable element in the urban centers. The Ukrainians (10 percent of the population) live mainly in the areas bordering on the Ukrainian SSR in the north, east, and south. The Russians, who make up 6 to 7 percent of the population, live mainly in the cities, as do the Jews, who formed 10 percent of the population before the Second World War. Lesser minorities in this multinational region are Bulgars, Gypsies, Greeks, and Armenians. Less than 20 percent of the population live in the cities.

The Moldavian SSR was formed in 1940 out of a section of the former Moldavian Autonomous SSR, which was established in 1924 as part of the Ukrainian SSR, and of the central major portion of Bessarabia, which together with Northern Bukovina had been ceded by Rumania in June, 1940. The Moldavian Autonomous SSR, which had been established mainly as an expression of the Soviet claim to Bessarabia, included seven districts (rayons) with a predominantly Ukrainian population which had been merged with the Moldavian elements in order to enhance the importance of the autonomous republic for political reasons. When the Moldavian SSR was established, the Ukrainian districts (including the towns of Balta and Kotovsk) were separated from the Moldavian area and returned to Odessa Oblast of the Ukrainian SSR. The northern and the southern districts of Bessarabia, including the towns of Khotin (in the north) and Izmail and Belgorod-Dnestrovskiy (in the south), were included in the Ukrainian SSR because of their predominantly Ukrainian and Russian elements. Until 1947 the Moldavian SSR consisted of six *uyezds* and of the old Soviet portion on the left bank of the Dniester; it was subdivided into rayons. The suppression of the *uyezds*, which left the republic directly divided into rayons on the pattern of the other small union republics (Georgia, Armenia, and so forth), indicates that the Moldavian SSR has completed the stage of gradual sovietization of its economy for which purpose the additional *uyezd* administration pattern had been maintained.

Although agriculture and livestock raising are the chief economic activities for the republic as a whole, the development of viticulture and the cultivation of fruits and vegetables is the most characteristic feature of the economy. The climate and the natural conditions of Moldavia have frequently been compared with those prevailing in the French Champagne as being exceedingly favorable to the planting of vineyards. The republic includes about one third of the vineyard acreage of the USSR.

The principal wine-growing district is centered on Kishinev and includes the wooded hill slopes in the center of the republic. Other important wine districts are around Kagul and Komrat and in the protected Dniester valley. Orchards are scattered through the entire region, but are especially important on the left bank of the Dnieper. Vegetables are concentrated in the same area, mainly around Tiraspol' and Slobodzeya. Grain crops, which occupy about 75 percent of the total area, are sown chiefly in the northern and southern steppe areas of Bessarabia. Corn is the main crop and is considered as the staple food of the local population, who use it in the preparation of *mamalyga* (corn porridge) and burn the stalks as fuel. Corn, which covers one third of the grain area, is followed closely by winter wheat, barley, and winter rye. During the post-war Five-Year Plan the introduction of rice into the Dniester flood plain will be studied. The chief industrial crops are tobacco, near Orgeyev and Dubossary, sugar beets, near Bel'tsy and Rybnitsa, soy beans and sunflowers, in the northern steepe. Flax and hemp are grown to some extent for oil-seed production. Among the new industrial crops, which are being introduced experimentally, are opium poppies, mustard, *kok-sagyz*, castor beans, caraway, and mint. The introduction of cotton into the southern steppe is also being studied. Dairy cattle and hogs are raised in the north, while in the drier southern steppe sheep and goats are the chief stock animals. Karakul sheep have been introduced in the extreme south, near Vulkaneshty.

On the basis of the agricultural production, the main processing industries are fruit and vegetable canning, wine making, distilling, flour milling, vegetable-oil extraction, tobacco processing, and sugar refining. Of lesser importance are tanning, knitting, woodworking, and quarrying industries. However, during the post-war Five-Year Plan a basis will be laid for the development of new industries associated with those based on the agricultural production. Projected are the establishment of a fertilizer industry, on the basis of phosphorite deposits found in the northern part of the republic, the development of coopering, on the basis of oak timber, as well as the manufacturing of agricultural machinery and of equipment for the wine-making and canning industries. To be used in the further development of industry are the new cement mills of Rybnitsa and Kishinev and the new glassworks of Floreshty. Hydroelectric installations on the Dniester (near Dubossary) and on the Reut River are intended to supply power to the local industrial centers.

The Moldavian SSR is relatively well served by rail lines, but does not possess any good north-south connections. Its principal railroads serve as lateral links between the trunk lines Galaţi-Iaşi-Chernovtsy (in Rumania) and Odessa-L'vov (in the Ukraine). Navigation is possible on the Dniester below Mogilev-Podol'skiy and on the Prut below Leovo. The chief export items are grapes, wine, fruits, nuts, hides, wheat, and canned goods.

Kishinev (Rumanian *Chişinău*) lies on the Byk River, a right affluent of the Dniester. It includes an old section in the river valley and a new city on the plateau amid the picturesque Kodry hills. It is the chief industrial center of the republic with large food industries. During the post-war Plan it will be the subject of a considerable industrial development, with the establishment of shoemaking, tanning, and knitting plants, a cement mill, brickworks, and a metalworking industry.

Bel'tsy (Rumanian *Bălţi*), on the Reut River, is the chief city of the northern part of the republic. A rail center, it has important oil-extraction, flour-milling, and sugar-refining industries.

Soroki (Rumanian *Soroca*) is a minor food-processing center (flour, beer, and oils) on the Dniester River.

Orgeyev (Rumanian *Orheiu*) is an old city which flourished under the Turks. It is located amid vineyards, orchards, and tobacco plantations and has handicraft and food industries.

Bendery (Rumanian *Tighina*) lies at the intersection of the chief lateral railway and the Dniester River. Its commercial and transportation importance is enhanced by the rich surrounding vineyards and orchards and its own canning industry.

Tiraspol', on the opposite bank of the Dniester River, was the capital of the former Moldavian Autonomous SRR. Its large fruit and vegetable canneries are of country-wide importance; it also has important wine-making, flour-milling and oil-extraction industries. Other centers on the left (former Soviet) bank of the Dnieper are the wine-making towns of Dubossary and Grigoriopol' and the sugar city of Rybnitsa, which is now becoming also a major cement producer.

Kagul (Rumanian *Cahul*) is the chief city of the southern steppes and the seat of a flour-milling and wine-making industry.

CHAPTER 25

Belorussian Soviet Socialist Republic

Capital, Minsk; area, 80,100, population, 7,220,000

THE BELORUSSIAN SSR is situated in the western section of the European USSR and is bordered by Poland in the west, the Ukraine in the south, and the Baltic republics in the north. It forms part of the East European plain and is separated by the Lithuanian-Belorussian upland into a small northern and a larger southern lowland.

GENERAL SURVEY

THE NORTHERN SECTION, in the vicinity of Polotsk, is an old moraine region drained by the Western Dvina. The upland, which extends in a broad chain of hills southwest-northeast across the republic, forms the main watershed between the Baltic and the Black Sea drainage areas. Of low average elevation and rising to more than 1,100 feet, it consists of a series of glacial end moraines and isolated groups of hills. The intervening depressions are the sites of river valleys (Western Dvina, Neman, upper Berezina, and their affluents) or are filled with sand and other quaternary deposits left by the retreating continental glaciers. Here and there appear remains of the primeval forest, of which the Belovezha Pushcha, on the Polish border, is the most important example. The entire region is a characteristic moraine land form, with lakes bounded by high rounded banks, remains of moraines blocking the original course of rivers, and by an abundance of pebbles and boulders throughout the fields. In the south, the relief gradually changes into a marshy depression along the Pripet River and its affluents. This is the Belorussian Poles'ye, also known as the Pripet Marshes, a swampy, poorly drained depression in which slowly meandering streams and creeks, with banks rising barely above the water level, form an intricate network of waterways having a multitude of branches and canals. Watersheds are poorly defined, and during the spring floods large areas become inundated. Drainage work has been an age-old preoccupation of the local population and was first undertaken toward the end of the last century. A considerable portion of the eastern Pripet Marshes has already been drained and converted into fertile pastures and cultivated land. The principal rivers of the area are the Pripet and its left affluents, the Yasel'da, the Sluch, and the Ptich' rivers, as well as the lower Berezina. In the east the marshes merge with the northern section of the Dnieper lowland of the Ukraine.

The climate is relatively moderate and humid and represents a transition between the maritime climate of north central Europe and the continental climate of the central European USSR. It has moderately cool summers, with a July mean temperature of 65° F, a regular year-round distribution of precipitation (20–24 inches annually), and a three-month winter season, with a January average of 20° F. Thaws frequently occur in January and February.

The marshes, which cover about 10 percent of the total area, constitute the principal type of unusable land. However, when drained, their soils become extremely fertile, due to the vast amounts of decomposed vegetable matter and the high phosphorus content. Elsewhere, the soils are of the glacial podsol type, poor in humus and mineral salts, and require the application of fertilizer for good yields. The best soil types, suitable for the growing of flax and orchard crops, lie in the eastern Orsha-Mogilev section and around Minsk. In the south, and lying outside the marshy area, poor sandy soils support chiefly potato crops. Nearly one third of the total area is forested. Belorussia is the meeting ground between the taiga type of forest (predominantly pine), which advanced from the northeast, and of broad-leaved deciduous trees (oak, maple, beech, and linden), which penetrated from the southwest. Conifers are generally found on the dry sandy eminences, while aspen and alder prosper in the damper locations. The Belorussian forests furnish excellent timber, suitable for woodworking and veneering industries, and are well served by timber-floating streams leading to the Baltic Sea (Western Dvina and Neman) and to the Ukraine (Dnieper).

The main mineral resources of Belorussia are peat, which constitutes

BELORUSSIAN SOVIET SOCIALIST REPUBLIC

the chief power source, quartz, the basis for the glass industry, pottery clays, building materials (limestone and cement rock), phosphorites, low-quality iron ore and lignite.

The chief population element, the Belorussians, also known as the White Russians, constitute about 80 percent of the population. They are closely related to the Russians and the Ukrainians, but form an ethnic group which has been less affected by the admixture of Finnish and Turco-Tatar strains. They live mainly in the rural areas, where they form over 90 percent of the population, while in the urban centers their share is often less than one half. Most important among the minorities are the Russians, who are scattered throughout the cities and are strongest in the area of Gomel', the Ukrainians along the southern border, and the Jews, who were largely exterminated during the Second World War. Most of the Poles were repatriated in the course of the population exchange following the establishment of the USSR-Polish frontier in 1945. Some Lithuanian elements are found along the border of the Lithuanian SSR.

The average population density is over 110 per square mile. The Pripet Marshes are most thinly settled; the greatest density is found in the areas of Vitebsk, Mogilev, Gomel', and in a few fertile districts southeast of Novogrudok. The urban population is largest (about 25 percent) in the old Soviet part, and scarcely reaches 20 percent in the former Polish territories. There are few large cities, and they are located at relatively long distances from each other. Most of the rural element live in small villages, usually located on land elevated above the low, marshy expanses.

The Belorussian SSR was originally organized in 1919, and the present oblast division was introduced in 1938 by the creation of five oblasts. Previously the republic had been divided into okrugs, and later directly into rayons. In 1939, following the partition of Poland, Western Belorussia was combined with former Soviet (Eastern) Belorussia, and the oblasts of Baranovichi, Belostok, Brest, Vileyka, and Pinsk were established in the newly annexed territories. The city of Vil'nyus (Vilna), which had briefly come under Belorussian control, was transferred to the then-independent republic of Lithuania. After Lithuania joined the USSR, in 1940, further slight modifications were made in the Belorussian-Lithuanian boundary in order to bring areas with a predominantly Lithuanian population within the Baltic republic. New territorial changes occurred in 1945, after the Second World War, when the

Soviet-Polish frontier was altered in favor of Poland on the basis of the
Curzon line and the city and district of Belostok (Białystok) were returned to Poland. This was followed by a partial territorial reorganization and the creation of new oblasts.

Belorussia is predominantly an agricultural region suffering from
poor yields and economic backwardness. The cool, damp climate and the
sandy and clayey soils favor the cultivation mainly of winter rye, potatoes, and oats. Summer barley, and forage grasses, mainly clover, are
also grown. Wheat is of secondary importance. Flax, although widely
grown in the northern section, is generally of less importance than in the
western European oblasts of the Russian SFSR. To be noted also is the
cultivation of buckwheat, a local food staple. The best conditions for
rye and potatoes are found in the east central section, from Minsk
throughout Vitebsk, Orsha, and Mogilev. Oats are best represented in the
area of Vitebsk, where they cover over 13 percent of the arable area. The
fertile drained sections of the Pripet Marshes furnish good yields of forage grasses, grains, hemp, flax, and even the rubber-bearing *kok-sagyz*.
While Belorussia has to import bread grains, its surplus potato crop
finds a wide range of applications as hog feed and raw material for the
starch-processing, distilling, and derived industries. Hog raising is most
widely developed on the basis of the potato crop and the by-products of
the distilling and vegetable-oil industries. Dairy farming, with its related
fodder and flax crops, is in second place. In the southern marshes, hemp
replaces flax to some extent, stock is bred largely for meat production,
and fishing is carried on in the rivers and the ponds. Orchard and garden
crops, as well as poultry raising, have local importance near the urban
centers.

The industries are based primarily on the agricultural production,
the lumber resources, and the mineral deposits. Flax and linen industries
are important in the Vitebsk area, and tanning in Minsk and other cen·
ters. The republic has the largest hog-bristle production of the Union.
Among the food industries are distilling, starch-processing, meat-
packing, dairy, oil-extraction, cheese, and fruit-canning establishments.
The lumber is especially valuable for the plywood and veneering industries. Aspen furnishes excellent material for the match mills, which,
with the paper mills, are of national importance. During the post-war
Five-Year Plan the introduction of heavy and textile industries, based
on imported raw material, is being emphasized. Peat, which constitutes

the principal power source of the republic, fuels a number of electric power plants, of which the *Belgres* installation, northeast of Orsha, is most important, with a capacity of over 20,000 kilowatts.

Of interest in the transportation scheme of the republic, which relies chiefly on its good railway network, are the small canals connecting the principal rivers across the low watersheds. Among them are the Dnieper-Bug Canal, between the Mukhavets (affluent of the Western Bug) and the Pina (affluent of the Pripet), the Oginskiy Canal, between the Yasel'da and the Shchara, an affluent of the Neman, and the Berezina Canal, between the upper Berezina and the Ulla, an affluent of the Western Dvina. These canals, which date from before the Bolshevik Revolution, are small and narrow and have been largely neglected. Reconstruction of the Dnieper-Bug Canal was begun in 1940, but was interrupted by the war.

Oblast Survey

Minsk Oblast
Area, 8,000, population, 840,000

Minsk Oblast is the central division of the Belorussian SSR. It is situated in the Lithuanian-Belorussian upland and drained by the Berezina, the upper Ptich', and the Svisloch' rivers. It has flax and dairy farming in the northeast, potato and hog raising in the east, and grains in the west. Lumbering, peat cutting, distilling, and woodworking are the chief rural industries.

Minsk, the capital of the Belorussian SSR, is the chief industrial and cultural center of the republic. It is situated on the Svisloch' River and the Moscow-Brest-Warsaw trunk railroad at the junction of lines to Vil'nyus and Gomel'. The seat of machine tool, instrument, radio, textile, and lumber mills, it is acquiring during the post-war Five-Year Plan such important industries as automobile, tractor, and bicycle works. It is the site of the Belorussian state university, an academy of sciences, and a swamp research institute. Its population was 231,000 in 1948.*

Borisov is a match and wood-distillation center at the intersection of the main rail line and the Berezina River. Napoleon's Grand Army crossed the river north of here in 1812.

* Estimate based on a local election.

Polotsk Oblast
Area, 6,900, population, 460,000

Polotsk Oblast, the northernmost of the republic, lies in the basin of the Western Dvina, in a swamp and lake district. Flax growing and dairy farming are the chief activities. The oblast was formed in 1944, astride the pre-1939 Soviet-Polish frontier.

Polotsk is a transportation and lumber center on the Western Dvina at the junction of five rail lines. It has sawmilling, flour, and meat-packing industries.

Vitebsk Oblast
Area, 7,600, population, 640,000

Vitebsk Oblast lies in the Smolensk-Moscow upland and is drained by the Western Dvina in the north and the Dnieper in the south. Flax and dairy farming are most important; truck produce and orchards are located near Vitebsk. Flax retting, textile milling, sawmilling, and glassworking are the chief industries.

Vitebsk is a major textile center, with linen, clothing, and knitting mills. Located at the junction of rail lines on the Western Dvina, it produces machine tools, optical goods, needles, agricultural machinery, tobacco, and linseed oil. Its lumber mills specialize in the manufacture of prefabricated houses and knotted-wood furniture.

Orsha, a rail center on the Dnieper River bend, south of Vitebsk, has a machine-tool plant and a linen mill. Sewing machines are produced in near-by Baran', to the southwest. North of Orsha, at Orekhovsk (until 1946, Orekhi-Vydritsa) is the largest power station of the republic, "*Belgres*," which is fueled by the peatworks of near-by Osintorf.

Mogilev Oblast
Area, 8,000, population, 840,000

Mogilev Oblast in the eastern part of the republic, lies in the Dnieper lowland and is drained by the Dnieper and the Sozh rivers. It has flax and dairy farming in the north and potato and hog raising in the south. The chief rural industries are flax retting, distilling, lumber and paper milling, and glassworking. Truck produce is grown in the vicinity of Mogilev.

Mogilev, on the Dnieper, is a transportation and industrial center, with machinery works (steam-driven tractors), an artificial fiber mill, tanning and clothing industries. It also produces hog bristles, furniture, and canned goods.

Gomel' Oblast
Area, 6,100, population, 700,000

Gomel' Oblast lies in the Dnieper lowland at the confluence of the Dnieper and the Sozh rivers. Potato and hog raising are the leading activities; flax and grains are also grown. The main industries are paper milling (Dobrush), glassworking (Kostyukovka, north of Gomel'), lumber milling, and peat working.

Gomel', a rail center on the Sozh River, produces machine tools, agricultural implements (especially for flax and potato crops), electrical equipment, clothing, and foods. It includes the left-bank suburb of Novo-Belitsa, with match works.

Rechitsa is a lumber center on the Dnieper and produces matches and prefabricated houses.

Bobruysk Oblast
Area, 7,600, population, 640,000

Bobruysk Oblast lies in the northern section of the Pripet Marshes and is drained by the Berezina, the Ptich', and the Sluch' rivers. It has potato and hog farming in the east and grains (rye, oats, and barley) in the west. Lumbering forms the basis for sawmilling, distillation, and woodworking plants.

Bobruysk, on the Berezina River, is a lumber center, with food and clothing industries. It has extensive peatworks to the northwest.

Slutsk is a food-processing point, with flour mills and a meat-packing plant.

Poles'ye Oblast
Area, 8,400, population, 420,000

Poles'ye Oblast lies entirely in the Pripet Marshes. It is largely wooded, swampy region with some agriculture (potatoes, hemp, and *kok-sagyz*) in the elevated or drained sections. Lumbering and peat working are the chief industries.

Mozyr', on the Pripet River, is the capital of Poles'ye Oblast and a transportation and lumber center. It has veneering and furniture works and prefabricated house construction.

Pinsk Oblast
Area, 6,300, population, 400,000

Pinsk Oblast is in the central, most sparsely settled, portion of the Pripet Marshes—a backward area, in which livestock raising and fishing are carried on.

Pinsk (Polish *Pińsk*), on the Pina River, an affluent of the Pripet, is a lumber and fish-trading center, with tanning, sawmilling, paper, and match industries. It is a naval flotilla base.

Brest Oblast
Area, 5,200, population, 520,000

Brest Oblast lies in the Pripet–Western Bug watershed and has marshy soils in the south and sands in the north. Lumbering (south) and grain farming (north) are engaged in.

Brest (Polish *Brześć nad Bugiem*), formerly called Brest-Litovsk, is the Soviet border station on the Moscow-Warsaw trunk railroad. It has metalworking, sawmilling, leather, and food industries.

Grodno Oblast
Area, 5,000, population, 600,000

Grodno Oblast includes the moraine hills of the Lithuanian-Belorussian upland in the south and the sandy Lida lowland in the north. It is drained by the Neman River. Grain and potatoes are the chief crops; hogs and cattle are raised. Sawmilling, dairying, tanning, and quarrying are the main industries.

Grodno, a border city on the Neman River, produces fine cloth, tobacco, metal goods, and food products. It has lumber and agricultural trade. Sugar is milled at Skidel' to the southeast.

Lida, a rail junction south of Vil'nyus, is an agricultural processing center and produces agricultural implements, rubber goods, and building materials (tiles, cement).

Baranovichi Oblast
Area, 5,300, population, 580,000

Baranovichi Oblast lies in the morainic hills which form the watershed between the Neman and the Pripet rivers. It produces grains (rye and oats) and potatoes and has an important building-materials industry (cement, bricks, glass, and tile).

Baranovichi (Polish *Baranowicze*) is a major rail center on the Moscow-Warsaw line. It has railroad shops, weaving, and tanning industries, and produces cement, glass, and food products.

Molodechno Oblast
Area, 5,700, population, 580,000

Molodechno Oblast (called Vileyka Oblast until 1944) lies in a lake and moraine region drained by the Viliya River. It has flax and dairy farming in the north and grows mainly grain in the south. Quarrying is an important industry.

Molodechno (Polish *Molodeczno*) is a rail junction on the Minsk-Vil'nyus line. It produces musical instruments, flour, and meat products.

Vileyka (Polish *Wilejka*) is a lumber and flour-milling center just north of Molodechno.

CHAPTER 26

Baltic Region

THE BALTIC REGION, which includes the union republics of Estonia, Latvia, and Lithuania, and Kaliningrad Oblast of the Russian SFSR, lies on the shores of the Baltic Sea in the northwestern part of the East European plain. It includes, in addition to the mainland, the Moonsund archipelago, off the entrance to the Gulf of Riga, in which the main islands are Sarema (Saaremaa), or Ösel, and Khiuma (Hiiumaa), or Dagö. Although the northern ports on the Gulf of Finland and the port of Riga, in the deep recess of the Gulf of Riga, freeze during the winter months, the ice cover is sufficiently thin so that navigation can be maintained with the help of icebreakers. Along the southern coast, at Liepaya (Liepāja) and Kaliningrad, the sea remains free from ice. Because of these favorable conditions, the ports of the Baltic Sea (from Tallin to Kaliningrad) are of exceptional importance as trade outlets for the products of the central European USSR.

The southern shore of the Gulf of Finland in the north is an abrupt escarpment of old limestone formations which extend eastward to Lake Ladoga and form many bays and natural harbors, including that of Tallin (Tallinn). On the Gulf of Riga and along the coast to the south, the character of the shore line changes radically. Pine-covered sand dunes extend along the low coast in several parallel ranges, and ports lie only at the mouth of rivers and in man-made locations. Shallow sand bars lie offshore.

The relief is a continuation of the northern section of the East European plain, with a typical glacial landscape. Morainic hills, composed of boulder clays and other debris left by the continental ice sheet, and occasional denuded plateaus of Paleozoic rocks alternate with glacial lake beds and other depressions filled with sand and gravel deposits. The uplands, which have been deeply dissected by surface waters, occasionally appear like the picturesque mountain terrain of a miniature Switzerland. With the exception of the narrow littoral belt, the entire region, including the offshore islands, has marked morainic features, such as an abundance of gravel and boulder fields, swampy, lake-filled depressions, and clayey and sand soil types. The main rivers are the short, but important Narva (Russian *Narova*) River, the outlet of Lake Peipus and a source of hydroelectric power, the Western Dvina River (Latvian *Daugava*), which also supplies water power, and the Neman River (Lithuanian *Nemunas*, Polish *Niemen*) which enters the Kurland Gulf, a shallow lagoon of the Baltic Sea.

The moderate continental climate is characterized by a low range between summer and winter temperatures, unlike the greater extremes which are common along the same latitude in the inland areas of the European USSR. The humid westerly winds produce a mild, damp climate, with moderate winters, cool summers, a precipitation of 20–25 inches yearly, and a high proportion of cloudy days. The poor glacial soils and the humid climate are favorable to the growth of mixed forests, where coniferous stands alternate with oak, birch, and aspen clusters, and the development of hay meadows. Except for oil shale in Estonia, peat, and construction materials (clay, sand, and limestone), the region is poor in mineral resources.

The total population of the Baltic Region is about 6 millions, of which 2.7 millions live in Lithuania, 1.8 millions in Latvia, 1 million in Estonia, and 600,000 in Kaliningrad Oblast of the Russian SFSR. In addition to the titular nationalities of the three republics, the population includes the Latgals of eastern Latvia, who are related to Latvians, as well as Russians, Belorussians, Jews, Poles, and Swedes. With the exception of Lithuania, where large villages are common, the rural population lives in small hamlets of three to seven households. About one third of the population is urban and resides in small towns.

The three Baltic republics, each of which represents an ethnographic unit, marked by a uniformity of language, history, and culture, were part of the Russian Empire prior to the First World War and became firmly linked with the Russian economy through trade and transportation routes. Following the Bolshevik Revolution, they separated from Russia and constituted themselves as separate independent states. In 1940, following Soviet military penetration, Estonia, Latvia, and Lithuania were annexed to the USSR as union republics. Because of the relatively higher level of material prosperity, special consideration was given to the republics with respect to administrative organization. Instead of introducing the current administrative structure of rayon and

BALTIC REGION

(Estonian, Latvian, Lithuanian SSRs)

village Soviet, the USSR government at first retained the existing divisions (*uyezd* and *volost*) and only gradually introduced the village Soviets. This process was completed in 1950, when the regular Soviet administrative system (rayon-village Soviet) was introduced into Estonia, Latvia, and Lithuania. Lithuania, the most populous of the three republics, was also divided into oblasts. In the northern part of East Prussia, however, which was assigned to the USSR by the Potsdam Conference of 1945 and was organized as the Kaliningrad Oblast of the Russian SFSR, no attempt was made to establish any kind of German or other autonomous unit. The German population, greatly reduced by evacuation before the Russian occupation, became a small minority among the Russians that immigrated from the central part of the European USSR. The Soviet administrative system, with all its attributes, was established in the new oblast as a matter of course.

The climatic conditions of the Baltic Region are generally favorable for agricultural development. Rye, oats, and barley are the most common grain crops, and potatoes are widely grown. Flax is cultivated largely for the production of linseed oil. Extensive hay meadows, fodder grasses, and forage grains support intensive dairy farming, especially toward the north. Hogs are raised on root vegetables. The chief agricultural export items are butter, eggs, and meat products (mainly bacon).

Except for the processing of oil shale in Estonia, the industries are centered in the ports and produce textiles, machines, and chemicals. Lumber is an important raw material for paper and plywood industries. The region has a dense rail network, in which the main trunk lines lead from the central European USSR to the large Baltic port cities. The chief centers are Tallin (Tallinn) Riga, Vil'nyus (Vilnius) Kaunas, and Kaliningrad.

Lithuanian Soviet Socialist Republic
Capital, Vil'nyus (Vilnius); area, 31,200, population, 2,700,000

The Lithuanian SSR is the southernmost of the three Baltic republics. It has the shortest coast line, only 25 miles long in the area of Klaypeda (Klaipėda). Its generally level terrain rises gently in the morainic hills of the western and the eastern sections. Lakes and swamps abound in the depressions. The forests which once covered the entire region have been largely cleared and now comprise only 20 percent of the area. The republic is drained by the Neman (Nemunas) and its affluents, the Viliya (Neris), the Nevyazh (Nevežys), and the Dubisa (Dubysa) rivers on the right, and the Sheshupa (Šešupė) on the left. The Neman is navigable below Kaunas, and for shallow-draught vessels below Alitus (Alytus).

The Lithuanians represent about four fifths of the total population and, except for small Latvian and Belorussian minorities, make up the bulk of the rural population. The principal non-Lithuanian groups, Russians, Jews, and Poles, belong chiefly to the urban elements. The rural settlements are villages of a much larger type than the small farming communities generally found in Latvia and Estonia.

The long-contested Vil'nyus district was awarded to Lithuania following the partition of Poland in 1939. In 1940, when Lithuania joined the USSR as a union republic, it also annexed from the Belorussian SSR a narrow strip of territory with a predominantly Lithuanian population. Its present territorial configuration was completed in January, 1945, when it reacquired the Memelland, which had been ceded to Germany in 1939.

In 1950 Lithuania was divided into the oblasts of Vil'nyus, Kaunas, Klaypeda, and Shaulyay.

Agriculture is the principal branch of the economy. Grains cover the major part of the sown area, mostly rye and oats. Potatoes are an important crop in connection with the raising of hogs; flax and forage grasses (mainly clover) are sown in rotation. A few areas are under sugar beets. In addition to hogs, dairy cattle and poultry are extensively raised.

Dairy farming forms the basis for the chief industries of the republic. Butter and dairy plants, meat-packing plants, and tanneries are scattered throughout the entire region. Sugar is milled in a number of places, including Mariyampole (Marijampolė) and Panevezhis (Panevėžys).

Lumbering furnishes raw material for woodworking plants and paper mills. The glass and cement industry is being developed under the postwar Five-Year Plan; peat-based power plants are under construction at Kaunas and Shaulyay. Fisheries are important along the coast, near Klaypeda. Textiles are manufactured from imported silk, wool, and cotton. The only local fuel resource is peat, which is processed widely into briquettes. Building materials are quarried. To be noted also are the health resorts of Birshtonas (Birštonas) and Druskininkay (Druskininkai) on the Neman River, south of Kaunas, and the sand-dune resorts on the coast in the vicinity of Klaypeda. Meat, bacon, butter, flax, and lumber products are the principal export items.

Vil'nyus (Vilnius—Polish *Wilno*, Russian *Vil'na*) lies amid forests and hills on the Viliya River, at the mouth of the Vileyka. Founded in the tenth century, it became the capital of Lithuania in the fourteenth century and the seat of a university in the sixteenth century. Following 125 years of Russian domination, it became one of the most contested cities of Europe in the period between the two World Wars. It was fought over by the Soviets, the Lithuanians, and the Poles in the years following the First World War and was part of Poland from 1922 until 1939. It is a major rail center on the Leningrad-Warsaw and Moscow-Minsk-Kaliningrad lines, with a population of 244,500.* It has metalworking industries, which produce agricultural implements, electric motors, and radio equipment, lumber, paper, and clothing mills, shoemaking and fertilizer plants, and large food industries. In 1947 the city limits were considerably expanded to incorporate the town of Nauya Vil'nya (Nauja Vilnia), six miles to the east and the seat of a prefabricated-house industry and the first machine-tool plant of Lithuania.

Kaunas (Russian *Kovno*), the former capital, is the chief industrial center of the republic, on the Neman River, at the mouth of the Viliya. It has rail shops, metalworks, an automobile repair plant, textile and knitting mills, and an important chemical industry, producing rubber goods, paints, and pharmaceutical products. Its lumber and match mills and tobacco, meat-packing and flour industries are also notable.

Klaypeda (Klaipėda—German *Memel*) is a major ice-free port north of the mouth of the Neman River. It has large pulp and paper industries, a veneering mill, textile plants, and produces superphosphate fertilizer. To the north, at Palanga, there are amber-processing works. To the south, on the Kurland Spit, a sand spit barring the lagoon known as Kurland Gulf, are the seaside resorts and fishing villages of Yuodkrante (Juodkrante), Preyla (Preila), and Nida.

Panevezhis (Panevėžys) is the most important sugar and flour-milling center of Lithuania; it has also metalworking, chemical, textile, and lumber industries.

Shaulyay (Šiauliai) has a large meat-packing and dairy industry, with associated tanning and shoe plants. Paper, bicycles, and alabaster are manufactured.

* An estimate based on the local election of 1948.

Latvian Soviet Socialist Republic
Capital, Riga ; area, 24,600, population, 1,800,000

The Latvian SSR lies in the middle Baltic Region, on the Gulf of Riga, which here penetrates deeply into the mainland. This largest of the Baltic republics contains the fertile Riga-Yelgava lowland in its center and morainic hills in Kurland, in the west, and Livonia, in the northeast. The latter region, because of its picturesque hilly landscape, is often called the "Livonian Switzerland." The coasts are low and covered with pine-covered sand dunes. The Western Dvina River (Latvian *Daugava*) enters the republic from Belorussia in the southeast and empties into the Gulf of Riga. It is important for timber flotage and as a source of hydroelectric power ; navigation is hampered by sand bars and rapids. Its chief tributary is the Lielupe River on the left. The western part of Latvia, generally known as Kurland, is drained by the Venta River, and the northern (Livonia) by the Gauya (Gauja) River. The forests, which cover 20 percent of the area, are found mainly in Kurland and in Livonia, where the maritime climate has its greatest influence.

The Latvians represent about 60 percent of the total population. The Latgals, who are predominantly Catholic and speak a dialect related to Lettish, constitute about 15 percent of the population and live mainly in Latgale, the southeastern section of the republic. Russians are the most important non-Latvian minority, followed by Jews, Belorussians, and Lithuanians along the eastern and southern frontiers. The predominantly Russian districts of Abrene or Jaunlatgale (now Pytalovo) and Kačanava (now Kachanovo), southwest of Pskov, were ceded to the newly formed Pskov Oblast of the Russian SFSR in 1945. With this cession, Latvia underwent its first teritorial change since the creation of the independent state in 1920.

Prior to the First World War the economy of Latvia was closely integrated with that of the Russian Empire. About one quarter of all Russian exports passed through the Latvian ports of Riga, Liepaya (Liepāja), and Ventspils. The ports, and mainly Riga, became the centers of important industries engaged in shipbuilding, machine construction, textile milling, and the manufacture of chemicals. During its independence Latvia developed its food and light industries to a large extent. At the present time Latvia's economy emphasizes its food industries, which are largely based on the raising of livestock. The dairy industry, which has plants scattered throughout all the small towns of the republic, mainly in the north and the west, leads the field. Meat packing, flour milling, and sugar refining are other activities. Next in importance are the engineering and the textile industries, which are concentrated at Riga and Liepaya. Also produced are matches, paper, rubber goods, chemicals, and tobacco. Fisheries are important along the coast, sardines, herring, and cod constituting the largest catch. Of all the Baltic republics, Latvia has the greatest tourist trade which descends yearly on the famous Riga beaches west of the city and the health resort (sulphur springs) of Kemeri near by.

Livestock raising is the chief agricultural occupation, with emphasis on dairy farming and milk, butter, and cheese production. Hogs are raised for bacon and other meat products, which together with eggs form the chief export items. The development of stock raising, as elsewhere in the Baltic Region, is favored by the humid climate and the abundance of meadowland. Crops are strongly slanted toward the production of fodder grasses and potatoes for stock feed. Grains cover about one half the sown acreage and are also partly used for forage. Rye, oats, and barley are emphasized. The main industrial crops are flax and sugar beets; garden crops are grown in a few suburban areas.

Power for the industry is furnished chiefly by the Kegums hydroelectric station on the Western Dvina, southeast of Ogre. This plant, which has a capacity of 55,000 kilowatts, is the only major water-power producer in the Baltic Region. The local peat supply, which is used in form of briquettes, is also of some importance in the industrial fuel scheme, although to a lesser extent than in Lithuania.

Riga, located on the Western Dvina, its center about 10 miles from the Gulf of Riga, of the Baltic Sea, is the largest city in the Baltic Region. An old city, dating from the early thirteenth century, it contains two thirds of all the Latvian industries. It is a large port, the terminus of a number of rail lines and of the timber flotage on the river. Its chief industries are its engineering enterprises, which produce rolling stock for electric trains, subways, and tramways, electrical equipment for automobiles, and telephone and radio apparatus. In its northeastern outskirts, on lake Kishozero, are superphospate and paper mills. Other products are textiles, glass, cement, rubber goods, and bicycles. Its port installations and shipyards extend along both sides of the river to the outer port of Daugavgriva, where most of the lumber is loaded. West of the city, between the Lielupe and the sea, on a narrow sand

spit, lies Rigas Yurmala (Rigas Jurmala), which the Russians call
Vzmor'ye. This noted vacation area, which consists of nine adjacent
seaside resorts extending for more than 10 miles along the beach, was
incorporated into the city in 1946. The population of Riga, which
amounted to about 400,000 on the eve of the Second World War, was
390,000 in 1947.*

South of Riga, on the railroad to Kaunas, is Yelgava (Jelgava—
German *Mitau*, Russian *Mitava*), the largest textile center of the
republic, engaged mainly in linen milling; it is also the seat of an important sugar industry.

The port of Liepaya (Liepāja—German *Libau*, Russian *Libava*), the
second largest of the republic, is ice-free nearly all year round. It has
important shipbuilding, docking, and naval-base installations. Site of
the only metallurgical (steel milling) plant of the Baltic Region, it has
railroad repair shops, machine construction works, and chemical, lumber, and fish-canning industries.

To the north is the third port of Latvia, Ventspils (German *Windau*,
Russian *Vindava*), which also engages in metalworking, lumber, and
light industries.

Daugavpils (German *Dünaburg*, Russian *Dvinsk*), the center of
Latgale, lies in the most densely settled portion of the republic, at the
intersection of important rail and highway routes. It has important
railroad shops, as well as metalworking, furniture, textile, and food
industries.

Estonian Soviet Socialist Republic

Capital, Tallin (Tallinn); area, 17,400, population, 1,000,000

The Estonian SSR is the northernmost Baltic republic, situated between
the gulfs of Finland in the north and Riga in the southwest. Its area
and population are smaller than those of either Latvia or Lithuania.
The republic includes the seventy islands of the Moonsund archipelago,
off the west coast, including Sarema (Saaremaa), Khiuma (Hiiumaa),
Mukhu (Muhu), and Vormsi.

In the northern part is a lowland, having large sandy and swampy
expanses. It breaks off abruptly on the coast of the Gulf of Finland,
forming cliff-like limestone escarpments. The coast here is deeply dissected and contains a large number of good natural harbors. Toward
the south the relief becomes hilly and rises in glacial moraines to over

* An estimate based on the Republic election.

1,500 feet. In the center lies the lake Vyrts-Yarv (Võrts Järv), which empties through the Emayogi (Emajõgi) into Lake Peipus on the eastern border of the republic. Lake Peipus is connected by the Narva River with the Gulf of Finland. The only other notable river is the Pyarnu (Pärnu), which flows southwest to the Gulf of Riga. The Estonian rivers are generally not navigable, but the numerous rapids provide a relatively large hydroelectric potential.

The Estonians represent more than 90 percent of the total population. The principal minorities are the Russians, mostly in the cities, and the Swedes, on the islands off the west coast and in the urban centers. As in Latvia, rural districts with a predominantly Russian population were separated from Latvia and annexed to the Russian SFSR. The territorial transfer which took place in 1945 involved the Petseri (now Pechory) district, which was incorporated by Pskov Oblast, and the narrow frontier strip on the right bank of the Narva River, which became part of Leningrad Oblast.

Estonia is considerably better supplied with mineral resources than are the other two Baltic republics. Most important are the oil-shale deposits between Lake Peipus and the Gulf of Finland, which form the basis of an industry characteristic of the local economy. The oil shale extends about sixty miles between Rakvere and Narva in reserves estimated at 1.5 to 2.5 billion tons. The yield is 20–30 percent. The product can be used as fuel in solid form, but produces a large proportion of ashes, reducing its caloric value. A method has been developed by which the ash residue can be converted into cement, thus rendering the use of the shale more economical. Distillation of the shale yields heavy oils and various other products used in the chemical industry. In recent years fuel gas has also been derived from the process. The center of the oil-shale district is Kokhtla-Yarve (Kohtla-Järve).

The textile industry assumes large proportions in the Estonian economy. There are large cotton mills at Narva and Tallin, and smaller weaving and flax-spinning enterprises in other towns. Forests, which cover 20 percent of the area, furnish lumber for match, paper, and furniture industries. Tyuri (Türi) is the chief paper-milling center. Blue clays along the Gulf of Finland coast supply a large cement mill at Kunda. The greater part of the metalworking industries is concentrated in Tallin, Tartu, and Pyarnu.

Dairy farming is the basic feature of the agricultural economy. Even more than in Latvia do meadows and pastures predominate over cultivated land. Most of the milk goes into butter production. Hog raising and poultry farming are other occupations. In addition to forage grasses and potatoes, grains are sown for animal feed (oats and barley) and for food (rye and wheat). Fishing is important along the seashore and in the large lakes.

Tallin (Tallinn—German *Reval*, Russian *Revel'*) lies on the coast of the Gulf of Finland, opposite Helsinki. It consists of the old city on the limestone plateau (at an elevation of 250 feet) and a new section on a coastal terrace adjoining the sea. An important, well-constructed port, it is also the seat of the major Estonian industries. Its principal activities are shipbuilding, machine construction (electrical equipment), cotton milling, paper milling, veneering, furniture making, and flour milling. The southwestern residential suburb of Nymme (Nõmme) lies within the city limits. The population in 1947 was 190,000.*

Tartu (German *Dorpat*, Russian *Yur'yev* or *Derpt*) is an old university city between lake Vyrts-Yarv and Lake Peipus. Its population was 50,000 in 1947.* Its agricultural machinery works, linen mills, and sawmills are important.

Pyarnu (Pärnu—German *Pernau*) is a port and commercial center at the northeast shore of the Gulf of Riga. Its lumber industry, with sawmills, match factories, and paper mills are notable.

Paldiski (Baltic Port) is a port west of Tallin, which is being developed as a naval base guarding the entrance to the Gulf of Finland.

Rakvere (German *Wesenberg*) is a linen and tanning center halfway between Tallin and Narva.

Kokhtla-Yarve (Kohtla-Järve), a new industrial city, lies at the center of the Estonian oil-shale district. It developed mainly after the Second World War, when a large oil-shale distillery was built here. A new pipe line, laid during the current Five-Year Plan, will carry fuel gas from the distillery to Leningrad for industrial and domestic consumption. It is estimated that in 1950 the population will be 25,000 to 30,000. The major oil-shale mines of the district are at Kiviyli (Kiviõli), Kukruse, at the end of a rail spur passing through Kokhtla-Yarve, Kyava (Käva), just southeast of the city, Kokhtla (Kohtla), a rail junction to the south, Yykhvi (Jõhvi) and Akhtme (Ahtme), southeast of Yykhvi, and the newly developed town of Vivikond (Viivikond), southwest of Vayvara (Vaivara).

Narva, on the Narva River, between Lake Peipus and the Gulf of

* Estimate based on the Republic election.

Finland, is an old fortress city, with the forts of Ivangorod and Hermannstadt on opposite banks of the river. It is noted as a textile center, the home of the Krengol'm (Kreenholm) cotton and linen mill, powered by a hydroelectric plant on the Narva River. The suburb of Ivangorod, on the right bank of the Narva, was placed into Leningrad Oblast of the Russian SFSR as the result of a boundary change in 1945.

Kaliningrad Oblast (Russian SFSR)
Capital, Kaliningrad; area, *c.* 6,100, population, 600,000

Kaliningrad Oblast was organized in the northern part of East Prussia, north of a line passing north of Goldap and Braniewo (German *Braunsberg*), which was assigned by the Berlin Conference in 1945 to the USSR. The oblast lies on the Baltic Sea and is bordered in the east by the Lithuanian SSR along the Neman River and in the south by Poland. The territory is level lowland rising slightly toward the south and characterized by a humid climate, with mild winters and cool summers. It is drained by the Neman in the northeast and by the Pregel' in the southeast. Along the coast it includes portions of the two lagoon-like inlets characteristic of this section of the Baltic Sea—Kurland Lagoon in the north and Vistula Lagoon in the south. Each lagoon is separated from the sea by a long, narrow sand bar (*Nehrung*), which leaves only a narrow passage at the northern end. Amber, peat, and lignite are the chief mineral resources.

As in the case of other territories formerly held by an enemy nation (Japanese part of Sakhalin and the Kurile Islands), no provision was made to establish the northern part of East Prussia as an autonomous area. Instead, the German population which was left at the time of the Russian occupation, estimated at 100,000, was deprived of minority rights similar to those provided for other nationalities in the USSR. Only in the field of education did the Russian administration officially acknowledge the existence of a German minority by establishing a limited number of German schools. After a brief existence as a special okrug, the area was organized as Königsberg Oblast in April, 1946, and renamed Kaliningrad Oblast in July, 1946. Since a Russian majority is mandatory in the population of the oblasts of the Russian SFSR, Russian immigration into the oblast was organized from the central European USSR, where a relatively high population density prevails in oblasts such as Smolensk, Bryansk, Pskov, Novgorod, Kostroma,

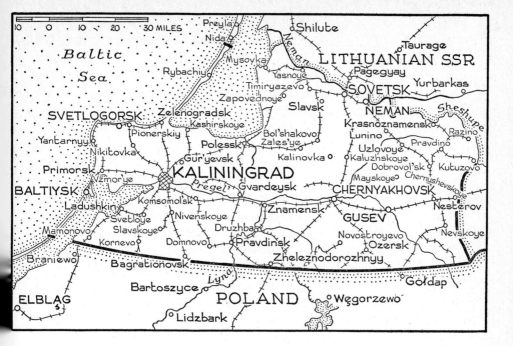

KALININGRAD OBLAST

GLOSSARY

Soviet Name	German Name (Name used 1938–45 in parentheses)	Soviet Name	German Name (Name used 1938–45 in parentheses)
Bagrationovsk	Preussisch Eylau	Nesterov	Stallupöhnen (Ebenrode)
Baltiysk	Pillau		
Bol'shakovo	Gross Skaisgirren (Kreuzingen)	Nevskoye	Pillupöhnen (Schlossbach)
Chernyakhovsk	Insterburg	Nikitovka	Marienhof
Chernyshevskoye	Eydtkuhnen (Eydtkau)	Nivenskoye	Wittenberg
		Novostroyevo	Trempen
Dobrovol'sk	Pillkallen	Pionerskiy	Neukuhren
		Polessk	Labiau
Domnovo	Domnau	Pravdino	Grumbkowkeiten (Grumbkowfelde)
Druzhba	Allenburg		
Gur'yevsk	Neuhausen	Pravdinsk	Friedland
Gusev	Gumbinnen	Primorsk	Fischhausen
Gvardeysk	Tapiau	Razino	Doristhal
Kaliningrad	Königsberg	Rybachiy	Rossitten
Kalinovka	Aulowönen (Aulenbach)	Slavsk	Heinrichswalde
		Slavskoye	Kreuzburg
Kaluzhskoye	Grünheide	Sovetsk	Tilsit
Kashirskoye	Schaaksvitte	Svetlogorsk	Rauschen
Komsomol'sk	Löwenhagen	Svetloye	Kobbelbude
Kornevo	Zinten	Timiryazevo	Neukirch
Krasnoznamensk	Lasdehnen (Haselberg)	Uzlovoye	Rautenberg
		Vzmor'ye	Grossheidekrug
Kutuzovo	Schirwindt	Yantarnyy	Palmnicken
Ladushkin	Ludwigsort	Yasnoye	Kaukehmen (Kuckerneese)
Lunino	Langwethen (Hohensalzburg)	Zales'ye	Mehlauken (Liebenfelde)
Mamonovo	Heiligenbeil		
Mayskoye	Mallwischken (Mallwen)	Zapovednoye	Seckenburg
		Zelenogradsk	Cranz (Kranz)
Mysovka	Karkeln		
Neman	Ragnit	Zheleznodorozhnyy	Gerdauen
		Znamensk	Wehlau

Vladimir, Ul'yanovsk, and Penza. Settlers also came from the Belorussian SSR.

The region is mainly agricultural, with grain crops (rye, oats, barley, and wheat) in the lowlands, tobacco near the Neman River, sugar beets, potatoes, root vegetables, and leguminous crops. Forage grasses (mainly clover) support large dairy-cattle herds. Hogs and horses are extensively raised. Flour milling, distilling, and flax retting are the chief rural industries. Lumber milling plays an important role in the economy; there are paper and pulp mills at Kaliningrad, Sovetsk, Neman, and Znamensk (formerly Wehlau). Fisheries abound along the coast, with the chief ports and processing plants at Primorsk (formerly Fischhausen), Zelenogradsk (formerly Cranz), and Rybachiy (formerly Rossitten), on the Kurland Spit. One of the most characteristic products of the oblast is amber, which is secured mainly at Yantarnyy (formerly Palmnicken). There are machine construction plants at Bagrationovsk (formerly Preussisch-Eylau), Nesterov (formerly Stallupönen), Ozersk (formerly Darkehmen), and railroad-repair works at Zheleznodorozhnyy (formerly Gerdauen). Cement is milled at Polessk (formerly Labiau).

Kaliningrad (formerly Königsberg) was the former capital of East Prussia. Situated near the mouth of the Pregel' River, it is an important port and industrial center. It has shipyards and machinery works, and produces freight cars and drilling machinery. There are paper and pulp mills, locomotive repair works, and electric power installations. A deepwater channel connects Kaliningrad, through the Vistula Lagoon, with its outer port of Baltiysk (formerly Pillau), a naval base and fishing port.

Chernyakhovsk (formerly Insterburg) is a rail center and the head of navigation on the Pregel' River. It has chemical and metalworking industries and produces food products (sugar, meat, and flour) and beverages.

Gusev (formerly Gumbinnen), on the railroad east of Chernyakhovsk, has flour mills and manufactures agricultural implements.

Sovetsk (formerly Tilsit) is a lumber-milling center on the Neman River. It has paper and pulp mills, distilleries, and produces dairy products. Just east, on the Neman River, is the city of Neman (formerly Ragnit), with lumber and paper mills.

On the Baltic coast north of Kaliningrad are a number of important health and seaside resorts, including Svetlogorsk (formerly Rauschen) and Pionerskiy (formerly Neukuhren), to the east.

CHAPTER 27

Karelo-Finnish Soviet Socialist Republic

Capital, Petrozavodsk; area, 68,900, population, 600,000

THE KARELO-FINNISH SSR is the northwesternmost republic of the USSR, extending about 400 miles along the Finnish border from Lake Ladoga in the south to the White Sea in the north. It lies on the eastern edge of the Fenno-Scandian crystalline shield, which has predominant granite and gneiss formations. The region has a pronounced glacial relief of scoured slopes, descending gradually from the watershed area along the border to the White Sea and the large lakes, boulder-strewn fields, and numerous lakes (up to 35,000), which comprise 15 percent of the total area. The largest lakes are Ladoga, Onega, and Vygozero, which has been enlarged with the construction of the White Sea–Baltic Canal. The lakes lie at different elevations and are connected by short torrential streams, which represent a great hydroelectric potential. The climate is the result of a combination of Arctic and Atlantic influences, of cold air masses from the north and temperate humid winds from the west. Considerable precipitation (up to 22 inches annually) and the reduced evaporation are conducive to the formation of marsh areas. Much of the soil is of the podsolic type. Two thirds of the territory is forested (conifers), and only 3 percent arable. Moreover, only 15 percent of the arable land is under cultivation; the remainder is used in the form of meadows. The principal mineral resources are building stone (granite, diabase, and marble), quartz, mica, iron ore, and nonferrous metals.

The population of the republic is 23 percent Karelian and Finnish and 63 percent Russian. The former groups live chiefly in the west and the southwest, the Russians in the east and the southeast, along the shores of the White Sea and lakes Onega and Ladoga. The average population density is very low (9 per square mile). Only in the south, where conditions are more favorable to agriculture, does the concentration reach 25 per square mile. The rural population lives in small villages which average five to ten households and are generally located on the banks of rivers and lake shores. Classified as urban is nearly one third of the total population; Petrozavodsk alone accounts for one half of the urban elements.

The Karelo-Finnish SSR was organized in 1940, on the basis of the former Karelian Autonomous SSR (formed in 1923 out of the provisional Karelian Workers' Commune) and the areas which Finland was forced to cede to the USSR at the conclusion of the Russo-Finnish war of 1939–40. These areas, which comprised the district of Kuolayarvi (Finnish *Salla*), the northern shores of Lake Ladoga, including the city of Sortavala, and the Karelian Isthmus, including the cities of Vyborg (Finnish *Viipuri*) and Priozersk (Finnish *Käkisalmi*), were largely cleared of their Finnish population, which upon the territorial transfer chose to move to Finland. A considerable Russian immigration was organized from the central European USSR in order to compensate for the loss of population in the annexed areas. Although the Karelo-Finnish SSR acquired in 1940 the major portion of the annexed areas (the southern half of the Karelian Isthmus was already incorporated into Leningrad Oblast at that time), the republic lost control over the remaining (northern) section of the Karelian Isthmus after the conclusion of the Finnish armistice, in 1944. Reasons for this territorial transfer which brought the entire Karelian Isthmus within Leningrad Oblast of the Russian SFSR can be found in the strategic and the economic spheres. It was probably found expedient for the Russian SFSR to have a common frontier with Finland, rather than to have an intervening belt of Karelian territory. However, it was also found to be economically sound to incorporate the industries of the Karelian Isthmus within the Leningrad orbit. Particularly was this necessary in the case of the Svetogorsk and the Raukhiala power plants on the Vuoksi River which supplied the Leningrad industrial area with hydroelectric power.

The mainstay of the economy is the lumber industry and allied activities. Lumbering has been mechanized to a high degree within the republic. Sawmills are found in many areas, but particularly along the Murmansk Railroad at the intersection of waterways. Prefabricated houses, plywood, paper, rosin, turpentine, cellulose, and other derivatives are produced. The chief sawmilling centers are Solomennoye, a northern suburb of Petrozavodsk, the towns of Nadvoitsy (furniture

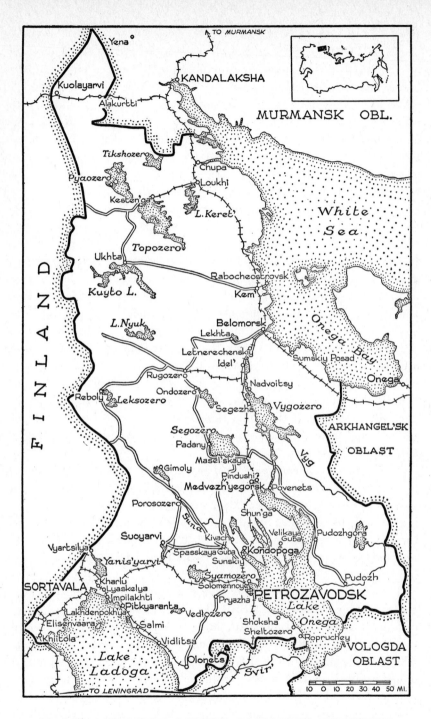

KARELO-FINNISH SOVIET SOCIALIST REPUBLIC

making), Idel', and Letnerechenskiy (prefabricated houses), along the Murmansk Railroad north of Segezha, and the lumber ports of Belomorsk and Kem' (with its outer port of Rabocheostrovsk). Plywood is milled at Lakhdenpokh'ya. Of special importance in the economy of the republic are the large paper-milling centers Segezha and Kondopoga, along the Murmansk line, and Pitkyaranta, Lyaskelya, Kharlu, and Suoyarvi, near and on the shores of Lake Ladoga. The paper centers are usually powered by hydroelectric stations; the Sunskiy plant on the Suna River, near Kondopoga, is most important. In lumber export, which is effected through the ports of Belomorsk, Kem', and Leningrad, the Karelo-Finnish SSR follows in second place after Arkhangel'sk Oblast.

The quarrying of building stone has become an important feature of the Karelian economy. Granite is secured at Shala, on the eastern shore of Lake Onega, quartzite, diabase, and sandstone at Shoksha, and Rop-Ruchey on the southwestern shore. Feldspar, mica, and pegmatite are quarried in the far north at Chupa and Loukhi. Marble is also obtained in the area of Sortavala. Among the metallic deposits are the iron ore of Gimoly, the lake iron-ore reserves found on the bottom of most large lakes of the republic, mainly Vygozero and Segozero, magnetite and titaniferous iron ore on the east shore of Lake Onega, at Pudozhgora, north of the mouth of the Vodla River. Copper is mined near Medvezh'-yegorsk and near Pitkyaranta, the seat of a nonferrous metallurgical industry.

Agriculture puts emphasis on dairy farming and on the raising of truck produce. In connection with the raising of dairy cattle, fodder grasses are extensively sown. Also, some grain (rye, barley, and oats) is grown in the republic; bread grains have to be largely imported from the Volga Region, along the Mariinsk Canal system. Fisheries are important in the lakes and in the White Sea, where Belomorsk is the processing center.

The transportation facilities of the republic are the major transit routes of the northwestern USSR. The Murmansk Railroad, which was originally constructed in 1916, later reconstructed and modernized, connects the Kola Peninsula in the north and Leningrad in the south. This line, officially called the Kirov Railroad, is the northernmost normal-gauge railway in the USSR. Its main branches extend westward to Kuolayarvi and on into Finland and, in the south, along the northern shore of Lake Ladoga, past Sortavala, to Vyborg. In 1940 the construction of the vital Belomorsk-Obozerskaya by-pass connected the Murmansk line with the Arkhangel'sk-Vologda-Moscow railroad to the east and made possible the continuing flow of Allied supplies through the port of Murmansk after the Germans had occupied the southern portion of the Murmansk Railroad itself. A West Karelian Railroad, 120 miles long, is scheduled for construction in the post-war period. Another transit route of great importance is the White Sea–Baltic Canal, constructed in 1933. This 140-mile route, equipped with nineteen locks, connects the White Sea port of Belomorsk with the town of Povenets, on Lake Onega, thus establishing an all-water route between the White Sea and the Baltic at Leningrad. The chief export items of the republic are lumber, wood products, paper, building stone, and mica.

Petrozavodsk, an important stop on the Murmansk Railroad, lies on the western shore of Lake Onega. It is the seat of the Onega metalworks, which produce steam engines, gas-generating equipment for lumber tractors and trailers, lumber machinery (electric saws, axes, and so forth). It has one of the main ski-manufacturing plants of the USSR, a cement mill, and mica-processing works, and produces prefabricated houses.

Sortavala, the largest city in the territory acquired from Finland in 1940, has metalworks, woolen mills, a furniture plant, and a leather and shoemaking industry. Marble is quarried in the vicinity. Vyartsilya, on the railroad north of Sortavala, has a metallurgical plant.

Kondopoga, north of Petrozavodsk, has paper and pulp mills (specializing in the output of newsprint) and a pegmatite-processing works, which produces glass, pottery, and porcelain. The industries are powered by the Sunskiy hydroelectric plant, as well as by a local installation.

Medvezh'yegorsk, at the northwestern tip of Lake Onega, is the administration center for the White Sea–Baltic Canal route. A major rail-water transfer point, it is connected by a rail spur with the town of Povenets at the southern end of the canal. It has lumber mills and furniture works. Just to the east, Pindushi builds river and lake barges. Copper mines and dolomite quarries are found near by.

Belomorsk (until 1933, Soroka) is a major port on the White Sea, at the northern end of the White Sea–Baltic Canal and at the junction of the Murmansk Railroad and the new line to Obozerskaya. It is the main lumber-exporting point of the republic, with lumber mills, fish canneries, and shipyards.

Appendix: Tables

TABLE 1

POPULATION OF THE UNION REPUBLICS OF THE USSR [a]

(BASED ON THE UNION AND REPUBLIC ELECTORAL DISTRICTS)

REPUBLIC	UNION ELECTION (1946)			REPUBLIC ELECTIONS (1947)		
	Population per District	Number of Districts	Population of Republic	Population per District	Number of Districts	Population of Republic
Russian SFSR	300,000	379	112,800,000	150,000	740	111,000,000
Ukrainian SSR	300,000	136	40,800,000	100,000	405	40,500,000
Belorussian SSR	300,000	31	9,300,000	20,000	361	7,220,000
Azerbaijan SSR	300,000	11	3,300,000	10,000	310	3,100,000
Georgian SSR	300,000	12	3,600,000	15,000	237	3,555,000
Armenian SSR	300,000	4	1,200,000	5,000	269	1,345,000
Kazakh SSR	300,000	20	6,000,000	20,000	300	6,000,000
Kirghiz SSR	300,000	5	1,500,000	5,000	298	1,490,000
Uzbek SSR	300,000	20	6,000,000	15,000	400	6,000,000
Tadzhik SSR	300,000	5	1,500,000	5,000	291	1,455,000
Turkmen SSR	300,000	4	1,200,000	5,000	234	1,170,000
Karelo-Finnish SSR	300,000	2	600,000	5,000	120	600,000
Moldavian SSR	300,000	9	2,700,000	10,000	266	2,660,000
Lithuanian SSR	300,000	10	3,000,000	15,000	180	2,700,000
Latvian SSR	300,000	7	2,100,000	15,000	120	1,800,000
Estonian SSR	300,000	4	1,200,000	10,000	100	1,000,000
USSR (total)	300,000	656	196,800,000	...	...	191,595,000

[a] The electoral districts for the 1946 Union election have apparently been based on prewar population data and thus do not present a true picture of the population of the USSR immediately after the Second World War. The electoral divisions for the 1947 Republic elections, however, appear to have been revised on the basis of postwar data, though only for a few republics. These revisions were downward to account for wartime population losses, as in the case of the Belorussian and the Baltic republics, or upward to account for postwar immigration, as in the case of the Armenian SSR. In other cases the 1947 electoral districts remain based on prewar data and the slight discrepancies with the 1946 population data are due merely to the more precise unit (as small as 5,000 per district) available for the Republic elections. The Ukrainian, Georgian, and Kirghiz SSR's, for instance, are areas where more precise, though prewar, population data could be imputed from the 1947 lists.

It appears that the 1947 population for the USSR as a whole would be closer to the true population immediately after the war than the 1946 data, in view of the fact that necessary downward revisions in war-devastated areas, such as the Ukraine, would be balanced by the required upward revisions in such remote areas as the Central Asian republics. The view is supported by the figure for the total population of the USSR imputed from the 1950 Union election (201,300,000). A population increase of about 10 millions through the period running from 1945–46 to 1950 would correspond to the previously observed annual increase of 1.23 percent.

TABLE 2

ADMINISTRATIVE-TERRITORIAL DIVISIONS OF THE USSR [a]

DIVISION	AREA (in square miles)	POPULATION Estimate 1947	Census 1939	CAPITAL	YEAR OF FORMA- TION OF DIVISION
Moscow (Moskva) Oblast	18,500	9,450,000	...	Moscow (Moskva)	1929
Yaroslavl' Oblast	14,250	1,500,000	...	Yaroslavl'	1936
Kostroma Oblast	22,400	1,050,000	...	Kostroma	1944
Ivanovo Oblast	9,500	1,500,000	...	Ivanovo	1929
Vladimir Oblast	10,350	1,350,000	...	Vladimir	1944
Ryazan' Oblast	18,200	2,100,000	...	Ryazan'	1937
Tula Oblast	9,300	1,500,000	...	Tula	1937
Central Industrial Region	102,500	18,450,000	...		
Orel Oblast	12,200	1,500,000	...	Orel	1937
Tambov Oblast	13,200	1,650,000	...	Tambov	1937
Voronezh Oblast	26,400	3,450,000	...	Voronezh	1934
Kursk Oblast	19,600	3,000,000	3,196,814	Kursk	1934
Central Black-Earth Region	71,400	9,600,000	...		
Bryansk Oblast	13,400	1,800,000	...	Bryansk	1944
Kaluga Oblast	11,600	1,050,000	...	Kaluga	1944
Smolensk Oblast	18,900	1,800,000	...	Smolensk	1937
Velikiye Luki Oblast	17,300	900,000	...	Velikiye Luki	1944
Kalinin Oblast	25,500	2,250,000	...	Kalinin	1935
European West	86,700	7,800,000	...		
Novgorod Oblast	20,700	1,050,000	...	Novgorod	1944
Pskov Oblast	12,200	900,000	...	Pskov	1944
Leningrad Oblast	32,800	4,800,000	...	Leningrad	1927
European Northwest	65,700	6,750,000	...		
Murmansk Oblast	57,800	450,000	291,188	Murmansk	1938
Komi Autonomous SSR	156,200	450,000	318,969	Syktyvkar	1936
Vologda Oblast	56,900	1,500,000	...	Vologda	1937
Arkhangel'sk (Archangel) Oblast	229,400	1,050,000	...	Arkhangel'sk (Archangel)	1937
Nenets National Okrug	67,300	30,000	...	Nar'yan-Mar	1929
European North	500,300	3,450,000	...		
Kirov Oblast	47,000	2,250,000	...	Kirov	1936
Gor'kiy Oblast	29,100	3,600,000	...	Gor'kiy	1936
Mari Autonomous SSR	8,900	600,000	579,456	Yoshkar-Ola	1936
Upper Volga Region	85,000	6,450,000	...		
Chuvash Autonomous SSR	7,100	1,050,000	1,077,614	Cheboksary	1925
Mordvinian Autonomous SSR	10,100	1,200,000	1,188,598	Saransk	1934

DIVISION	AREA (in square miles)	POPULATION Estimate 1947	POPULATION Census 1939	CAPITAL	YEAR OF FORMATION OF DIVISION
Tatar Autonomous SSR	26,100	2,850,000	2,919,423	Kazan'	1920
Penza Oblast	16,700	1,500,000	...	Penza	1939
Ul'yanovsk Oblast	14,400	1,200,000	...	Ul'yanovsk	1943
Kuybyshev Oblast	20,800	1,950,000	...	Kuybyshev	1936
Middle Volga Region	95,200	9,750,000	...		
Saratov Oblast	39,500	2,400,000	...	Saratov	1936
Stalingrad Oblast	49,100	1,800,000	...	Stalingrad	1936
Astrakhan' Oblast	35,600	750,000	...	Astrakhan'	1943
Lower Volga Region	124,200	4,950,000	...		
Volga Region	304,400	21,150,000	...		
Crimean Oblast	10,000	1,050,000	1,126,824	Simferopol'	1945
Rostov Oblast	40,300	2,550,000	...	Rostov	1937
Krasnodar Kray	32,800	3,000,000	3,172,885	Krasnodar	1937
Adyge Autonomous Oblast	1,700	300,000	241,773	Maykop	1922
Stavropol' Kray	29,600	1,500,000	...	Stavropol'	1924
Cherkess Autonomous Oblast	1,540	100,000	92,534	Cherkessk	1928
Kabardinian Autonomous SSR	4,600	300,000	...	Nal'chik	1936
North Ossetian Autonomous SSR	3,500	450,000	...	Dzaudzhikau	1936
Groznyy Oblast	12,700	600,000	...	Groznyy	1944
Dagestan Autonomous SSR	14,700	900,000	930,527	Makhachkala	1921
Lower Don and Northern Caucasus	138,200	9,300,000	...		
Sverdlovsk Oblast	74,600	3,000,000	2,512,175	Sverdlovsk	1934
Molotov Oblast	65,900	2,250,000	2,082,166	Molotov	1938
Komi-Permyak National Okrug	12,000	200,000	...	Kudymkar	1929
Chelyabinsk Oblast	33,900	2,100,000	...	Chelyabinsk	1934
Udmurt Autonomous SSR	16,200	1,200,000	1,220,007	Izhevsk	1934
Bashkir Autonomous SSR	55,400	3,000,000	3,144,713	Ufa	1919
Chkalov Oblast	47,400	1,800,000	1,677,013	Chkalov	1934
Urals	293,400	13,350,000	...		
Kaliningrad Oblast	6,100	600,000	...	Kaliningrad	1946
Russian SFSR in Europe	1,578,700	91,500,000	...		
Chernigov Oblast	12,200	1,700,000	...	Chernigov	1932
Chernovtsy Oblast	3,200	900,000	...	Chernovtsy	1940
Dnepropetrovsk Oblast	12,600	2,200,000	...	Dnepropetrovsk	1932
Drogobych Oblast	4,000	1,200,000	...	Drogobych	1939
Izmail Oblast	4,800	700,000	...	Izmail	1940

TABLE 2 (*Continued*)

ADMINISTRATIVE-TERRITORIAL DIVISIONS OF THE USSR [a]

DIVISION	AREA (in square miles)	POPULATION *Estimate* 1947	*Census* 1939	CAPITAL	YEAR OF FORMATION OF DIVISION
Kamenets-Podol'skiy Oblast	8,000	1,800,000	...	Proskurov	1937
Khar'kov Oblast	12,000	2,500,000	...	Khar'kov	1932
Kherson Oblast	10,600	700,000	...	Kherson	1944
Kiev (Kiyev) Oblast	15,900	3,500,000	...	Kiev (Kiyev)	1932
Kirovograd Oblast	9,600	1,100,000	...	Kirovograd	1939
L'vov Oblast	4,300	1,500,000	...	L'vov	1939
Nikolayev Oblast	7,500	800,000	...	Nikolayev	1937
Odessa Oblast	10,800	1,800,000	...	Odessa	1932
Poltava Oblast	13,200	2,200,000	...	Poltava	1937
Rovno Oblast	8,000	1,200,000	...	Rovno	1939
Stalino Oblast	10,200	3,000,000	...	Stalino	1938
Stanislav Oblast	5,400	1,300,000	...	Stanislav	1939
Sumy Oblast	9,400	1,700,000	...	Sumy	1939
Ternopol' Oblast	5,300	1,500,000	...	Ternopol'	1939
Transcarpathian (Zakarpatskaya) Oblast	5,000	900,000	...	Uzhgorod	1946
Vinnitsa Oblast	10,600	2,300,000	...	Vinnitsa	1932
Volyn' Oblast	7,700	1,100,000	...	Lutsk	1939
Voroshilovgrad Oblast	10,300	1,800,000	...	Voroshilovgrad	1938
Zaporozh'ye Oblast	10,400	1,300,000	...	Zaporozh'ye	1939
Zhitomir Oblast	11,600	1,800,000	...	Zhitomir	1937
Ukrainian SSR	222,600	40,500,000	...	Kiev (Kiyev)	1917
Baranovichi Oblast	5,300	580,000	...	Baranovichi	1939
Bobruysk Oblast	7,600	640,000	...	Bobruysk	1944
Brest Oblast	5,200	520,000	...	Brest	1939
Gomel' Oblast	6,100	700,000	...	Gomel'	1938
Grodno Oblast	5,000	600,000	...	Grodno	1944
Minsk Oblast	8,000	840,000	...	Minsk	1938
Mogilev Oblast	8,000	840,000	...	Mogilev	1938
Molodechno Oblast	5,700	580,000	...	Molodechno	1939
Pinsk Oblast	6,300	400,000	...	Pinsk	1939
Poles'ye Oblast	8,400	420,000	...	Mozyr'	1938
Polotsk Oblast	6,900	460,000	...	Polotsk	1944
Vitebsk Oblast	7,600	640,000	...	Vitebsk	1938
Belorussian SSR	80,100	7,220,000	...	Minsk	1919
Azerbaijan SSR	33,100	3,100,000	3,209,727	Baku	1920
Nakhichevan' Autonomous SSR	2,100	160,000	...	Nakhichevan'	1924
Nagorno-Karabakh Autonomous Oblast	1,700	130,000	...	Stepanakert	1923
Georgian SSR	29,400	3,555,000	3,542,289	Tbilisi (Tiflis)	1921
Abkhaz Autonomous SSR	3,300	330,000	...	Sukhumi	1921

DIVISION	AREA (in square miles)	POPULATION Estimate 1947	Census 1939	CAPITAL	YEAR OF FORMATION OF DIVISION
Adzhar Autonomous SSR	1,100	195,000	...	Batumi	1921
South Ossetian Autonomous Oblast	1,500	120,000	...	Stalinir	1922
Armenian SSR	11,500	1,345,000	1,281,599	Yerevan (Erivan')	1920
Transcaucasia	74,000	8,000,000	...		
Moldavian SSR	13,100	2,660,000	...	Kishinev	1940
Lithuanian SSR	31,200	2,700,000	...	Vil'nyus (Vilnius)	1940
Latvian SSR	24,600	1,800,000	...	Riga	1940
Estonian SSR	17,400	1,000,000	...	Tallin (Tallinn)	1940
Karelo-Finnish SSR	68,900	600,000	...	Petrozavodsk	1940
USSR in Europe	2,110,600	155,980,000	...		
Kurgan Oblast	27,500	900,000	...	Kurgan	1943
Tyumen' Oblast	526,300	900,000	...	Tyumen'	1944
Khanty-Mansi National Okrug	215,500	110,000	...	Khanty-Mansiysk	1930
Yamal-Nenets National Okrug	258,800	40,000	...	Salekhard	1930
Omsk Oblast	53,800	1,500,000	...	Omsk	1934
Novosibirsk Oblast	69,000	2,100,000	...	Novosibirsk	1937
Tomsk Oblast	121,400	600,000	...	Tomsk	1944
Altay Kray	101,000	2,400,000	...	Barnaul	1937
Gorno-Altay Autonomous Oblast	35,800	150,000	161,431	Gorno-Altaysk	1922
Kemerovo Oblast	36,900	1,950,000	...	Kemerovo	1943
Western Siberia	935,900	10,350,000	...		
Krasnoyarsk Kray	928,000	2,100,000	1,940,002	Krasnoyarsk	1934
Khakass Autonomous Oblast	24,000	300,000	270,655	Abakan	1930
Evenki National Okrug	285,900	25,000	...	Tura	1930
Taymyr National Okrug	316,700	25,000	...	Dudinka	1930
Tuva Autonomous Oblast	66,100	150,000	...	Kyzyl	1944
Irkutsk Oblast	301,900	1,200,000	1,286,696	Irkutsk	1937
Ust'-Orda Buryat-Mongol National Okrug	8,000	100,000	...	Ust'-Ordynskiy	1937
Buryat-Mongol Autonomous SSR	135,700	600,000	542,170	Ulan-Ude	1923
Chita Oblast	168,200	1,050,000	...	Chita	1937
Aga Buryat-Mongol National Okrug	9,400	30,000	...	Aginskoye	1937
Yakut Autonomous SSR	1,182,300	450,000	400,544	Yakutsk	1922
Eastern Siberia	2,782,200	5,550,000	...		
Amur Oblast	139,000	575,000	...	Blagoveshchensk	1948
Khabarovsk Kray	965,400	1,250,000	...	Khabarovsk	1938

TABLE 2 (*Continued*)

ADMINISTRATIVE-TERRITORIAL DIVISIONS OF THE USSR [a]

DIVISION	AREA (in square miles)	POPULATION Estimate 1947	POPULATION Census 1939	CAPITAL	YEAR OF FORMA- TION OF DIVISION
Kamchatka Oblast	490,400	150,000	...	Petropavlovsk	1932
Koryak National Okrug	151,700	20,000	...	Palana	1930
Chukchi National Okrug	274,500	20,000	...	Anadyr'	1930
Lower Amur Oblast	202,700	150,000	...	Nikolayevsk	1934
Jewish Autonomous Oblast	13,800	150,000	108,419	Birobidzhan	1934
Khabarovsk area (unorganized)	111,500	650,000	...		
Magadan-Kolyma area (unorganized)	137,100	150,000	...		
Maritime Kray	64,900	1,475,000	907,220	Vladivostok	1938
Sakhalin Oblast	35,400	300,000	...	Yuzhno-Sakhalinsk	1947
Kurile Islands	5,700	15,000	...		
Far East	1,204,700	3,600,000	...		
Russian SFSR in Asia	4,922,800	19,500,000	...		
Russian SFSR	6,501,500	111,000,000	...	Moscow (Moskva)	1917
Including border seas:	6,533,600				
Akmolinsk Oblast	59,000	440,000	...	Akmolinsk	1939
Aktyubinsk Oblast	114,700	300,000	...	Aktyubinsk	1932
Alma-Ata Oblast	41,700	520,000	...	Alma-Ata	1932
Dzhambul Oblast	52,000	320,000	...	Dzhambul	1939
East Kazakhstan Obl. (Vostochno-Kazakhstan)	37,300	500,000	...	Ust'-Kamenogorsk	1932
Gur'yev Oblast	98,600	240,000	...	Gur'yev	1938
Karaganda Oblast	156,700	460,000	...	Karaganda	1932
Kokchetav Oblast	28,600	320,000	...	Kokchetav	1944
Kustanay Oblast	76,700	400,000	...	Kustanay	1936
Kzyl-Orda Oblast	88,900	300,000	...	Kzyl-Orda	1938
North Kazakhstan Obl. (Severo-Kazakhstan)	17,600	360,000	...	Petropavlovsk	1936
Pavlodar Oblast	53,600	260,000	...	Pavlodar	1938
Semipalatinsk	67,600	360,000	...	Semipalatinsk	1939
South Kazakhstan Obl. (Yuzhno-Kazakhstan)	61,500	640,000	...	Chimkent	1932
Taldy-Kurgan Oblast	46,200	300,000	...	Taldy-Kurgan	1944
West Kazakhstan Obl. (Zapadno-Kazakhstan)	60,900	280,000	...	Ural'sk	1932
Kazakh SSR	1,061,600	6,000,000	6,145,937	Alma-Ata	1936
Dzhalal-Abad Oblast	9,200	220,000	...	Dzhalal-Abad	1939
Frunze Oblast	6,000	500,000	...	Frunze	1939

DIVISION	AREA (in square miles)	POPULATION Estimate 1947	Census 1939	CAPITAL	YEAR OF FORMA- TION OF DIVISION
Issyk-Kul' Oblast	16,300	180,000	...	Przheval'sk	1939
Osh Oblast	17,000	390,000	...	Osh	1939
Talas Oblast	6,400	90,000	...	Talas	1944
Tyan'-Shan' Oblast	21,200	110,000	...	Naryn	1939
Kirghiz SSR	76,100	1,490,000	1,459,301	Frunze	1936
Garm Oblast	7,600	165,000	...	Novabad	1939
Kulyab Oblast	4,600	190,000	...	Kulyab	1939
Leninabad Oblast	9,400	500,000	...	Leninabad	1939
Stalinabad Oblast	9,700	555,000	...	Stalinabad	1939
Gorno-Badakhshan Autonomous Oblast	23,600	45,000	...	Khorog	1925
Tadzhik SSR	54,900	1,455,000	1,485,091	Stalinabad	1929
Andizhan Oblast	1,600	600,000	...	Andizhan	1941
Bukhara Oblast	49,600	465,000	...	Bukhara	1938
Fergana Oblast	3,100	720,000	...	Fergana	1938
Kashka Darya Oblast	11,300	405,000	...	Karshi	1943
Khorezm Oblast	1,900	315,000	...	Urgench	1938
Namangan Oblast	2,400	450,000	...	Namangan	1941
Samarkand Oblast	12,300	960,000	...	Samarkand	1938
Surkhan Darya Oblast	7,700	300,000	...	Termez	1941
Tashkent Oblast	5,900	1,350,000	...	Tashkent	1938
Kara-Kalpak Autono- mous SSR	61,600	435,000	...	Nukus	1932
Uzbek SSR	157,400	6,000,000	6,282,446	Tashkent	1924
Ashkhabad Oblast	87,600	430,000	...	Ashkhabad	1939
Chardzhou Oblast	35,900	240,000	...	Chardzhou	1939
Mary Oblast	34,700	265,000	...	Mary	1939
Tashauz Oblast	29,000	235,000	...	Tashauz	1939
Turkmen SSR	187,200	1,170,000	1,253,985	Ashkhabad	1924
Central Asia	475,600	10,115,000	...		
USSR in Asia	6,460,000	35,615,000	...		
USSR	8,570,600	191,595,000	...	Moscow (Moskva)	1922

Including border seas:
8,600,000

a The greater part of the data has been taken from the Administrative-Territorial Guide of the USSR as of January 1, 1949, supplemented by the author's administrative file on the USSR. This information includes the names of the divisions, their capitals and date of formation, as well as the area in square kilometers, which has been converted into square miles and rounded off in most cases to the nearest 100 square miles.

The 1947 population estimates have been computed from the election district lists for the 1947 Republic elections, in which data was based in part on prewar and in part on postwar population figures (see footnote *a*, Table 1).

These estimates, which are of necessity only approximate, are too low for areas where migration is known to have taken place. Kaliningrad Oblast (1950 estimate, 900,000) and Sakhalin Oblast (1950 estimate, 900,000) have had considerable immigration from other sections of the USSR, while the Armenian SSR (1950 estimate, 1,500,000) received immigrants from abroad (see also notes on 1950 election districts in Section on Methodology, pp. xv–xvi).

The 1939 census has been indicated only for purposes of comparison in the few cases of administrative divisions that have undergone negligible or no territorial changes since 1939.

TABLE 3

POPULATION OF CITIES WITH OVER 50,000 INHABITANTS [a]

	POPULATION Dec. 17, 1926	Jan. 17, 1939	PERCENTAGE INCREASE OVER 1926	ESTIMATED POSTWAR POPULATION (1946–48)
		RUSSIAN SFSR		
Central Industrial Region				
Moscow (Moskva)	2,029,425	4,137,018	203.9	4,500,000
Yaroslavl'	114,277	298,065	260.8	300,000
Ivanovo	111,460	285,069	255.8	300,000
Tula	155,005	272,403	175.7	300,000
Shcherbakov	55,546	139,011	250.3	150,000
Kostroma	73,732	121,205	164.4	150,000
Orekhovo-Zuyevo	62,841	99,329	158.1	...
Ryazan'	50,919	95,358	187.3	...
Serpukhov	55,891	90,766	162.4	...
Noginsk	38,494	81,024	210.5	...
Perovo	23,711	77,727	327.8	...
Stalinogorsk	...	76,207	...	...
Kineshma	34,110	75,378	221.0	...
Kolomna	30,767	75,139	244.2	...
Podol'sk	19,793	72,422	365.9	...
Babushkin	15,624	70,480	451.1	...
Kovrov	26,584	67,163	252.6	...
Vladimir	39,654	66,761	168.4	...
Lyublino	8,391	64,332	766.7	...
Kuntsevo	9,978	60,963	611.0	...
Mytishchi	17,054	60,111	352.5	...
Shuya	34,475	57,950	168.1	...
Yegor'yevsk	29,674	56,340	189.9	...
Central Black-Earth Region				
Voronezh	121,612	326,836	268.7	300,000
Tambov	72,256	121,285	167.9	150,000
Kursk	82,440	119,972	145.5	...
Orel	75,968	110,567	145.5	..
Michurinsk	49,853	70,202	140.8	...
Lipetsk	21,439	66,625	310.8	..
Borisoglebsk	39,788	52,055	130.8	...
Yelets	43,239	50,888	117.7	...
European West				
Kalinin	108,413	216,131	199.4	300,000
Smolensk	78,520	156,677	199.5	150,000
Kaluga	51,565	89,484	173.5	...
Bryansk	45,962	87,473	190.3	...
Bezhitsa	36,040	82,331	228.4	...
Vyshniy Volochek	32,022	63,642	198.7	...
Rzhev	32,810	54,081	164.8	...

	POPULATION		PERCENTAGE INCREASE OVER 1926	ESTIMATED POSTWAR POPULATION (1946–48)
	Dec. 17, 1926	Jan. 17, 1939		
European Northwest				
Leningrad	1,690,065	3,191,304	188.8	3,300,000
Pskov	43,226	59,898	138.6	...
European North				
Arkhangel'sk	76,774	281,091	366.1	300,000
Murmansk	8,777	117,054	1333.6	150,000
Vologda	57,976	95,194	164.2	...
Upper Volga Region				
Gor'kiy	222,356	644,116	289.7	900,000
Kirov	62,097	143,181	230.6	250,000
Dzerzhinsk	8,910	103,415	1160.7	...
Middle Volga Region				
Kazan'	179,023	401,665	224.4	500,000
Kuybyshev	175,636	390,267	222.2	600,000
Penza	91,924	157,145	171.0	250,000
Ul'yanovsk	70,130	102,106	145.6	200,000
Syzran'	50,293	77,679	154.5	150,000
Chapayevsk	13,529	57,995	428.7	...
Lower Volga Region				
Stalingrad	151,490	445,476	294.1	400,000
Saratov	219,547	375,860	171.2	500,000
Astrakhan'	184,301	253,655	137.6	300,000
Engel's	34,345	73,279	213.4	...
Vol'sk	35,272	55,053	156.1	...
Crimea				
Simferopol'	87,213	142,678	163.6	...
Sevastopol'	74,551	111,946	150.2	...
Kerch'	35,690	104,471	292.7	...
Northern Caucasus and Lower Don				
Rostov-on-Don	308,103	510,253	165.6	500,000
Krasnodar	161,843	203,946	126.0	200,000
Taganrog	86,444	188,808	218.4	150,000
Groznyy	97,087	172,468	177.6	...
Shakhty	41,043	155,081	377.9	...
Dzaudzhikau	78,346	127,172	162.3	...
Novorossiysk	67,941	95,280	140.2	...
Makhachkala	33,552	86,847	258.8	...
Stavropol'	58,640	85,100	145.1	...
Armavir	74,523	83,677	112.3	...
Novocherkassk	62,274	81,286	130.5	...
Maykop	53,033	67,302	126.9	...
Pyatigorsk	40,674	62,875	154.6	...
Kislovodsk	25,913	51,289	197.9	...

TABLE 3 *(Continued)*

POPULATION OF CITIES WITH OVER 50,000 INHABITANTS [a]

	POPULATION Dec. 17, 1926	Jan. 17, 1939	PERCENTAGE INCREASE OVER 1926	ESTIMATED POSTWAR POPULATION (1946–48)
Urals				
Sverdlovsk	140,300	425,544	303.3	600,000
Chelyabinsk	59,307	273,127	460.5	500,000
Molotov	119,776	255,196	213.1	450,000
Ufa	98,537	245,863	249.5	300,000
Izhevsk	63,211	175,740	278.0	200,000
Chkalov	123,283	172,925	140.3	200,000
Nizhniy Tagil	38,820	159,864	411.8	250,000
Magnitogorsk	...	145,870	...	200,000
Zlatoust	48,219	99,272	205.9	150,000
Orsk	13,581	65,799	484.5	100,000
Serov	33,345	64,719	194.1	...
Berezniki	16,138	63,575	393.9	...
Lys'va	27,279	51,192	187.7	...
Kamensk-Ural'skiy	5,367	50,897	948.3	...
Western Siberia				
Novosibirsk	120,128	405,589	337.6	750,000
Omsk	161,684	280,716	173.6	500,000
Stalinsk	3,894	169,538	4353.8	200,000
Barnaul	73,858	148,129	200.6	200,000
Tomsk	92,274	141,215	153.0	150,000
Kemerovo	21,726	132,978	612.1	200,000
Prokop'yevsk	10,717	107,227	1000.5	150,000
Leninsk-Kuznetskiy	19,645	81,980	417.3	...
Biysk	45,561	80,190	176.0	...
Tyumen'	50,340	75,537	150.1	...
Anzhero-Sudzhensk	30,199	71,079	235.4	...
Kurgan	27,996	53,224	190.1	...
Eastern Siberia				
Irkutsk	108,129	243,380	225.1	300,000
Krasnoyarsk	72,261	189,999	262.9	300,000
Ulan-Ude	28,918	129,417	447.5	150,000
Chita	61,526	102,555	166.7	150,000
Cheremkhovo	14,485	65,907	455.0	...
Yakutsk	10,558	52,888	500.9	...
Far East				
Vladivostok	107,980	206,432	191.2	300,000
Khabarovsk	52,045	199,364	383.1	300,000
Komsomol'sk	...	70,746	...	150,000
Voroshilov	35,344	70,628	199.8	150,000
Blagoveshchensk	61,205	58,761	96.0	...

	POPULATION Dec. 17, 1926	Jan. 17, 1939	PERCENTAGE INCREASE OVER 1926	ESTIMATED POSTWAR POPULATION (1946–48)

Kaliningrad Oblast

Kaliningrad	...	372,164 (1939)	...	150,000
Sovetsk	...	59,105 (1939)	...	...
Chernyakhovsk	...	48,711 (1939)	...	...

Kazakh SSR

Alma-Ata	45,395	230,528	507.8	260–300,000
Karaganda	...	165,937	...	220,000
Semipalatinsk	56,871	109,779	193.0	110,000
Petropavlovsk	47,361	91,678	193.6	100,000
Akmolinsk	12,781	...	...	90,000
Chimkent	21,018	74,185	353.0	80,000
Dzhambul	24,761	62,723	253.3	75,000
Ural'sk	36,352	66,201	182.1	60,000
Gur'yev	12,003	...	...	60,000
Leninogorsk	9,469	...	...	60,000
Kzyl-Orda	22,624	...	...	55,000
Balkhash	...	...	...	50–75,000
Ust'-Kamenogorsk	13,908	...	...	50,000

Uzbek SSR

Tashkent	323,613	585,005	180.8	600,000
Samarkand	105,206	134,346	127.7	150,000
Andizhan	73,465	83,691	113.9	90,000
Kokand	69,324	84,665	122.1	75,000
Namangan	73,640	77,351	105.0	75,000
Bukhara	46,778	50,382	107.7	60,000
Margelan	44,327	...	...	45,000
Chirchik	...	...	...	45,000

Turkmen SSR

Ashkhabad	51,593	126,580	245.3	120,000
Chardzhou	13,950	54,739	392.4	55,000
Mary	21,633	c. 37,100	125.5	50,000
Krasnovodsk	10,082	c. 23,600	233.6	30,000

Tadzhik SSR

Stalinabad	5,607	82,540	1472.1	110,000
Leninabad	37,480	...	...	55,000
Ura-Tyube	21,056	...	...	25,000

Kirghiz SSR

Frunze	36,610	92,659	253.1	140,000
Osh	30,639	...	...	40,000
Dzhalal-Abad	9,657	...	...	30,000

Azerbaijan SSR

Baku	453,333	809,347	178.5	800,000
Kirovabad	57,393	98,743	172.1	110,000

Table 3 (*Continued*)

Population of Cities with Over 50,000 Inhabitants [a]

	POPULATION Dec. 17, 1926	Jan. 17, 1939	PERCENTAGE INCREASE OVER 1926	ESTIMATED POSTWAR POPULATION (1946–48)
GEORGIAN SSR				
Tbilisi (Tiflis)	294,044	519,175	176.6	540,000
Kutaisi	48,196	81,479	169.0	90,000
Batumi	48,474	70,807	146.1	75,000
Rustavi	...	...	...	c. 50,000 by 1950
ARMENIAN SSR				
Yerevan (Erivan')	64,613	200,031	309.6	255,000
Leninakan	42,313	67,707	160.0	75,000
UKRAINIAN SSR				
Kiev (Kiyev)	513,637	846,293	164.8	900,000
Khar'kov	417,342	833,432	199.7	900,000
Odessa	420,862	604,223	143.6	600,000
Dnepropetrovsk	236,717	500,662	211.5	500,000
Stalino	174,230	462,395	265.4	500,000
L'vov	...	316,177 (1931)	...	400,000
Zaporozh'ye	55,744	289,188	518.8	300,000
Makeyevka	79,421	240,145	302.4	300,000
Zhdanov	63,920	222,427	348.0	200,000
Voroshilovgrad	71,765	213,007	296.8	200,000
Krivoy Rog	38,228	197,621	517.0	200,000
Nikolayev	104,909	167,108	159.3	200,000
Dneprodzerzhinsk	34,150	147,829	432.9	...
Poltava	91,984	130,305	141.7	...
Chernovtsy	...	112,427 (1930)	...	...
Gorlovka	23,125	108,693	470.0	...
Kirovograd	66,467	100,331	150.9	...
Kherson	58,801	97,186	165.3	...
Zhitomir	76,678	95,090	124.0	...
Konstantinovka	25,303	95,087	375.8	...
Kramatorsk	12,348	93,350	756.0	...
Vinnitsa	57,990	92,868	160.1	...
Kremenchug	58,832	89,553	152.2	...
Yenakiyevo	24,329	88,246	362.7	...
Melitopol'	25,289	75,735	299.5	...
Slavyansk	28,771	75,542	262.6	...
Kadiyevka	17,224	68,360	396.9	...
Chernigov	35,234	67,356	191.2	...
Berdichev	55,613	66,306	119.2	...
Sumy	44,213	63,883	144.5	...
Stanislav	...	60,256 (1931)	...	...
Nikopol'	14,214	57,841	406.9	...
Artemovsk	37,780	55,165	146.0	...
Voroshilovsk	16,040	54,794	341.6	...
Cherkassy	39,511	51,693	130.8	...
Osipenko	26,408	51,664	195.6	...
Krasnyy Luch	12,425	50,829	409.1	...

	POPULATION		PERCENTAGE INCREASE	ESTIMATED POSTWAR POPULATION
	Dec. 17, 1926	Jan. 17, 1939	OVER 1926	(1946–48)
		MOLDAVIAN SSR		
Kishinev	...	114,896 (1930)	...	110,000
		BELORUSSIAN SSR		
Minsk	131,803	238,772	181.2	231,000 (1948)
Gomel'	86,409	144,169	166.8	120,000
Vitebsk	98,857	167,424	169.4	80,000
Mogilev	50,222	99,440	198.0	80,000
Bobruysk	51,296	84,107	164.0	80,000
Grodno	...	49,819 (1931)	...	60,000
Brest	...	48,435 (1931)	...	60,000
		LITHUANIAN SSR		
Vil'nyus (Vilna)	...	208,000 (1937)	...	244,500 (1948)
Kaunas	...	108,200 (1938)	...	...
Klaypeda (Memel)	...	41,297 (1940)	...	...
		LATVIAN SSR		
Riga	...	383,699 (1935)	...	390,000
Liepaya	...	57,172 (1935)	...	75,000
Daugavpils	...	45,071 (1935)	...	45,000
		ESTONIAN SSR		
Tallin (Tallinn)	...	137,792 (1934)	...	190,000
Tartu	...	58,876 (1934)	...	50,000
		KARELO-FINNISH SSR		
Petrozavodsk	27,105	69,728	257.3	71,500

a Data on 1926 and 1939 population figures and the percentage increase have been taken from the preliminary census report of the 1939 census. For new cities that developed since 1926, no 1926 population figure nor percentage increase has been indicated. In the case of Blagoveshchensk, a city of the Far East, a decrease has been observed between the 1926 and 1939 census figures. This fact was not pointed out in the original Soviet publication, which showed no percentage increase, as in the case of newly developed cities.

The estimated postwar population figures have been computed from the election district lists of 1946 and 1947. In a few cases, more precise figures have been available from local elections of 1948.

For cities that were absorbed by the USSR since the 1939 census, the latest census or official estimate has been used.

TABLE 4

MAJOR ETHNIC GROUPS OF THE USSR AND THEIR AUTONOMOUS
POLITICAL DIVISIONS [a]

ETHNIC GROUPS REPORTED IN 1939 CENSUS

ETHNIC GROUP	NUMBER	TYPE OF POLITICAL DIVISION	TOTAL POPULATION OF POLITICAL DIVISION	TITULAR GROUP: PERCENT OF TOTAL POPULATION	RUSSIANS: PERCENT OF TOTAL POPULATION
Russian	c. 100,000,000 (99,019,929 in 1939)	SFSR	111,000,000	73	73
Ukrainian	c. 36,000,000 (28,070,404 in 1939)	SSR	40,500,000	80	9
Belorussian	c. 10,000,000 (5,267,431 in 1939)	SSR	7,220,000	81	7
Uzbek	4,844,021	SSR	6,000,000	76	6
Tatar	4,300,336	Autonomous SSR	2,850,000	50	42
Kazakh	3,098,764	SSR	6,000,000	57	20
Azerbaijani (Turks)	2,274,805	SSR	3,100,000	63	10
		Nakhichevan' Autonomous SSR	160,000	84	2
Georgian	2,248,566	SSR	3,555,000	61	4
Lithuanian	c. 2,200,000 (32,342 in 1939)	SSR	2,700,000	80	3
Armenian	2,151,884	SSR	1,345,000	84	2
		Nagorno-Karabakh Autonomous Oblast	130,000	89	1
Moldavian	c. 2,100,000 (260,023 in 1939)	SSR	2,660,000	65	7
Jewish	c. 2,000,000 (3,020,141 in 1939)	Autonomous Oblast	150,000	50	40
Latvian and Latgal	c. 1,600,000 (126,900 in 1939)	SSR	1,800,000	76	12
Mordvinian	1,451,429	Autonomous SSR	1,200,000	37	57
Chuvash	1,367,930	Autonomous SSR	1,050,000	80	16
Tadzhik	1,228,964	SSR	1,455,000	78	1
		Gorno-Badakhshan Autonomous Oblast	45,000	90	1
Estonian	c. 1,100,000 (142,465 in 1939)	SSR	1,000,000	91	7
Kirghiz	884,306	SSR	1,490,000	67	12
Peoples of Dagestan	857,371	Autonomous SSR	900,000	65	13
Bashkir	842,925	Autonomous SSR	3,000,000	24	40
Turkmen	811,769	SSR	1,170,000	72	8
Polish	626,905	None	...	...	...
Udmurt	605,673	Autonomous SSR	1,200,000	52	43
Mari	481,262	Autonomous SSR	600,000	51	44

ETHNIC GROUP	NUMBER	TYPE OF POLITICAL DIVISION	TOTAL POPULATION OF POLITICAL DIVISION	TITULAR GROUP: PERCENT OF TOTAL POPULATION	RUSSIANS: PERCENT OF TOTAL POPULATION
Komi	408,724	Komi Autonomous SSR	450,000	92	6
		Komi-Permyak National Okrug	200,000	...	...
Ossetian	354,547	Autonomous SSR and	450,000	84	7
		Autonomous Oblast	120,000	69	1
Bulgarian	c. 300,000 (113,479 in 1939)	None	...	...	...
Greek	285,896	None	...	...	...
Karelian	252,559 }	c. 400,000 SSR	600,000	23	63
Finn	143,074 }				
Kara-Kalpak	185,775	Autonomous SSR	435,000	38	2
Korean	180,412	None	...	...	...
Kabardinian	164,106	Autonomous SSR	300,000	60	11
Adyge	87,973	Adyge Autonomous Oblast	300,000	45	26
(Cherkess)		Cherkess Autonomous Oblast	100,000	7	4
Tuvinian	c. 85,000 (Not listed in 1939)	Autonomous Oblast	150,000	57	30
Abkhaz	58,969	Autonomous SSR	330,000	28	6
Khakass	52,602	Autonomous Oblast	300,000	50	47
Oyrot (Altaic)	47,717	Gorno-Altay Autonomous Oblast	150,000	36	52
			...	...	...
Kurd	45,866	None	...	...	...
Iranian	39,037				
Chinese	29,620	None	...	...	...
Czech, Slovak	26,919	None	...	...	...
Arab	21,793	None	...	...	...
Assyrians	20,207	None	...	...	...

OTHER MAJOR ETHNIC GROUPS REPORTED IN 1926 CENSUS

ETHNIC GROUP	NUMBER	TYPE OF POLITICAL DIVISION	TOTAL POPULATION OF POLITICAL DIVISION	TITULAR GROUP: PERCENT OF TOTAL POPULATION	RUSSIANS: PERCENT OF TOTAL POPULATION
Yakut	240,709	Autonomous SSR	450,000	82	10
Buryat-Mongol	237,501	Buryat-Mongol Autonomous SSR	600,000	44	53
		Ust'-Orda Buryat-Mongol National Okrug b	100,000	...	...
		Aga Buryat-Mongol National Okrug b	30,000	...	...
Evenki (Tungus)	37,546	National Okrug	25,000	...	...
Khanty (Ostyak)	22,306	National Okrug	110,000	...	...
Mansi (Vogul)	5,754				
Nentsy (Samoyed)	15,462	Nenets National Okrug	30,000	...	...
		Yamal-Nenets National Okrug	40,000	...	...
		Taymyr National Okrug c	25,000	...	...

TABLE 4 *(Continued)*

MAJOR ETHNIC GROUPS OF THE USSR AND THEIR AUTONOMOUS POLITICAL DIVISIONS [a]

ETHNIC GROUPS REPORTED IN 1939 CENSUS

ETHNIC GROUP	NUMBER	TYPE OF POLITICAL DIVISION	TOTAL POPULATION OF POLITICAL DIVISION	TITULAR GROUP: PERCENT OF TOTAL POPULATION	RUSSIANS: PERCENT OF TOTAL POPULATION
Luoravetlany		Chukchi National	20,000	...	...
(Chukchi)	12,332	Okrug	20,000	...	...
Nymylany		Koryak National	20,000	...	...
(Koryak)	7,439	Okrug	20,000	...	...

a The ethnic groups are listed in the order of their present estimated numbers. The designations are taken from the 1939 census, except where the author has added an explanatory term in parenthesis, e.g., Azerbaijani (Turks); Adyge (Cherkess). The preliminary 1939 census report listed all ethnic groups of the USSR with more than 20,000 people, except those of eastern and northern Siberia. For the ethnic groups not reported in the preliminary 1939 figures, the 1926 census has been used.

The number of people shown for each ethnic group is taken from the 1939 census or the 1926 census, except where their number was changed substantially as the result of Soviet territorial acquisitions since 1939. In these cases estimates of the present population are followed by the 1939 census figures. The postwar estimates have been taken from many sources and are very approximate. Attention is called to the changes in the number of Jews, which rose from 3 millions in 1939 to nearly 5 millions in 1940 as a result of Soviet territorial expansion, but fell to an estimated 2 million through the German extermination of the Jews during the Second World War.

The political division of each ethnic group bears the same name as the corresponding nationality, except where indicated. Certain groups, such as the Komi and the Cherkess, form more than one political division. Others are not identified with any major political division of their own.

The total population of the political divisions is taken from Table 1.

The percentage of the titular group and of the Russians in the total population of each political division is based largely on the 1926 census (with some later estimates) and are not compatible with the 1939 population figures. For example, the percentage of Kazakhs in the Kazakh SSR (57% in 1926) must be less than 50% according to the later population figures, assuming even that all Kazakhs of the USSR live within the confines of the Kazakh SSR.

A number of nationalities that were included in the 1939 census report and were formerly identified with their own political divisions have been accused of collaborating with the Germans during the Second World War and deprived of their identity as separate nationalities. They are no longer listed in Soviet demographic statistics.

These nationalities are: (number according to 1939 census)

Germans	1,423,534	Ingush	92,074
Chechen	407,690	Karachay	75,737
Kalmyk	134,327	Balkar	42,666

A seventh ethnic group, that of the Crimean Tatars, has similarly been deprived of its cultural identity. Their number, estimated at 200,000 before the Second World War, was included in the total number of Tatars in the 1939 census.

b Once included within the Buryat-Mongol Autonomous SSR, the two Buryat-Mongol national okrugs were constituted as separate units in 1937 when the intervening Russian-majority areas were incorporated into Irkutsk and Chita oblasts.

c In the Taymyr National Okrug (formerly known as the Dolgan-Nenets National Okrug), the titular ethnic groups are the Nentsy and the Dolgans, a small Turkic tribe which numbered 656 in the 1926 census.

Selected Bibliography

THE PRESENT BIBLIOGRAPHY includes material other than current periodicals examined in the course of the preparation of this book. It is restricted largely to works of geography and related fields that have appeared since the end of the Second World War. Regional studies of particular sections of the USSR have not been included. Brief comments have been written to describe the general features of each item.

Attention is called to The Soviet Economy, a Selected Bibliography of Materials in English, by Harry Schwartz, Syracuse University Press, 1949, for an excellent survey of English-language materials in fields related to the geography of the USSR, including general studies of the USSR, economic geography, population and migration, economic plans, Soviet statistics, industry, agriculture, transportation, and foreign trade.

Balzak, S. S., V. F. Vasyutin, and Ya. G. Feigin. Economic Geography of the USSR. American edition edited by Chauncy D. Harris. Translated from the Russian by Robert M. Hankin and Olga Adler Titelbaum. New York, The Macmillan Company, 1949. This is a Soviet text used in higher educational institutions of the USSR and selected as a representative work on economic geography as part of the Russian Translation project of the American Council of Learned Societies. Although colored by official Communist dogma, it is nevertheless a most complete and detailed treatment arranged largely on a topical plan. Unfortunately, the original Russian edition dates from 1940, and the translated work is thus rather out-of-date.

Baranskiy, N. N. Ekonomicheskaya Geografiya SSSR (Economic Geography of the USSR). 5th edition. Moscow, Uchpedgiz, 1939; 8th edition, 1947; 9th edition, 1948; 10th edition, 1949.

This basic textbook for Soviet secondary schools has been used extensively in formulating the plan and general outline of the present volume, particularly the regional arrangement by political divisions.

Berg, L. S. Priroda SSSR (Nature of the USSR). OGIZ, Moscow, 1937 ; 2d ed., 1938.

French Translation : Les Régions naturelles de l'URSS. Paris, Payot, 1941.

English Translation : The Natural Regions of the USSR. New York, The Macmillan Company, 1950.

The basic volume on the topic of physico-geographical zones of the USSR. Typical of the Soviet approach to physical geography in its emphasis of climate, soils, and especially, flora and fauna.

Berg, L. S. Geograficheskiye Zony Sovetskogo Soyuza (The Geographical Zones of the Soviet Union) Moscow, OGIZ, 1947.

An expanded edition of the previous item, but covering only tundra, forest, and wooded steppe.

Borisov, A. A. Klimaty SSSR (Climates of the USSR). Moscow, Uchpedgiz, 1948.

A most useful work on the climates of the Soviet Union, which are here treated on a topical and regional basis. It contains much analytical and synoptic climatological material, presented in form of maps and tables.

Chefranov, S. V. Fizicheskaya Geografiya SSSR (Physical Geography of the USSR). 4th edition. Moscow, Uchpedgiz, 1944 ; 5th edition, 1946 ; 8th edition, 1949.

An elementary, concise textbook for Soviet secondary schools, that furnished material for the regional survey of the present volume.

Cressey, George B. The Basis of Soviet Strength. New York, McGraw-Hill, 1945.

A lively, stimulating geography of the USSR, giving only briefly the characteristics of the physical pattern, the resources, and the regions of the USSR.

Dobrynin, B. F. Fizicheskaya Geografiya SSSR (Physical Geography of the USSR). Moscow, Uchpedgiz, 1948.

An advanced text covering the European part of the USSR, the Urals, and the Caucasus, with detailed treatment of vegetation, soils, geomorphology, and climate. It is supplemented by Suslov's book on the Asiatic USSR.

Fichelle, Alfred. Géographie physique et économique de l'URSS. Paris: Payot, 1946.

The poorest example of recent French publications, full of misstatements and factual errors.

Germany. Generalstab des Heeres. Abteilung für Kriegskarten und Vermessungswesen. Militärgeographische Angaben über das europäische und das asiatische Russland. Berlin, 1941–42.

A series of German military-geographical studies of the regions of the USSR, including descriptive text, town gazetteers, views, and special military maps. The information is based largely on the Great Soviet World Atlas, Vol. II.

George, Pierre. URSS, Haute Asie, Iran. Paris, Presses Universitaires de France, 1947.

The best of recent French studies of the USSR; it contains a section on Arctic problems and a preliminary survey of the postwar Five-Year Plan.

Gray, G. D. B. Soviet Land; the country, its people, and their work. London, A. and C. Black, 1947.

A topical geography, superficial, but well illustrated. The factual information is not always correct.

Gregory, J. S., and D. W. Shave. The USSR; a geographical survey. London, G. G. Harrap & Co., Ltd., 1944, and New York, J. Wiley and Sons, 1946.

One of the most complete geographies of the USSR in English, containing general and regional sections. Although it contains much valuable material, the data is generally of prewar vintage. Even the 3d edition (September, 1947) barely mentions any war-time developments and omits postwar problems.

Jorré, Georges. L'URSS; la terre et les hommes. Paris: Société d'éditions françaises et internationales, 1946.

One of the better French studies, hampered, however, by the lack of recent data and the use of old place names.

Leimbach, Werner. Die Sowjetunion; Natur, Volk und Wirtschaft. Stuttgart, Franckh'sche Verlag, 1950.

One of the best geographies of the postwar period, this volume treats every aspect of the USSR in a topical manner. It is up-to-date and takes account of all recent Soviet developments. Among its outstanding features are the abundance of available statistical production data, grouped in 115 tables, 99 topical maps, 65 well-chosen photos, and a

200-item bibliography. Highly recommended for all readers of German.

Lorimer, F. The Population of the Soviet Union: History and Prospects. Geneva, League of Nations, 1946.

A basic work on the topic of Soviet population, based largely on primary source materials. Its scholarly approach is seldom found in books on the USSR.

Mandel, William M. A Guide to the Soviet Union. New York, Dial, 1946.

Book One presents a cursory survey of the economic geography of the constituent republics of the USSR. Postwar data on the economy is given in Book Five.

Mikhaylov (Mikhailov), N. N. Na Karte Rodiny (On the Map of the Motherland). Moscow, 1947.

A fascinating popular study of the changes in the geography of the USSR between 1917 and 1947.

Mikhaylov, N. N. Russkaya Zemlya (The Russian Land). Moscow, Molodaya Gvardiya, 1946.

Describes in travelogue style the geography of the Russian SFSR, stressing the postwar development of the country.

Mikhailov, N. N., and V. Pokshishevsky. Soviet Russia; the land and its people. New York, Sheridan House, 1948.

An economic geography similar in treatment to the foregoing work, but covering the entire USSR.

Pavlov, M. Ya., and V. P. Goroshchenko. Geografiya SSSR (Geography of the USSR). Moscow, Uchpedgiz, 1946.

A textbook for teachers' colleges, using the physico-geographical approach by natural vegetation regions.

Pavlov, M. Ya. Geografiya SSSR (Geography of the USSR). Moscow, Uchpedgiz, 1948.

A revised edition of the foregoing work, containing new material regarding recent economic developments and a greatly expanded regional section by union republics.

Schwartz, Harry. Russia's Postwar Economy. Syracuse, Syracuse University Press, 1947, 119 pp.

Describes war-time and postwar developments in Soviet industry, agriculture, and transportation.

Simmons, Ernest J., ed. USSR: a concise handbook. Ithaca, Cornell University Press, 1947.

A symposium of encyclopedia-type articles on various topics, including the geography, of the USSR.

Suslov, S. P. Fizicheskaya Geografiya SSSR (Physical Geography of the USSR). Moscow, Uchpedgiz, 1947.

An advanced text covering the Asiatic part of the USSR, with the the customary emphasis on such problems as climate, vegetation, soils, flora, and fauna. It is a companion work to Dobrynin's book.

Timasheff, N. S. "The Postwar Population of the Soviet Union," *American Journal of Sociology*, September, 1948.

Attempts to estimate postwar population of the USSR on the basis of data concerning particular age groups. The result is substantially lower than the population estimate based on the postwar election districts.

Voznesensky, N. A. The Economy of the USSR during World War II. Washington, D.C., Public Affairs Press, 1948.

An official Soviet economic history of the last war, it is a basic source of data regarding the development of the economy.

Zakon o Pyatiletnem Plane Vosstanovleniya i Razvitiya Narodnogo Khozyastva SSSR na 1946–1950 gg. (Law of the Five-Year Plan of Reconstruction and Development of the National Economy of the USSR, 1946–50). Moscow, OGIZ, 1946.

Extensive use has been made of the administrative-territorial guides of the USSR and the Russian SFSR, which appear periodically. The following editions were used particularly.

USSR

Russian SFSR. Narodnyy Komissariat Vnutrennykh Del. Statisticheskiy Otdel. Administrativno-Territorial'noye Deleniye SSSR. 8th edition. Moscow, 1929.

USSR. Tsentral'nyy Ispolnitel'nyy Komitet. Administrativno-Territorial'noye Deleniye Soyuza SSR. Moscow, Vlast' Sovetov, 1931.

—— Administrativno-Territorial'noye Deleniye Soyuza SSR na 1 marta 1937. Moscow, Vlast' Sovetov, 1937.

USSR. Verkhovnyy Sovet. Prezidium. Sekretariat. Informatsionno-Statisticheskiy Otdel. SSSR: Administrativno-Territorial'noye Deleniye Soyuznykh Respublik na 1 oktyabrya 1938 g. Moscow, Vlast' Sovetov, 1938.

—— SSSR: Administrativno-Territorial'noye Deleniye Soyuznykh Respublik na 1 yanvarya 1941 g. Moscow, 1941.

—— SSSR: Administrativno-Territorial'noye Deleniye Soyuznykh Respublik na 1 yanvarya 1946 g. Moscow, 1946.

—— SSSR : Administrativno-Territorial'noye Deleniye Soyuznykh Respublik na 1 yanvarya 1947 g.

—— SSSR : Administrativno-Territorial'noye Deleniye Soyuznykh Respublik na 1 yanvarya 1949 g.

RUSSIAN SFSR

Russian SFSR. Verkhovnyy Sovet. Prezidium. Sekretariat. Informatsionno-Statisticheskiy Otdel. RSFSR : Administrativno-Territorial'noye Deleniye na 1 aprelya 1941 g.

—— na 1 iyunya 1945 g.

—— na 1 yanvarya 1948 g.

Mention must also be made of the Great Soviet World Atlas (Bol'shoy Sovetskiy Atlas Mira), 2 vols. 1937–39, which furnished an invaluable cartographic basis for the study of war-time and postwar developments in the geography of the USSR.

Lists of election districts used for the imputation of the population of the USSR and its constituent republics were obtained from the following newspaper sources. Except for the Pravda issue of October 17, 1945, which was devoted to the 1946 elections to the Supreme Soviet of the USSR, all local republic newspapers refer to the 1947 elections to the Supreme Soviets of the constituent republics.

Bakinskiy Rabochiy, December 3–4, 1946 (Azerbaijan SSR).

Kazakhstanskaya Pravda, December 7, 1946 (Kazakh SSR).

Kommunist, December 4, 1946 (Armenian SSR).

Kommunist Tadzhikistana, December 7–8, 1946 (Tadzhik SSR).

Pravda, October 17, 1945 (USSR ; 1946 election).

Pravda, November 30, 1946 (Russian SFSR).

Pravda, January 12, 1950 (USSR ; 1950 election).

Pravda Vostoka, December 3–4, 1946 (Uzbek SSR).

Radyans'ka Ukraina, December 3, 1946 (Ukrainian SSR).

Sovetskaya Belorussiya, December 3, 1946 (Belorussian SSR).

Sovetskaya Estoniya, December 8, 1946 (Estonian SSR).

Sovetskaya Kirgiziya, December 3, 1946 (Kirghiz SSR).

Sovetskaya Latviya, December 3, 1946 (Latvian SSR).

Sovet Turkmenistany, December 10, 1946 (Turkmen SSR).

Zarya Vostoka, December 8, 1946 (Georgian SSR).

No local republic election district lists could be located for the Lithuanian, Moldavian, and Karelo-Finnish SSR's.

A vast amount of material was obtained from the following periodicals:

Pravda.
Izvestiya.
Vedomosti Verkhovnogo Soveta SSSR.
Vokrug Sveta.
Geografiya v Shkole.

Index

Abakan, 283 (*map*), 297 (*map*); industries, 293; population, 292

Abakan range, 292

Abastumani, 425, 427 (*map*), 429

Abaza, ethnic group, 224

Abdulino, 235 (*map*), 255, 256, 258

Abez', 155 (*map*)

Abkhaz, ethnic group, 411, 412, 425, 431

Abkhaz Autonomous Soviet Socialist Republic, 427 (*map*); area: economy: population, 431

Ablaketka, 358, 359 (*map*)

Abrau-Dyurso, 211 (*map*), 219, 220

Abrene, 148, 485; *see also* Pytalovo

Achinsk, 283 (*map*), 290, 291, 297 (*map*)

Achisay, 339 (*map*), 362

Achi-Su, 211 (*map*), 232

Aday-Khokh, mountain, 427 (*map*)

Adimi, 321 (*map*), 328

Adler, 211 (*map*), 219

Administrative-territorial divisions, 41-48; *tables* showing area, capital, population, year of formation, 500-505

Adrasman, 381 (*map*), 385, 395 (*map*)

Adyge, ethnic group, 213, 218, 220, 224, 225

Adyge Autonomous Oblast, 211 (*map*), area: population, 220

Adzhar, ethnic group, 411, 412, 425, 432

Adzhar Autonomous Soviet Socialist Republic, 427 (*map*); area: economy: population, 432

Adzharis-Tskhali River, 432

Aga (Aginskiy) Buryat-Mongol National Okrug, 283 (*map*), 297 (*map*), 302; agriculture: area and population, 304

Agadyr', 339 (*map*)

Agdam, 415 (*map*)

Agdzhabedy, 415 (*map*)

Agine-Afanas'yevskiy, 321 (*map*)

Aginskiy—, *see* Aga—

Aginskoye, 297 (*map*), 304

Agricultural machinery works, 79; Central Asia, 395; European South: largest plant of USSR, 216; Kazakh SSR, 347, 354, 355; Kirghiz SSR, 374; Transcaucasia, 423; Ukrainian SSR, 454, 456, 461, 463; Ural Region, 254; Uzbek SSR, 390; Western Siberia, 267

Agriculture, 54-68; attempted on a regional quasi-self-sufficient basis, 65; regional specialization, 65 ff.; *see also* Dairying; Drainage; Dry farming; Farming; Farms; Fertilizers; Irrigation; Livestock; *also names of products, e.g.,* Grain; *and see further subhead* agriculture, *under names of territorial divisions*

Agryz, 183 (*map*), 189, 235 (*map*)

Ahtme, *see* Akhtme

Ai—, *see* Ay—

Ainu, ethnic group, 332, 333

Akchatau, 339 (*map*), 355

Akhalkalaki, 427 (*map*)

Akhalkhevi, 427 (*map*)

Akhaltsikhe, 426, 427 (*map*)

Akhan-Garan, 395 (*map*)

Akhmedly, 415 (*map*)

Akhsu, 415 (*map*)

Akhta, 421 (*map*)

Akhtala, 421 (*map*), 422

Akhtme, 489

Akhtuba River, 171, 195 (*map*)

Akhtyrka, 437 (*map*)

Akhuryan, 421 (*map*), 422

Akkerman, *see* Belgorod-Dnestrovskiy

Akkermanovka, 259

Ak-Mechet', *see* Kzyl-Orda

Akmolinsk, 339 (*map*), 346, 354

Akmolinsk Oblast, 339 (*map*); agriculture: area: mineral resources: population, 354

Aksarka, 261 (*map*)

Aksenovo-Zilovskoye, 297 (*map*)

Akstafa, 415 (map)
Ak-Su, health resort, 376
Ak-Su, river, 340, 360
Aksuat, 339 (map)
Ak-Tau, range, 396
Aktyubinsk, 338 (map); industries, 352
Aktyubinsk Oblast, 338 (map), area and population: mineral deposits, 352
Aktyuz, 373 (map), 374, 376
Akutikha, 275, 279 (map), 359 (map)
Akzhal, 357, 359 (map)
Akzhar, 359 (map)
Alabuka, 373 (map), 395 (map)
Alagez, 421 (map)
Alagez, Mount, see Aragats, Mount
Alagir, 211 (map), 228
Alai, see Alay
Alakurtti, 495 (map)
Alanskoye, 211 (map)
Alapayevsk, 235 (map), 239, 241 (map), 243
Alatyr', 183 (map), 186
Alaverdi, 421 (map), 422
Alay range, 365, 378
Alay valley, 378
Alazan' River, 415 (map), 417, 427 (map)
Alchevsk, see Voroshilovsk
Aldan, 283 (map), 305, 307, 311 (map); administrative okrug, 44, 307
Aldan highway, 91
Aldan plateau, 304; geologic shield, 20
Aldan River, 22, 283 (map), 304, 305
Alei—, see Aley—
Alekhovshchina, 145 (map)
Aleksandriya, 437 (map), 456
Aleksandropol', see Leninakan
Aleksandrov, 105 (map), 115 (map); industries, 121
Aleksandrov-Gay, 195 (map), 198, 404
Aleksandrovka, see Kuybyshevka
Aleksandrovsk (Ukrainian SSR), see Zaporozh'ye
Aleksandrovsk, or Aleksandrovsk-Sakhalinskiy, 311 (map), 331 (map), 332, 333
Aleksandrovsk-Grushevskiy, see Shakhty
Aleksandrovskiy, 241 (map)
Aleksandrovskoye, 279 (map)
Alekseyevka (Amur Oblast), see Svobodnyy
Alekseyevka, Kazakh SSR, 339 (map), 359 (map)
Alekseyevka (Kuibyshev Oblast), 183 (map), 192
Alekseyevka (Saratov Oblast), 195 (map)

Alekseyevka (Voronezh Oblast), 127 (map)
Aleksin, 105 (map)
Alex—, see Aleks—
Aley River, 359 (map)
Aleysk, 274, 279 (map), 359 (map)
Alga, 338 (map), 352
Ali-Bayramly, 415 (map)
Alitus, 481 (map)
Allakh-Yun', 283 (map), 305
Alma-Ata, 50, 334, 339 (map), 346; industries, 347, 361
Alma-Ata Oblast, 339 (map); agriculture: area, 360; industries, 361; population, 360
Almalyk, 391, 394, 395 (map)
Almaznaya, 451 (map), 452
Alpine geosyncline, 12, 13, 14
Alpine vegetation zone, 33
Altai, see Altay
Altay Kray, 53, 265, 279 (map), 359 (map); agriculture: area and population, 274; mineral resources, 274
Altay Mountains, 17 (map), 260, 262, 274, 275, 334, 336, 341, 356, 358, 359 (map); climate, 263; forest zone, 264; formation, 20; mineral resources, 264, 344
Altay tribes, 41, 53, 98, 265, 275
Altayskaya, see Chesnokovka
Altayskoye, 275, 359 (map)
Alty-Agach, 415 (map)
Altynay, 241 (map)
Aluksne, 481 (map)
Aluminum, industry, 78, 150, 241, 265, 424, 443, 454; see also Bauxite
Alupka, 205 (map), 209
Alushta, 205 (map), 208
Alyaty, 415 (map); oil fields, 416; railroad to Dzhulfa, 422
Alygdzher, 297 (map)
Alytus, see Alitus
Alzamay, 297 (map)
Amamlu, 421 (map), 422
Amangel'dy, 338 (map)
Amasiya, 421 (map)
Amazar, 297 (map)
Ambarchik, 283 (map), 307, 311 (map)
Amber, 14, 492
Ambrolauri, 427 (map)
Amderma, 155 (map), 169
Amgun' River, 321 (map)
Amu Darya, river, 23, 364, 365, 366, 380, 381 (map), 388, 389 (map), 400, 401 (map), 407, 408; canals to connect with Murgab and Tedzhen rivers, 403; with Caspian Sea, 403; cotton, 399, 403

Amur Oblast, 47, 311 (*map*), 315-18, 317 (*map*), 321 (*map*); agriculture, 316, 318; area, 315; gold, 316; population, 315; topography: transportation routes, 316

Amur region, climate, 27; forest zone, 31, 313; location, 308

Amur River, 22, 23, 302, 310, 311 (*map*), 313, 315, 317 (*map*), 321 (*map*), 331 (*map*)

Amurstal', steel mills, 320

Amurzet, 321 (*map*)

Amvrosiyevka, 451 (*map*)

Anabar hills, 281; geologic shield, 20

Anabar River, 285; gold placers, 306

Anadyr', 311 (*map*), 325, 326

Anadyr', Gulf of, 326

Anadyr' range, 20, 282

Anadyr' River, 310

Anan'yev, 436 (*map*), 465 (*map*)

Anan'yevo, 373 (*map*)

Anapa, 211 (*map*), 219

Andi, ethnic group, 231

Andizhan, city, 389 (*map*), 395 (*map*); railroad center: industries, 393

Andizhan, town, 395 (*map*); oil and natural-gas fields, 391, 393

Andizhan Oblast, 389 (*map*), 395 (*map*); area and population: economy, 393; industry, 393

Andreapol', 135 (*map*)

Andreyevsk, 296, 297 (*map*)

Andronovskoye, 145 (*map*)

Angara River, 283 (*map*), 284, 297 (*map*); iron deposits, 296; navigation route, 299; projected hydroelectric installations, 299

Angren, 389 (*map*), 395 (*map*); coal-mining center, 391, 394, 396

Angren River, 388, 394, 395 (*map*)

Anikshchyay, 481 (*map*)

Ani-Pemza, 421 (*map*), 422

Aniva, 330, 331 (*map*)

Anna, 127 (*map*)

Annenskiy Most, 155 (*map*)

Anopino, 115 (*map*)

Anthracite, 72, 239, 248; used in power stations, 75

Antimony, 38, 374, 378, 394

Antsla, 481 (*map*)

Anuchino, 327 (*map*)

Anzhero-Sudzhensk, 277, 279 (*map*), 280

Aparan, 421 (*map*)

Apatite, 10, 38, 159, 160

Apatity, 161 (*map*), 162

Ape, 481 (*map*)

Aprelevka, 115 (*map*)

Aprel'sk, 296

Aprelya, 28 [April 28], 415 (*map*)

Apsheron Peninsula, 413, 415 (*map*); fisheries, 418; irrigation scheme, 62; petroleum deposits, 14, 36, 219, 221, 416, 418 (*see also* Baku); salt obtained from sea, 414

Apsheron-Port, 415 (*map*)

Apsheronsk, 211 (*map*), 219

Arabat spit, or Arabat tongue, 9, 205 (*map*)

Aragats (*Alagez*) Mount, 421 (*map*)

Araks River, *see* Aras River

Aral Kara-Kum, desert, 335, 362

Aral Sea, 23, 335, 338 (*map*), 365, 389 (*map*); area: depth, 337; fisheries, 340, 348; phosphorite and saltpeter, 362; salinity, 339

Aral'sk, 338 (*map*), 363

Aralsul'fat, 338 (*map*), 362

Ararat, 421 (*map*), 423

Aras (*Araks*) River, 410, 414, 415 (*map*), 420; agricultural region, 423

Aravan, 395 (*map*)

Archangel, *see* Arkhangel'sk

Arctic Circle, 154, 157; agriculture, 289; cities within, 162, 165, 292

Arctic islands, 157, 167; economic activity: population, 169

Arctic Ocean, 5-6; coastal lowlands, 283; navigation aids established, 91; Northern Sea Route, 90 f.

Ardatov, 183 (*map*), 187

Ardon River, 211 (*map*); hydroelectric plant, 227

Area of administrative-territorial divisions, 500-505

Argamach, 127 (*map*), 130

Argun' River, 4, 297 (*map*), 302, 310; lead-zinc ore sites, 302, 303

Arkadak, 195 (*map*)

Arkhangel'sk (Archangel), 155 (*map*), 168; industries, 168

Arkhangel'sk Oblast, 167-68; area: population, 167; transportation routes, 167

Arkhangel'skoye, 155 (*map*)

Arkhara, 317 (*map*)

Arkul', 173 (*map*)

Armavir, 211 (*map*), 219, 220

Armenian plateau, 409, 410

Armenian Soviet Socialist Republic, 412, 421 (*map*), 420-24; agriculture, 423; area, 420; cities over 50,000, 509; climate, 420; industries, 423; mineral de-

Armenian SSR (*continued*)
posits, 422 f.; population, 420, 422; water power, 422
Armenians, 41; immigration from abroad, 422, 505n; in European South, 207, 228, 230; in Moldavian SSR, 466; in Transcaucasia, 414, 419, 422, 425, 431
Arpa-chay, 421 (*map*)
Arsenic, 38, 374, 379, 414
Arsk, 183 (*map*)
Artashat, 421 (*map*)
Artel'nyy, 241 (*map*)
Artem, 321 (*map*), 327 (*map*), 328, 329
Artema, Imeni, 451 (*map*)
Artem Island, 415 (*map*), 416
Artemovsk (Krasnoyarsk Kray), 290, 297 (*map*)
Artemovsk (Ukrainian SSR), 443, 450, 451 (*map*)
Artemovskiy (Irkutsk Oblast), 296, 297 (*map*)
Artemovskiy (Rostov Oblast), 217, 451 (*map*)
Artemovskiy (Sverdlovsk Oblast), 241 (*map*)
Artik, 421 (*map*), 422
Artsiz, 465 (*map*)
Artyshta, 279 (*map*)
Arys', 339 (*map*), 349, 362
Arys' River, 340, 362
Arzamas, 173 (*map*), 186
Asbest, 52, 241 (*map*), 242
Asbestos, 239, 242, 243
Asbestovskiy, 241 (*map*), 243
Asha, 241 (*map*), 249
Ashkhabad, 401 (*map*), 402, 403; industries, 405
Ashkhabad Oblast, 401 (*map*), 402, 404-406; agriculture: area, 404; industrial towns, 405 f.; natural resources: population, 404
Ashtarak, 421 (*map*)
Asia, *see* Central Asia; USSR in Asia
Asino, 273, 279 (*map*)
Askaniya-Nova, 437 (*map*)
Askiz, barite, 292
Assa River, 361
Astara, 415 (*map*)
Astrakhan', 10, 195 (*map*); fishing and fish processing: industries: population, 202
Astrakhan' Oblast, 194, 195 (*map*), 200, 201-03; area and population: economy, 201; fish processing centers, 202; transportation, 202
Ataki, 465 (*map*)

Atasuskiy, 339 (*map*), 355
Atbasar, 339 (*map*), 354
Atbashi, 373 (*map*)
Atkarsk, 195 (*map*)
Atrek River, 401 (*map*)
At-Uryakh, 324
Auce, *see* Autse
Aulie-Ata, Auliye-Ata, *see* Dzhambul
Automobiles, assembly plants, 456, 463; production, 79; ZIS, 113
Automobile transportation, 91
Autonomous territorial divisions, 44 ff.; *see also under names of individual territorial divisions*
Autse, 481 (*map*)
Avachinskaya Sopka, 311
Avars, in European South, 213, 231; in Russian SFSR, 98; in Siberia, 41
Aviation, 92
Ay, river, 235 (*map*), 241 (*map*)
Ayaguz, 339 (*map*), 357, 359 (*map*)
Ayaguz River, 357, 359 (*map*)
Ayakhta, 297 (*map*)
Ayan, 311 (*map*), 323
Aydabul', 339 (*map*)
Aydar River, 451 (*map*)
Aydyrlinskiy, 235 (*map*), 258
Aynazhi, 481 (*map*)
Ayzpute, 481 (*map*)
Azerbaijan (Azerbaydzhan) Soviet Socialist Republic, 412, 413-19; agriculture, 417; area, 413; cities over 50,000, 509; climate, 414; fishing industry, 417; hydroelectric power, 414; iron, 412; irrigation scheme, 62; mineral resources, 414, 416; mineral springs, 414; principal oil region of USSR, 416; population, 413, 414; railway routes: roads, 418; textile industry, 412
Azerbaijani or Azerbaijani Turks, ethnic group, 40, 411, 413
Azizbekov, 421 (*map*)
Azov, 205 (*map*), 216
Azov, Sea of, 9, 205 (*map*), 437 (*map*), 445; navigation, 90
Azov-Podolian shield, 18
Azovstal', steel mills, 442, 452
Azov uplands, 435

Babay (Ukrainian SSR), 436 (*map*)
Babay coal field (Bashkir ASSR), 255
Babayevo, 155 (*map*)
Babintsy, 436 (*map*)
Babushkin (Buryat-Mongol ASSR), 283 (*map*), 297 (*map*), 302

Babushkin (Moscow Oblast), 113, 114, 115 (*map*)
Bai—, *see* Bay—
Bailovo, 415 (*map*)
Bakal, 241 (*map*), 248, 249
Bakanas, 339 (*map*)
Bakharden, 401 (*map*)
Bakhchisaray, 51, 205 (*map*), 207
Bakhmach, 437 (*map*)
Bakhmut, *see* Artemovsk (Ukrainian SSR)
Bakhty, 339 (*map*), 359 (*map*)
Bakinskikh Komissarov, Imeni, 26, 401 (*map*), 404
Bakr-Uzyak, 235 (*map*), 254
Baksanges (Baksan hydroelectric station), 211 (*map*), 226
Baksan River, 211 (*map*)
Baksan valley, upper, ceded to Georgian SSR, 225, 427 (*map*)
Baksheyevo, 115 (*map*)
Baku, 10, 415 (*map*), 418; cracking plants, 416; irrigation scheme, 62; machinery works, 416; oil region of major importance, 36, 48, 412, 418; population, 418; *see also* Apsheron Peninsula
Bakuriani, 427 (*map*), 429
Balabanovo, 115 (*map*), 135 (*map*)
Baladzhary, 415 (*map*)
Baladzholskiy, 359 (*map*)
Balakhany, 415 (*map*), 416
Balakhna, 173 (*map*), 178, 179, 180
Balaklava, 51, 205 (*map*), 206, 207
Balakleya, 437 (*map*)
Balakovo, 195 (*map*), 197
Balashikha, 115 (*map*)
Balashov, 195 (*map*), 198
Balbagar, 300
Baley, 297 (*map*), 303
Balezino, 235 (*map*), 253
Balkany, 248
Balkar-Kabardinian (now Kabardinian) Autonomous SSR, part of, added to Georgian SSR, 225, 426, 427 (*map*); *see also* Kabardinian Autonomous SSR
Balkars, ethnic group, 213, 225, 514
Balkhan range, 365, 404; bentonite, 402; coal, 405
Balkhash, city, 339 (*map*), 356
Balkhash, Lake, 23, 337, 339 (*map*), 340, 356; copper, 344; fisheries, 348, 360
Balta, 436 (*map*), 441, 465 (*map*), 466
Bălţi, *see* Bel'tsy
Baltic Region, 479-92, 481 (*map*), 491 (*map*); agriculture, 482; chemical industry, 484, 485, 487, 488, 492; climate, 480; ethnic groups, 41; fishing industries, 484, 489, 492; lumber industries, 482, 483, 488, 489; metallurgical industry, 487; population, 480; topography, 479; *see also* Estonian SSR; Latvian SSR; Lithuanian SSR
Baltic Sea, 8, 16 (*map*), 90, 479
Baltic shield, *see* Fenno-Scandian shield
Baltic-White Sea Canal, *see* White Sea–Baltic Canal
Baltiysk, 52, 491 (*map*), 492
Bal'tser, *see* Krasnoarmeysk (Saratov Oblast)
Balyaginskiy, 303
Balzer, *see* Krasnoarmeysk (Saratov Oblast)
BAM, *see* Baykal-Amur *magistral*
Bank, 415 (*map*)
Bar, 436 (*map*)
Baraba Steppe, 264; dairy products, 272, 273
Barabash, 327 (*map*)
Barabinsk, 261 (*map*), 273
Baran', 471 (*map*)
Baranovichi, 471 (*map*), 478
Baranovichi Oblast, 471 (*map*), 472; area and population, 477
Baranovskiy, 327 (*map*)
Barbalo, Mount, 427 (*map*)
Barda, 415 (*map*)
Barents Sea, 5, 16 (*map*), 155 (*map*); fishing, 162
Barguzin, 297 (*map*)
Barguzin range, 300
Barguzin River, 300
Barite, deposits, 292, 405, 427
Barnaul, 261 (*map*), 266, 274, 279 (*map*), 359 (*map*); industries, 275
Barsuki, 335
Bartang, 381 (*map*)
Barvenkovo, 451 (*map*)
Barysh, 183 (*map*), 191
Barzas, 277, 279 (*map*)
Basargechar, 421 (*map*)
Bashanta, 205 (*map*)
Bashkir Autonomous Soviet Socialist Republic, 44, 235 (*map*), 237, 241 (*map*), 253-56; agriculture, 254; area, 253; industrial centers, 255-56; industries, 254; mineral resources, 253; oil fields, 254, 256; population, 253; railroads, 255
Bashkirs, ethnic group, 40, 98; in Urals, 237, 243, 252, 254; in Volga Region, 184
Baskaya, *see* Gremyachinsk
Baskunchak, Lake, 23, 195 (*map*), 202
Bataisk, *see* Bataysk

Batalpashinsk, *see* Cherkessk
Batamshinskiy, 338 (*map*), 352
Bataysk, 205 (*map*), 217
Batetskiy, 145 (*map*)
Batken, 395 (*map*)
Batraki, 183 (*map*), 193
Batumi, 9, 416, 427 (*map*), 432
Batylinskiy, 305
Batyr' (or Karagiye) Sink, 18, 335
Baunt, 300
Bauska, 481 (*map*)
Bautino, 351
Bauxite, 38, 78, 153, 238, 290, 354
Bayan-Aul, 339 (*map*)
Bayan-Tumen, *see* Choybalsan
Baychunas, 338 (*map*), 346, 351
Baykal-Amur *magistral* trunk line, 88, 298, 316
Baykal, Lake, 23, 283 (*map*), 284, 297 (*map*); fishing industry, 298; mica, 296; navigation route, 299, 301; oil wells, 300; sable reserve, 301
Baykal Range, 282, 295
Baykit, 283 (*map*), 293
Baykonur, 338 (*map*), 345, 346, 355
Baymak, 235 (*map*), 253, 255, 256
Bayram-Ali, 401 (*map*), 406
Baysun, 389 (*map*)
Bazarnyy Syzgan, 183 (*map*), 191
Bednodem'yanovsk, 183 (*map*)
Begovat, 77, 389 (*map*), 391, 394, 395 (*map*), 396
Bek-Budi, *see* Karshi
Bel'agachskiy, 359 (*map*)
Belaya Kalitva, 205 (*map*), 215, 451 (*map*)
Belaya River (Bashkir ASSR), 234, 235 (*map*), 241 (*map*), 253
Belaya River (Krasnodar Kray), 211 (*map*)
Belaya Tserkov', 436 (*map*), 446
Belebelka, 145 (*map*)
Belebey, 235 (*map*)
Belev, 105 (*map*)
Belgorod, 127 (*map*), 133
Belgorod-Dnestrovskiy, 436 (*map*), 457, 465 (*map*), 466
Belgres power station, 474, 475; *see also* Orekhovsk
Belichi, 436 (*map*)
Belinskiy, 183 (*map*)
Belogorsk, 205 (*map*), 208
Belogor'ye, 261 (*map*)
Belokany, 415 (*map*)
Belomorsk, 495 (*map*), 496, 497
Beloomut, 115 (*map*)
Beloostrov, 153 (*map*)

Belopol'ye, 437 (*map*)
Belorechka, 241 (*map*)
Beloretsk, 235 (*map*), 237, 253, 255
Belorussian Poles'ye, *see* Pripet Marshes
Belorussians, in Baltic Region, 480, 483, 484; in Belorussian SSR, 472; in Ukrainian SSR, 440; in USSR, 40
Belorussian Soviet Socialist Republic, 469-78; agriculture, 473; area, 469; cities over 50,000, 510; climate: drainage: forests, 470; industries, 473; lumber industries, 476, 477; mineral resources, 470 f.; oblast survey, 47, 474-78; population, 469, 472; soils, 470; *see further under names of oblasts as listed on p. 502*
Belostok, 472, 473
Belotsarsk, *see* Kyzyl
Belousovka, 358, 359 (*map*)
Belovezha Pushcha, 469
Belovo, 277, 279 (*map*)
Belozersk, 155 (*map*)
Bel'tsy, 464, 465 (*map*), 468
Belukha, mountain, 262, 359 (*map*)
Belush'ye or Belush'ya Guba, 155 (*map*), 169
Belyy, 135 (*map*)
Belyye Berega, 135 (*map*)
Belyy Gorod, 415 (*map*), 418
Bendery, 465 (*map*), 468
Berchogur, 338 (*map*), 346
Berd, 421 (*map*)
Berd' River, 279 (*map*)
Berdichev, 436 (*map*), 458
Berdsk, 273, 279 (*map*)
Berdyansk, *see* Osipenko
Berdyaush, 241 (*map*)
Beregovo, 436 (*map*)
Berelyakh, 324
Bereza, 471 (*map*)
Berezina River, 469, 470, 471 (*map*), 474, 476
Berezniki, 235 (*map*), 237, 241 (*map*), 245, 247
Berezovka, 436 (*map*)
Berezovo, 261 (*map*)
Berezovskiy, 241 (*map*), 242
Berezovskoye, 303
Berikul'skiy, 279 (*map*)
Bering Sea, 6, 308, 311 (*map*)
Bering Strait, 6, 325
Berislav, 437 (*map*)
Beriya, Imeni, 421 (*map*)
Berlik, 339 (*map*)
Bertys Bay, *see* Balkhash
Beshtau, mountain, 210
Beslan, 211 (*map*), 227

Bessarabia, 41, 456, 464, 466; acquisition of, from Rumania, 459; ceded to USSR, 441; Moldavian territory joined to, 441

Bestobe, 339 (*map*)

Bet-Pak-Dala, desert, 334, 336, 343; meteorological station, 339 (*map*)

Bezhetsk, 135 (*map*), 141

Bezhitsa, 50, 135 (*map*), 138

Białystok, *see* Belostok

Bibi-Eybat, 415 (*map*)

Bidzhan River, 322

Biel—, *see* Bel—

Bikin, 321 (*map*)

Bikin River, 321 (*map*)

Bil'gya, 415 (*map*)

Bina, 415 (*map*)

Binagady, 415 (*map*)

Bira, 321 (*map*)

Bira River, 322

Birakan, 321 (*map*)

Birilyussy, 297 (*map*)

Birobidzhan, 311 (*map*), 321 (*map*), 322, 323

Birshtonas, 483

Birsk, 235 (*map*), 241 (*map*)

Birštonas, *see* Birshtonas

Biryusa, 296

Biržai, *see* Birzhay

Birzhay, 481 (*map*)

Bityug River, 127 (*map*), 131

Biya River, 261 (*map*), 262, 279 (*map*), 359 (*map*)

Biysk, 275, 279 (*map*), 359 (*map*)

Black-Earth Region, *see* Central Black-Earth Region

Black Mountains, 210

Black Sea, 8, 11, 14, 205 (*map*), 366, 427 (*map*), 437 (*map*), 465 (*map*); navigation, 90; ports, 9, 445, 455

Black Sea littoral, 424, 429; resort area, 431; petroleum, 425

Black Sea lowland, 19, 435, 454-57

Blagodarnoye, 211 (*map*)

Blagodat', Mount, 234, 241 (*map*)

Blagoveshchensk (Amur Oblast), 311 (*map*), 315, 317 (*map*); industries, 318; population, 316

Blagoveshchensk (Bashkir ASSR), 235 (*map*), 241 (*map*), 254

Bobriki, *see* Stalinogorsk

Bobrinets, 437 (*map*)

Bobrov, 127 (*map*)

Bobruisk, *see* Bobruysk

Bobruysk, 471 (*map*), 476

Bobruysk Oblast, 471 (*map*); area: economy: population, 476

Bochkarevo, *see* Kuybyshevka

Bodaibo, *see* Bodaybo

Bodaybo, 296, 297 (*map*), 299

Bogdanovich, 241 (*map*)

Bogdarin, 297 (*map*), 300

Bogorodchany, 460

Bogoroditsk, 105 (*map*)

Bogorodsk, 173 (*map*), 179

Bogorodskoye, 321 (*map*)

Bogoslovsk, *see* Karpinsk

Bogotol, 291, 297 (*map*)

Boguchany, 297 (*map*)

Boguchar, 127 (*map*)

Bokombayevskoye, 373 (*map*)

Bokovo-Antratsit, 451 (*map*)

Bokovskaya, 205 (*map*)

Boksitogorsk, 52, 145 (*map*), 152

Bol'dzhuan, 381 (*map*)

Bolekhov, 436 (*map*), 460

Bolgrad, 436 (*map*), 465 (*map*)

Bolnisi, 427 (*map*), 429

Bologoye, 135 (*map*)

Bolokhov, 127 (*map*)

Bolokhovo, 105 (*map*)

Bolon', 321 (*map*)

Bolotnoye, 273, 279 (*map*)

Bol'shakovo, 491 (*map*)

Bol'shaya Izhora, 153 (*map*)

Bol'shaya Vishera, 145 (*map*)

Bol'she-Narymskoye, 359 (*map*)

Bol'shevik Island, 6

Bol'shezemel'skaya Tundra, 158, 169

Bol'shoy Dzhezkazgan, 339 (*map*), 355, 356; *see also* Dzhezkazgan

Bol'shoye Polpino, 135 (*map*)

Bol'shoy Tokmak, 437 (*map*)

Bomnak, 316, 317 (*map*)

Bondyuzhskiy, 183 (*map*)

Boom Gorge, 375

Bor, 173 (*map*)

Borate deposits, 347, 351

Borislav, 436 (*map*), 443, 460

Borisoglebsk, 127 (*map*), 132

Borisov, 471 (*map*), 474

Borisovka (Kazakh SSR), 339 (*map*)

Borisovka (Maritime Kray), 327 (*map*)

Boris Vil'kitskiy Strait, 6

Borki, 436 (*map*)

Borodino, 465 (*map*)

Borodyanka, 436 (*map*)

Borovichi, 144, 145 (*map*), 147

Borovlyanka, 279 (*map*), 359 (*map*)

Borovoye, 339 (*map*), 354

Borovsk (Kaluga Oblast), 115 (*map*), 135 (*map*)

Borovsk (Molotov Oblast), 241 (*map*), 247

Borshchovochnyy Range, 302
Borysław see Borislav
Borzhomi, 425, 427 (*map*), 428, 429
Borzya, 297 (*map*), 303
Boshchekul', 344, 357
Boshnyakovo, 331 (*map*)
Botoma River, 306
Boyarka-Budayevka, 436 **(*map*)**
Braslav, 471 (*map*)
Bratsk, 297 (*map*)
Bredy, 235 (*map*), 248
Brest, 471 (*map*), 477
Brest Oblast, 471 (*map*), 472; area and population, 477
Brest-Litovsk, *see* Brest
Breytovo, 105 (*map*)
Brichany, 465 (*map*)
Brody, 436 (*map*)
Bromine, 402, 404
Bronnitsy, 115 (*map*)
Brovary, 436 (*map*)
Bryansk, 135 (*map*), 138
Bryansk Oblast, 135 (*map*); agriculture: area, 137; cities, 138; industries: mineral resources, 138; population, 137
Brześć nad Bugiem, see Brest
Bucha, 436 (*map*)
Budennovsk, 211 (*map*), 223
Budennovskiy, 451 (*map*)
Budennyy, 373 (*map*)
Budogoshch, 145 (*map*)
Budy, 436 (*map*)
Budzhak Steppe, 464, 465 (*map*)
Bug Liman, 455
Bug River, 471 (*map*); *see also* Southern Bug River
Bugrino, 155 (*map*), 169
Bugul'ma, 183 (*map*), 189
Buguruslan, 36, 183 (*map*), 235 (*map*), 259
Bui—, *see also* Buy—
Buinsk, 183 (*map*), 189
Bukachacha, 297 (*map*), 303
Bukhara, 389 (*map*), 398; oasis, 369, 388
Bukhara Jews in Central Asia, 368
Bukhara Oblast, 389 (*map*), 397-98; area and population, 397; industries, 398
Bukhtarma River, 341, 358, 359 (*map*)
Buki, 395 (*map*)
Bukovina, Northern, 466; acquisition of, from Rumania, 459
Bukuka, tungsten, 303
Bulgarians, in European South, 207; in Moldavian SSR, 466; in Ukrainian SSR, 440, 457
Bulun, 306

Bureya, 317 (*map*)
Bureya Range, 309, 317 (*map*), 321 (*map*)
Bureya River, 310, 316, 317 (*map*), 321 (*map*); coal basin, 36, 314, 319, 320; gold, 313
Burkhalinskiy, 305
Burlyu-Tobe, 339 (*map*), 360
Buryat-Mongol Autonomous Soviet Socialist Republic, 297 (*map*), 300-302; agriculture, 301; area, 300; highways: industries, 301; mineral resources, 300; population: topography, 300
Buryat-Mongols, ethnic group, 41, 98, 288, 289, 296, 300, 302
Buturlinovka, 127 (*map*), 132
Butysh, 235 (*map*), 252
Buurdu, 376
Buy, 105 (*map*), 118, 119
Buynaksk, 211 (*map*), 232
Buzovny, 415 (*map*)
Buzuluk, 235 (*map*), 259
Byandovan, 415 (*map*), 416
Byel—, *see* Bel—
Byk River, 465 (*map*), 468
Bykhov, 471 (*map*)
Bytosh, 135 (*map*)
Byul'-Byuly, 415 (*map*)
Bzyb' River, 427 (*map*)

Cahul, see Kagul
Camel raising, 258, 362
Canals, 62, 63, 89, 384, 385, 474
Canning industry and equipment, 79; *see also* Fishing industries
Capitals of administrative-territorial divisions, 500-505
Carpathian Mountains, 16 (*map*), 434, 435, 459, 463; elevation: extent, 438; formation, 14, 20; petroleum fields, 37, 439, 443
Carpatho-Ukraine, *see* Transcarpathian Oblast
Caspian Sea, 9, 11, 15, 338 (*map*), 415 (*map*); area, 337; coastwise shipping, 90; desert zone, 32; fish-breeding area, 171; fisheries, 337, 348, 403, 418; fish processing industries, 196, 201, 202; lowland, 19, 193, 350; ports, 10; railroad line, new, 202; salinity, 337; shores, 18
Caucasian ethnic group, in Russian SFSR, 98; in Transcaucasia, 411
Caucasus, formation, 14, 20; health and summer resorts, 26; hydroelectric resources, 75; irrigation project, 63; manganese deposits, 14; petroleum, 74; soils,

33; subtropical forest vegetation, 32; *see also* Greater Caucasus range; Lower Don and Northern Caucasus; Transcaucasia

Cement milling, 198, 220, 328

Central Asia, 364-408; agriculture, 368; area, 364, 505; capitals, 505; climate, 26, 366; highest points, 15; highways, 370; irrigation schemes, 62 (*see also* Irrigation); mineral resources, 367; mining industry, 369; industrial regions, 68, 390; petroleum regions, 367, 369, 404; political divisions, 368; population, 368, 505; soils, 33; topography, 364; transportation routes, 369; vegetation, 32, 367; *see also* Kirghiz SSR; Tadzhik SSR; Turkmen SSR; Uzbek SSR

Central Black-Earth Region, 102, 125-33; agriculture, 128; cities over 50,000, 506; climate, 125 f.; industries, 129; population: soils, 126; topography, 125; wheat, 100; *see further under names of oblasts as listed on p. 500*

Central Industrial Region, 98, 105-24; administrative-territorial divisions, 102; agriculture, 109; cities, 107; cities over 50,000, 506; climate, 106; imports and exports, 110; industrial enterprises, 68, 107 ff.; metallurgical industry, 77; mineral resources, 106; population, 106; power, 108; soil and vegetation, 106; textile industry, 81; topography, 105; transportation, 109; *see further under names of oblasts as listed on p. 500*

Central Russian upland, 15, 19, 125, 134

Cernăuţi, see Chernovtsy

Cetatea Albă, see Belgorod-Dnestrovskiy

Chaadayevka, 183 (*map*)

Chadan, 295, 297 (*map*)

Chagala, 405

Chagan-Uzun, 261 (*map*), 276, 359 (*map*)

Chagda, 283 (*map*)

Chagoda, 155 (*map*)

Chamchakly, 401 (*map*)

Changyrtash, 374, 379, 395 (*map*)

Chapayevo, 338 (*map*)

Chapayevsk, 50, 183 (*map*), 193

Chaplino, 437 (*map*)

Chaplygin, 105 (*map*)

Chardara, 339 (*map*)

Chardzhou, 401 (*map*), 402, 407; railroad to Kungrad and Aleksandrov-Gay, 398, 403, 404, 408

Chardzhou Oblast, 401 (*map*), 402; area and population: economy, 407

Chardzhuy, *see* Chardzhou

Char River, 359 (*map*)

Charskiy, 339 (*map*), 359 (*map*)

Chasov-Yar, 451 (*map*)

Chatkal range, 388

Chatyrkël', Lake, 373 (*map*)

Chausy, 471 (*map*)

Chauvay, 373 (*map*), 374, 378, 395 (*map*)

Chayek, 373 (*map*)

Chayvo, 331 (*map*)

Cheboksary, 183 (*map*), 186

Chechen, ethnic group, 213, 228, 229, 514

Chechen-Ingush Autonomous SSR, 51, 226, 228; autonomous oblast, 229; dissolved, 46, 213; territory distributed, 229; part of, added to Georgian SSR, 427

Chekalin, 105 (*map*)

Chekhov, 330, 331 (*map*)

Chekunda, 320, 321 (*map*)

Cheleken, 401 (*map*), 402, 404

Chelkar, 338 (*map*), 352

Chelkar-Tengiz, Lake, 340, 352, 353

Chelyuskin, Cape, 3, 17 (*map*), 294

Chelyabinsk, 235 (*map*), 241 (*map*); coal, 13, 36, 234; industry, 249, 250; population: power station, 250; tractor plant, 237

Chelyabinsk Oblast, 235 (*map*), 237, 241 (*map*), 248-51; agriculture, 250; area: climate, 248; heavy industry, 249; minerals, 248; population: topography, 248

Chemical industry, 80; Baltic Region, 484, 485, 487, 488, 492; Eastern Siberia, 299; European Northwest, 150; European South, 217, 222, 224, 230, 232; geographical dispersion of new plants, 80; Kazakh SSR, 347, 352, 357, 361, 362; Moscow Oblast, 111; Russian SFSR, 99; Transcaucasia, 412, 416, 422, 423, 426, 430; Turkmen SSR, 405; Ukrainian SSR, 442 f., 449, 450, 452, 454, 458, 459, 460, 461; Urals, 237, 242, 245, 246, 247, 250, 251, 255, 258; Uzbek SSR, 390, 391, 393, 396; Volga Region, 179, 180, 185, 188, 189, 198, 200; Western Siberia, 265, 274, 277, 278, 280

Cherdyn', 241 (*map*)

Cheremiss, *see* Mari

Cheremkhovo, 283 (*map*), 297 (*map*); coal basin, 36, 288, 296, 299

Cheremshan River, 183 (*map*)

Cheremukhovo, 239

Cherepanovo, 273, 279 (*map*)

Cherepovets, 155 (*map*), 167

Cherkassy, 437 (*map*), 446

Cherkess, or Circassian, ethnic group, in European South, 41, 98, 213, 218, 220, 221, 224, 225

Cherkess Autonomous Oblast, 45, 211 (*map*); area, 224; chemical industry, 222; economy: population, 224

Cherkessk, 50, 211 (*map*), 224

Chermoz, 241 (*map*), 245

Chernaya Kholunitsa, 173 (*map*)

Chernigov, 437 (*map*), 458

Chernigov Oblast, 437 (*map*); area: economy: population, 458

Chernigovka, 327 (*map*)

Chernikovsk, 235 (*map*), 241 (*map*), 255

Chernogorsk, 283 (*map*), 293, 297 (*map*)

Chernomorskoye, 205 (*map*)

Chernorech'ye, 229

Chernovskiye Kopi, 303, 304

Chernovtsy, 436 (*map*), 459

Chernovtsy Oblast, 436 (*map*), area and population: economy, 459; territory acquired from Rumania, 441, 459

Chernushka, 241 (*map*)

Chernyakhovsk, 52, 491 (*map*), 492

Chernyshevskaya, 205 (*map*)

Chernyshevskoye, 491 (*map*)

Chernyye Gory, 210

Chernyy Gorod, 415 (*map*), 418

Chernyy Irtysh River, 341

Chernyy Yar, 195 (*map*)

Cherskiy range, 17 (*map*), 20, 283, 305

Chertkovo, 205 (*map*), 216

Cherusti, 115 (*map*)

Cherven, 471 (*map*)

Chesha Bay, 5

Chesnokovka, 275, 279 (*map*), 359 (*map*)

Chiatura, 427 (*map*), 430

Chibizhek, 290

Chib'-Yu, *see* Ukhta

Chiili, 338 (*map*)

Chik, 279 (*map*)

Chikishlyar, 401 (*map*)

Chikoy, 301

Chikoy River, 297 (*map*)

Chilia Nouă, see Kiliya

Chilik, 339 (*map*)

Chimbay, 389 (*map*), 399

Chimion, 391, 393, 395

Chimkent, 339 (*map*); industries, 362

Chinaz, 395 (*map*)

Chinese Dungans, *see* Dungans

Chinese Eastern Railway, 303

Chinese in Soviet Far East, 314

Chingiz-Tau, range, 336, 357

Chinnai, *see* Krasnogorsk

Chiragidzor, 415 (*map*), 416

Chirchik, 389 (*map*), 391, 395 (*map*), 396

Chirchik River, 340, 366, 388, 394, 395 (*map*), 396

Chishmy, 235 (*map*)

Chişinău, see Kishinev

Chistopol', 183 (*map*), 189

Chistoye, 173 (*map*)

Chistyakovo, 437 (*map*), 442, 451 (*map*), 452

Chita, 283 (*map*), 297 (*map*), 303; industries, 304

Chita Oblast, 283 (*map*), 297 (*map*), 302-04, 314; agriculture, 303; area: climate, 302; economy, 303; forests: mineral resources, 302 f.; population: topography, 302; transportation routes, 303

Chkalov, 50, 235 (*map*), 258, 345; industries, 259

Chkalov Oblast, 235 (*map*), 237, 256-59; agriculture, 257; area, 256; climate, 257; industries, 258; mineral deposits, 257; population: topography, 256

Chkalovo, 331 (*map*)

Chkalovsk, 173 (*map*)

Chkalovskoye, 327 (*map*)

Chokhatauri, 427 (*map*)

Chokpak, 346, 362

Chokurdakh, 283 (*map*), 307

Chortkov, 436 (*map*), 462

Chorukh-Dayron, 385, 395 (*map*)

Choybalsan, 297 (*map*), 303

Chrome (Chromite, Chromium), 38, 78; Kazakh SSR, 347, 349, 352; Urals, 245, 253, 256, 257

Chu, 85, 339 (*map*), 349, 355

Chu-Ili Mountains, 337

Chu River, 339 (*map*), 340, 361, 371, 375; irrigation canal project, 62, 375; valley, 375, 379; crops, 374, 376

Chudovo, 145 (*map*), 147

Chudskoye Lake, *see* Peipus, Lake

Chugunash, 279 (*map*)

Chuguyev, 436-37 (*map*)

Chuguyevka, 327 (*map*)

Chukchi, *see* Luoravetlany

Chukchi-Anadyr' region, 308, 311; climate, 313; coal deposits, 314; tundra, 313

Chukchi National Okrug, 311 (*map*), 318; area and population, 325; industries: mineral resources, 326

Chukchi peninsula, 283; ethnic group on, 314

Chukchi Sea, 6, 310 (*map*)

Chukhloma, 105 (*map*)

Chulak-Kurgan, 339 (*map*)
Chulak-Tau, 339 (*map*), 361
Chul'man, 283 (*map*), 305
Chulym, 261 (*map*)
Chulym River, 261 (*map*), 279 (*map*), 297 (*map*); brown-coal mines, 290
Chumikan, 311 (*map*), 321 (*map*)
Chumysh River, 279 (*map*)
Chuna River, 297 (*map*)
Chupa, 495 (*map*)
Chusovaya River, 234, 241 (*map*)
Chusovoy, 235 (*map*), 241 (*map*), 244, 245
Chust, 389 (*map*), 394, 395 (*map*)
Chuvash, ethnic group, 40, 98, 182, 185, 186, 188, 189, 194
Chuvash Autonomous Soviet Socialist Republic, 183 (*map*); area: capital, 185; industrial centers, 186; industries: population: topography, 185
Chuya highway, 91, 276
Chuya range, 262
Circassian, *see* Cherkess
Cities, administration, 48; with population over 50,000, 506-11
Citrus fruits, 55, 432
Clays, fire-proof or refractory, 38, 258, 423; kaolin, 38, 290
Climate, 24-27; coldest area of world, 27; continental type, 24; high and low pressure areas, 25
Coal, anthracite, 72, 239, 248; anthracite dust used in power stations, 75; brown-coal mines, 290, 300, 303, 427 (*see also* Lignite); coking coal, 36, 72, 73, 74, 164, 254, 265, 303, 320, 374; gasification, 69, 75, 300; Jurassic, 13; Middle Carboniferous period, 12; sapropelite variety, 264, 277
Coal deposits, Central Asia, 368, 369; Donets Basin, 12, 73, 217, 276, 441; Eastern Siberia, 287, 288, 290, 292, 293, 296, 302, 303, 306; European South, 215; Karaganda Basin, 12, 74, 265, 345, 346, 354, 355; Kazakh SSR, 36, 344, 345, 346, 351, 352, 355 ff. *passim*, 362; Kirghiz SSR, 373, 374, 378, 379; Kuznetsk Basin, 12, 33, 73, 264, 265, 276 f. (*see also* Kuznetsk Basin); Moscow Basin, 74; reserves of USSR, 33-34; Russian SFSR, 96; Soviet Far East, 313 f., 318, 325, 328, 332; Tadzhik SSR, 383, 386; Transcaucasia, 425, 431; Turkmen SSR, 405, 406; Ukrainian SSR, 439, 441, 451, 452, 460; Urals, 243, 255, 257, 258; Uzbek SSR, 390, 391, 395, 396; Western Siberia, 264, 265, 276

Coasts, description of, 5-10
Cobalt, 38, 414
Colchis lowland, *see* Kolkhida
"Cold pole," 312
Collective farming, *see* Farming
Commander (Komandorskiye) Islands, 7, 309, 310 (*map*), 324; ethnic group on, 314, 325
Commerce and transportation, 82-92
Copper, European North, 160; Kazakh SSR, 344, 347, 355 ff. *passim;* reserves of USSR, 37; smelters and refineries, 78, 239, 347, 355, 356, 391, 395; Transcaucasia, 412, 422; Urals, 238, 239, 253, 256 ff. *passim;* Uzbek SSR, 391, 395
Corn *kombinat,* 227
Corundum, 38, 355
Cossacks, in European South, 210, 218
Cotton, Central Asia, 59, 369; dry-farming methods, 59, 60, 67, 454; Egyptian, 383; irrigation, 62; Kazakh SSR, 362; Kirghiz SSR, 378, 379; Tadzhik SSR, 383, 385; Transcaucasia, 413; Uzbek SSR, 391
Crab-canning installations, 324
Crimea (Crimean Oblast), 46, 51, 53, 102, 205 (*map*), 204-9, 437 (*map*); agriculture, 207; area, 204; cities, 209, cities over 50,000, 507; climate, 25, 206; exports, 208; history, 207; imports, 209; natural resources, 208; phosphoric iron ore, 206; population, 204, 207; resorts, 26; soils, 33; topography, 204, 206; transportation, 208; vegetation, 32
Crimean Mountains, 205 (*map*); formation, 14, 20
Crimean Tatars, 514
Crops, industrial, 60; geographical displacement, 59; rotation, 58; selective and crossbreeding processes of resistant types, 55
Cryolite, 257
Curzon line, 4, 441, 473
Czortków, see Chortkov

Dagestan Autonomous Soviet Socialist Republic, 211 (*map*), 212, 213, 228, 230-32; agriculture: area, 230; ethnic groups, 231; industrial centers, 232; industries: population, 230
Dagestanskiye Ogni, 211 (*map*), 231
Dagö, island, *see* Khiuma
Dagomys, 211 (*map*)
Dairying, 63-64, 66, 67, 166, 266, 267, 274,

Dairying (*Continued*)
276; *see also* Livestock; *see further sub-head* agriculture, *under names of territorial divisions*
Dalmatovo, 261 (*map*)
Dal'stroy, development project, 323
Dambuki, 317 (*map*)
Dams, *see* Hydroelectric stations
Danilov, 105 (*map*)
Danilovka, 339 (*map*), 354
Dankov, 105 (*map*)
Darasun, 297 (*map*), 303
Daraut-Kurgan, 373 (*map*)
Darganata, 401 (*map*)
Darghins, 98, 231
Darg-Kokh, 211 (*map*)
Darnitsa, 436 (*map*), 446
Darvaza, 401 (*map*), 402, 405
Dashava, 436 (*map*), 461
Dashkesan, 415 (*map*), 416, 426
Datta, 322
Daubikhe River, 327 (*map*)
Daugava River, 481 (*map*); *see also* Western Dvina River
Daugavgriva, port of, 486
Daugavpils, 481 (*map*), 487
David-Gorodok, 471 (*map*)
Davlekonovo, 235 (*map*)
Debal'tsevo, 451 (*map*), 452
Dedovsk, 115 (*map*)
Degtyarka, 241 (*map*)
De Long Island, 6, 307
Delyatin, 460
Dema, 255
Demidov, 135 (*map*)
Demyansk, 145 (*map*)
Denau, 389 (*map*)
Derbent, 211 (*map*), 232
Derbeshkinskiy, 183 (*map*)
Derbinskoye, 331 (*map*)
Dergachi (Saratov Oblast), 195 (*map*)
Dergachi (Ukrainian SSR), 436 (*map*)
Derpt, see Tartu
Deserts, change in nomadic type of stock-raising in, 64; climate, 32; effort to raise livestock, maintain wells in, 403; exploitation of agricultural potential, 61; irrigation, 407; Kazakh SSR, 343; soil, 32; Turkmen SSR, 400
Desna River, 135 (*map*), 434, 436 (*map*), 446, 458
Detskoye Selo, *see* Pushkin
Deynau, 401 (*map*)
Dezhnev, Cape, 3, 17 (*map*)
Dickson, *see* Dikson
Didbiran, 321 (*map*)
Dikson, 283 (*map*), 294

Dilizhan, 421 (*map*)
Diomede Islands, 6, 325
Disna, 471 (*map*)
Divichi, 415 (*map*)
Divisions, *see* Administrative-territorial divisions
Divnoye, 211 (*map*)
Dmitriyev-L'govskiy, 127 (*map*)
Dmitriyevskoye, *see* Talas
Dmitrov, 105 (*map*), 111, 115 (*map*)
Dmitrovsk-Orlovskiy, 127 (*map*)
Dneprodzerzhinsk, 437 (*map*), 442, 453
Dneproges, see Dnieper hydroelectric station
Dnepropetrovsk, 437 (*map*), 442, 453
Dnepropetrovsk Oblast, 437 (*map*); area: industries: population, 453
Dnieper Bend, 452-54; agriculture, 453; heavy industry center, 452; industrial centers, 453
Dnieper-Bug Canal, 474
Dnieper hydroelectric station (*Dneproges*), 76, 438, 442, 443, 444, 454
Dnieper lowlands, 19, 435; glacier, 18
Dnieper ridge, 434, 435
Dnieper River, 19, 22, 135 (*map*), 435, 437 (*map*), 446, 447, 448, 452, 453, 471 (*map*), 475, 476; navigation, 438, 444; valley, 15; viticulture, 467
Dniester River, 22, 435, 436 (*map*), 438, 459, 462, 464, 465 (*map*); hydroelectric installations, 467; navigation, 468; liman, 457; viticulture, 467
Dobele, 481 (*map*)
Dobromil', 436 (*map*), 460
Dobropol'ye, 451 (*map*)
Dobrovol'sk, 491 (*map*)
Dobrush, 471 (*map*), 476
Dobryanka, 241 (*map*), 245
Dokshitsy, 471 (*map*)
Dokshukino, 211 (*map*), 225
Dolgan-Nenets National Okrug, *see* Taymyr National Okrug
Dolgany in Eastern Siberia, 288, 290, 293
Dolina, 436 (*map*), 460
Dolinsk, 330, 331 (*map*), 333
Dombarovskiy, 235 (*map*), 257, 258
Domnovo, 491 (*map*)
Domodedovo, 115 (*map*)
Don, Lower, *see* Lower Don
Donbas, *see* Donets Basin
Donets Basin, or Donbas, 451 (*map*); coal-mining center, 217; coal reserves, 12, 73, 276, 441; extent of mining area: industrial regions served, 73; heavy machine construction, 442; industrial de-

velopment, 449-51; mineral resources, 449; population, 440, 451; port, 452; power-transmission system, 451; rail network, 451; rail trunk to Moscow, 444; salt and mercury deposits, 439

Donets ridge, 215, 434, 435

Don River, 22, 127 (*map*), 195 (*map*), 214-17 *passim*, 205 (*map*), 451 (*map*); drainage basin, 170

Donskoy, 105 (*map*), 111

Dormidontovka, 321 (*map*)

Dorogobuzh, 135 (*map*)

Dorokhovo, 115 (*map*)

Dorpat, see Tartu

Dossor, 338 (*map*), 346, 351

Dostafyur, 414

Drezna, 115 (*map*)

Drissa, 471 (*map*)

Drogobych, 436 (*map*), 443, 460

Drogobych Oblast, 436 (*map*), 441, 459, 460; industrial centers, 461

Drohobycz, see Drogobych

Druskininkay, 481 (*map*), 483

Druzhba, 491 (*map*)

Druzhina, 283 (*map*)

Druzhkovka, 450, 451 (*map*)

Druzhnaya Gorka, 145 (*map*)

Dry farming, 60, 61, 67

Dubenskiy, 258

Dubisa River, 481 (*map*), 483

Dubossary, 465 (*map*), 468

Dubovka (Moscow Oblast), 111

Dubovka (Stalingrad Oblast), 195 (*map*), 199

Dubovskoye, 205 (*map*)

Dubrovka, 151, 153 (*map*)

Dubrovno, 471 (*map*)

Dubysa River, *see* Dubisa River

Dudergof (Duderhof), 51

Dudinka, 283 (*map*), 293, 294

Dudorovskiy, 135 (*map*)

Due, 331 (*map*), 332

Dukhovshchina, 135 (*map*)

Dukshtos, 481 (*map*)

Dünaburg, see Daugavpils

Dunay, 327 (*map*)

Dungans (Chinese Moslems), in Central Asia, 368; in Kazakh SSR, 345, 348, 360; in Kirghiz SSR, 376

Dushak, 401 (*map*)

Dusheti, 427 (*map*)

Duzkend, see Akhuryan

Dvigatel'stroy, *see* Kaspiysk

Dvina Bay, 5

Dvina-Pechora lowland, 156

Dvina River, Northern, *see* Northern Dvina River

Dvina River, Western, *see* Western Dvina River

Dvinsk, see Daugavpils

Dyat'kovo, 135 (*map*), 138

Dyes, from cotton tree, 55; vegetable, 61

Dykh-Tau, mountain, 211 (*map*), 224, 427 (*map*)

Dyurbel'dzhin, 373 (map)

Dyushambe, *see* Stalinabad

Dyushambinka River, 386

Dzagidzor, 421 (*map*), 422

Dzaudzhikau, 50, 211 (*map*), 227, 228

Dzerzhinsk (Belorussian SSR), 471 (*map*)

Dzerzhinsk (Gor'kiy Oblast), 173 (*map*), 179, 180

Dzerzhinsk (Ukrainian SSR), 451 (*map*)

Dzhagdy Range, 317 (*map*)

Dzhalal-Abad, 373 (*map*), 379, 395 (*map*)

Dzhalal-Abad Oblast, 373 (*map*); area and population: economy, 379

Dzhalinda, 317 (*map*)

Dzhambeyty, 338 (*map*)

Dzhambul, 50, 339 (*map*), 361, 362, 379

Dzhambul Oblast, 339 (*map*); area and population: economy, 361

Dzhangi-Dzhol, 373 (*map*), 395 (*map*)

Dzhankoy, 205 (*map*), 207, 208

Dzharat, 415 (*map*)

Dzhargalan, 373 (*map*), 374, 377

Dzharkent, *see* Panfilov

Dzhar-Kurgan, 389 (*map*)

Dzhava, 427 (*map*), 433

Dzhebel, 401 (*map*)

Dzhekonda, 305

Dzhetygara, 338 (*map*), 353

Dzhety-Oguz, 377

Dzhezdinskiy, 339 (*map*), 355

Dzhezkazgan, 339 (*map*), 344, 354, 355

Dzhida River, 297 (*map*), 300, 302; *see also* Gorodok

Dzhirgatal', 381 (*map*)

Dzhizak, 389 (*map*), 396

Dzhugdzhur Range, 283, 305

Dzhul'fa, 415 (*map*), 419

Dzhuma, 389 (*map*)

Dzungarian Ala-Tau, 336, 360; zinc, 344

Dzungarian Gates, 336

Dzhusaly, 338 (*map*)

Earthquakes, 206, 310, 410

Eastern Belt Highway, 350

Eastern Slavs, 40

East European plain, 18 ff.; climate, 25; covered by ice, 18; rivers, 22; uplands, 19; *see also* Baltic Region

East-Kazakhstan Oblast, 339 (*map*), 359 (*map*); area and population: mineral resources, 358

East Prussia, 4; northern part organized as Kaliningrad Oblast (*q.v.*), 482, 490; place names in northern, changed to Russian toponymics, 52, 491 (*map*)

East Siberian Sea, 6, 311 (*map*)

Echmiadzin, 421 (*map*)

Economic pattern, USSR, 54-92; agriculture, 54-67; industry, 68-81; in state of flux, 47; transportation and commerce, 82-92

Ege-Khaya, 283 (*map*), 306

Ekhabi, 331 (*map*), 332

Ekibastuz, 339 (*map*), 346, 357

Ekimchan, 317 (*map*), 321 (*map*)

El'brus, Mount, 14, 210, 211 (*map*), 212, 224, 426 (*map*)

El'dikan, 283 (*map*), 305

Electric power stations, *Belgres* station, 474, 475; fuels utilized in, 75; Moscow Oblast, 111; *see also* Hydroelectric stations

Elekmonar, 359 (*map*)

Elektrogorsk, 52, 115 (*map*)

Elektroperedacha, *see* Elektrogorsk

Elektrostal', 52, 77, 111, 115 (*map*)

Elisenvaara, 495 (*map*)

Elista, *see* Stepnoy

El'ton, 195 (*map*)

El'ton, Lake, 195 (*map*)

Emayogi, 488

Emba River, 338 (*map*), 340, 352; petroleum fields, 13, 345, 349 ff. *passim*

Emba, town, 338 (*map*)

Emerald mines, 239

Emi River, 481 (*map*)

Endybal'sk, 306

Engel's, 195 (*map*), 198

Enso, *see* Svetogorsk

Ergeni Hills, *see* Yergeni Hills

Erivan, *see* Yerevan

Ertil', 127 (*map*)

Eskimos, 41, 314

Estonians, 41; in Baltic Region, 488; in Western Siberia, 265

Estonian Soviet Socialist Republic, 45, 479, 481 (*map*), 487-90; administrative organization, 480; agriculture, 488; area, 487; cities over 50,000, 511; geography, 487; mineral resources, 488; population, 480, 487; shale, extraction of combustible, 75; textile industry, 488

Esutoru, see Uglegorsk

Ethnic groups, and their autonomous political divisions, 512-14; deprived of identity as separate nationalities, 514; eleven important, 40-41; rank occupied by any given, 45; *see further under names of groups, e.g.,* Belorussians

Etorofu Island, 333

Eucalyptus, 63

Eupatoria, *see* Yevpatoriya

European North, 102, 154-69; agriculture, 158; cities over 50,000, 507; climate, 157; forests and tundras, 158; natural resources, 159; population, 158; role in Union economy, 159; topography, 154; *see further under names of oblasts as listed on pp. 102, 500*

European Northwest, 102, 143-53; agriculture, 146; cities over 50,000, 507; climate: forests, 145; industries, 145; lakes, 143; mineral resources: population, 145; power stations, 146; soils, 145; topography, 143; *see further under names of oblasts as listed on pp. 102, 500*

European South, 204-32; agriculture, 207 f.; chemical industry, 217, 222, 224, 230, 232; climate, 206 f.; history, 207; industrial centers, 209; mineral resources, 206, 208; railroads, 208; relief and physical geography, 204-6

European West, 102, 134-42; agriculture, 135 f.; cities over 50,000, 506; climate: forests, 135; industries, 9; oblasts, 137-42; population, 135; topography, 134; transportation, 137; *see further under names of oblasts as listed on pp. 102, 500*

Evenki (Tungus), in Soviet Far East, 318, 332; in Eastern Siberia, 41, 53, 288, 289, 290, 293, 296, 300, 302, 305

Evenki National Okrug, 283 (*map*), 290, 297 (*map*); area and population, economy, 293

Eveny (Lamuts) in Eastern Siberia, 288, 305; in Soviet Far East, 323, 324, 325

Eyshishkes, 481 (*map*)

Faleshty, 465 (*map*)

Farab, 401 (*map*)

Farab-Pristan', 401 (*map*)

Far East, *see* Soviet Far East

Farkhad, dam and hydroelectric station, 369, 391, 394, 395 (*map*), 396

Fastov, 436 (*map*)

Fatezh, 127 (*map*)

Fedchenko Glacier, 365, 380

Feldspar, 38

Fenno-Scandian shield, 10, 18, 493

Feodosiya, or Theodosia, 205 (map), 209

Fergana, 389 (map), 393, 395 (map)

Fergana Oblast, 393, 395 (map)

Fergana Range, 366

Fergana Valley, 14, 365, 366, 371, 380, 395 (map); canals, 62, 395 (map); coal and iron deposits, 368; cotton, 369, 378, 379, 383, 392; industries and industrial crops, 374; irrigation system, 384; mineral resources, 372, 374; mining, 383; petroleum, 374, 390, 391; rail network, 375, 393

Fergana Valley, sulphur deposits, 368, 391; textile industry, 394; see also Andizhan Oblast; Fergana Oblast; Leninabad Oblast; Namangan Oblast

Ferroalloys, 253, 347, 352; ferromanganese, 412, 426

Ferruginous springs, 223, 224

Fertilizers, 58, 278, 443, 445, 467; potash fertilizers, 80; superphosphate, 38

Fiber plants, 55, 60, 66, 376

Finland, territory lost to USSR, 148

Finland, Gulf of, 153 (map), 479, 481 (map), 487, 488

Finno-Ugric ethnic group, in Eastern Siberia, 288; Russian SFSR, 98; Urals, 243, 247; Western Siberia, 264

Finns, western, or Baltic, 41; in Karelo-Finnish SSR, 493

Firyuza, 401 (map), 405

Fishing industries, Baltic Region, 484, 489, 492; Barents Sea, 162; Eastern Siberia, 298, 301; European North, 159, 162, 169; European South, 208, 215, 220, 231; Far East, 65; Karelo-Finnish SSR, 496; Kazakh SSR, 337, 348, 350, 351, 363; Russian SFSR, 100; Soviet Far East, 315, 319, 323, 324, 325, 328, 332; Transcaucasia, 417; Turkmen SSR, 403, 405; Ukrainian SSR, 457; Volga Region, 201 f.; Western Siberia, 269, 270

Flax, 60, 66, 177

Floreshty, 465 (map), 467

Fodder crops, 62, 63

Fontan, 456

Food industry, 81, 383; processing centers, 197, 208; see also agriculture; Fishing industries

Foreign trade, 90

Forest zones, 30-31

Fort Shevchenko, 338 (map), 351

Fosforitnaya station, 173 (map)

Fosforitnyy, 52, 105 (map), 115 (map)

Franz-Josef Land, 5, 155 (map), 167, 169

Fridenfel'd (Friedenfeld), 51

Friedland, 52

Frolovo, 195 (map), 199

Fruits, 369

Frunze, city (Kirghiz SSR), 373 (map), 376

Frunze, town (Kirghiz SSR), 374, 378, 395 (map)

Frunze (Ukrainian SSR), 451 (map)

Frunze Oblast, 373 (map); area, 375; agriculture: industries, 376; main economic region of the Kirghiz SSR, 375; population, 375

Fur, hunting and trapping of fur-bearing animals, 65, 306; processing industry, 176; production in Khabarovsk Kray, 319; seal reserve, 325

Furmanov, 105 (map), 120

Furukamappu, see Yuzhno-Kuril'sk

Gadyach, 437 (map)

Gagra (formerly Gagry), 427 (map), 431

Gali, 427 (map), 431

Galich, 105 (map)

Gandzha, see Kirovabad

Ganyushkino, 338 (map), 351

Garm, 381 (map), 383, 387

Garm Oblast, 381 (map); area and population: livestock, 387

Gasan-Kuli, 401 (map), 403, 405

Gas pipe lines, see Natural gas pipe lines

Gastello, 331 (map)

Gatchina, 50, 145 (map), 152, 153 (map)

Gaudan, 401 (map)

Gauja River, see Gauya River

Gaurdak, 368, 401 (map), 402, 407

Gauya River, 481 (map), 485

Gavrilov-Yam, 105 (map)

Gayduk, 211 (map)

Gazalkent, 395 (map)

Gelendzhik, 211 (map), 219

Gems, 38, 239

Genichesk, 205 (map), 437 (map)

Geokchay, 415 (map)

Geokmaly, 415 (map)

Geok-Tepe, 401 (map)

Georgian Military Road, 227, 228, 413, 429

Georgians, in the Caucasus, 41; in European South, 228; in Transcaucasia, 41, 411, 414, 431, 432, 433

Georgian Soviet Socialist Republic, 51, 222, 412, 427 (map), 424-30; agriculture, 428; area, 424; cities over 50,000, 509; climate, 424 f.; coal mines, 412; economic importance, 426; health re-

Georgian SSR (*continued*)
sorts, 429; heavy industry, 426; highways, 429; mineral resources, 425; population, 424, 425; subtropical crops, 426, 428, 431; territory of liquidated autonomous units added to, 213, 426; transportation facilities, 429; water power, 425
Georgiyevka, 359 (*map*)
Georgiyevsk, 211 (*map*), 223
Geral'd Island, 311 (*map*), 326
Gerdauen, *see* Zheleznodorozhnyy
Gergebil', 211 (*map*), 232
German Volga, *see* Volga German
Gidrotorf, 173 (*map*), 179
Gigant, 205 (*map*), 216
Gilyaks, *see* Nivkhi
Gimoly, 495 (*map*), 496
Girvas, 161 (*map*)
Gissar, 381 (*map*); range, 383, 388; valley, 380, 384
Gizel'don, 211 (*map*), 227
Gizhduvan, 389 (*map*), 398
Gizhiga, 311 (*map*); bay, 325
Glauber salt, 232, 274, 368, 404
Glazov, 235 (*map*), 252
Glubokiy, 205 (*map*), 216, 451 (*map*)
Glubokoye (Belorussian SSR), 471 (*map*)
Glubokoye (Kazakh SSR), 358, 359 (*map*)
Glukhov, 437 (*map*)
Gnadenburg, *see* Vinogradnoye
Gokcha Lake, *see* Sevan Lake
Gold, Eastern Siberia, 38, 282, 287, 290, 292, 296, 300, 302, 303, 305; Kazakh SSR, 38, 344, 353 ff. *passim;* Kirghiz SSR, 377; Soviet Far East, 38, 313, 314, 315, 319, 320, 323; Tadzhik SSR, 383, 386, 387; Urals, 38, 239, 253, 256, 257, 258; Western Siberia, 264, 274 f., 279
Golden Horn Bay, 329
Golds, *see* Nanay
Golodnaya Step', 336, 362, 388
Golovinskaya, 296
Golyy Karamysh, *see* Krasnoarmeysk (Saratov Oblast)
Gomel', 471 (*map*), 476
Gomel' Oblast, 471 (*map*); area: economy: population, 476
Goose Lake, 300
Goragorskiy, 211 (*map*), 229
Gorbatov, 173 (*map*)
Gorchakovo, 395 (*map*)
Goreloye, 127 (*map*)
Gori, 427 (*map*), 430

Goris, 421 (*map*)
Gorki, 471 (*map*)
Gor'kiy, 173 (*map*); fairs, 180; industries, 179, 180; population, 180; railroad to Kotel'nich, 84
Gor'kiy Oblast, 173 (*map*), 178-80; agriculture, 179; area and population: economic position, 178; industries, 77, 179
Gorlovka, 442, 450, 451 (*map*)
Gornaya Shoriya, 278
Gorno-Altay Autonomous Oblast, 53, 265, 279 (*map*), 359 (*map*); area and population, 275; ethnic groups, 275 f.; highway: industries, 276
Gorno-Altaysk, 261 (*map*), 276, 359 (*map*)
Gorno-Badakhshan Autonomous Oblast, 381 (*map*), 382; area: population, 387
Gornozavodsk, 330, 331 (*map*); coal, 332
Gornyak (Altay Kray), 274, 359 (*map*)
Gornyak (Chelyabinsk Oblast), 250
Gornyatskiy, 155 (*map*), 165
Gornyy, 195 (*map*)
Gorodenka, 460
Gorodets, 173 (*map*), 179
Gorodishche, 183 (*map*)
Gorodok (Belorussian SSR), 471 (*map*)
Gorodok (Buryat-Mongol ASSR), 283 (*map*), 297 (*map*), 300, 302
Gorokhovets, 105 (*map*)
Gorskiy, *see* Goragorskiy
Gorskoye, 451 (*map*)
Goryn' River, 436 (*map*), 461, 471 (*map*)
Gousany, 415 (*map*)
Grain, belts, 59; grain-hemp-potato zone, 66; grain-sunflower zone, 67; Kuban' steppes, 213; Moldavian SSR, 467; Ukrainian SSR, 441, 454
Graphite, 38, 290
Grayvoron, 127 (*map*)
Greater Caucasus range, 209, 210, 409, 413, 431, 432; agricultural products, 417; ethnic and linguistic groups, 98; mountain tribes, 425; resorts, 223
Greater Uzen' River, 195 (*map*)
"Great Volga" scheme, 63, 172 f., 186, 196, 199, 246, 247
Great Fergana Canal, 385
Great Gissar Canal, 384
Greeks, in European South, 207, 228; in Moldavian SSR, 466; in Transcaucasia, 425, 431
Gremikha, 161 (*map*)
Gremyachinsk, 241 (*map*), 244
Grigoriopol', 465 (*map*), 468
Grimm, *see* Kamenskiy

Grodekovo, 321 (*map*), 327 (*map*)

Grodno, 471 (*map*), 477

Grodno Oblast, 471 (*map*); area and population, 477

Grossevichi, 322

Groznyy, 211 (*map*), 230; oil fields, 36, 74, 229, 230; pipe line from, 443

Groznyy Oblast, 213, 228-30; agriculture, 229; area, 228; economic importance, 229; history, 228; industrial cities, 230; population: topography, 228; transportation, 230

Gruzino, 145 (*map*), 147

Gryazi, 127 (*map*)

Gubakha, 241 (*map*), 244

Guberniya, 44

Gubkin, 37, 127 (*map*)

Gudauta (formerly Gudauty), 427 (*map*), 431

Gudermes, 211 (*map*), 230

Gukasyan, 421 (*map*)

Gukovo, 215, 451 (*map*)

Gulbene, 481 (*map*)

Gul'cha, 373 (*map*)

Gumbinnen, *see* Gusev

Gumista River, hydroelectric station, 431

Gumry, *see* Leninakan

Gundorovka, 215, 451 (*map*)

Gunt River, 387

Gurdzhaani, 427 (*map*)

Gur'yev, 338 (*map*), 347, 351; railroad to Orsk, 349, 350

Gur'yev Oblast, 338 (*map*); area and population: mineral deposits, 351

Gur'yevsk (Kaliningrad Oblast), 491 (*map*)

Gur'yevsk (Kemerovo Oblast), 277, 279 (*map*)

Gurzuf, 205 (*map*), 209

Gusev, 481 (*map*), 491 (*map*), 492

Gus'-Khrustal'nyy, 105 (*map*), 115 (*map*), 121

Gutay, 303

Gvardeysk, 52, 491 (*map*)

Gydan range, *see* Kolyma range

Gyda Peninsula, 6

Gypsies, in Moldavian SSR, 466

Gypsum, 12, 202, 257, 258, 464

Gyul'bakht, 415 (*map*)

Gyumush, 421 (*map*), 422

Gyuzdek, 415 (*map*)

Gzhatsk, 135 (*map*), 140

Handicraft industries, Central Industrial Region, 109, 121; co-operatives, 111; Volga Region, 177

Health resorts, Baltic Region, 483, 486, 492; Caucasus: Crimea, 26; Eastern Siberia, 303; European South, 208, 214, 220, 222, 223, 232; Kazakh SSR, 354; Kirghiz SSR, 376, 377, 378; Transcaucasia, 414, 429, 431, 433; Ukrainian SSR, 454, 456, 461; Urals, 257

Heavy industry, 68, 79; Central Asia, 368; Kazakh SSR, 361; Transcaucasia, 426; Ukrainian SSR, 442, 449; Urals, 237, 239, 240, 249 f., 252; Uzbek SSR, 390; Western Siberia, 266; *see also* Machine-building industries: Metallurgy; Nonferrous metallurgical industry

Heavy metallurgy, 412; raw materials, 439

Hematite, 238, 257

Hemp, 60

Hemp-grain-potato zone, 66

Herald Island, *see* Geral'd Island

High-voltage power lines of USSR, 99

Highways, construction projects, 92; Kirghiz SSR, 375; lack of good, 91; Tadzhik SSR, 384; *see also* Military roads

Hiiumaa, island, *see* Khiuma

Hogs, 63, 64, 448

Honto, *see* Nevel'sk

Hooker I., 155 (*map*), 169

Hotin, see Khotin

Hot springs, 284, 303, 310

Hunting, 306

Hydrography, 21-23

Hydroelectric power stations, Baltic Region, 480, 486, 488, 490; Eastern Siberia, 284, 299; European North, 162; European Northwest, 149; European South, 226, 227, 232; European West, 141; "Greater Volga" scheme, 172, 186, 199, 246, 247; Karelo-Finnish SSR, 493, 494, 496, 497; Kazakh SSR, 347, 356, 358; Kirghiz SSR, 376; Moldavian SSR, 467; Transcaucasia, 62, 412, 414, 422, 425, 426, 430, 431, 432; Transcaucasian projects, 416, 420, 422; Ukrainian SSR, 438, 442; Uzbek SSR, 391, 394, 396; Volga River, 63, 73, 108, 172, 174, 179, 186, 192, 199, 246, 247; Western Siberia, 274

Ibresi, 183 (*map*)

Ice age, 14 ff.; fossilized ice, 284; vegetation, 27

Ichki-Grammatikovo, *see* Sovetskiy

Idel', 495 (*map*), 496

Idritsa, 135 (*map*)

Idzhevan, 421 (*map*)
Igarka, 283 (*map*), 291, 292
Iksha, 115 (*map*)
Ilanskiy, 291, 297 (*map*)
Iletskaya Zashchita, *see* Sol'-Iletsk
Ili, 339 (*map*)
Ili River, 336, 339 (*map*), 340, 360
Il'ich, 339 (*map*), 362, 395 (*map*)
Il'ich Bay, oil fields, 416
Il'ich works, 452
Ilim, 297 (*map*)
Ilim River, iron deposits, 296
Ilimpiya Rayon, 48
Il'inskiy, 330, 331 (*map*)
Il'men, Lake, 143, 145 (*map*)
Ilovaysk, 451 (*map*)
Ilovlinskaya, 195 (*map*)
Ilovlya River, 195 (*map*)
Il'skiy, 211 (*map*), 219
Ilukste, 481 (*map*)
Il'yaly, 401 (*map*)
Iman, 321 (*map*), 328
Iman River, 321 (*map*)
Imandra, Lake, 161 (*map*)
Imeni, *see following proper name*
Imeretia, 428
Imeretians, in Transcaucasia, 411
Imishly, 415 (*map*)
Impilakhti, 495 (*map*)
Imtandzha, 306
Inderborskiy, 338 (*map*), 347, 351
Indiga, 155 (*map*)
Indigirka River, 283 (*map*), 285, 304;
    lowlands, 20
Industrial'nyy, 325
Industriya state farm, 162
Industry, 68-81; characterized by large
    enterprises: smaller-scale construction,
    69; chemical, 80; coal, 72 ff.; food, 81;
    fuel, 72-75; heavy, 79 f.; hydroelectric
    potential, 75 f.; *kombinat* type, 69 ff.;
    location pattern, 68; lumber, 80; metal-
    lurgy, 76 ff.; output, 68; petroleum, 74;
    power sources, 72; *see also names of
    specific centers or regions*
Ingermanland, 44
Ingichka, 389 (*map*)
Ingoda River, 297 (*map*), 302
Ingul River, 455, 456
Ingulets River, 456
Ingur River, 425, 427 (*map*), 428, 431
Ingush ethnic group, 228; dispersed: na-
    tional identity lost, 213, 229, 514
Inkur, 297 (*map*)
Innokent'yevskiy, 321 (*map*), 322
Insterburg, *see* Chernyakhovsk

Inta, 155 (*map*), 164
Inya River, 279 (*map*)
Inza, 183 (*map*), 191
Inzer, 235 (*map*), 253
Inzhavino, 127 (*map*)
Iodine, deposits, 404; processing plant,
    402
Iokan'ga, 161 (*map*)
Iokan'ga River, 161 (*map*)
Iolotan', 401 (*map*), 406
Ionava, 481 (*map*)
Ionishkis, 481 (*map*)
Iora River, 415 (*map*), 417, 427 (*map*)
Iranian ethnic group, 41, 98; in Central
    Asia, 368; in Transcaucasia, 411
Irbit, 235 (*map*), 243
Irgiz, 338 (*map*)
Irgiz River (Kazakh SSR), 338 (*map*),
    340
Irgiz River (Saratov Oblast), 183 (*map*),
    195 (*map*)
Irkeshtam, 373 (*map*)
Irkutsk, 283 (*map*), 296, 297 (*map*), 299
Irkutsk Oblast, 283 (*map*), 297 (*map*),
    295-300; agriculture, 297; area, 295;
    forests, 296; mineral resources, 296;
    navigation route, 299; population, 295,
    296; power resources, 296 ff.; railroads,
    298; topography, 295
Irmino, 451 (*map*)
Iron deposits, Central Asia, 368; Central
    Black-Earth Region, 126, 133; Eastern
    Siberia, 292, 296, 303, 306; exchange of
    coal and, between Urals and Kuznetsk
    Basin, 68; formation, 14; Karelo-
    Finnish SSR, 496; Kazakh SSR, 345;
    magnetic, 133; phosphoric, 206; Russian
    SFSR, 96; Transcaucasia, 412; Ukrain-
    ian SSR, 439, 441; Urals, 234, 238, 248,
    253, 255, 256, 257; USSR, 37; Volga
    Region, 176; Western Siberia, 278
Iron and steel mills, 76 ff.; coking process,
    449; Kazakh SSR, 347; new center, 159;
    pig iron or rolled steel, 239; Ukrainian
    SSR, 442, 453; Volga Region, 178, 179;
    see also Steel industry
Irpen', 436 (*map*)
Irrigation, Central Asia, 62, 369; Chu
    Valley, 375, 377; dry steppe and desert
    regions, 55, 63, 407; European South,
    222; "Great Volga" scheme, 172 f.;
    Tadzhik SSR, 384; Turkmen SSR, 403,
    408; Uzbek SSR, 393, 394
Irsha, 290
Irtysh-Ob' system, *see* Ob'-Irtysh system
Irtysh River, 260, 261 (*map*), 262, 263,

271, 336, 339 (*map*), 356, 357, 358 (*map*), 358; hydroelectric plant, 347; tributaries, 340, 341
Isheyevka, 183 (*map*)
Irtyshskoye, 339 (*map*)
Is, 241 (*map*)
Iset' River, 234, 240 (*map*)
Isfana, 373 (*map*), 395 (*map*)
Isfara, 395 (*map*)
Ishim, 261 (*map*), 264, 268, 269
Ishim River, 263, 338-39 (*map*), 340, 352, 353
Ishim Steppe, 264, 353
Ishimbay, 36, 235 (*map*), 254, 256
Ishkashim, 381 (*map*)
Isil'-Kul', 261 (*map*), 271
Iskander, 395 (*map*)
Iski-Naukat, 395 (*map*)
Iskininskiy, 338 (*map*), 346, 351
Iskitim, 273, 279 (*map*)
Ismail, see Izmail
Issyk-Ata, 376
Issyk-Kul', Lake, 23, 366, 371, 372, 373 (*map*), 374, 375, 377
Issyk-Kul' Oblast, 53, 373 (*map*); area, 376; economy, 377; population, 376
Istra, 115 (*map*)
Itaka, 303
Itel'meny (Kamchadals), 41, 314, 325
Itum-Kale, *see* Akhalkhevi
Iturup or Etorofu Island, 333
Ivangorod, 145 (*map*), 490
Ivanishchi, 115 (*map*)
Ivan'kovo, 135 (*map*), 141
Ivanovka (Amur Oblast), 317 (*map*)
Ivanovka (Maritime Kray), 327 (*map*)
Ivanovo, 44, 105 (*map*), 108
Ivanovo Oblast, 105 (*map*); area, 119; industries, 119 f.; population: topography, 119
Ivanovo-Voznesensk, *see* Ivanovo
Ivanteyevka, 115 (*map*)
Ivashchenkovo, *see* Chapayevsk
Ivdel', 235 (*map*), 241 (*map*), 243
Ivot, 135 (*map*)
Izberbash, 211 (*map*), 232
Izhevsk, 235 (*map*), 252, 253
Izhma (town), 165, 173 (*map*)
Izhma (village), 173 (*map*)
Izhma River, 155 (*map*)
Izhmorskoye, 279 (*map*)
Izhora works, 152
Izmail, 436 (*map*), 457, 465 (*map*), 466
Izmail Oblast, 436 (*map*), 441; area and population, 456; economy, 457
Izumrud, 52, 239, 241 (*map*)

Izvestkovyy, 321 (*map*), 322
Izyum, 437 (*map*), 448, 451 (*map*)

Jäniskoski, *see* Yaniskoski
Japan, Sea of, 7, 311 (*map*), 321 (*map*), 326, 327 (*map*); ice condition of ports, 91
Japanese in Soviet Far East, 332
Japanese territories, sovietization of former: localities renamed, 52, 330, 331 (*map*)
Japhetic ethnic group, 228; languages, 41
Jasper, 264
Jaunlatgale, *see* Pytalovo
Jelgava, *see* Yelgava
Jewish Autonomous Oblast, 311 (*map*), 318, 321 (*map*); area and population: industries: mineral resources, 322
Jews, 41, 514; in Baltic Region, 480, 483, 485; Belorussian SSR, largely exterminated, 472; Central Asia, 368; European South, 207, 228; Moldavian SSR, 466; Soviet Far East, 314; Transcaucasia, 425; Ukrainian SSR, 440
Jõhvi, *see* Yykhvi
Juodkrante, *see* Yuodkrante

Kaakhka, 401 (*map*)
Kabakovsk, *see* Serov
Kabaktan, 305
Kabardinian Autonomous Soviet Socialist Republic, 211 (*map*), 213, 224-26; agriculture, 225; area, 224; industry, 225; population: topography, 224
Kabardinians, 41; in European South, 213, 224, 225
Kabardinka, 211 (*map*)
Kabardino-Balkar Autonomous SSR, Balkar nationality dissolved, 213, 225, 514
Kačanava, *see* Kachanovo
Kachanovo, 148, 485
Kachug, 297 (*map*)
Kadamdzhay, 374n
Kadiyevka, 50, 442, 451 (*map*), 452
Kadzharan, 421 (*map*), 422
Kadzhisay, 372, 373 (*map*), 377
Kafan, 421 (*map*), 422
Kaffa, *see* Feodosiya
Kafirnigan River, 380, 381 (*map*), 386; cotton valley, 383, 386
Kagan, 389 (*map*), 398; railroad to Stalinabad, 397, 407
Kaganovich (Moscow Oblast), 105 (*map*), 111, 115 (*map*), 124
Kaganovich (Tula Oblast), 105 (*map*), 123

Kaganovicha, Imeni, L. M., 415 (map)
Kaganovichesk, 401 (map)
Kagul, 465 (map), 467, 468
Kakhetia, 425, 428
Kakhi, 415 (map)
Kakhovka, 437 (map), 455
Käkisalmi, see Priozersk
Kalach (Stalingrad Oblast), 195 (map);
  railroad to Tsaritsyn, 82
Kalach (Voronezh Oblast), 127 (map),
  132
Kalachinsk, 261 (map), 271
Kalai-Khumb, 381 (map)
Kalakan, 297 (map)
Kalarash, 465 (map)
Kalba Range, 336, 358
Kalinin, 49, 135 (map), 141 f.
Kalinina, Imeni, 415 (map)
Kalinina, Imeni M. I., 173 (map)
Kalininabad, 395 (map)
Kalinindorf, 52
Kaliningrad (Kaliningrad Oblast), Bal-
  tic port, formerly Königsberg, 8, 52,
  479, 482, 491 (map); port and indus-
  trial center, 492
Kaliningrad (Moscow Oblast), 115 (map)
Kaliningrad Oblast, 479, 482, 491 (map),
  490-92; administrative system, 482;
  agriculture, 492; amber, 14; area, 490;
  cities over 50,000, 509; mineral re-
  sources, 490; population, 480, 490
Kalinin Oblast, agriculture, 135 (map),
  141; area, 140; description, 140; indus-
  tries, 141, 142; mineral resources, 141;
  population, 140; timber, 141
Kalininsk, 401 (map)
Kalininskoye, 52
Kalinkovichi, 471 (map)
Kalinovka, 491 (map)
Kalmanka, 279 (map)
Kal'mius River, 451 (map)
Kalmyk Autonomous SSR, abrogated, 46,
  51, 194, 195 (map), 200, 201, 216
Kalmyk national rayon, abrogated, 216
Kalmykovo, 338 (map)
Kalmyks, deprived of identity as separate
  nationality, 514; in Volga Region, 172,
  194, 201
Kaluga, 135 (map), 139
Kaluga Oblast, 135 (map); agriculture:
  area, 138; industries: mineral resources,
  139; population, 138
Kaluzhskoye, 491 (map)
Kalvariya, 481 (map)
Kal'ya, 239, 241 (map)
Kalyazin, 135 (map), 142

Kama River, 170, 173 (map), 183 (map),
  234, 235 (map), 237, 241 (map); diversion of northern waters of Pechora to
  the Volga via, 246; hydroelectric plant,
  246, 247
Kambarka, 235 (map), 252
Kamchadals, see Itel'meny
Kamchatka Oblast, 311 (map), 318; area
  and population: industries, 324; mineral resources, 325
Kamchatka peninsula, 17 (map), 282, 308,
  309, 311 (map), 333; climate, 312; ethnic
  groups, 314, 324, 325; naval bases, 7, 91;
  oil fields, 314, 325; tundra belt, 30;
  volcanoes, 20, 309, 310
Kamchatka River, 309, 310; valley, 313
Kamen', or Kamen' on the Ob' (Kamen'-
  na-Obi), 261 (map), 274, 275
Kamenets-Podol'skiy, 436 (map), 447
Kamenets-Podol'skiy Oblast, 52; 436
  (map); area: economy: population, 447
Kamenka (Ivanovo Oblast), 105 (map)
Kamenka (Moldavian SSR), 465 (map)
Kamenka (Penza Oblast), 183 (map)
Kamenka (Voronezh Oblast), 127 (map)
Kamenka-Dneprovskaya, 437 (map)
Kamen'-Kashirskiy, 436 (map)
Kamennogorsk, 145 (map)
Kamenolomni, 217, 451 (map)
Kamen' Rybolov, 327 (map)
Kamensk or Kamensk-Shakhtinskiy (q.v.)
Kamenskiy, 195 (map), 197
Kamenskoye, 311 (map)
Kamensk-Shakhtinskiy, 205 (map), 217,
  415 (map)
Kamensk-Ural'skiy, 235 (map), 239, 241
  (map), 243
Kamysh-Burun, 205 (map), 209
Kamyshin, 195 (map), 200
Kamyshlov, 235 (map), 241 (map), 243
Kanaker, 421 (map); power station, 420
Kanash, 183 (map), 186
Kandagach, 338 (map), 349, 352
Kandalaksha, 161 (map), 162, 163
Kandalaksha, Gulf of, 5, 161 (map)
Kangalasskiye Kopi, 306
Kanibadam, 381 (map), 383, 385, 395
  (map)
Kanin, 155 (map)
Kanin Peninsula, 155 (map)
Kansay, 381 (map), 385, 395 (map)
Kansk, 283 (map), 290, 291, 297 (map);
  brown-coal basin, 290
Kant, 52, 372 (map), 376
Kantagi, 339 (map), 362
Kantemirovka, 127 (map)

Kaolin clay, 38, 290
Kara, 155 (*map*)
Karabakh upland, 409
Karabalty, 376
Karabanovo, 105 (*map*), 115 (*map*), 121
Karabash, 241 (*map*), 248, 249, 251
Karabekaul, 401 (*map*)
Kara-Bogaz-Gol, 232, 368, 401 (*map*), 402, 404, 405; gulf, 9, 401 (*map*), 404
Karabulak, 339 (*map*), 360
Karachala, 417
Karachay, ethnic group, 221, 225, 514
Karachay Autonomous Oblast, 46, 51, 213, 221; added to Georgian SSR, 426
Karachay-Cherkess Autonomous Oblast, abolished, 45, 221, 222, 224
Karachev, 135 (*map*), 138
Karadag (Azerbaijan SSR), 415 (*map*)
Kara-Dag (Crimea), 206
Kara Darya, 366, 393
Karafuto (Southern Sakhalin), 314, 329; *see also* Sakhalin Oblast
Karaganda, 36, 254, 339 (*map*), 345, 355; coal basin, 12, 74, 265, 345, 346, 354, 355
Karaganda Oblast, 339 (*map*); area: economy, 355; industrial centers, 356; population, 355
Kara Gates, *see* Karskiye Vorota
Karagiye, *see* Batyr'
Karaidel'skiy, 235 (*map*), 241 (*map*)
Kara-Irtysh River, 341
Kara-Kala, 401 (*map*)
Kara-Kalpak Autonomous Soviet Socialist Republic, 346, 389 (*map*), 390, 397, 398-99; area, 398; industries, 399; population, 398, 399; transportation, 399
Kara-Kalpaks, in Uzbek SSR, 368, 399
Kara-Kirghiz, ethnic group, became Kirghiz (*q.v.*), 53
Kara-Kirghiz Autonomous Oblast, 372
Kara-Kirghiz Autonomous SSR, 368
Karakol, *see* Przheval'sk
Karakul', 381 (*map*); lake, 366, 387
Karakul sheep, 396, 397, 403, 404, 467
Kara-Kum Canal, 62, 403, 406, 407
Kara-Kum desert, 364, 400, 401 (*map*), 404, 408; development of, 403; sulphur deposits, 368, 402
Kara-Mazar, 385, 395 (*map*)
Kara River, 155 (*map*)
Kara Sea, 6, 155 (*map*), 261 (*map*), 262
Karasu, 373 (*map*), 378, 395 (*map*)
Karasubazar, *see* Belogorsk
Kara-Tag, 386
Karatal River, 340, 360

Kara-Tau range (Gur'yev Oblast), 335, 346, 351
Kara-Tau range (South Kazakhstan Oblast), 337, 344, 362
Kara-Tyube, 374
Karaul, 283 (*map*)
Kara-Unkurt, *see* Kum-Bel'
Karavan, 373 (*map*), 395 (*map*)
Karelia (Karelian Autonomous SSR), 18, 45, 46, 494
Karelian Isthmus, 143, 148, 150; incorporated into Leningrad Oblast, 494
Karelians, 41, 493
Karelo-Finnish Soviet Socialist Republic, 45, 148, 495 (*map*), 493-97; area, 493; cities over 50,000, 511; fishing industries, 496; lumber industries, 494; metallurgical industries, 497; mineral resources, 493, 496; paper-milling centers, 496; population: topography, 493; transportation facilities, 496
Kargat, 261 (*map*)
Kargopol', 155 (*map*)
Karintorf, 173 (*map*), 178
Karkaralinsk, 339 (*map*)
Karl Libknekht, 127 (*map*)
Karlyuk, 401 (*map*)
Karpinsk, 235 (*map*), 241 (*map*), 242
Karpogory, 155 (*map*)
Karpushikha, 241 (*map*)
Karsakpay, 338 (*map*), 355, 356
Karsava, 481 (*map*)
Karshi, 389 (*map*), 397
Karskiye Vorota (Kara Gates), strait, 6, 155 (*map*), 157
Karyagino, 415 (*map*)
Karymskoye, 297 (*map*)
Kashin, 135 (*map*)
Kashira, 105 (*map*), 114, 115 (*map*)
Kashirskoye, 491 (*map*)
Kashiwabara, *see* Severo-Kuril'sk
Kashka Darya, river, 397
Kashka-Darya Oblast, 389 (*map*), 390; area and population: industries, 397
Kashka-Su, 377
Kashpirovka, 183 (*map*), 193
Kasimov, 105 (*map*), 123
Kasli, 241 (*map*), 249
Kaspi, 427 (*map*), 428
Kaspiysk, 211 (*map*), 232
Kaspiyskiy, 195 (*map*), 202
Kassansay, 394, 395 (*map*)
Kastornoye, 127 (*map*)
Katangli, 311 (*map*)
Katav-Ivanovsk, 241 (*map*), 249
Kataysk, 241 (*map*), 261 (*map*), 267

Katon-Karagay, 359 (*map*)
Katta-Kurgan, 389 (*map*), 396, 397; Uzbek Sea, 62
Katunki, 173 (*map*)
Katun' Range, 262, 359 (*map*)
Katun' River, 261 (*map*), 279 (*map*), 359 (*map*)
Katyk, 451 (*map*)
Kaunas, 481 (*map*), 482, 483, 484
Kaunchi, *see* Yangi-Yul'
Käva, *see* Kyava
Kawakami, *see* Sinegorsk
Kayakent, 211 (*map*), 232
Kayshyadoris, 481 (*map*)
Kazachinskoye, 297 (*map*)
Kazak, *see* Kazakh
Kazakh, town, 415 (*map*)
Kazakhs, 40, 53; in Kazakh SSR, 345, 351, 360, 361; in Kirghiz SSR, 372; in Uzbek SSR, 399; in Western Siberia, 265; *see also* Kirghiz
Kazakh Soviet Socialist Republic (Kazakhstan), 47, 334-63; agricultural economy, 348; agricultural zones, basic, 348; area, 334, 345; chemical industry, 352, 357, 361, 362; cities over 50,000, 509; climate, 341; cotton region, 362; deserts, 343; economic importance of rivers, 341; fishing industries, 337, 348, 350, 351, 363; fuel bases, 345; general survey, 334-50; gold, 344, 353 ff. *passim;* hydrography, 337; industrial progress, 348; industries based on agricultural and livestock products, 347; lumber industries, 347; metallurgical industries, 346, 347, 354, 355, 356; mineral resources, 344 ff.; mining and metallurgical section, 355; oblast survey, 350-63; petroleum, 344-47 *passim,* 351; population, 334, 345, 346, 499; power industries, 346; railroads, 348 ff.; role of railroads in industrial development, 85; soils, 343; topography, 334-37; transportation, 348 ff.; vegetation, 343; water-power resources, 347; *see further under names of oblasts as listed on p. 504*
Kazakhstan, republic, *see* Kazakh Soviet Socialist Republic
Kazakhstan, town, 338 (*map*)
Kazakh upland, 334, 335, 344, 354, 355, 356
Kazaks, *see* Kazakhs
Kazalinsk, 338 (*map*)
Kazan', 44, 183 (*map*), 184, 188, 189; railroad to Sverdlovsk, 84
Kazandzhik, 401 (*map*)

Kazanshukur, 359 (*map*)
Kazanskaya, 205 (*map*)
Kazarman, 373 (*map*)
Kazatin, 436 (*map*)
Kazbeg, 427 (*map*)
Kazbek, Mount, 14, 211 (*map*), 212, 427 (*map*)
Kazhim, 155 (*map*), 165
Kazi-Magomed, 415 (*map*)
Keda, 427 (*map*)
Kedabek, 414, 415 (*map*), 416
Kedaynyay, 481 (*map*)
Kegums, hydroelectric station, 486
Kel'badzhar, 415 (*map*)
Keles, 395 (*map*)
Kelif Uzboy, 407
Kel'my, 481 (*map*)
Kel'temashat, 362
Kem', 495 (*map*), 496
Kemeri, 486
Kemerovo, 261 (*map*), 265, 279 (*map*), 280
Kemerovo Oblast, 261 (*map*), 265, 272, 279 (*map*), 276-80; agriculture, 279; area, 276; coal-mining centers, 280; coal reserves, 276 ff.; industrial region, 277; metallurgical centers, 280; minerals, 277; population, 276; *see also* Kuznetsk Basin
Kempendyay River, 306
Kenaf, 55, 61, 227, 376
Kenderlyk River, 346, 359 (*map*)
Kendyr', 55, 376
Kengir, 356
Kenimekh, 389 (*map*)
Kerch', 37, 205 (*map*), 208, 209; peninsula, 204
Kerchevskiy, 241 (*map*)
Kerch' Strait, 9, 205 (*map*)
Keret', Lake, 495 (*map*)
Kergez, 415 (*map*)
Kerki, 401 (*map*), 407
Kerkichi, 401 (*map*)
Kerki Oblast, former, 402, 407
Kermine, 389 (*map*)
Kerva, 115 (*map*)
Kesten'ga, 495 (*map*)
Ketmen' range, 336, 360
Ketmen'-Tyube valley, 379
Kety, in Eastern Siberia, 288, 290
Kexholm, *see* Priozersk
Keyla, 481 (*map*)
Khaapsalu, 481 (*map*)
Khabarovo, 155 (*map*)
Khabarovsk, 311 (*map*), 319, 320, 321 (*map*)

Khabarovsk area, 311 (*map*), 321 (*map*), 319-22, area, 319; mineral resources, 320; organization, 319; population, 319

Khabarovsk Kray, 47, 311 (*map*), 314; administrative divisions: area and population, 318; importance in national economy, 319

Khachmas, 415 (*map*)

Khadyzhenskiy, 211 (*map*), 219

Khadzhibey Liman, 456

Khakass, ethnic group, in Kirghiz SSR, 372; in Siberia, 41, 98, 288, 290

Khakass Autonomous Oblast, 290, 292, 297 (*map*); area, 292; gold mining, 292; industries, 292; iron ore deposits, 279; population, 292

Khalach, 401 (*map*)

Khalilovo, 235 (*map*), 257, 258, 259

Khal'mer-Sede, 261 (*map*)

Khal'mer-Yu, 155 (*map*), 169

Khalturin, 173 (*map*)

Khamar-Daban range, 282, 300

Khanabad, 395 (*map*)

Khanka, Lake, 313, 321 (*map*), 327 (*map*), 328; lowland, 309; Ussuri plain, 328, 329

Khankendy, *see* Stepanakert

Khanlar, 415 (*map*)

Khan-Tengri, mountain, 373 (*map*)

Khanty (Ostyaks), in Siberia, 41, 53, 264, 269, 273

Khanty-Mansi National Okrug, 261 (*map*), 265; area and population: industries, 269

Khanty-Mansiysk, 261 (*map*), 269

Khapcheranga, 297 (*map*), 303

Khar'kov, 436-37 (*map*), 442, 448

Khar'kov Oblast, 436-37 (*map*), 447; area and population: industries, 448

Kharlu, 495 (*map*), 496

Kharovsk, 155 (*map*)

Khartsyzsk, 451 (*map*)

Khasavyurt, 211 (*map*), 232

Khashuri, 427 (*map*)

Khatanga, 283 (*map*); gulf, 6; river, 285

Khaudag, 389 (*map*), 391, 397

Khaydarkan, 373 (*map*), 374, 378, 395 (*map*)

Khem-Belder, *see* Kyzyl

Khemchik River, 295

Kherson, 437 (*map*), 442, 445, 455

Kherson Oblast, 437 (*map*); area: population: ports, 455

Khevsurs, tribe in Transcaucasia, 411, 425

Khibiny Mountains, 10, 19, 38, 78, 156, 161 (*map*); mining district, 160, 162

Khiitola, 495 (*map*)

Khilok, 297 (*map*)

Khimki, 112, 115 (*map*)

Khislavichi, 135 (*map*)

Khiuma (Hiiumaa), island, 479, 481 (*map*), 487

Khiva, 389 (*map*), 398

Khiva (or Khorezm) oasis, 364, 390, 398

Khodzhent, *see* Leninabad

Khodzheyli, 389 (*map*), 399

Kholbon, 303

Kholm, 135 (*map*)

Kholmogory, 155 (*map*); dairy breed, 167

Kholmsk, 330, 331 (*map*), 333

Kholuy, 105 (*map*)

Khoper River, 183 (*map*), 195 (*map*)

Khor, 321 (*map*)

Khorezm (or Khiva) oasis, 364, 390, 398

Khorezm Oblast, 53, 389 (*map*); area and population: industries, 398

Khorezm Soviet People's Republic, 368

Khorlovo, 115 (*map*)

Khorly, 437 (*map*), 455

Khorog, 381 (*map*), 387

Khorol', 327 (*map*)

Khor River, 321 (*map*)

Khoseda-Khard, 155 (*map*)

Khosta, 211 (*map*), 220

Khotin, 436 (*map*), 460, 465 (*map*), 466

Khot'kovo, 115 (*map*)

Khram River, 425, 427 (*map*)

Khrenovoye, 127 (*map*), 131

Khrom-Tau, 338 (*map*), 352

Khudat, 415 (*map*)

Khulo, 427 (*map*)

Khungari, 321 (*map*)

Khurdalan, 415 (*map*)

Khust, 436 (*map*)

Khuzhir, 297 (*map*)

Khvalynsk, 195 (*map*)

Khvatovka, 195 (*map*)

Khvoynaya, 145 (*map*)

Kianly, 401 (*map*)

Kichiga, 325

Kiev, 44, 436 (*map*), 442, 446, 461

Kiev Oblast, 436 (*map*), 443, 445; area and population: economy, 446

Kikhchik, 324

Kil'din Island, 161 (*map*)

Kil'dinstroy, 161 (*map*)

Kilingi-Nymme, 481 (*map*)

Kiliya, 436 (*map*), 457, 465 (*map*)

Kim, 383, 385, 395 (*map*)

Kimry, 135 (*map*), 142

Kinel', 183 (*map*), 192, 193

Kineshma, 105 (*map*), 120

Kingisepp, 145 (*map*), 150

Kirda, 395 (*map*)

Kirensk, 283 (*map*), 296, 297 (*map*)

Kireyevka, 105 (*map*), 124

Kirghiz, 40, 53; in Central Asia, 368; in Kirghiz SSR, 372, 378; in Tadzhik SSR, 387; in Uzbek SSR, 393; *see also* Kara-Kirghiz; Kazakhs

Kirghiz Autonomous Oblast made a union republic, 45, 372

Kirghiz Autonomous SSR, 345, 368, 372

Kirghizia, *see* Kirghiz SSR

Kirghiz range, 375

Kirghiz Soviet Socialist Republic, 371-79; agriculture, 374; area, 371; general survey, 371-75; cities over 50,000, 509; foremost producer of mercury and antimony, 378; general survey, 371-75; heavy machinery, 374; highways, 374; industries, 374; livestock region, 377; main economic region, 375; metals, non-ferrous and rare, 374; mineral resources, 373 f.; oblasts in, 47; oblast survey, 375-79; petroleum, 374, 379; population, 372; power resources, 374; railroads, 375; *see further under names of oblasts as listed on pp. 504-5*

Kirghizstan, *see* Kirghiz SSR

Kirillov, 155 (*map*)

Kirishi, 145 (*map*)

Kirov (Kaluga Oblast), 135 (*map*), 139

Kirov (Kirov Oblast), 173 (*map*), 176, 177

Kirova, Imeni (Azerbaijan SSR), 415 (*map*)

Kirova, Imeni (Tadzhik SSR), 381 (*map*)

Kirovabad (Azerbaijan SSR), 415 (*map*), 416, 418

Kirovabad (Tadzhik SSR), 381 (*map*)

Kirovakan, 421 (*map*), 423

Kirovgrad, 235 (*map*), 239, 241 (*map*), 242

Kirovo, 395 (*map*)

Kirov Oblast, 173 (*map*), 176-77; agriculture, 177; area and population, 176; industries: mineral resources, 176; topography, 176; trade routes, 177

Kirovo-Chepetskiy, 173 (*map*), 177

Kirovograd, 437 (*map*), 456

Kirovograd Oblast, 437 (*map*); area: economy: population, 456

Kirov Railroad, 162, 496

Kirovsk (Azerbaijan SSR), 415 (*map*)

Kirovsk (Murmansk Oblast), 160, 161 (*map*), 163

Kirovsk (Turkmen SSR), 401 (*map*)

Kirovskiy (Amur Oblast), 317 (*map*), 324

Kirovskiy (Astrakhan' Oblast), 195 (*map*), 202

Kirovskiy (Maritime Kray), 327 (*map*)

Kirovskiy (Kazakh SSR), 339 (*map*)

Kirovskoye (Kirghiz SSR), 373 (*map*)

Kirovskoye (Sakhalin Oblast), 331 (*map*)

Kirs, 173 (*map*), 178

Kirsanov, 127 (*map*)

Kirya, 183 (*map*)

Kirzhach, 105 (*map*), 115 (*map*), 121

Kirzhak, suburb of Ufa, 255

Kiselevsk, 277, 279 (*map*), 280

Kishinev, 465 (*map*), 467, 468

Kishozero, lake, 486

Kislovodsk, 210, 211 (*map*), 214, 222, 223

Kitab, 389 (*map*), 397

Kitoy, 298

Kivach, 495 (*map*)

Kivdinskiy, 317 (*map*), 318

Kiviõli, *see* Kiviyli

Kiviyli, 481 (*map*), 489

Kiya River, 278, 279 (*map*)

Kizel, 36, 234, 235 (*map*), 241 (*map*), 244

Kizlyar, 211 (*map*), 230; okrug, 228

Kizyl-Arvat, 401 (*map*), 405

Kizyl-Atrek, 401 (*map*)

Kizyl-Kiya, 372, 373 (*map*), 374, 378, 395 (*map*)

Kizyl-Kup, 405

Kizyl-Su, 401 (*map*), 405

Klaipeda, *see* Klaypeda

Klavdiyevo-Tarasovo, 436 (*map*)

Klaypeda (Klaipeda), Baltic port, 8, 481 (*map*), 482, 483, 484

Klerk, 327 (*map*), 328

Kletnya, 135 (*map*)

Kletsk, 471 (*map*)

Klimovichi, 471 (*map*)

Klimovsk, 115 (*map*)

Klin, 105 (*map*), 111, 115 (*map*)

Klin-Dmitrov ridge (or upland), 105, 134

Klintsy, 135 (*map*), 138

Klukhori, 51, 211 (*map*), 213, 222, 426, 427 (*map*)

Klukhori Pass, 431

Klyaz'ma River, 105 (*map*), 114, 115 (*map*), 119

Klyuchevskaya Sopka, 21, 310

Knyazhaya Guba, 161 (*map*)

Kobi, 415 (*map*)

Kobrin, 471 (*map*)

Kobuleti, 427 (*map*)

Kochenevo, 279 (*map*)

Kochetovka, 127 (*map*)

Kochkorka, 373 (*map*)

Kochura, 279 (*map*)
Kodor River, 427 (*map*)
Kodry, 464, 465 (*map*), 468
Kodyma, 465 (*map*)
Kogal'nik River, 465 (*map*)
Kohtla, *see* Kokhtla
Kohtla-Järve, *see* Kokhtla-Yarve
Koivisto, *see* Primorsk
Kokand, 389 (*map*), 393, 394, 395 (*map*)
Kokayty, 389 (*map*)
Kokchetav, 339 (*map*), 354
Kokchetav Oblast, 339 (*map*), 353; area and population, 353; economy, 354
Kokhila, 481 (*map*)
Kokhma, 105 (*map*)
Kokhtla, 489
Kokhtla-Yarve, 481 (*map*), 488, 489
Kok-sagyz, 55, 61
Koksovyy, 215, 451 (*map*)
Koktash, 381 (*map*)
Kokuy, 303
Kok-Yangak, 372, 373 (*map*), 379, 395 (*map*)
Kola, 161 (*map*), 163
Kolanguy, 303
Kola Peninsula, 18, 37, 154, 155 (*map*), 160 ff. *passim,* 161 (*map*)
Kol'chugino (Kemerovo Oblast), *see* Leninsk-Kuznetskiy
Kol'chugino (Vladimir Oblast), 105 (*map*), 115 (*map*), 121
Kolguyev, Island, 5, 155, 157, 167, 169
Kolkhida, 63, 410
Kologriv, 105 (*map*)
Kolomak, 436 (*map*)
Kolomna, 105 (*map*), 111, 114, 115 (*map*)
Kolomyya, 436 (*map*), 460
Kolpakovskiy, 324
Kolpashevo, 261 (*map*), 274
Kolpino, 145 (*map*), 152, 153 (*map*)
Kolpny, 127 (*map*)
Koltubanovskiy, 235 (*map*), 258
Koluton, 339 (*map*)
Kolyberovo, 115 (*map*)
Kolyma highway, 92
Kolyma range, 20, 282
Kolyma River, 285, 310, 311 (*map*); gold-mining basin, 7, 313, 318; lowlands, 20
Kolyubakino, 115 (*map*)
Kolyvan', 274, 279 (*map*), 359 (*map*)
Komarichi, 135 (*map*)
Komarovka, 436 (*map*)
Komarovo (Bashkir ASSR), 235 (*map*), 253, 255, 256
Komarovo (Novgorod Oblast), 145 (*map*), 146

Kombinat, 68, 69; *see also* Ural-Kuzbas *kombinat*
Komi, ethnic group, 41, 53; in European North, 163; in Urals, 98, 243, 247; in Western Siberia, 274
Komi Autonomous Soviet Socialist Republic, 155 (*map*), 163-65; area, 163; natural resources, 164; population: topography, 163
Kominterna, Imeni, 145 (*map*), 147
Kominternovskiy, 173 (*map*)
Komi-Permyak National Okrug, 235 (*map*), 241 (*map*); administrative okrug converted into, 46; agriculture: area and population, 247
Komi-Permyaks, ethnic group, 98, 237, 243, 247
Kommunar, 292, 297 (*map*)
Komrat, 465 (*map*), 467
Komsomolets, 338 (*map*)
Komsomolets Island, 6
Komsomol'sk (Ivanovo Oblast), 105 (*map*), 120
Komsomol'sk (Kaliningrad Oblast), 491 (*map*)
Komsomol'sk (Khabarovsk Kray), 50, 77, 311 (*map*), 319, 320, 321 (*map*)
Komsomol'skoye, 451 (*map*)
Konakhkend, 415 (*map*)
Konakovo, 135 (*map*)
Kondinskoye, 261 (*map*)
Kondoma River, 278, 279 (*map*)
Kondopoga, 495 (*map*), 496, 497
Kondrovo, 135 (*map*), 139
Konevo, 155 (*map*)
Königsberg, *see* Kaliningrad
Konosha, 155 (*map*), 167
Konotop, 437 (*map*), 449
Konstantinovka (Amur Oblast), 317 (*map*)
Konstantinovka (Ukrainian SSR), 450, 451 (*map*)
Konstantinov Kamen', 157
Konstantinovskiy (Rostov Oblast), 205 (*map*)
Konstantinovskiy (Yaroslavl' Oblast), 105 (*map*)
Konzhakovskiy Kamen', 234, 241 (*map*)
Kopet Dagh range, 20, 364, 365, 400, 404
Kopeysk, 241 (*map*), 248, 250
Koreans, in Soviet Far East, 314
Koreiz, 205 (*map*)
Korkino, 241 (*map*), 248, 250
Kornevo, 491 (*map*)
Korocha, 127 (*map*)
Korosten', 436 (*map*), 458

Korsakov, 52, 330, 331 (*map*), 333
Koryak National Okrug, 311 (*map*), 318, 325
Koryak range, 282
Koryaks, *see* Nymylany
Koschagyl, 338 (*map*), 346, 351
Koshtan-Tau, mountain, 224
Kosikha, 279 (*map*)
Kosino, 173 (*map*)
Koslan, 155 (*map*)
Kosmach, 436 (*map*), 460
Kosmynino, 105 (*map*)
Kospash, 241 (*map*), 244
Kosta-Khetagurovo, 211 (*map*)
Kostino, 115 (*map*)
Kostopol', 436 (*map*)
Kostroma, 64, 105 (*map*), 118
Kostroma Oblast, 105 (*map*) area, economy, population, 118
Kostroma River, 105 (*map*)
Kostyukovka, 471 (*map*), 476
Kos'ya, 239, 241 (*map*)
Kotel'nich, 173 (*map*), 177
Kotel'nikovskiy, 195 (*map*), 205 (*map*)
Kotlas, 155 (*map*), 168
Kotlin Island, 153 (*map*)
Kotovsk (Tambov Oblast), 127 (*map*), 131, 255n
Kotovsk (Ukrainian SSR), 436 (*map*), 441, 465 (*map*), 466
Kotovskoye, 465 (*map*)
Kounradskiy, 339 (*map*), 344, 354, 355
Kovda, 161 (*map*)
Kovel', 436 (*map*), 462
Kovno, see Kaunas
Kovrov, 105 (*map*), 122
Kovylkino, 183 (*map*), 187
Kovzhinskiy Zavod, 155 (*map*)
Kowel, see Kovel'
Koysara, 377
Koytash, 389 (*map*)
Kozel'sk, 135 (*map*)
Kozhevnikovo (Krasnoyarsk Kray), 283 (*map*)
Kozhevnikovo (Tomsk Oblast), 279 (*map*)
Kozhva, 155 (*map*)
Kozlov, *see* Michurinsk
Kozlovka, 183 (*map*)
Koz'modem'yansk, 173 (*map*), 181
Kramatorsk, 437 (*map*), 442, 450, 451 (*map*)
Krapivino, 279 (*map*)
Krasavino, 155 (*map*), 166
Krasino, 155 (*map*)
Kraskino, 321 (*map*), 327 (*map*), 328

Kraslava, 481 (*map*)
Krasnaya Glinka, 183 (*map*), 192
Krasnaya Gorbatka, 105 (*map*), 121
Krasnaya Rechka, 321 (*map*)
Krasnaya Shapochka, 239
Krasnoarmeysk (Moscow Oblast), 115 (*map*)
Krasnoarmeysk (Saratov Oblast), 51, 195 (*map*), 197, 200
Krasnoarmeyskoye, 451 (*map*)
Krasnodar, 211 (*map*), 219
Krasnodar Kray, 211 (*map*), 217-20, 222; agriculture, 218; area, 217; petroleum, 218; population, 217, 218; transportation, 219
Krasnodon, 451 (*map*), 452
Krasnofarfornyy, 145 (*map*), 147
Krasnogorovka, 451 (*map*)
Krasnogorsk (Moscow Oblast), 115 (*map*)
Krasnogorsk (Sakhalin Oblast), 330, 331 (*map*)
Krasnogorskiy, 173 (*map*)
Krasnograd, 437 (*map*)
Krasnogvardeysk (Leningrad Oblast), *see* Gatchina
Krasnogvardeysk (Samarkand Oblast), 389 (*map*)
Krasnogvardeyskiy, 241 (*map*)
Krasnogvardeyskoye, 205 (*map*)
Krasnokamsk, 36, 241 (*map*), 244, 245, 247
Krasnokokshaysk, *see* Yoshkar-Ola
Krasnolesnyy, 127 (*map*)
Krasnooktyabr'skiy, 376
Krasnoostrovskiy, 145 (*map*), 150
Krasno-Perekopsk, 205 (*map*), 208
Krasnosel'kup, 261 (*map*), 270
Krasnosel'sk, 421 (*map*)
Krasnoslobodsk, 183 (*map*), 187
Krasnotur'insk, 235 (*map*), 241 (*map*), 242, 243
Krasnoufimsk, 241 (*map*), 243
Krasnoural'sk, 235 (*map*), 239, 241 (*map*), 242
Krasnousol'skiy, 235 (*map*), 254
Krasnovishersk, 235 (*map*), 241 (*map*), 245, 246
Krasnovodsk, 10, 401 (*map*), 402, 403, 405
Krasnovodsk Oblast, former, 402, 406
Krasnoyarsk, 283 (*map*), 290, 291, 297 (*map*)
Krasnoyarsk Kray, 283 (*map*), 288, 289-94; area: population: topography, 289
Krasnoyarsk Kray proper, 283 (*map*),

290-92, 297 (*map*); agriculture, 291; area and population, 290; industries: mineral resources, 290

Krasnoye, 51, 195 (*map*)

Krasnoye Ekho, 115 (*map*)

Krasnoye Selo, 153 (*map*)

Krasnozavodsk, 115 (*map*)

Krasnoznamensk, 491 (*map*)

Krasnyy (Tuva Autonomous Oblast), *see* Kyzyl

Krasnyy (Udmurt Autonomous SSR), *see* Mozhga

Krasnyy Bor, 153 (*map*)

Krasnyye Baki, 173 (*map*)

Krasnyy Kholm, 135 (*map*)

Krasnyy Klyuch, 235 (*map*), 241 (*map*), 254

Krasnyy Kut, 195 (*map*)

Krasnyy Liman, 451 (*map*)

Krasnyy Luch, 442, 451 (*map*), 452

Krasnyy Oktyabr', 115 (*map*)

Krasnyy Profintern, 105 (*map*)

Krasnyy Steklovar, 173 (*map*), 181

Krasnyy Sulin, 205 (*map*), 216, 451 (*map*)

Krasnyy Tekstil'shchik, 195 (*map*), 197

Krasnyy Tkach, 115 (*map*)

Krays, named for their administrative centers, 52; organization, 46; term, 47

Krechevitsy, 145 (*map*)

Kreenholm, *see* Krengol'm

Kremenchug, 437 (*map*), 449

Kremenets, 436 (*map*), 462

Kremennaya, 451 (*map*)

Krengol'm, 490

Krestovaya, 155 (*map*)

Kresttsy, 145 (*map*)

Kretinga, 481 (*map*)

Krichev, 471 (*map*)

Krivoy Rog, 10, 437 (*map*), 442, 448; iron-ore region, 37, 439, 441, 442, 449, 452, 453

Kromy, 127 (*map*)

Kronshtadt (Kronstadt), 8, 51, 151, 153 (*map*)

Kropachevo, 241 (*map*), 249

Kropotkin (Irkutsk Oblast), 296, 297 (*map*)

Kropotkin (Krasnodar Kray), 211 (*map*), 219, 220

Krustpils, 481 (*map*)

Krutaya, 155 (*map*)

Kryukov, 437 (*map*), 449

Krzemieniec, see Kremenets

Krzhizhanovsk, 244

Kuba, 415 (*map*), 417

Kuban' River, 22, 210, 211 (*map*), 212,

217 ff. *passim,* 427 (*map*); delta drainage, 63; steppes: grain-producing region, 213; waters diverted to Manych and Yegorlyk rivers, 63

Kubinka, 112, 115 (*map*)

Kudymkar, 235 (*map*), 248

Kugal'nik Liman, 456

Kugitang, 401 (*map*), 407

Kui—, *see* Kuy—

Kukisvumchorr, 161 (*map*), 163

Kukmor, 183 (*map*), 188

Kukruse, 489

Kukshik, *see* Pervomayskiy

Kulanak, 373 (*map*)

Kuldiga, 481 (*map*)

Kul'dur, 321 (*map*)

Kulebaki, 77, 173 (*map*), 178

Kulomzino, 271

Kulotino, 145 (*map*), 147

Kul'sary, 351

Kuludzhunskiy, 358, 359 (*map*)

Kulunda, 261 (*map*), 274, 275, 357

Kulunda Steppe, 264, 274, 275, 356, 357

Kulyab, 381 (*map*), 386

Kulyab Oblast, 381 (*map*); area and population: agriculture, 386

Kumak, 235 (*map*)

Kumand, tribe, in Western Siberia, 276

Kumara, 317 (*map*)

Kuma River, 211 (*map*); Manych Depression, 19, 210, 212

Kum-Bel', 373 (*map*), 374

Kunda, 481 (*map*), 488

Kungey Ala-Tau, 376

Kungrad, 389 (*map*), 399

Kungur, 235 (*map*), 241 (*map*), 245, 247

Kuntsevo, 113, 114, 115 (*map*)

Kunya-Urgench, 401 (*map*)

Kuolayarvi, 494, 495 (*map*)

Kupishkis, 481 (*map*)

Kupyansk, 437 (*map*), 448

Kurama Range, 383, 385, 495 (*map*)

Kura River, 212, 409, 414, 415 (*map*), 427 (*map*); agricultural area, 425; cotton, 417; dam, reservoir, and power plant, 62, 417; fisheries, 418; irrigation scheme, 62

Kurashasayskiy, 338 (*map*), 352

Kurba River, 300

Kurchum River, 341, 358

Kurds in Transcaucasia, 411, 425

Kuressare, 481 (*map*)

Kurgal'dzhino, 339 (*map*); lake, 340

Kurgan, 261 (*map*), 267

Kurgan Oblast, 250, 261 (*map*), 265, 266-67; agriculture, 267; area, 266; indus-

Kurgan Oblast (*Continued*)
tries, 267; population, 266; railroads, 267; topography, 266

Kurganovka, 279 (*map*)

Kurgan-Tyube, 381 (*map*), industries, 383, 386

Kurgan-Tyube Oblast, former, 383

Kurile Islands, 308, 309, 310, 311 (*map*), 329, 490; area, 333; localities renamed, 52, 330; population, 333; Soviet annexation of, 314; volcanic activity, 20

Kuril'sk, 311 (*map*), 330, 333

Kurland, 485

Kurland Gulf (or Lagoon), 480, 484, 490

Kurlovskiy, 115 (*map*)

Kurmenty, 373 (*map*), 377

Kurovskoye, 115 (*map*)

Kurshenay, 481 (*map*)

Kursk, 10, 37, 127 (*map*), 133

Kursk Oblast, 127 (*map*); agricultural centers, 133; agriculture, 132; industries, 132, 133; area and population, 132

Kusa, 241 (*map*), 249

Kusary, 415 (*map*)

Kushchevskaya, 211 (*map*)

Kushka, 3, 401 (*map*), 403, 406

Kushmurun, 338 (*map*), 353

Kushnarenkovo, 235 (*map*), 254

Kushunnai, *see* Il'inskiy

Kushva, 238, 241 (*map*), 242

Kustanay, 338 (*map*), 353

Kustanay Oblast, 338 (*map*); area and population: economy, 353

Kutais, 211 (*map*), 219

Kutaisi, 425, 426, 427 (*map*), 430

Kutkashen, 415 (*map*)

Kutulik, 297 (*map*), 300

Kutuzovo, 491 (*map*)

Kuty, 460

Kuuli-Mayak, 401 (*map*), 404

Kuvandyk, 235 (*map*), 257

Kuvasay, 393, 395 (*map*)

Kuvshinovo, 135 (*map*), 141

Kuyaly, 339 (*map*)

Kuybyshev (Kuybyshev Oblast), 183 (*map*), 184, 192

Kuybyshev (Novosibirsk Oblast), 261 (*map*), 272

Kuybyshev (Tatar ASSR), 183 (*map*), 189

Kuybyshevka or Kuybyshevka-Vostochnaya, 317 (*map*), 318

Kuybyshevo (Crimean Oblast), 205 (*map*)

Kuybyshevo (Kazakh SSR), 338 (*map*)

Kuybyshevo (Rostov Oblast), 451 (*map*)

Kuybyshevo (Turkmen SSR), 401 (*map*)

Kuybyshevo (Uzbek SSR), 395 (*map*)

Kuybyshev Oblast, 183 (*map*), 191-93; agriculture, 192; area, 191; hydroelectric power project, 192; industrial centers, 193; natural resources, 192; population, 191

Kuybyshevskiy Zaton, 183 (*map*), 188

Kuyto Lake, 495 (*map*)

Kuyurgaz coal fields, 255

Kuzbas, *see* Kuznetsk Basin

Kuzedeyevo, 279 (*map*)

Kuzino, 241 (*map*)

Kuznetsk (Kemerovo Oblast), *see* Stalinsk

Kuznetsk (Penza Oblast), 183 (*map*), 190

Kuznetsk Ala-Tau, 260, 264, 280

Kuznetsk Basin (Kuzbas), 260, 272, 279 (*map*); chemical industry, 265; coal deposits, 12, 33, 73, 264, 265, 276 f.; industrial development, 99, 277; iron ore for metallurgical mills, 249, 265; metallurgical industry, 77, 265; urban concentration, 97; water power, 265; *see also* Kemerovo Oblast

Kuzomen', 161 (*map*)

Kyakhta, 283 (*map*), 297 (*map*), 301

Kyardla, 481 (*map*)

Kyava, 489

Kyshtym, 235 (*map*), 241 (*map*), 248, 249, 251

Kytlym, 241 (*map*)

Kytmanovo, 279 (*map*)

Kyurdakhany, 415 (*map*)

Kyurdamir, 415 (*map*)

Kyzyl, 283 (*map*), 295, 297 (*map*)

Kyzyl-Burun, 415 (*map*)

Kyzyl-Khoto, *see* Kyzyl

Kyzyl-Kum Desert, 335, 358, 362, 364, 389 (*map*), 398, 399

Kyzyl-Mazhalyk, 295

Kyzyl-Ray Mountains, 336

Kyzyl-Su, river, 373 (*map*), 380, 381 (*map*)

Kzyl-Kuga, 338 (*map*)

Kzyl-Orda, 338 (*map*), 346, 363

Kzyl-Orda Oblast, 338 (*map*); area and population: economy, 362

Kzyltuu, 339 (*map*)

Laba River, 211 (*map*), 218

Labaznoye, 311 (*map*)

Labiau, *see* Polessk

Labinsk, 211 (*map*), 219

Lachin, 415 (map)
Ladoga Lake, 23, 143, 148, 153 (map), 479, 493, 494, 495 (map), 496
Ladozhskoye Ozero, 153 (map)
Ladushkin, 491 (map)
Lagan', see Kaspiyskiy
Lakhdenpokh'ya, 495 (map), 496
Lakhtinskiy, 152, 153 (map)
Lakinskiy, 115 (map)
Laks, ethnic group, 213, 231
Lal'sk, 173 (map), 177
Lamuts, see Eveny
La Pérouse Strait, 331 (map), 332
Laptev Sea, 6, 304
Lars, 427 (map)
Lar'yak, 261 (map)
Latgale, 485, 487
Latgals, in Baltic Region, 41, 480, 485
Latnaya, 127 (map)
Latvians, in Baltic Region, 41, 483, 485
Latvian Soviet Socialist Republic, 45, 479, 481 (map), 485-87; administrative organization, 480; agriculture, 486; area, 485; cities over 50,000, 511; industries, 485; population, 480, 485
Lazdiyay, 481 (map)
Lazo, 327 (map)
Lbishchevo, see Chapayevo
Lead-zinc ores, 38, 78; Eastern Siberia, 302, 303, 306; Kazakh SSR, 347, 355, 362; Kirghiz SSR, 374, 376; Soviet Far East, 326; Western Siberia, 274; see also Zinc
Lebedin, 437 (map)
Lebedyan', 105 (map)
Lebyazh'ye (Kazakh SSR), 339 (map)
Lebyazh'ye (Kurgan Oblast), 261 (map)
Lefu River, 327 (map)
Legostayevo, 279 (map)
Lekhta, 495 (map)
Leksozero, lake, 495 (map)
Lena River, 21, 22, 283 (map), 284, 285, 297 (map), 304, 311 (map); coal-bearing basin, 36, 306; fishing establishments, 306; navigation route, 299
Lenger, 339 (map), 345, 346, 362
Leninabad, 381 (map) 383, 384, 385, 395 (map)
Leninabad Oblast, 381 (map), 395 (map); area and population: economy, 385
Leninakan, 410, 421 (map), 423, 424; plateau, 420; steppe, 423
Leningori, 427 (map)
Leningrad, 68, 145 (map), 150, 151, 153 (map); Baltic port, 8; fuel resources, 149; industrial suburbs, 144; machine

construction center, 98; metallurgical base for, 78
Leningrad Oblast, 145 (map); 148-52; agriculture, 150; area, 148; climate, 149; industries, 150; natural resources, 149; population: topography, 148
Leninogorsk, 339 (map), 347, 358, 359 (map)
Lenin Peak, 365
Leninpol', 373 (map)
Leninsk, 393, 395 (map)
Leninskaya Sloboda, 173 (map)
Leninskiy, 173 (map)
Leninskoye (Jewish Autonomous Oblast), 321 (map)
Leninskoye (Kirov Oblast), 173 (map)
Leninsk-Kuznetskiy, 277, 279 (map), 280
Leninsk-Turkmenskiy, see Chardzhou
Lenkoran, 414, 415 (map), 417
Lentekhi, 427 (map)
Lentvaris, 481 (map)
Leonidovo, 331 (map)
Leovo, 465 (map)
Lepaya, see Liepaya
Lepel', 471 (map)
Lepsa River, 341, 360
Lepsy, 339 (map)
Lerik, 415 (map)
Lesghians, 41, 98, 231
Lesnoy, 161 (map), 162
Lesogorsk, 330, 331 (map)
Lesogorskiy, 145 (map)
Lesopil'noye, 321 (map)
Lesozavodsk, 52, 321 (map), 328
Lesozavodskiy (Kirov Oblast), 173 (map), 178
Lesozavodskiy (Murmansk Oblast), 161 (map), 162
Lesser Caucasus, 409, 419; industrial base, 416
Lesser Uzen' River, 195 (map)
Letnerechenskiy, 495 (map), 496
Levikha, 238, 241 (map)
Levshino, 245, 246
L'gov, 127 (map), 133
Liakhvi River, 432
Liaotung Peninsula, naval base of Port Arthur, 3, 91
Libau, see Liepaya
Libava, see Liepaya, 487
Lida, 471 (map), 477
Lielupe River, 481 (map), 485
Liepāja, see Liepaya
Liepaya (Liepāja), Baltic port, 8, 479, 481 (map), 485; engineering and tex-

Liepaya (Liepāja) (*Continued*)
tile industries, 486; shipbuilding, docking, and naval-base installations, 487
Lifudzin, 321 (*map*), 328
Lignite, 36, 69, 72, 73; industry, 445; mines and mining centers, 239, 248, 446, 456, 463; used in power stations, 75
Ligovo, 153 (*map*)
Likhoslavl', 135 (*map*)
Likhovskoy, 216, 451 (*map*)
Likhvin, *see* Chekalin
Likino-Dulevo, 115 (*map*)
Limbazhi, 481 (*map*)
Limestone, 38, 206, 445
Linen-milling centers, 81, 141
Lipetsk, 77, 127 (*map*), 132
Lipiya, 173 (*map*), 179
Lipkany, 464, 465 (*map*)
Lisichansk, 451 (*map*)
Lisiy Nos, 153 (*map*)
Liski, 127 (*map*)
Listvyanskiy, 279 (*map*), 296
Lithuanian-Belorussian upland, 19, 134
Lithuanians, in Baltic Region, 41, 472, 483, 485
Lithuanian Soviet Socialist Republic, 479, 481 (*map*), 482-84; accession of, 45; administrative organization, 480; agriculture, 483; area, 482; cities over 50,000, 511; population, 480, 482; topography, 482
Litovko, 321 (*map*)
Little Khingan range, 309, 322
Litvino, *see* Sosnovoborsk
Livadiya, 205 (*map*), 209
Livestock, distribution of, 63, 445
Livestock raising, Baltic Region, 486; Central Asia, 369; Eastern Siberia, 301; in desert, 64, 403; Kirghiz SSR, 374; nomadic type, 64; Transcaucasia, 413; Western Siberia, 276; *see also* Dairying
Livny, 127 (*map*), 129
Lobva, 240, 241 (*map*)
Local government, 47; urban, 48
Lodeynoye Pole, 145 (*map*)
Lok-Batan, 415 (*map*)
Lokhvitsa, 437 (*map*)
Loknya, 135 (*map*)
Lomonosov, 145 (*map*), 152, 153 (*map*)
Lomonosovo, 135 (*map*)
Lopatin, 211 (*map*), 231
Lopatino, *see* Volzhsk
Lori steppe, 420, 423
Losinoostrovsk, *see* Babushkin (Moscow Oblast)

Lotta River, 161 (*map*)
Loukhi, 162, 495 (*map*), 496
Lovat' River, 135 (*map*), 145 (*map*)
Lovozero, 161 (*map*)
Lower Amur lowland, 309
Lower Amur Oblast, 311 (*map*), 318, 321 (*map*); area and population: industries: mineral resources, 323
Lower Don and Northern Caucasus, 205 (*map*), 211 (*map*); 209-14; agriculture, 214; cities over 50,000, 507; climate, 212; ethnic groups that lost their national identity, 213; grain-producing region, 213; industries, 214; mineral springs, 210; population, 213; resorts, 214, 223; topography, 209 ff.; transportation, 214; *see further under names of oblasts as listed on pp. 102, 501*
Lower Tunguska River, 283 (*map*), 297 (*map*)
Lower Varzob, power station, 383, 386
Lower Volga Region, 195 (*map*); 193-96; agriculture, 196; climate, 194; deposits left by Caspian Sea, 19; industries, 196; population, 194; topography, 193; *see further under names of oblasts as listed on p. 501*
Lozovaya, 437 (*map*)
Loz'va River, 235 (*map*), 241 (*map*)
Lubny, 437 (*map*)
Luck, *see* Lutsk
Ludzha, 481 (*map*)
Luga, 145 (*map*)
Lugansk, *see* Voroshilovgrad
Luga River, 145 (*map*)
Lugovoy, 339 (*map*); railroad to Rybach'ye, 374, 376
Lukachek, 316, 317 (*map*)
Lukhovitsy, 115 (*map*)
Lukoyanov, 173 (*map*)
Lumber and lumbering industry, centers, 80, 200 (*see also* Sawmilling centers); Baltic Region, 482, 483, 488, 489; Belorussian SSR, 476, 477; Central Industrial Region, 108; Eastern Siberia, 290, 291, 296; European North, 159, 166, 168; European Northwest, 150; Georgian SSR, 431; Karelo-Finnish SSR, 494; Kazakh SSR, 347; Novgorod Oblast, 146; Russian SFSR, 100; Soviet Far East, 319, 328, 332; Ukrainian SSR, 461; Urals, 240, 245, 252, 253, 254; Volga Region, 175, 177, 179, 181, 185, 197, 200; Western Siberia, 266, 268, 271, 273, 274
Lumber *kombinat*, 69

Luninets, 471 (*map*)
Lunino (Kaliningrad Oblast), 491 (*map*)
Lunino (Penza Oblast), 183 (*map*)
Lun'yevka, 241 (*map*)
Luoravetlany (Chukchi), in Eastern Siberia, 41, 305, 314, 325
Lutsk, 436 (*map*), 461
Luza, 173 (*map*), 177
L'vov, 436 (*map*), 441, 442, 462
L'vov Oblast, 436 (*map*), 459, 462-63; area and population, 462
Lwów, *see* L'vov
Lyakhov Island, 6, 307
Lyamino, 241 (*map*), 245
Lyangar, 389 (*map*), 391, 396
Lyangosovo, 173 (*map*)
Lyaskelya, 495 (*map*), 496
Lychkovo, 145 (*map*)
Lyskovo, 173 (*map*)
Lys'va, 241 (*map*), 245
Lyuksemburgi, *see* Bolnisi
Lyuban', 145 (*map*)
Lyubertsy, 114, 115 (*map*)
Lyubinskiy, 261 (*map*), 271
Lyublino, 113, 114, 115 (*map*)
Lyubotin, 436-37 (*map*)
Lyubytino, 145 (*map*)
Lyudinovo, 135 (*map*), 139

Machine-building industries, 79, 217; Baltic Region, 492; Central Industrial Region, 107, 111, 120; Eastern Siberia, 288, 290; European South, for petroleum industry, 220; European West, 150; Kazakh SSR, 347, 361; Kirghiz SSR, 374; Russian SFSR, 99; Tadzhik SSR, 383; Transcaucasia, 412, 423, 429; Ukrainian SSR, 442, 448, 449, 456, 463; Urals, 239, 241, 249, 254, 255, 258; Uzbek SSR, 395; Western Siberia, 266; *see also* Agricultural machinery works; Heavy industry
Madniskhevi, 222
Madona, 481 (*map*)
Magadan, 7, 311 (*map*), 318, 324
Magadan-Kolyma Area, 311 (*map*); area and population: gold, 323
Magdagachi, 317 (*map*)
Magnesium salts, 244 f., 362, 460
Magnetite, 37, 133, 234, 250
Magnitka, 241 (*map*), 248, 249
Magnitnaya Mountain, 234, 248
Magnitogorsk, 235 (*map*), 250, 251; coal shipped to, 346; iron, 37; metallurgical plant, 77, 99, 237, 239; railway to Abdulino, 255, 256

Mago, 321 (*map*), 323
Mai—, see May—
Makanchi, 359 (*map*)
Makarakskiy, 278, 279 (*map*)
Makarov (Sakhalin Oblast), 330, 331 (*map*)
Makarov (Ukrainian SSR), 436 (*map*)
Makar'yev, 105 (*map*)
Makat, 338 (*map*), 346, 351
Makeyevka, 442, 450, 451 (*map*)
Makhachkala, 10, 51, 211 (*map*), 232
Makharadze, 427 (*map*)
Makinsk, 339 (*map*), 346, 355
Maksatikha, 135 (*map*)
Malatiya, 423
Malaya Kheta River, 294
Malaya Sopcha, 161 (*map*), 163
Malaya Vishera, 145 (*map*)
Malgobek, 211 (*map*), 228
Malka River, 211 (*map*)
Malmyzh, 173 (*map*)
Maloarkhangel'sk, 127 (*map*)
Malomal'sk, 239, 241 (*map*)
Malo-Uchalinskiy, 235 (*map*), 254
Maloyaroslavets, 115 (*map*), 135 (*map*)
Malozemel'skaya Tundra, 158, 169
Malyye Barsuki, 335
Malyye Karmakuly, 155 (*map*)
Mama, 296, 297 (*map*)
Mamadysh, 183 (*map*), 189
Mamlyutka, 339, (*map*)
Mammoths, 284; ivory deposits, 307
Mamonovo, 491 (*map*)
Manganese, 78; Caucasus, 14, 37; Eastern Siberia, 290, 291, 296; Kazakh SSR, 345, 351, 355; Transcaucasia, 412, 425, 426; Ukrainian SSR, 14, 37, 439, 441, 453; Urals, 238, 253, 256; Western Siberia, 278
Mangut, 303
Mangyshlak peninsula, coal mines, 346; depressions, 335; fisheries, 351; manganese, 345; mineral deposits, 351
Mansi (Voguls), tribe in Siberia, 41, 53, 264, 269
Manych River, 205 (*map*), 211 (*map*); canal project, 223
Manzovka, 321 (*map*), 327 (*map*)
Maoka, *see* Kholmsk
Maral deer, 276
Maralik, 421 (*map*)
Mardakert, 415 (*map*)
Mardakyany, 415 (*map*)
Marelisi, 428
Marevo, 145 (*map*)
Marganets, 437 (*map*), 453

Margelan, 393, 394, 395 (*map*)
Mari (Cheremiss) 41, 53, 98, 172, 173, 181, 184, 188
Mari Autonomous Soviet Socialist Republic, 173 (*map*), 180-81; agriculture, 181; area and population, 180; ethnic distribution, 181; industries, 181
Mariinsk, 278, 279 (*map*), 280
Mariinsk canal system, 89, 109, 146; fisheries, 496
Mariinskiy Posad, 183 (*map*)
Mar'inka, 451 (*map*)
Maritime Kray, 27, 47, 53, 311 (*map*), 314, 321 (*map*), 326-29; agriculture, 328; area: climate, 327; coal-mining industry, 328; communications, 328; population: topography, 327
Mariupol', *see* Zhdanov
Mariyampole, 481 (*map*)
Mariyets, 173 (*map*), 181
Markovo, 311 (*map*)
Marks, 51, 195 (*map*), 197
Marsyaty, 238, 241 (*map*)
Martuni, 415 (*map*), 421 (*map*)
Marxstadt, *see* Marks
Mary, 401 (*map*), 402, 406
Mary oasis, *see* Murgab oasis
Mary Oblast, 401 (*map*); 402; area and population: economy, 406
Masally, 415 (*map*)
Masel'skaya, 495 (*map*)
Mashtagi, 415 (*map*)
Mashuk, mountain, 210
Maslovo, 241 (*map*)
Maslyanino, 279 (*map*)
Massandra, 209
Matay, 339 (*map*)
Matcha, 381 (*map*)
Matochkin Shar, settlement, 155 (*map*)
Matochkin Shar, strait, 6, 155 (*map*), 157, 169
Matsesta, 211 (*map*), 214, 220
Matveyev Island, 155 (*map*), 167
Matveyev Kurgan, 451 (*map*)
Maya River, 317 (*map*)
Maykain, 339 (*map*), 357
Maykop, 36, 74, 211 (*map*), 220
Maylisay, 373 (*map*), 374, 379, 395 (*map*)
Mayna, 183 (*map*)
Mayskiy (Amur Oblast), 317 (*map*)
Mayskiy (Kabardinian ASSR), 211 (*map*), 225
Mayskoye, 491 (*map*)
Mazheykyay, 481 (*map*)
Mazul'skiy, manganese mines, 291

Mednogorsk, 235 (*map*), 258, 259
Medveditsa River, 195 (*map*)
Medvedok, 173 (*map*)
Medvezh'yegorsk, 495 (*map*), 496, 497
Medyn', 135 (*map*)
Megalomania, policy directed against, 69
Megri, 421 (*map*), 423
Melekess, 183 (*map*), 191
Meleuz, 235 (*map*), 254
Melitopol', 437 (*map*), 454
Mel'nikovo, 279 (*map*)
Melovoye, 205 (*map*), 437 (*map*)
Memel, see Klaypeda
Memelland, 483
Mendeleyevo, 235 (*map*)
Menzelinsk, 183 (*map*), 189
Mercury deposits, 38, 276, 374, 378
Merefa, 436 (*map*), 437 (*map*)
Merke, sugar refinery, 361
Meshchera, 105 (*map*), 122
Meshchovsk, 135 (*map*)
Mestia, 427 (*map*)
Metallurgical industries, 76 ff.; coal for, 73, 74; chrome and nickel-steel project, 78; giant plants, 77; in Baltic Region, 487; Central Asia, 391; European South, 208, 216, 221; Karelo-Finnish SSR, 497; Kazakh SSR, 346, 347, 354, 355, 356; Leningrad area, project, 78, 149; Russian SFSR, 99; Soviet Far East, 315, 320; Tadzhik SSR, 383; Ukrainian SSR, 449, 450, 452, 453, 454; Urals, 237, 239, 242, 245; 248 ff., 253, 254, 255, 258, 259; Uzbek SSR, 396; Volga Region, 178, 200; Western Siberia, 265, 280
Metallurgy, nonferrous, 78; European South, 227; Kazakh SSR, 347, 358; Ukrainian SSR, 443; Urals, 238, 239, 249; Western Siberia, 265, 277, 278; *see also under industries, e.g.,* Copper, smelters and refineries
Metals, rare, 368, 425
Metals, nonferrous, 238, 328, 368
Methane, *see* Natural gas
Mezen', 155 (*map*), 168
Mezen' River, 155 (*map*)
Mezinovskiy, 115 (*map*)
Mga, 153 (*map*)
Mgachi, 331 (*map*), 332
Mglin, 135 (*map*)
Miass, 235 (*map*), 241 (*map*), 248, 251
Miass River, 241 (*map*), 234
Miazhik, 415 (*map*)
Mica, 38, 290, 296

Michurinsk, 127 (*map*), 131
Middle Amur lowland, 316
Middle Volga Kray, former, 187
Middle Volga Region, 183 (*map*), 181-84; agriculture, 184; climate, 182; exports and imports: industrialization drive, 184; petroleum resources, 182; topography, 181 f.; *see further under names of oblasts as listed on p. 500 f.*
Mikha Tskhakaya, 427 (*map*)
Mikhaylov, 105 (*map*), 123
Mikhaylovka (Maritime Kray), 327 (*map*)
Mikhaylovka (Stalingrad Oblast), 195 (*map*), 199
Mikhaylovskiy, 261 (*map*), 359 (*map*), 274
Mikhaylovskiy Khutor, 437 (*map*)
Mikhrevo, 115 (*map*)
Mikoyan, 421 (*map*)
Mikoyana, Imeni, 324
Mikoyan-Shakhar, *see* Klukhori
Mili steppe, irrigation canals, 417
Military roads, European South, 227, 228, 413, 429, 431
Millerovo, 205 (*map*), 216, 451 (*map*)
Millet, 59, 61
Milyutinskaya, 205 (*map*)
Mineralnyye Vody, 211 (*map*), 223
Mineral resources, 33-38; Central Asia, 367; European North, 159, 160; European South, 206; Soviet Far East, 315, 320; Ukrainian SSR, 449; Urals, 234, 238, 253, 257; Volga Region, 172, 174, 176; Western Siberia, 264
Minerals, formed in Pre-Cambrian deposits, 10; of Devonian nonmetallic, 12, 38; of Jurassic period, 13; of Silurian period, 11
Mineral springs, European South, 210, 223; Transcaucasia, 410, 414, 425, 429; Ukrainian SSR, 456, 461, 463
Mingechaur, 415 (*map*), 416
Mingechaur Sea, 62, 415 (*map*), 417
Mining, *see under names of products, e. g.,* Coal; Sulphur
Minorities, national, 101
Minorskiy, 305
Minsk, 469, 471 (*map*), 474
Minsk Oblast, 471 (*map*); area: industries: population, 474
Minusinsk, 283 (*map*), 288, 290, 292, 297 (*map*); coal basin, 289
Min'yar, 241 (*map*), 249
Mirabilite, *see* Glauber salt
Mir-Bashir, 415 (*map*)

Mirgorod, 437 (*map*)
Mirzaani, 426, 427 (*map*)
Mirzachul', 395 (*map*)
Mirzoyan, *see* Dzhambul
Mishelevka, 298
Misheronskiy, 115 (*map*)
Mishkino, 261 (*map*)
Mitau, see Yelgava
Mitava, see Yelgava
Mitoginskiy, 324
Mius River, 451 (*map*)
Mizur, 211 (*map*), 227
Mogilev, 471 (*map*), 475
Mogilev Oblast, 471 (*map*); area: industries: population, 475
Mogilev-Podol'skiy, 436 (*map*), 447, 465 (*map*)
Mogocha, 297 (*map*)
Mogochin, 261 (*map*), 273
Mogol-Tau, mountain, 395 (*map*)
Mogoytuy, 304
Mogzon, 297 (*map*)
Mointy, 85, 339 (*map*), 349, 355
Moksha River, 183 (*map*)
Moldavian Autonomous SSR, 45, 46, 441, 464, 466, 468
Moldavians, in Bessarabia, 41; in Moldavian SSR, 464; in Ukrainian SSR, 457
Moldavian Soviet Socialist Republic, 45, 441, 465 (*map*), 464-68; agriculture, 466 f.; area, 464; cities over 50,000, 510; industries, 467; mineral resources, 464; population, 464; railroads, 467 f.
Molochansk, 437 (*map*)
Molodechno, 471 (*map*), 478
Molodechno Oblast, 471 (*map*); area and population: economy, 478
Molodeczno, see Molodechno
Mologa, 116
Molotov, 235 (*map*), 237, 241 (*map*), 245, 246
Molotovabad, 395 (*map*)
Molotova, Imeni V. M., 173 (*map*), 179
Molotovo (Georgian SSR), 427 (*map*)
Molotovo (Uzbek SSR), 395 (*map*)
Molotov Oblast, 235 (*map*), 237, 241 (*map*), 243-47; agriculture, 245; area: coal: forests, 243; industrial area projected, 246; industrial cities, 246 f.; lumbering, 245; metallurgical industry, 245; mineral resources, 244; population, 243; transportation, 245
Molotovsk (Arkhangel'sk Oblast), 155 (*map*), 168
Molotovsk (Kirov Oblast), 173 (*map*), 177

Molybdenum, 38, 78 f.; Central Asia, 374, 377, 391, 396; European South, 226; Eastern Siberia, 300, 303; Kazakh SSR, 355; Kirghiz SSR, 377; Soviet Far East, 320; Transcaucasia, 414, 422

Monchegorsk, 161 (*map*), 162, 163

Monche-tundra, mineral reserves, 160

Mongolian ethnic group, in Western Siberia, 276; *see also* Buryat-Mongols

Monsoons, 25, 27, 312, 326

Moonsund archipelago, 479, 487

Moraines, 15, 19, 469

Mordvinian Autonomous Soviet Socialist Republic, 183 (*map*); agriculture, 187; area, 186; capital, 186; industries, 187; population, 186

Mordvinians, 41, 98, 172, 182, 185, 186, 188, 189, 194

Morozova, Imeni, 153 (*map*)

Morozovsk, 205 (*map*), 216

Morshansk, 127 (*map*), 131

Moryakovskiy Zaton, 273, 279 (*map*)

Mor'ye, 153 (*map*)

Mosal'sk, 135 (*map*)

Moscow, 44, 105 (*map*), 115 (*map*); area, 110; history and description of city, 113; industries, 113, 114; lignite basin, 36, 73, 74, 122, 123; machine construction, 107; population, 110; port and rail facilities, 112; reconstruction project, 113; scientific and cultural institutions, 113

Moscow Canal, 89, 109, 111, 115 (*map*), 135 (*map*), 141

Moscow Oblast, 105 (*map*), 115 (*map*), 110-16; agriculture, 111; area, 110; exports and imports, 112; industry, 110; population: topography, 110

Moscow-Volga Canal, *see* Moscow Canal

Moshkovo, 279 (*map*)

Moskal'vo, 331 (*map*), 332

Moskva, *see* Moscow

Moskva River, 105 (*map*), 112, 115 (*map*)

Mospino, 451 (*map*)

Mosty, 471 (*map*)

Mototomari, *see* Vostochnyy

Motovilikha, *see* Molotov

Mountain-building processes, 12 ff.

Mountain tourism and climbing, 226, 227

Mozdok, 211 (*map*), 226, 228

Mozhaysk, 105 (*map*), 115 (*map*)

Mozhga, 235 (*map*), 252, 253

Mozyr', 471 (*map*), 476

Msta River, 140, 145 (*map*)

Mstera, 105 (*map*), 121

Mstislavl', 471 (*map*)

Mtsensk, 127 (*map*)

Mtskheta, 427 (*map*), 428

Mud baths, 208, 223, 456

Mugan' steppe, irrigation canals, 417

Mugodzhar Mountains, 335; mineral deposits, 345, 349, 350, 352

Mukachevo, 436 (*map*), 463

Mukhanovo, 183 (*map*), 192

Mukhu (Muhu), 487

Mukry, 401 (*map*)

Muk-Su, river, 381 (*map*)

Mulberry trees, 384, 385, 393

Mullino, *see* Oktyabr'skiy (Bashkir ASSR)

Mullovka, 183 (*map*), 191

Mumra, 195 (*map*), 202

Mundybash, 278, 279 (*map*)

Munkács, see Mukachevo

Munku-Sardyk, mountain, 20, 282

Murashi, 173 (*map*), 177

Murgab, 381 (*map*)

Murgab oasis, 403, 406

Murgab River, 364, 387, 400, 401 (*map*); canal to connect with Amu Darya and Tedzhen rivers, 403; cotton, 403, 406; reservoirs, 403

Murman coast, 157

Murmansk, 155 (*map*), 161 (*map*), 162

Murmansk Oblast, 161 (*map*), 160-63; area: capital: mineral reserves, 160; population: territorial acquisitions, 160

Murmansk (Kirov) Railroad, 162, 494, 496, 497

Murmashi, 161 (*map*)

Murom, 105 (*map*), 122

Murygino, 173 (*map*), 177

Murzabek, 381 (*map*)

Mustvee, 481 (*map*)

Muyaldy, 339 (*map*)

Muynak, 389 (*map*), 399

Muyun-Kum, 361

Muztor, 373 (*map*), 379

Myski, 279 (*map*)

Mysovka, 491 (*map*)

Mysovsk, *see* Babushkin Buryat-Mongol Autonomous SSR

Mytishchi, 113, 114, 115 (*map*)

Myyzakyula, 481 (*map*)

Naberezhnyye Chelny, 183 (*map*)

Nadezhdinsk, *see* Serov

Nadezhdinskaya, 327 (*map*)

Nadvoitsy, 494, 495 (*map*)

Nadvornaya, 460

Naftalan, 36, 414, 415 (*map*)

Nagayevo, 7, 324

Nagorno-Karabakh Autonomous Oblast, 415 (*map*), 416; area: industries: population, 419
Nagornoye, 51, 153 (*map*)
Nagornskiy, 240, 241 (*map*)
Nagornyy, 283 (*map*), 305
Naihoro, *see* Gornozavodsk
Nakhichevan', 414, 415 (*map*), 419
Nakhichevan' Autonomous Soviet Socialist Republic, 415 (*map*), 416; area: economy: population, 419
Nakhodka, 321 (*map*), 327 (*map*), 328, 329
Nal'chik, 211 (*map*), 226
Namangan, 389 (*map*), 394, 395 (*map*)
Namangan Oblast, 389 (*map*); area and population: economy, 395
Nanay (Golds), 41, 314, 318, 319
Napareuli, 427 (*map*)
Narodnaya, Mount, 155 (*map*), 157
Naro-Fominsk, 105 (*map*), 115 (*map*)
Narova River, *see* Narva River
Narva, 145 (*map*), 481 (*map*), 488, 489
Narva River, 145 (*map*), 480, 481 (*map*), 488, 489, 490
Nar'yan-Mar, 155 (*map*), 169
Narym Range, 336
Narym River, 341, 358
Naryn River, 366, 373 (*map*), 377, 379, 395 (*map*)
Naryn (Kirghiz SSR), 373 (*map*), 377, 378
Naryn (Uzbek SSR), 395 (*map*)
Narynkol, 339 (*map*)
Naryshevo, *see* Oktyabr'skiy (Bashkir ASSR)
Naryshkino, 127 (*map*)
Nasosnyy, 415 (*map*)
National autonomy, 44
Nationalities, deprived of their identity as separate nationalities, 514 (*see also* Ethnic groups)
Natural-gas, fields: Kazakh SSR, 350, 351; Turkmen SSR, 405; Ukrainian SSR, 443, 460, 461; Urals, 257; Uzbek SSR, 393; Volga Region, 37, 192; pipe lines, 75, 192, 197, 229, 393
Nau, 381 (*map*), 395 (*map*)
Nauja Vilnia, *see* Nauya Vil'nya
Naushki, 297 (*map*), 301
Nauya Vil'nya, 484
Naval bases, Baltic Region, 489, 492; districts of Porkkala and Port Arthur controlled by USSR, 3; European North, 161; Soviet Far East, 7, 91, 322; submarine base in Soviet Far East, 329

Navlya, 135 (*map*)
Nayoshi, *see* Lesogorsk
Nazarovo, 290, 297 (*map*)
Nazimovo, 327 (*map*), 328
Nebit-Dag, 52, 401 (*map*), 402, 404, 406
Nebolchi, 145 (*map*)
Nefteabad, 383, 385, 395 (*map*)
Neftechala, 36, 415 (*map*), 416
Neftegorsk, 52, 211 (*map*), 219, 221
Negoreloye, 471 (*map*)
Neklyudovo, 173 (*map*)
Nelidovo, 135 (*map*), 140
Nel'ma, 321 (*map*), 322
Neman, 481 (*map*), 491 (*map*), 492
Neman River, 22, 469, 470, 471 (*map*), 477, 480, 481 (*map*), 482, 491 (*map*); navigation, 483
Nemunas River, *see* Neman River
Nenets National Okrug, 155 (*map*), 164, 167; area: capital, 168; population, 169
Nentsy (Samoyed) people, 41, 53; in Eastern Siberia, 288, 290, 293; in European North, 169; in Western Siberia, 264, 270
Nephelite, 38, 78, 159, 160
Nerchinsk, 297 (*map*), 303
Nerchinskiy Zavod, 302
Nerekhta, 105 (*map*), 118, 119
Neris River, 481 (*map*); *see also* Viliya River
Nerpa seal, 285
Nesterov, 491 (*map*)
Nesvizh, 471 (*map*)
Neukuhren, *see* Pionerskiy
Neva River, 22, 145 (*map*), 153 (*map*), 156
Nevel, 135 (*map*)
Nevel'sk, 330, 331 (*map*), 333
Never, 317 (*map*); highway from, 305
Nevežys River, *see* Nevyazh River
Nevinnomyssk, 211 (*map*), 223; canal, 63, 211 (*map*), 222, 223
Nevskoye, 491 (*map*)
Nev'yansk, 240, 241 (*map*)
Nevyazh River, 483
New Siberian (Novo-Sibirskiye) Islands, 6, 17 (*map*), 281, 284, 307
Neya, 105 (*map*)
Nezametnyy, *see* Aldan
Nezhin, 437 (*map*), 458
Nganasany (Tavgiytsy), in Eastern Siberia, 290, 293
Nickel deposits, European North, 160; Kazakh SSR, 347, 349, 352; Urals, 257
Nickel refinery, 78, 241
Nida, 481 (*map*), 484
Niemen River, *see* Neman River

Nikel', 159, 160, 161 (*map*)
Nikitinka (Kazakh SSR), 359 (*map*)
Nikitinka (Smolensk Oblast), 135 (*map*)
Nikitovka (Kaliningrad Oblast), 491 (*map*)
Nikitovka (Ukrainian SSR), 450, 451 (*map*)
Nikolayev, 9, 437 (*map*), 442, 445, 455
Nikolayevka, 322
Nikolayev Oblast, 437 (*map*); area: economy: population, 455
Nikolayevsk (Lower Amur Oblast), 311 (*map*), 321 (*map*), 323, 331 (*map*)
Nikolayevsk (Saratov Oblast), *see* Pugachev
Nikolayevskiy, 195 (*map*)
Nikol'sk, 155 (*map*)
Nikol'skaya Pestravka, 183 (*map*), 190
Nikol'skiy Khutor, 183 (*map*), 190
Nikol'skoye, 195 (*map*)
Nikol'sk-Ussuriyskiy, *see* Voroshilov
Nikopol', 37, 437 (*map*), 439, 452, 453
Nikulyasy, 153 (*map*)
Niskakoski, acquired by USSR, 160
Niva River, 161 (*map*), 162, 163
Nivenskoye, 491 (*map*)
Nivkhi (Gilyaks), ethnic group, 14, 314, 318, 332
Nivskiy, 161 (*map*), 163
Nizhne-Angarsk, 297 (*map*)
Nizhnegorskiy, 205 (*map*), 208
Nizhne-Ilimsk, 297 (*map*)
Nizhne-Kolymsk, 307
Nizhne-Stalinsk, 305
Nizhne-Troitskiy, 235 (*map*), 254
Nizhneudinsk, 297 (*map*), 298
Nizhniy Baskunchak, 195 (*map*), 202
Nizhniye Sergi, 239, 241 (*map*)
Nizhniy Lomov, 183 (*map*), 190
Nizhniy Novgorod, *see* Gor'kiy
Nizhniy Pyandzh, 381 (*map*), 384
Nizhniy Tagil, 37, 80, 235 (*map*), 240, 241 (*map*), 242
Nizhniy Ufaley, 241 (*map*)
Nizhnyaya Salda, 239, 241 (*map*)
Nizhnyaya Tunguska River, *see* Lower Tunguska River
Nizhnyaya Tura, 241 (*map*)
Noda, *see* Chekhov
Nogaysk, 437 (*map*)
Noginsk (Krasnoyarsk Kray), 293
Noginsk (Moscow Oblast), 105 (*map*), 111, 114, 115 (*map*)
Nogliki, 331 (*map*)
Nõmme, *see* Nymme
Nor-Bayazet, 421 (*map*)

Nordvik, 283 (*map*), 293, 294
Noril'sk, 283 (*map*), 293, 294
North Caucasus, *see* Northern Caucasus
Northeast Passage, 91
Northern Bukovina, ceded to USSR, 441
Northern Caucasus, *see* Lower Don and Northern Caucasus
Northern Donets River, 205 (*map*), 435, 437 (*map*), 438, 448, 451 (*map*)
Northern Dvina River, 22, 155 (*map*), 156
Northern Sea Route, 266, 285, 306, 315, 326; chief ports, 91, 270, 307
Northern Uvals, 15, 156, 173 (*map*), 176
North-Kazakhstan Oblast, 339 (*map*); area and population, 353
North Ossetian Autonomous Soviet Socialist Republic, 211 (*map*), 213, 225, 226-28, 432; agriculture, 227; area, 226; economic assets, 227; hydroelectricity and nonferrous metallurgy: military roads, 227; population: topography, 226
North Pechora Railroad, 84; link between Solikamsk and, 246
Nota River, 161 (*map*)
Novabad, 381 (*map*), 387
Novaya Bukhara, *see* Kagan
Novaya Ivanovka, 465 (*map*)
Novaya Kazanka, 338 (*map*)
Novaya Ladoga, 145 (*map*)
Novaya Lyalya, 240, 241 (*map*)
Novaya Slobodka, 105 (*map*), 120
Novaya Vodolaga, 436 (*map*)
Novaya Zemlya, 6, 155 (*map*), 157, 167, 169
Novgorod, 145 (*map*), 147
Novgorod Oblast, 145 (*map*), 146-47; area, economy, population, 146
Novgorod-Severskiy, 437 (*map*)
Novikovo, 331 (*map*)
Novo-Aleksandrovsk, 331 (*map*)
Novo-Annenskiy, 195 (*map*)
Novoasbest, 239, 241 (*map*)
Novo-Aydar, 451 (*map*)
Novo-Belitsa, 476
Novobogatinskoye, 338 (*map*)
Novocherkassk, 205 (*map*), 216, 217, 451 (*map*)
Novo-Ekonomicheskoye, 451 (*map*)
Novograd-Volynskiy, 436 (*map*), 458
Novogroznenskiy, 211 (*map*), 229
Novogrudok, 471 (*map*), 472
Novokazalinsk, 338 (*map*)
Novokhopersk, 127 (*map*)
Novokiyevka, 317 (*map*)
Novokurovka, 321 (*map*)
Novo-Lyubino, *see* Lyubinskiy

Novo-Mariinsk, *see* Anadyr'
Novo-Moskovsk, 437 (*map*), 453
Novo-Nazyvayevka, 261 (*map*), 271
Novo-Nikolayevskaya, 195 (*map*)
Novo-Omsk, *see* Kulomzino
Novo-Pavlovka, 303
Novorossiysk, 9, 211 (*map*), 220
Novoselovskoye, 205 (*map*)
Novoshakhtinsk, 205 (*map*), 215, 217, 451 (*map*)
Novosibirsk, 261 (*map*), 266, 272, 279 (*map*)
Novo-Sibirskiye Islands, *see* New Siberian Islands
Novosibirsk Oblast, 261 (*map*), 265; area: industries: population: rail lines, 272
Novosil', 127 (*map*)
Novosokol'niki, 135 (*map*)
Novostroyevo, 491 (*map*)
Novo-Troitsk, 78, 235 (*map*), 258, 259
Novo-Ukrainka, 437 (*map*)
Novo-Urgench, *see* Urgench
Novouzensk, 195 (*map*)
Novo-Zavidovskiy, 135 (*map*), 141
Novozybkov, 135 (*map*), 138
Novyy, 278, 279 (*map*)
Novyy Chardzhuy, *see* Chardzhou
Novyy Donbass, 451 (*map*)
Novyy Margelan, *see* Fergana
Novyy Oskol, 127 (*map*)
Novyy Port, 261 (*map*), 270
Noyemberyan, 421 (*map*)
Nukha, 415 (*map*), 417
Nukus, 389 (*map*), 399
Nura River, 340, 347, 354, 355
Nura-Tau, range, 396
Nurlat, 183 (*map*)
Nyandoma, 155 (*map*)
Nyazepetrovsk, 241 (*map*), 249
Nyda, 261 (*map*)
Nymme, 489
Nymylany (Koryaks), ethnic group, 41, 314, 325
Nytva, 241 (*map*), 245
Nyuk, Lake, 495 (*map*)
Nyukzha River, 316, 317 (*map*)
Nyuvchim, 155 (*map*)

Oases, Central Asia, 364, 388, 400
Ob', town, 279 (*map*)
Ob', river, *see* Ob' River
Ob' Bay (or Gulf), 6, 261 (*map*), 262
Obdorsk, *see* Salekhard
Obi-Garm, 381 (*map*)
Obikhingou River, 381 (*map*)
Oblasts, intra-kray, 47; named for their

administrative centers, 52; organization, 46
Obluch'ye, 321 (*map*)
Oboyan', 127 (*map*)
Obozerskaya, 155 (*map*)
Ob' River, 21, 22, 260, 261 (*map*), 262, 279 (*map*); Irtysh system, 22, 23, 237; potential source of hydroelectric energy, 274
Obruchevo, 389 (*map*), 395 (*map*)
Obshchiy Syrt, 19, 171, 195 (*map*), 234, 235 (*map*), 257
Obsidian, 423
Ochakov, 437 (*map*)
Ochamchire, 427 (*map*), 431
Ochemchiri, *see* Ochamchire
Ocher, 235 (*map*), 245
Ochiai, *see* Dolinsk
October Revolution, *see* Oktyabr'skaya Revolyutsiya
Odessa, 9, 436 (*map*), 443, 445, 455, 456, 465 (*map*)
Odessa Oblast, 436 (*map*), 441, 466; area and population: economy, 455 f.
Oduly (Yukagirs), ethnic group, 288, 305, 324
Ogarevka, 105 (*map*), 124
Oginskiy Canal, 471 (*map*), 474
Oglangly, 401 (*map*), 404
Ogre, 481 (*map*)
Ogurchinskiy Island, 405
Oil, *see* Petroleum
Oil-bearing plants, 61
Oil shale deposits, 13, 72-75 *passim;* Baltic Region, 488; Volga Region, 190
Oka-Don lowlands, 18, 19
Oka River, 105 (*map*), 110, 114, 115 (*map*), 173 (*map*), 178, 180, 297 (*map*)
Okha, 311 (*map*), 331 (*map*), 332
Okhansk, 241 (*map*), 245
Okhotsk, 311 (*map*), 323
Okhotsk, Sea of, 7, 308, 311 (*map*), 321 (*map*), 331 (*map*); climate, 312; ice condition of ports, 91; littoral, 308, 309, 313
Oknitsa, 465 (*map*)
Okrugs, abolition of administrative, 44, 47; formation of rational, 46
Oktemberyan, 421 (*map*), 423
Oktyabr'skaya Revolyutsiya (October Revolution), canal, 231; island, 6
Oktyabr'skiy (Amur Oblast), 316, 317 (*map*)
Oktyabr'skiy (Bashkir ASSR), 183 (*map*), 235 (*map*); area: petroleum center: population, 256

Oktyabr'skiy (Frunze Oblast), 376
Oktyabr'skiy (Kirov Oblast), 173 (map)
Oktyabr'skiy (Komi ASSR), 155 (map), 165
Oktyabr'skiy (Ryazan' Oblast, near Mikhaylov), 105 (map), 123
Oktyabr'skiy (Ryazan' Oblast, near Skopin), 105 (map), 122
Oktyabr'skiy (Sakhalin Oblast), 331 (map), 332
Oktyabr'skoye (Crimea Oblast), 205 (map)
Oktyabr'skoye (Kirghiz SSR), 395 (map)
Oktyabrya, Imeni, 11, 303
Okulovka, 145 (map)
Olekma River, 282, 297 (map), 303, 317 (map)
Olekminsk, 283 (map), 307
Olenek, 283 (map)
Olenek River, 285
Ol'ga, 321 (map), 328, 329
Ol'ginka, 451 (map)
Ol'khon Island, 296, 297 (map), 298
Olkhovskiy, see Artemovsk
Olonets, 495 (map)
Olovyannaya, 297 (map), 303
Ol'shany, 436 (map)
Ol'viopol', see Pervomaysk
Olyutorskoye, 311 (map), 325
Omsk, 261 (map), 266, 271
Omsk Oblast, 261 (map), 265; area, 270; industrial centers, 271; physico-economic zones, 271; population, 270
Omutninsk, 173 (map), 176, 178
Ondozero, 495 (map)
Onega, 155 (map), 168
Onega Bay, 5, 495 (map)
Onega, Lake, 23, 143, 145 (map), 155 (map), 493, 495 (map), 496, 497
Onega metalworks, Petrozavodsk, 497
Onega River, 155 (map)
Onguday, 359 (map)
Oni, 427 (map)
Onon River, 297 (map), 302
Oparino, 173 (map), 177
Opechenskiy Posad, 145 (map)
Opium, 377, 467
Opochka, 135 (map)
Opol'ye, 105 (map), 117, 121
Oranienbaum, see Lomonosov
Oranzherei, 195 (map), 202
Ordubad, 415 (map), 419
Ordzhonikidze (Dnepropetrovsk Oblast), 437 (map), 453
Ordzhonikidze (North Ossetian ASSR), see Dzaudzhikau

Ordzhonikidze (Stalino Oblast), see Yenakiyevo
Ordzhonikidzeabad, 381 (map)
Ordzhonikidzegrad, see Bezhitsa
Ordzhonikidze Kray, former, 221, 228
Ordzhonikidzevskiy, 211 (map)
Oredezh, 145 (map)
Orekhi-Vydritsa, see Orekhovsk
Orekhovo-Zuyevo, 105 (map), 111, 114, 115 (map)
Orekhovsk, 471 (map), 474, 475
Orel, 127 (map), 129
Orel Oblast, 127 (map); area: industries: population, 129
Orel' River, 437 (map), 448
Orenburg, see Chkalov
Orgeyev, 465 (map), 468
Orgtrud, 115 (map)
Orheiu, see Orgeyev
Orichi, 173 (map)
Orlik, 297 (map)
Orlovo, 331 (map)
Orochen, 305
Orogeny, see Mountain-building processes
Orotukan, 324
Or' River, 235 (map)
Orsha, 471 (map), 475
Orsk, 235 (map), 237, 257, 258, 259, 338 (map), 347, 351; Khalilovo district, 255, 257, 258
"Orsk Sea," 259
Orto-Tokoy, 373 (map); reservoir, 62, 375, 377
Osa, 241 (map)
Ösel, island, see Sarema
Osetrovo, 296
Osh, 373 (map), 378, 395 (map); highway to Khorog, 387
Oshkur'ya, 155 (map)
Oshmyany, 471 (map)
Osh Oblast, 373 (map); area and population: economy, 378
Osinniki, 277, 279 (map), 280
Osintorf, 475
Osipenko, 437 (map), 443, 445, 454
Osipovichi, 471 (map)
Oskol River, 127 (map), 437 (map), 448
Os'mino, 145 (map)
Ossetian Military Road, 227, 228, 413, 429
Ossetians, ethnic group, in European South, 213, 226; in Russian SFSR, 41, 98; in Transcaucasia, 411, 412, 425, 433
Ostashkov, 135 (map), 142
Ostrogozhsk, 127 (map)
Ostrov, 145 (map), 148
Ostrovnoye, 311 (map)

Ostyako-Vogul'sk, *see* Khanty-Mansiysk

Ostyaks, *see* Khanty

Ostyak-Vogul National Okrug, *see* Khanty-Mansi National Okrug

Otar, 339 (*map*)

Otepya, 481 (*map*)

Otomari, see Korsakov

Otradnoye, 153 (*map*)

Ovruch, 436 (*map*)

Oyash, 279 (*map*)

Oyat' River, 145 (*map*)

Oymyakon, climate, 24, 27, 283 (*map*), 286; plateau, 282

Oyrot Autonomous Oblast, *see* Gorno-Altay Autonomous Oblast

Oyrot (Oyrat) ethnic group, 41, 53, 265, 275

Oyrot-Tura, *see* Gorno-Altaysk

Oysungur, *see* Novogroznenskiy

Oytal, 339 (*map*)

Ozernaya, hydroelectric station, 420

Ozernovskiy, 324

Ozersk, 491 (*map*)

Ozerskiy, 331 (*map*)

Ozery, 105 (*map*), 115 (*map*)

Ozherel'ye, 115 (*map*)

Ozinki, 195 (*map*), 197

Ozocerite, deposits, 385, 404, 460; plants for processing, 402, 461

Pabrade, 481 (*map*)

Pachel'ma, 183 (*map*), 190

Pacific Ocean, 7; access to, 91; climate, 25; naval bases, 7, 91

Padany, 495 (*map*)

Pagegyay, 481 (*map*)

Pakhotnyy, 359 (*map*)

Pakhta-Aral, cotton plantation, 362

Pakhtusovo, 155 (*map*)

Palana, 311 (*map*), 325

Palanga, 481 (*map*)

Palattsy, 359

Paldiski, 8, 481 (*map*), 489

Palekh, 105 (*map*), 120

Paleoasiatic, ethnic group, 41, 98; in Eastern Siberia, 288; in Soviet Far East, 314, 318, 319, 324

Pallasovka, 195 (*map*)

Palmnicken, *see* Yantarnyy

Palvantash, 393, 395 (*map*)

Pamir, 365; climate, 366, 382; gold, 383; salt steppes and salt lakes, 367

Pamir-Alay mountain system, 14, 23, 365, 371, 378, 380, 388; Alpine meadows, 33; formation, 20

Pamir highway, 92, 375, 378, 384

Pamir River, 381 (*map*), 387

Pamyati 13 Bortsov, 291

Pamyat' Parizhskoy Kommuny, 173 (*map*)

Panevezhis, 481 (*map*), 484

Panfilov, 339 (*map*), 360

Panj (Pyandzh) River, 365, 380, 381 (*map*), 387

Pap, 395 (*map*)

Paper and pulp-milling industry, 80, 81, 99, 150, 166, 167, 168, 177, 187, 332, 453, 489, 496

Parakhino-Poddub'ye, 145 (*map*), 147

Paramushir Island, 333

Parfenovo, 279 (*map*)

Parfino, 145 (*map*), 146

Pargolovo, 153 (*map*)

Parizhskaya Kommuna, 451 (*map*), 452

Parkent, 395 (*map*)

Pärnu, *see* Pyarnu

Paromnaya, 195 (*map*)

Pashiya, 241 (*map*), 245

Pashskiy Perevoz, 145 (*map*)

Pastures, summer and winter, 64 f., 66, 67

Pasvalis, 481 (*map*)

Patom plateau, 296

Pats-Joki, river, 161 (*map*)

Pavelets, 105 (*map*), 122

Pavlodar, 339 (*map*), 357

Pavlodar Oblast, 339 (*map*); area and population: mineral resources, 357

Pavlograd, 437 (*map*), 453

Pavlovo, 173 (*map*), 179

Pavlovsk (Altay Kray), 275, 279 (*map*), 359 (*map*)

Pavlovsk (Leningrad Oblast), 145 (*map*), 152, 153 (*map*)

Pavlovsk (Voronezh Oblast), 127 (*map*)

Pavlovskiy, 235 (*map*), 245

Pavlovskiy Posad, 111, 114, 115 (*map*)

Payde, 481 (*map*)

Pay-Khoy, mountain range, 155 (*map*), 157

Peat, 37, 72, 73, 75; extracting machinery, 79; power stations, 69, 75; of Siberia, 31; techniques in working, 69; Ukrainian SSR, 445, 446, 447

Pechatkino, 167

Pechenezhin, 460

Pechenga, 161 (*map*); district, acquired by USSR, 4, 160

Pechora, 155 (*map*)

Pechora Bay, 5

Pechora River, 22, 155 (*map*), 156, 235,

Pechora River (*Continued*)
246; basin: coal, 12, 36, 164, 169;
petroleum deposits, 11

Pechory district, 148, 481 (*map*), 488

Peipus (Chudskoye) Lake, 143, 145
(*map*), 480, 481 (*map*), 488

Peleduy, 297 (*map*), 306

Pendzhikent, 381 (*map*), 383, 385

Peno, 135 (*map*), 140

Penza, 183 (*map*), 190

Penza Oblast, 183 (*map*); agriculture:
area, 189; industries, 190; population:
topography, 189

Perechin, 463

Pereginsko, 436 (*map*), 460

Perekop Isthmus, 204, 205 (*map*)

Peresechnaya, 436 (*map*)

Pereslavl'-Zalesskiy, 105 (*map*), 118

Perevoloki, 183 (*map*), 192

Pereyaslav-Khmel'nitskiy, 437 (*map*)

Perm', *see* Molotov

Permskoye, *see* Komsomol'sk

Pernau, see Pyarnu

Perovo, 113, 114, 115 (*map*)

Perovsk, *see* Kzyl-Orda

Persians, in European South, 228; in
Turkmen SSR, 402

Pervomaysk, 436 (*map*), 456

Pervomayskiy (Bashkir ASSR), 254

Pervomayskiy (Frunze Oblast), 376

Pervomayskiy (Kemerovo Oblast), 279
(*map*)

Pervomayskiy (Kirov Oblast), 173 (*map*)

Pervomayskoye, 205 (*map*)

Pervoural'sk, 235 (*map*), 241 (*map*),
242

Peschanoye, 195 (*map*)

Peski, 115 (*map*)

Peskovka (Kirov Oblast), 173 (*map*),
178

Peskovka (Ukrainian SSR), 436 (*map*)

Pesochnyy, 153 (*map*)

Pestovo, 145 (*map*)

Petergof (Peterhof), *see* Petrodvorets

Peter the Great Bay, fish canning and
processing, 328

Petrikov, 471 (*map*)

Petrodvorets, 51, 145 (*map*), 152, 153
(*map*)

Petrograd, *see* Leningrad

Petrokrepost', 51, 145 (*map*), 152, 153
(*map*)

Petroleum industry, cracking plants, 193,
416; dearth in drilling machinery, 75;
loading ports, 416, 432; manufacture
of machines for, 220; pipe lines, 192,

220, 229, 230, 347; products, 258; refineries, 406, 416, 427

Petroleum reserves, 36-37, 72, 73; Cen-
tral Asia, 367, 369; Eastern Siberia,
293, 300, 306; European North, 164;
European South, 218-21 *passim*, 229,
232; Kazakh SSR, 344-47 *passim*, 351;
Kirghiz SSR, 374, 379; principal regions
of USSR, 14, 74, 404, 416; Russian
SFSR, 96; Soviet Far East, 325, 332;
Tadzhik SSR, 383; Transcaucasia, 412,
416, 425, 426; Turkmen SSR, 402, 404;
Ukrainian SSR, 439, 443, 449, 460, 461;
Urals, 234, 244, 254, 256, 257, 258;
Uzbek SSR, 390, 391, 393, 397; Volga
Region, 172, 188, 192

Petropavlovsk (Kamchatka Oblast), 7,
91, 311 (*map*), 315, 325

Petropavlovsk (Kazakh SSR), 261
(*map*), 339 (*map*), 353; railroad to
Balkhash, 354

Petropavlovskiy, 195 (*map*)

Petrovsk (Dagestan ASSR), *see* Makhachkala

Petrovsk (Saratov Oblast), 195 (*map*),
197

Petrovsk or Petrovsk-Zabaykal'skiy, 283
(*map*), 297 (*map*), 303, 304

Petrozavodsk, 493, 494, 495 (*map*),
497

Petsamo, *see* Pechenga

Petseri, *see* Pechory

Petukhino, 261 (*map*)

Pevek, 311 (*map*)

Pezas, 279 (*map*)

Phosphate, *see* Phosphorite

Phosphorite, 38, 80, 190, 352, 362, 467

Phosphorite, fertilizer industry, 347, 352,
361, 445; converted into fertilizer, 361,
445; mining of, 447

Physical setting, USSR, 3-38; location
and boundaries, 3-5; seas and coasts, 5-
10; geologic history, 10-15; structure
and relief, 15-20; hydrography, 21-23;
climate, 24-26; soils and vegetation, 27-
33; mineral resources, 33-38

Pig iron, *see* Iron

Pikalevo, 145 (*map*)

Pikhtovka, 279 (*map*)

Pillau, *see* Baltiysk

Pil'tun, 331 (*map*)

Pina River, 477

Pindushi, 495 (*map*), 497

Pinega, 155 (*map*)

Pinega River, 155 (*map*)

Pinsk, 471 (*map*), 477

Pinsk Oblast, 471 (*map*), 472; area: population, 477
Pioner, 279 (*map*)
Pioner Island, 6
Pionerskiy, 491 (*map*), 492
Pipe lines, natural gas, 75, 192, 197, 229, 393; petroleum and petroleum products, 192, 220, 229, 230, 347, 412; shale gas, 75
Pirsagat, 415 (*map*), 416
Piryatin, 437 (*map*)
Pishpek, *see* Frunze
Pistachio-nut woods, 404, 406
Pit-Gorodok, 290, 297 (*map*)
Pitkyaranta, 495 (*map*), 496
Pivan, 321 (*map*)
Place names, *see* Toponymy
Planting, shelter-belt, 58, 174
Plast, 235 (*map*), 248, 251
Plastun, 321 (*map*), 328
Platinum, 38, 239, 306
Plavsk, 105 (*map*)
Plesetsk, 155 (*map*)
Plunge, 481 (*map*)
Pobeda Peak, 20, 365, 373 (*map*)
Pobedino, 331 (*map*), 333
Pobedinskiy, 105 (*map*), 122
Pochep, 135 (*map*)
Pochinok, 135 (*map*)
Podchinnyy, 195 (*map*)
Poddor'ye, 145 (*map*)
Podkamennaya Tunguska, *see* Srednyaya Tunguska River
Podkarpatska Rus, 463
Podlesnoye', 51, 195 (*map*)
Podol'sk, 105 (*map*), 114, 115 (*map*)
Podporozh'ye, 145 (*map*), 149
Podunskaya, 279 (*map*)
Pokhvistnevo, 183 (*map*), 192, 193
Pokrovka (Kirghiz SSR), 373 (*map*)
Pokrovka (Maritime Kray), 327 (*map*)
Pokrovsk (Saratov Oblast), *see* Engel's
Pokrovsk (Yakut ASSR), 283 (*map*)
Pokrovsk-Ural'skiy, 239, 241 (*map*)
Pola, 145 (*map*)
Poland, annexation of territory from, 440, 459, 483
Pola River, 145 (*map*)
Polar stations, 293, 294, 307, 326
Poles, in Baltic Region, 480, 483; in Ukrainian SSR, 440; in Western Siberia, 265; repatriated, 472
Polessk, 491 (*map*), 492
Poles'ye, 434, 461; agriculture, 443, 457; industries, 458; population density, 440
Poles'ye Oblast, 471 (*map*); area: industries: population, 476

Polevskoy, 235 (*map*), 241 (*map*), 242
Poliny Osipenko, Imeni, 321 (*map*)
Polist' River, 145 (*map*)
Political framework, 39-53; population, 39-41; administrative-territorial divisions, 41-48; toponymy, 49-53
Polotsk, 471 (*map*), 475
Polotsk Oblast, 471 (*map*); area, economy, population, 475
Polovinka (Khabarovsk Area), *see* Umal'tinskiy
Polovinka (Molotov Oblast), 241 (*map*), 244
Poltava, 437 (*map*), 448, 449
Poltava Oblast, 437 (*map*), 443, 447; area and population: economy, 448
Poltoratsk, *see* Ashkhabad
Polunochnoye, 241 (*map*), 243
Polyarnyy, 161 (*map*), 163
Ponoy, 161 (*map*)
Ponoy River, 161 (*map*)
Pontonnyy, 153 (*map*)
Popasnaya, 451 (*map*)
Popova, 327 (*map*)
Population, USSR, 39-41; of administrative-territorial divisions, 500-505; cities over 50,000, 506-11; of the Union Republics, 499
Porkhov, 145 (*map*), 148
Porkkala, naval base district, 3
Poronay River, 331 (*map*)
Poronaysk, 52, 311 (*map*), 330, 331 (*map*), 333
Porosozero, 495 (*map*)
Portages, 82
Port Apsheron, oil-loading port, 418
Port Arthur, naval base district, 3, 91
Port Il'icha, 415 (*map*)
Ports, 8-10
Port-Vladimir, 161 (*map*), 162
Poselok Severnykh Promyslov Ozera No. 6, *see* Sartas
Posevnaya, 279 (*map*)
Poshekhon'ye-Volodarsk, 105 (*map*)
Pospelikha, 261 (*map*), 274, 359 (*map*)
Postavy, 471 (*map*)
Pos'yet, 327 (*map*), 328, 329
Pos'yet Gulf, 308
Potash deposits, Urals, 12, 38, 234, 244, 257
Potatoes, 61, alcohol and synthetic rubber produced from, 80
Potato-grain-hemp zone, 66
Poti, 9, 426, 427 (*map*), 430
Poultry, 64
Povenets, 495 (*map*), 497

Povolzh'ye, see Volga Region

Povorino, 127 (*map*)

Power, most common sources, 72; *see also* Coal; Hydroelectric power; Oil shale; Peat; Petroleum

Power stations, Belorussian SSR (Belgres power station), 474, 475; Central Industrial Region, 108; European Northwest, 146; Tadzhik SSR, 383; Ukrainian SSR, 442; Volga Region, 173, 192; *see also* Electric power stations; Hydroelectric stations

Poyarkovo, 317 (*map*)

Pravda, 331 (*map*)

Pravdino, 491 (*map*)

Pravdinsk (Gor'kiy Oblast), 173 (*map*), 179, 180

Pravdinsk (Kaliningrad Oblast), 491 (*map*)

Pravdinskiy, 115 (*map*)

Precious and semiprecious stones, 38, 234, 264

Precious metals, 239

Precipitation, Central Asia, 26; desert zone, 32; East European plain, 25; steppe zone, 31

Precision instruments, 79, 463

Predivinsk, 291, 297 (*map*)

Prefabricated houses, 69, 181, 245, 476

Pregel' River, 490, 491 (*map*), 492

Pregradnaya, 211 (*map*), 222

Prenay, 481 (*map*)

Presnogor'kovka, 338 (*map*)

Preyla, 481 (*map*), 484

Priamur'ye, see Amur region

Pribalkhash, *see* Balkhash

Priluki, 437 (*map*), 458

Primorsk (Kaliningrad Oblast), 491 (*map*)

Primorsk (Leningrad Oblast), 145 (*map*), 148

Primorsko-Akhtarsk, 211 (*map*)

Primor'ye, see Soviet Far East, southern coastal area

Primor'ye range, 282

Priozersk (Käkisalmi or Kexholm), 145 (*map*), 148, 494

Pripet Marshes, 434, 469, 476; converted into cultivated land, 470; drainage, 63; population, 472

Pripet (or Pripyat') River, 434, 446, 470, 471 (*map*)

Pristan' Lavak, 401 (*map*)

Pristan' Przheval'sk, 373 (*map*)

Privolzhsk, 105 (*map*), 120

Privolzhskiy, 195 (*map*)

Prokhladnyy, 211 (*map*), 226

Prokop'yevsk, 277, 279 (*map*), 280

Proletariy, 145 (*map*)

Proletarsk (Tadzhik SSR), 395 (*map*)

Proletarsk (Ukrainian SSR), 451 (*map*)

Proletarskaya, 205 (*map*)

Proletarskiy (Kursk Oblast), 127 (*map*)

Proletarskiy (Moscow Oblast), 115 (*map*)

Promyshlennaya, 279 (*map*)

Proskurov, 436 (*map*), 447

Provid
eniya, 311 (*map*), 326

Prut River, 436 (*map*), 438, 459, 460, 464, 465 (*map*), 468

Pruzhany, 471 (*map*)

Pryazha, 495 (*map*)

Przheval'sk, 373 (*map*), 377

Psel River, 127 (*map*), 437 (*map*), 448, 449

Pshaves, tribe in Transcaucasia, 411, 425

Psirtskha, 427 (*map*)

Pskent, 395 (*map*)

Pskov, 145 (*map*), 148

Pskov Lake, 143

Pskov Oblast, 145 (*map*), 147-48; area: population, 147; districts ceded to, 485

Ptich' River, 470, 474, 476

Puchezh, 105 (*map*), 120

Pudozh, 495 (*map*)

Pudozhgora, 495 (*map*), 496

Pugachev, 195 (*map*), 198

Pugachevo, 331 (*map*)

Pulkovo, 153 (*map*)

Pulozero, 161 (*map*)

Pulp and paper mills, *see* Paper and pulp-milling industry

Pumice, 422

Pushkin, 145 (*map*), 152, 153 (*map*)

Pushkino (Azerbaijan SSR), 415 (*map*)

Pushkino (Moscow Oblast), 111, 115 (*map*)

Pushkino (Saratov Oblast), 195 (*map*)

Pustoshka, 135 (*map*)

Putyatin, *see* Nazimovo

Puyko, 261 (*map*)

Pyandzh River, *see* Panj River

Pyaozero, lake, 495 (*map*)

Pyarnu, 481 (*map*), 488, 489

Pyarnu River, 488

Pyasina River, 293

Pyatigorsk, 210, 211 (*map*), 222, 223

Pyatikhatki, 437 (*map*)

Pyltsama, 481 (*map*)

Pytalovo, 145 (*map*), 148, 485

Rabocheostrovsk, 495 (*map*), 496

Radioactive ore deposit, 38, 378
Radvilishkis, 481 (*map*)
Ragnit, *see* Neman
Railroads, construction program, 82-88, 349; electrified, 85; Kazakh SSR, 348 ff.; Kirghiz SSR, 375; radiating lines centered at Moscow, 83; Saratov Oblast, 198; Tadzhik SSR, 384; Ural Region, 255, 256, 258; Western Siberia, 275
Railway-car and locomotive works, 79, 180, 242, 301, 453
Rainfall, *see* Precipitation
Rakhovo, 463
Rakh'ya, 152, 153 (*map*)
Rakitnoye, 127 (*map*)
Rakityanka, 235 (*map*), 259
Rakvere, 481 (*map*), 488, 489
Ramenskoye, 115 (*map*)
Ramie, 55, 61
Ramon', 127 (*map*)
Ranenburg, *see* Chaplygin
Rang-Kul', 381 (*map*), 387
Rapla, 481 (*map*)
Rare metals, 368, 425; *see also* Precious metals
Raseynyay, 481 (*map*)
Rasskazovo, 127 (*map*), 130
Rastyapino, *see* Dzerzhinsk
Raukhiala (Rauhiala), 149, 494
Rauschen, *see* Svetlogorsk
Rava-Russkaya, 436 (*map*)
Raychikhinsk, 317 (*map*), 318
Rayevskiy, 235 (*map*)
Rayons, 46, 47 f.; named for administrative centers, 53; subordinated to oblast, kray, or republic, 44
Razdel'naya, 436 (*map*)
Razdolinsk, 290, 297 (*map*)
Razdol'noye (Crimea Oblast), 205 (*map*)
Razdol'noye (Maritime Kray), 327 (*map*), 328
Razdorskaya, 205 (*map*), 216, 451 (*map*)
Razino, 491 (*map*)
Reboly, 495 (*map*)
Rebrikha, 279 (*map*), 359 (*map*)
Rechitsa, 471 (*map*), 476
Regar, 381 (*map*)
Regional Survey, 93-497
Reindeer, 64, 66, 159, 162, 169, 270, 294, 306, 319; experimental station, 169, 328
Relief and structure, 15-20
Remontnoye, 205 (*map*)
Reni, 436 (*map*)
Reservoirs, "Great Volga" scheme, 186, 196, 199, 246, 247; "Orsk Sea," 259; Orto-Tokoy reservoir, Chu valley, 62, 375, 377; projected, on watershed of the Vychegda, 63; Turkmen SSR, 403; Uzbek SSR, 397
Reshetikha, 173 (*map*), 179
Resorts, Baltic Region, 483, 484, 486, 487, 492; Caucasus, 26; European South, 208, 214, 219, 220, 222, 223, 226; provision for creation of, 48; Transcaucasia, 431, 432, 433; Turkmen SSR, 405; Ukrainian SSR, 454
Retavas, 481 (*map*)
Reutov, 115 (*map*)
Reut River, 467, 468
Reval, see Tallin
Revda, 239, 241 (*map*), 242
Revel', see Tallin
Reyneke, 327 (*map*)
Rezekne, 481 (*map*)
Rezh, 241 (*map*)
Rezina, 465 (*map*)
Rice cultivation, 59, 362
Riga, 8, 479, 481 (*map*), 482, 485, 486, 487
Riga, Gulf of, 479, 481 (*map*), 485, 487, 488
Rigas Yurmala (Rigas Jurmala), 487
Rioni, 427 (*map*)
Rion River, 212, 409, 427 (*map*), 428; hydroelectric station, 426, 430; lowland, 424
River systems, 21-23, 88; of Russian SFSR, 95; opened to navigation, 89; rapids, 22; role in development of the economy, 82
Rodniki, 105 (*map*), 119
Rogachev, 471 (*map*)
Rogan', 436 (*map*)
Rokishkis, 481 (*map*)
Roman-Kosh, 206
Romanovka (Moldavian SSR), 465 (*map*)
Romanovka (Saratov Oblast), 195 (*map*)
Romany, 415 (*map*)
Romny (Amur Oblast), 317 (*map*)
Romny (Ukrainian SSR), 437 (*map*), 439, 449
Ropruchey, 495 (*map*)
Roshal', 115 (*map*)
Roshchino, 145 (*map*), 153 (*map*)
Roslavl', 135 (*map*)
Ros' River, 436 (*map*), 446
Rossel'mash, agricultural machinery works, 216, 217
Rossosh', 127 (*map*)
Rostov or Rostov-on-Don, 205 (*map*), 216
Rostov (Yaroslavl' Oblast), 105 (*map*), 118

Rostov Oblast, 194, 205 (*map*); 214-17; agriculture, 216; area, 214; climate: coal fields, 215; industrial centers, 217; industries, 216; population, 214, 216; topography, 214

Roven'ki, 451 (*map*), 452

Rovno, 436 (*map*), 461

Rovno Oblast, 436 (*map*), 441, 459; area: industries: population, 461

Rovnoye, 195 (*map*), 197

Równe, see Rovno

Rozovka, 451 (*map*)

Rtishchevo, 195 (*map*), 198

Rubber-bearing plants, 55, 61, 403

Rubezhnoye, 437 (*map*), 451 (*map*), 452

Rubtsovsk, 261 (*map*), 275, 359 (*map*)

Rudnichnyy (Chelyabinsk Oblast), 248

Rudnichnyy (Kirov Oblast), 173 (*map*), 176, 178, 235 (*map*)

Rudnichnyy (Molotov Oblast), 244

Rudnichnyy (Sverdlovsk Oblast), 241 (*map*)

Rudnya, 135 (*map*)

Rudolf Island, 5, 155 (*map*), 169

Rugozero, 495 (*map*)

Rukhlovo, *see* Skovorodino

Rusanovo, 155 (*map*)

Rushan, 381 (*map*)

Russian Federation, *see* Russian SFSR

Russian platform, 11; invaded by Jurassic sea, 13; marine invasion of Cretaceous period, 13; petroleum, 36; raised sections, 18

Russians, in Baltic Region, 480, 482, 483, 485, 488, 490; Belorussian SSR, 472; Central Asia, 368; Eastern Siberia, 287, 290, 293, 296, 300, 302, 305; European South, 207, 213, 216, 218, 220, 225, 226, 228, 229, 231; Karelo-Finnish SSR, 493; Kazakh SSR, 345, 348, 351, 352, 360, 361; Kirghiz SSR, 372, 376, 379; Moldavian SSR, 466; Russian SFSR, 97; Soviet Far East, 314, 318, 319, 324, 332, 333; Transcaucasia, 414, 425, 431; Turkmen SSR, 402; Ukrainian SSR, 440, 456; Urals, 237, 243, 252, 254; USSR, 40; Volga Region, 172, 174, 181, 182, 185, 186, 188, 189, 194; Western Siberia, 264, 267, 269, 270, 273, 276

Russian Soviet Federated Socialist Republic (SFSR), agriculture, 100; area, 95; autonomous units liquidated, 427; cities over 50,000, 506-9; ethnic and linguistic groups, 98, 101; exports and imports, 101; geographical regions, 102; industrialization, 98 ff.; leading and most important republic, 45; lumbering, 100; mineral resources, 96 f.; national okrugs within, 46; natural resources, 96; oblasts and krays, 47; population, 95, 97, 504; proclaimed, 44; Russian majority mandatory in population of oblasts of, 490; topography, 95; transportation, 100; vegetation and soils, 96; *see also* Central Black-Earth Region; Central Industrial Region; Eastern Siberia; European North; European Northwest; European South; European West; Soviet Far East: Urals: Volga Region: Western Siberia

Rustavi, 412, 416, 426, 427 (*map*), 430, 432

Rutaka, *see* Aniva

Rutchenkovo, 451 (*map*)

Ruthenia, *see* Transcarpathian Oblast

Rutsava, 481 (*map*)

Ruyena, 481 (*map*)

Ruza, 115 (*map*)

Ruzayevka, 183 (*map*), 187

Ryapina, 481 (*map*)

Ryazan', 105 (*map*), 123, 186

Ryazan' Oblast, 105 (*map*); agriculture, 123; area, 122; industries, 123; natural resources: population: topography, 122

Ryazhsk, 105 (*map*), 123

Rybachiy, 491 (*map*), 492

Rybachiy Peninsula, 160, 161 (*map*)

Rybach'ye, 373 (*map*), 377

Rybatskoye, 153 (*map*)

Rybinsk, *see* Shcherbakov

Rybinsk Reservoir ("Rybinsk Sea"), 105 (*map*), 108, 109, 116, 166, 167, 417

Rybnitsa, 465 (*map*), 467, 468

Rybnovsk, 331 (*map*), 332

Rykovo, *see* Yenakiyevo

Ryl'sk, 127 (*map*)

Ryshkany, 465 (*map*)

Rzhev, 135 (*map*), 141

Saaremaa, *see* Sarema

Saatly, 415 (*map*)

Sabirabad, 415 (*map*)

Sable reserve, 301

Sablya, Mount, 155 (*map*)

Sabunchi, 415 (*map*)

Sachkhere, 427 (*map*)

Sadki, 235 (*map*), 259

Sadon, 211 (*map*), 227

Sadovoye, 51, 195 (*map*)

Safonovo, 135 (*map*)

Sagiz, 338 (*map*)

St. Petersburg, *see* Leningrad

Sakhalin Island, 20, 308, 311 (*map*), 329, 490; climate, 312; coal deposits, 36, 314; forests, 313; localities renamed, 52, 331; oil fields, 37, 314; topography, 309

Sakhalin Oblast, 329-33, 331 (*map*); agriculture, 332; area, 329; industries, 332; Japanese territories renamed, 331; minerals, 332; population, 329, 332; railways, 332; separated from Khabarovsk Kray, 314

Saki, 205 (*map*)

Sakmara River, 235 (*map*)

Saksaul'skiy, 338 (*map*)

Saksaul tree, 367

Salair, 277, 279 (*map*)

Salair Ridge, 260, 264, 279

Saldus, 481 (*map*)

Salekhard (Salegard), 51, 261 (*map*), 270

Salgir River, 204, 205 (*map*)

Salla, see Kuolayarvi

Salmi, 495 (*map*)

Sal River, 205 (*map*)

Sal'sk, 205 (*map*), 216

Salt, chemical industry based on, 347; Kazakh SSR, 347; Krasno-Perekopsk works, 208; produced from brine at Berezniki, 247; stratum in Lake Baskunchak, 38, 202; Ukrainian SSR, 450, 452; Urals, 244, 247, 257

Saltpeter, 362

Sal'yany, 415 (*map*)

Sama, 241 (*map*)

Samagaltay, 297 (*map*)

Samara, *see* Kuybyshev (Kuybyshev Oblast)

Samara Bend (of Volga River), 170, 182; hydroelectric power complex, 192

Samara River, 182, 235 (*map*), 257

Samarga, 321 (*map*)

Samarkand (Kazakh SSR), *see* Temir-Tau

Samarkand (Uzbek SSR), 389 (*map*), 392, 396; oasis, 369, 388

Samarkand Oblast, 389 (*map*); area and population: economy, 396

Samarovo, 261 (*map*), 269

Sambor, 436 (*map*), 461

Samoyeds, *see* Nentsy

Samsonovo, 401 (*map*)

Samtredia, 427 (*map*)

Samur-Divichi Canal, 62, 415 (*map*)

Samur River, 211 (*map*), 415 (*map*)

Samus', 273, 279 (*map*)

Sanatoriums, in Urals for dry-air and kumiss cures, 257; on Black Sea littoral, 431

Sanchursk, 173 (*map*)

Sangar, 283 (*map*), 306

San River, 441

Sapropelite coal, 277

Sara, 235 (*map*), 258

Saraktash, 235 (*map*), 258

Sarala, 292, 297 (*map*)

Saran', 356

Saransk, 183 (*map*), 187

Sarany, 241 (*map*), 245

Sarapul, 235 (*map*), 253

Sarata, 465 (*map*)

Saratov, 36, 195 (*map*), 197, 198

Saratov Oblast, 194, 195 (*map*), 196-98; agriculture: area, 196; cities, 198; industries: mineral resources, 197; population, 196; railroads, 198

Sarema (Saaremaa), island, 479, 481 (*map*), 487

Sarepta, *see* Krasnoarmeysk (Stalingrad Oblast)

Sarez Lake, 387

Sarkand, 339 (*map*)

Sarny, 436 (*map*)

Sars, 241 (*map*), 245

Sartas, 401, 405 (*map*)

Sary-Agach, 362, 395 (*map*)

Sary-Ishik-Otrau, desert, 336 f.

Sary-Su, river, 339 (*map*), 340, 355; escarpments, 336

Sasovo, 105 (*map*)

Sas-Tyube, 339 (*map*)

Satka, 241 (*map*), 248, 249

Saur range, 346, 358

Sawmilling centers, 80, 81, 165, 168, 181, 185, 190, 290

Sayan Mountains, 17 (*map*), 283, 300

—— Eastern: altitude, 295; gold-bearing area, 290

Sayat, 401 (*map*)

Sayda-Guba, 161 (*map*), 162

Schlüsselburg, *see* Petrodvorets

Seal, *nerpa,* 285

Seal hunting, 159, 169, 319, 350, 351

Sea otter reserve, 325

Seas, 5-10

Sebastiya, 423

Sebezh, 135 (*map*)

"Second Baku," oil fields, 36, 73, 172, 182, 188

Segezha, 495 (*map*), 496

Segozero, lake, 495 (*map*), 496

Selemdzha River, 316, 317 (*map*), 321 (*map*); gold, 313

Selenga River, 297 (*map*), 300, 301

Seligdar, 305

Seliger, Lake, 134
Selishche, 135 (*map*)
Selizharovo, 135 (*map*), 141, 149
Selkups, ethnic group, 270
Semenov, 173 (*map*), 179
Semenovka, 327 (*map*)
Semiluki, 127 (*map*), 132
Semiozernoye, 338 (*map*)
Semipalatinsk, 339 (*map*), 357, 359 (*map*)
Semipalatinsk Oblast, 358, 359 (*map*); area and population: economy, 357
Semi-precious stones, 239
Semiz-Bugu, 339 (*map*), 355
Sengiley, 183 (*map*), 191
Senno, 471 (*map*)
Sentas, 359 (*map*)
Serafimovich, 195 (*map*), 199
Serakhs, 401 (*map*)
Serdobsk, 183 (*map*)
Serdtse-Kamen, Cape, 326
Seregovo, 155 (*map*)
Sergach, 173 (*map*)
Sergeyevka (Maritime Kray), 327 (*map*)
Sergeyevka (Ukrainian SSR), 451 (*map*)
Sergiyevskiy, 235 (*map*), 252
Sergo, *see* Kadiyevka
Sericulture, in Central Asia, 64; Kirghiz SSR, 379; Tadzhik SSR, 384, 386; Transcaucasia, 64, 413, 417, 428; Turkmen SSR, 404; Uzbek SSR, 393
Sernyy Zavod, 401 (*map*), 402, 405
Serov, 235 (*map*), 241 (*map*), 242
Serpukhov, 105 (*map*), 114, 115 (*map*)
Seryshevo, 317 (*map*)
Sesame, 403
Sestroretsk, 151, 153 (*map*)
Šešupė River, *see* Sheshupa River
Sevan, 420, 421 (*map*)
Sevan Lake, 409, 420, 421 (*map*); Zanga hydroelectric project, 420
Sevastopol', 9, 205 (*map*), 209
Severnaya Zemlya (North Land), 6, 281
Severnyy Kommunar, 235 (*map*), 245
Severnyy Rudnik No. 3, bauxite deposits, 239
Severnyy Suchan, 329
Severokamsk, 37, 244
Severo-Kuril'sk, 311 (*map*), 330, 333
Severoural'sk, 235 (*map*), 241 (*map*), 242, 243
Severo-Yeniseyskiy, 283 (*map*), 290, 297 (*map*)
Sevsk, 135 (*map*)
Seymchan, 324
Seym River, 127 (*map*), 437 (*map*)

Seytler, *see* Nizhnegorskiy
Shaartuz, 381 (*map*)
Shabbaz, 399
Shadrinsk, 261 (*map*), 267
Shagonar, 295, 297 (*map*)
Shakhimardan, 395 (*map*)
Shakhristan, 395 (*map*)
Shakhrisyabz, 389 (*map*), 397
Shakhta, 244
Shakhtersk, 330, 331 (*map*), 332
Shakhtinskiy, 205 (*map*)
Shakhty, 205 (*map*), 215, 217, 451 (*map*)
Shakhun'ya, 173 (*map*)
Shakyay, 481 (*map*)
Shale, *see* Oil shale
Shalya, 241 (*map*)
Shalym, 279 (*map*)
Shamary, 241 (*map*)
Shamkhor, 415 (*map*)
Shamlug, 422
Shana, *see* Kuril'sk
Sharovka, 436 (*map*)
Shar'ya, 105 (*map*), 118
Shatsk, 105 (*map*)
Shatura, 75, 105 (*map*), 113, 115 (*map*)
Shaturtorf, 115 (*map*)
Shaulyay, 481 (*map*), 483, 484
Shchara, mountain, 224
Shcheglovsk, *see* Kemerovo
Shchekino, 105 (*map*), 124
Shchelkovo, 115 (*map*)
Shcherbakov, 105 (*map*), 108, 117, 118
Shchigry, 126, 127 (*map*), 133
Shchors, 50, 437 (*map*)
Shchuchinsk, 339 (*map*), 354
Shchuch'ye, 261 (*map*)
Shchurovo, 115 (*map*)
Shebalino, 359 (*map*)
Shebekino, 127 (*map*)
Sheduva, 481 (*map*)
Sheep, breeds, 64, 222; karakul breed, 396, 397, 403, 404, 467
Sheepskin processing, 177, 188
Shelabolikha, 279 (*map*)
Shelon' River, 145 (*map*)
Shelter-belt planting, 58, 174
Sheltozero, 495 (*map*)
Shemakha, 415 (*map*), 417
Shemonaikha, 339 (*map*), 359 (*map*)
Shenkursk, 155 (*map*)
Shepetovka, 436 (*map*), 447
Sherlovaya Gora, 303
Sheshupa River, 483, 491 (*map*)
Shikhany, 195 (*map*)
Shikhikaya, 415 (*map*)
Shikhovo, 415 (*map*)

Shikuka, see Poronaysk

Shilka, 297 (*map*)

Shilka River, 282, 297 (*map*), 302, 310

Shilovo, 105 (*map*)

Shilute, 481 (*map*)

Shimanovskiy, 317 (*map*)

Shimsk, 145 (*map*)

Shipbuilding industry, Baltic Region, 492; Eastern Siberia, 296, 306; European South, 217, 220; Ukrainian SSR, 446, 452-56 *passim;* Volga Region, 166, 168, 177, 180, 185, 188, 200; Western Siberia, 268

Shipping, ocean and coastal, 90

Shiraki steppe, 425, 426

Shiraura, *see* Vzmor'ye

Shiringushi, 183 (*map*), 187

Shirokaya Pad', 331 (*map*), 332

Shirutori, see Makarov

Shirvintos, 481 (*map*)

Shklov, 471 (*map*)

Shkotovo, 327 (*map*)

Shlisselburg, *see* Petrokrepost'

Shoksha, 495 (*map*)

Shollar, 415 (*map*)

Shorsu, 390, 391, 393, 395 (*map*)

Shortandy, 339 (*map*)

Shoyna, 155 (*map*)

Shpola, 437 (*map*)

Shtergres, 442, 451 (*map*)

Shubany, 415 (*map*)

Shubar-Kuduk, 338 (*map*), 347, 352

Shugozero, 145 (*map*)

Shugurovo, 183 (*map*), 188

Shumerlya, 183 (*map*), 185

Shun'ga, 495 (*map*)

Shurab, 381 (*map*), 383, 385, 395 (*map*)

Shuryshkary, 261 (*map*)

Shusha, 415 (*map*), 419

Shushenskoye, 297 (*map*)

Shushtalep, 278, 279 (*map*)

Shuvelyany, 415 (*map*)

Shuya, 105 (*map*), 120

Shvenchenelyay, 481 (*map*)

Shvenchenis, 481 (*map*)

Šiauliai, *see* Shaulyay

Sibay, 235 (*map*), 253, 256

Siberia, ethnic groups, 41, 46, 98; forests, 31; formation of *guberniya,* 44; gold lode deposits and other minerals, 10; industrial district, 99; industrial output, 69; industrial regions, new, created, 68; iron, 37; natural resources, 72; rivers, 22; structure and relief, 20; transportation, 101; tundra belt, 27; wheat, 100

—— Central: plateau, 20

—— Eastern, 103, 281-307; agriculture, 288 f.; chemical industry, 299; cities over 50,000, 508; climate, 26, 285 f.; economy, 288; ethnic and linguistic groups, 98; gold, 282, 287, 290, 292, 296, 300, 302, 303, 305; highlands, 20, 282 ff.; metallurgical region, 78; mineral resources, 287; natural limits and political administrative boundaries, 288; petroleum, 293, 300, 306; population, 287; soil, 286; taiga, 287, 289; topography, 281; transportation, 289; trees, 30; uplands, 281, 282; vegetation, 287; waterways, 284-85; *see further under names of oblasts as listed on p. 503*

—— Western, 102, 260-80; administrative units, 265; agriculture, 266; area, 260; chemical industry, 265, 274, 277, 278, 280; cities over 50,000, 508; climate, 26, 263; coal, 264, 265, 276; dairy farming, 63; ethnic and linguistic groups, 98; lowland, 18, 20, 356; marshes, 31; metallurgical industries, 265; mineral resources, 264; population, 264; railroads, 275; rivers, 260 ff.; soil, 263; topography, 260; vegetation, 263; wild life, 31; *see further under names of oblasts as listed on p. 503*

Signakhi, 427 (*map*)

Sigulda, 481 (*map*)

Sikhote-Alin' range, 309, 321 (*map*), 326, 327 (*map*), 328

Silk industry, 403, 423

Silova River, 155 (*map*), 169

Silver, 302

Sim, 241 (*map*), 249

Simbirsk, *see* Ul'yanovsk

Simeiz, 205 (*map*), 209

Simferopol', 205 (*map*), 209

Sinancha, 321 (*map*), 328

Sindi, 481 (*map*)

Sinegorsk, 330, 331 (*map*), 332

Sinegorskiy, 451 (*map*)

Sinel'nikovo, 437 (*map*)

Siniy Shikhan, 235 (*map*), 258

Sinyavino, 152, 153 (*map*)

Sisian, 421 (*map*)

Sivaki, 317 (*map*)

Sivash (or Putrid) Sea, 9, 204, 205 (*map*)

Siverskiy, 145 (*map*)

Skadovsk, 437 (*map*), 455

Skal'nyy, 241 (*map*), 244

Skidel', 471 (*map*), 477

Skobelev, *see* Fergana

Skopin, 105 (*map*), 122

Skovorodino, 311 (*map*), 317 (*map*), 318
Skuodas, 481 (*map*)
Slantsy, 145 (*map*), 149
Slavgorod (Altay Kray), 261 (*map*), 274, 275
Slavgorod (Belorussian SSR), 471 (*map*)
Slavsk, 491 (*map*)
Slavskoye, 491 (*map*)
Slavyanka (Kazakh SSR), 395 (*map*)
Slavyanka (Maritime Kray), 327 (*map*), 328
Slavyanoserbsk, 451 (*map*)
Slavyansk, 450, 451 (*map*)
Slobodskoy, 173 (*map*), 178
Slobodzeya, 465 (*map*)
Slonim, 471 (*map*)
Sluch' River, 436 (*map*), 461, 470
Slutsk (Bobruysk Oblast), 471 (*map*), 476
Slutsk (Leningrad Oblast), *see* Pavlovsk
Slyudyanka, 296, 297 (*map*)
Smela, 437 (*map*), 446
Smidovich (Arkhangel'sk Oblast), 155 (*map*)
Smidovich (Jewish Autonomous Oblast), 321 (*map*)
Smiltene, 481 (*map*)
Smirnovskiy, 339 (*map*)
Smolensk, 44, 135 (*map*), 139
Smolensk-Moscow uplands, 19, 105, 134
Smolensk Oblast, 135 (*map*); area and population, 139; industries, 140
Smolyaninovo, 327 (*map*)
Snezhnoye, 451 (*map*)
Sobinka, 105 (*map*), 115 (*map*)
Sochi, 211, (*map*), 214, 220
Soda industry, 274, 443, 450, 452
Sofiysk, 320, 321 (*map*)
Soils, 27-33
Sokhondo Peak, tin-mining, 303
Sokh River, 395 (*map*)
Sokol (Sakhalin Oblast), 331 (*map*)
Sokol (Vologda Oblast), 155 (*map*), 167
Sokolovka, 327 (*map*), 328
Soldatskoye, 395 (*map*)
Soligalich, 105 (*map*), 118
Solikamsk, 234, 235 (*map*), 237, 241 (*map*), 245
Sol'-Iletsk, 234, 235 (*map*), 257, 258
Solnechnogorsk, 115 (*map*)
Solntsedar, 211 (*map*), 219
Solomennoye, 494, 495 (*map*)
Solotvin, 460, 463
Solovetskiye Islands, 155 (*map*), 167
Solov'yevsk, 317 (*map*)
Solton, 279 (*map*)

Sol'tsy, 145 (*map*)
Sol'vychegodsk, 12, 155 (*map*)
Sonkovo, 135 (*map*)
Son-Kul', lake, 373 (*map*)
Sonskiy, 292
Sormovo, 180
Soroca, see Soroki
Sorochinsk, 235 (*map*)
Soroka, *see* Belomorsk
Soroki, 465 (*map*), 468
Sorokino, 279 (*map*)
Sortavala, 494, 495 (*map*), 497
Sosna River, 127 (*map*)
Sosnovka (Chuvash ASSR), 183 (*map*)
Sosnovka (Kirov Oblast), 173 (*map*)
Sosnovka (Murmansk Oblast), 161 (*map*)
Sosnovka (Tambov Oblast), 127 (*map*)
Sosnovo (Leningrad Oblast), 145 (*map*), 153 (*map*)
Sosnovoborsk, 183 (*map*), 190
Sosnovo-Ozerskoye, 297 (*map*)
Sos'va, 241 (*map*); railroad to Alapayevsk, 243
Sos'va River, 235 (*map*), 241 (*map*)
Southern Bug River, 435, 436 (*map*), 438, 447, 456
Southern Sakhalin Oblast, former, 329
South-Kazakhstan Oblast, 339 (*map*); area and population: cotton, 362
South Ossetian Autonomous Oblast, 427 (*map*); area: population, 432
South Siberian Railroad, 346, 353; construction project, 349; eastern terminus of trunk line, 298; route, 275, 280; western part of overall Siberian project, 88
Sovetsk (Kaliningrad Oblast), 481 (*map*), 491 (*map*), 492
Sovetsk (Kirov Oblast), 173 (*map*)
Sovetskaya Gavan', 311 (*map*), 319, 321 (*map*), 322, 331 (*map*)
Sovetskiy (Crimean Oblast), 205 (*map*), 208
Sovetskiy (Leningrad Oblast), 145 (*map*)
Soviet Far East, 103, 308-33; agricultural areas, 315; area, 308; cities over 50,000, 508; climate, 312; exports, 314; fishing industries, 308, 315, 319, 323, 324, 325, 328, 332; gold, 313, 314, 315, 319, 320, 323; industries, new, 315; lumber industries, 319, 328, 332; metallurgical industries, 315, 320; mineral resources, 37, 313, 315, 320; northern sections, 310; petroleum, 325, 332; population, 314; southern coastal area (Maritime region), 308, 309, 313; transportation and

freight-transshipment center, 320; typography, 308; transportation routes, 308, 315; vegetation, 313; *see further under names of oblasts as listed on pp. 503-4*

Soviet Federated Socialist Republic, *see* Russian Soviet Federated Socialist Republic

Soviet of Nationalities, small divisions not represented, 46

Soviets, local, 45, 46, 47

Sozh River, 471 (*map*), 475, 476

Spas-Demensk, 135 (*map*)

Spas-Klepiki, 105 (*map*), 115 (*map*)

Spassk, *see* Kuybyshev (Tatar ASSR)

Spasskaya Guba, 495 (*map*)

Spassk-Dal'niy, 321 (*map*), 327 (*map*), 328

Spassk-Ryazanskiy, 105 (*map*)

Spokoynyy, 305

Sredne-Kolymsk, 283 (*map*)

Sredne-Serebrovsk, *see* Vtoroy-Orochen

Sredneural'sk, 241 (*map*), 242

Srednikan, 324

Sredniy Urgal, 320, 321 (*map*)

Srednyaya Nyukzha, 316, 317 (*map*)

Srednyaya (Middle) Tunguska River, 17 (*map*), 284, 297 (*map*)

Sretensk, 297 (*map*), 303

Stalinabad, 381 (*map*), 383, 384, 386

Stalinabad Oblast, 381 (*map*), agriculture: area and population, 385

Stalingrad, 120, 195 (*map*), 199, 200

Stalingrad Oblast, 194, 195 (*map*) 199-200; agriculture: area, 199; "Greater Volga" scheme, 172, 199; mineral resources, 199; population, 199; territorial changes, 200; Volga-Don Canal, 112, 171, 200

Stalinir, 427 (*map*), 433

Stalino (Turkmen SSR), 401 (*map*)

Stalino (Ukrainian SSR), 437 (*map*), 442, 450, 451 (*map*)

Stalino (Uzbek SSR), 395 (*map*)

Stalinogorsk, 105 (*map*), 114

Stalino Oblast, 437 (*map*), 449; area and population: industries, 450, 451 (*map*)

Stalin Peak, 20, 365, 380, 381 (*map*)

Stalinsk (Jewish Autonomous Oblast), 321 (*map*)

Stalinsk (Kemerovo Oblast), 261 (*map*), 266, 277, 279 (*map*), 280

Stalinskiy, 339 (*map*)

Stalin works, automobiles, 113

Stanichno-Luganskoye, 451 (*map*)

Stanislav, 436 (*map*), 460

Stanislav Oblast, 436 (*map*), 441, 459; area: economy: population, 460

Stanovoy range, 20, 282, 317 (*map*)

Star', 135 (*map*), 138

Staraya Bukhara, *see* Bukhara

Staraya Russa, 145 (*map*), 147

Staritsa, 135 (*map*)

Starobel'sk, 437 (*map*)

Staro-Beshevo, 451 (*map*)

Starodub, 135 (*map*)

Starodubskoye, 331 (*map*)

Staro-Konstantinov, 436 (*map*)

Staryy Krym, 205 (*map*), 208

Staryy Merchik, 436 (*map*)

Staryy Oskol, 127 (*map*), 133

Staryy Salavan, 183 (*map*)

Stavropol' (Kuybyshev Oblast), 36, 183 (*map*), 192

Stavropol' (Stavropol' Kray), 50, 211 (*map*), 223

Stavropol' Kray, 194, 211 (*map*), 213, 221-24, 226; agriculture, 222; area: climate, 221; coal, 222; communication: industries, 223; population, 221; resorts, 223; topography, 221

Stavropol' plateau, 18

Steel industry, 76 ff.; Baltic Region, 487; European South, 208; Kazakh SSR, 347, 356; Transcaucasia, 412, 430; Ukrainian SSR, 442, 452, 453, 454; Urals, 239, 242, 243, 249, 252, 254, 255, 256; Uzbek SSR, 391; Volga Region, 178, 179; Western Siberia, 265; *see also* Iron and steel mills

Stepanakert, 415 (*map*), 419

Stepana Razina, Imeni, 173 (*map*)

Stepanavan, 421 (*map*)

Stepnoy, 51, 195 (*map*), 203

Stepnoye, 205 (*map*)

Stepnyak, 339 (map), 354, 355

Steppes, dry or semi-desert, 32; irrigation, 63; soil, 31; vegetation, 31, 264

Sterlitamak, 235 (*map*), 256

Stock-raising, *see* Livestock

Stolboukha, 339 (*map*), 359 (*map*)

Stolbovaya, 115 (*map*)

Stolbtsy, 471 (*map*)

Stolin, 471 (*map*)

Stony Tunguska River, *see* Srednyaya Tunguska River

Storojinet, see Storozhinets

Storozhevsk, 155 (*map*)

Storozhinets, 436 (*map*), 459

Stoyba, 316, 317 (*map*)

Strel'na, 153 (*map*)

Strizhi, 173 (*map*)

Structure and relief, 15-20
Strunino, 105 (*map*), 115 (*map*)
Stryy, 436 (*map*), 461
Stupino, 105 (*map*), 114, 115 (*map*)
Styr' River, 436 (*map*)
Suchan, 321 (*map*), 327 (*map*), 328, 329
Sudak, 205 (*map*), 208
Sudogda, 105 (*map*), 122
Sudzha, 127 (*map*)
Sudzukhe, 327 (*map*)
Sufi-Kurgan, 373 (*map*)
Sugar-beet areas, 60, 66, 132, 376, 444, 448, 449
Sugar-refining industry, 52, 376, 443, 446-49 *passim;* by-products as feed for live-stock, 443, 444, 445
Suifen River, 327 (*map*)
Sukhinichi, 135 (*map*)
Sukhona River, 155 (*map*), 156
Sukhoy Log, 239, 241 (*map*)
Sukhumi (formerly Sukhum), 427 (*map*), 431
Sukhumi military road, 223, 413, 429, 431
Suksun, 241 (*map*)
Sulak River, 211 (*map*), 212, 231
Sula River, 437 (*map*), 448, 449
Sulimov, *see* Cherkessk
Sulphur mines, 38, 368, 374, 391, 402, 405
Sulphur springs, 223, 430, 486
Sulphur works, 258
Sultangulovo, 183 (*map*), 193
Sulyukta, 372, 373 (*map*), 378, 395 (*map*)
Sumbar River, 401 (*map*)
Sumgait, 415 (*map*), 416
Sumgait River, 416
Sumskiy Posad, 495 (*map*)
Sumy, 437 (map), 449
Sumy Oblast, 437 (*map*), 439, 447; area and population: economy, 449
Suna River, 495 (*map*), 496
Sundzha River, 211 (*map*)
Sunflowers, 59, 61, 67, 452, 453
Sunskiy, 495 (*map*), 496, 497
Suoyarvi, 495 (*map*), 496
Superphosphate plants, 80, 394, 422, 443
Surakhany, 415 (*map*), 416
Surami, 429
Surami range, 409
Sura River, 173 (*map*), 183 (*map*)
Surazh (Belorussian SSR), 471 (*map*)
Surazh (Bryansk Oblast), 135 (*map*)
Surgut (Kuybyshev Oblast), 183 (*map*)
Surgut (Tyumen' Oblast), 261 (*map*)
Surkhab River, 380, 381 (*map*), 387
Surkhan Darya, river, 397

Surkhan-Darya Oblast, 53, 389 (*map*); area and population: industries, 397; petroleum, 391
Surovikino, 195 (*map*)
Susamyr, 373 (*map*)
Suslonger, 173 (*map*), 181
Susuman, 311 (*map*), 324
Suvorovo, 465 (*map*)
Suyetikha, 298
Suyfun River, 327 (*map*)
Suzdal', 105 (*map*), 122
Suzun, 279 (*map*)
Svalyava, 463
Svans, tribe in Transcaucasia, 411, 425
Svatovo, 437 (*map*)
Sverdlovo, 195 (*map*)
Sverdlovsk (Sverdlovsk Oblast), 235 (*map*), 240, 241 (*map*)
Sverdlovsk (Ukrainian SSR), 442, 451 (*map*), 452
Sverdlovsk Oblast, 235 (*map*), 237, 238-43; agriculture, 240; area: development, 238; industries, 240; mineral resources, 238 ff.; new major industrial region, 242; population, 238; transportation, 240
Svetlaya, 321 (*map*), 328
Svetlogorsk, 491 (*map*), 492
Svetloye, 491 (*map*)
Svetlyy, 296, 297 (*map*)
Svetogorsk (Enso), hydroelectric station, 145 (*map*), 149, 494
Sviritsa, 145 (*map*)
Svir' River, 145 (*map*), 149
Svir'stroy, 145 (*map*), 149
Svisloch' River, 474
Sviyaga River, 183 (*map*), 191*n*
Svobodnyy, 317 (*map*), 318
Swedes in Baltic Region, 480, 488
Syamozero, lake, 495 (*map*)
Syas' River, 145 (*map*)
Syas'stroy, 145 (*map*), 150
Syava, 173 (*map*)
Sychevka, 135 (*map*)
Syktyvkar, 51, 155 (*map*), 165
Sylva, 241 (*map*), 245
Synthetic rubber, 80, 150, 422, 424
Syr-Dar'inskiy, 395 (*map*)
Syr Darya, river, 23, 335, 337, 338 (*map*), 340, 362, 365, 366, 380, 381 (*map*), 388, 394, 395 (*map*), dam on, 62
Syrskiy, 127 (*map*)
Sysert, 241 (*map*)
Sysola River, 155 (*map*)
Syuginskiy, *see* Mozhga
Syzran', 182, 183 (*map*), 193

Tables, 499-514
Taboshar, 381 (*map*), 385, 395 (*map*)
Tadzhikabad, 381 (*map*)
Tadzhik Autonomous SSR, 368, 382, 390
Tadzhikistan, *see* Tadzhik SSR
Tadzhiks, 41, 368, 382, 387
Tadzhik Soviet Socialist Republic, 380-87, 381 (*map*); agriculture, 384; area, 380; cities over 50,000, 509; climate, 382; coal, 383, 386; general survey, 380-84; industries, 383; irrigation systems, 384; mineral resources, 382, 383; oblasts in, 47; oblast survey, 385-87; population, 380, 382; transportation routes, 384; *see further under names of oblasts as listed on p. 505*
Taganrog, 205 (*map*), 216, 217
Taiga, 30
Takeli, 385, 395 (*map*)
Takhta (Lower Amur Oblast), 321 (*map*)
Takhta (Turkmen SSR), 401 (*map*)
Takhta-Bazar, 401 (*map*)
Takhta-Kupyr, 389 (*map*)
Talas, 373 (*map*), 379
Talas Ala-Tau, range, 379
Talas Oblast, 373 (*map*); area and population: economy, 379
Talas River, 339 (*map*), 340, 361, 371, 379; agriculture in valley, 374
Taldy-Kurgan, 339 (*map*), 360
Taldy-Kurgan Oblast, 339 (*map*); area and population: economy, 360
Talgi, 211 (*map*), 232
Talin, 421 (*map*)
Tallin (Tallinn), 8, 479, 481 (*map*), 482, 487, 488, 489
Tal'menka, 279 (*map*)
Tal'noye, 436 (*map*)
Talsi, 481 (*map*)
Tal'tsy, 298
Talysh, ethnic group, 411, 414
Talysh range, 409, 414
Taman', 211 (*map*)
Tambov, 127 (*map*), 130, 255n
Tambovka, 317 (*map*)
Tambov Oblast, 127 (*map*); agriculture: area: industries: population, 130
Tamdy-Bulak, 389 (*map*), 397
Tanning industry, 188
Tannu-Tuva, *see* Tuva Autonomous Oblast
Tapa, 481 (*map*)
Tara, 261 (*map*), 271
Tarakliya, 465 (*map*)
Tarbagatay range, 336, 357
Targyn, 359 (*map*)

Tarnopol', *see* Ternopol'
Tarta, 405
Tartar, *see* Tatar
Tartu, 481 (*map*), 488, 489
Tarussa, 135 (*map*)
Tas-Buget, 338 (*map*); dam, 362
Tashauz, 401 (*map*), 408
Tashauz Oblast, 401 (*map*), 402; area and population: economy, 408
Tashino, 77, 173 (*map*), 179
Tashkent, 369, 388, 389 (*map*), 390, 395 (*map*)
Tashkent oasis, 366, 388; cotton, 369; rice, 392
Tashkent Oblast, 389 (*map*), 395 (*map*), 394-96; area and population: economy, 394; industrial centers, 396
Tashkepristroy, 401 (*map*)
Tashkumyr, 372, 373 (*map*), 379, 395 (*map*)
Tash-Suleyman, 378
Tashtagol, 278, 279 (*map*), 359 (*map*)
Tashtyp, 297 (*map*)
Tatar Autonomous Soviet Socialist Republic, 37, 183 (*map*), 187-89; agriculture, 188; area, 187; capital, 187; industrial centers, 188-89; industries, 188; petroleum, 188; population, 187, 188; topography, 187 f.
Tatarbunary, 465 (*map*)
Tatars, 40, 98; in Crimea, resettled, lost national identity, 207; in Ukrainian SSR, 440; Urals, 237, 243, 252, 254; Volga Region, 172, 181, 182, 185, 186, 188, 189, 194; Western Siberia, 265, 267
Tatarsk, 261 (*map*), 273
Tatar Strait, 309, 331 (*map*); climate, 312; fishing settlements, 323; Sovetskaya Gavan', fishing port and naval base, 7, 91, 322
Tatary, Gulf of, 321 (*map*)
Tats, ethnic group, 414
Tauchik, 338 (*map*)
Taurage, 481 (*map*)
Tau-sagyz, 55, 61
Tauz, 414, 415 (*map*)
Tavda, 235 (*map*)
Tavda River, 234, 235 (*map*), 241 (*map*)
Tavil'-Dara, 381 (*map*)
Tavolzhan, 339 (*map*), 357
Tavrichanka, 327 (*map*), 328
Tayga, 279 (*map*)
Taymyr National Okrug, 283 (*map*), 290; area and population: economy, 293
Taymyr Peninsula, 15, 290, 293

Tayncha, 339 (*map*)
Tayshet, 283 (*map*), 297 (*map*), 298
Taz Bay, 6, 262
Taz River, 261 (*map*), 262
Tbilisi, 50, 425, 426, 427 (*map*), 429
Tch—, *see* Ch—
Tea, principal producer, 432; processed, 219
Teberda, 211 (*map*), 222, 426, 427 (*map*)
Tedzhen, 401 (*map*), 403, 404
Tedzhen River, 364, 400, 401 (*map*), 404; canal to connect with Amu Darya and Murgab rivers: reservoirs, 403
Tedzhenstroy, 401 (*map*)
Tekeli, 339 (*map*), 360
Telavi, 427 (*map*)
Tel'bes, 279 (*map*)
Teleneshty, 465 (*map*)
Telenget, ethnic group, 276
Teletskoye Lake, 23, 359 (*map*)
Tel'manovo, 451 (*map*)
Tel'shay, 481 (*map*)
Temir, 338 (*map*)
Temir-Khan-Shura, *see* Buynaksk
Temir-Tau (Kazakh SSR), 52, 339 (*map*), 347, 355, 356
Temir-Tau (Kemerovo Oblast), 278, 279 (*map*)
Temnikov, 183 (*map*), 187
Temryuk, 211 (*map*)
Temut, ethnic group, 275
Tengiz Lake, 340, 354
Teplaya Gora, 241 (*map*), 245
Teplitz Bay, 155 (*map*)
Terek River, 22, 211 (*map*), 212, 227
Teriberka, 161 (*map*)
Termez, 389 (*map*), 397
Terminal moraines, *see* Moraines
Terney, 321 (*map*), 328
Ternopol', 436 (*map*), 462
Ternopol Oblast, 436 (*map*); 441, 459; area and population, 462
Terskey Ala-Tau, 376
Terter River, 419
Tertiary epoch, deposits, 14; vegetation, 27
Tesovo-Netyl'skiy, 145 (*map*)
Teterev River, 436 (*map*), 446, 458
Tetyukhe, 321 (*map*), 328, 329
Tetyukhe-Pristan', 321 (*map*), 328
Tetyushi, 183 (*map*)
Textile industry, areas of concentration, 81; Central Industrial Region, 108; Ivanovo Oblast, 119; milling machinery, 79; Moscow Oblast, 111, 114; raw materials, 81, 392; textile *kombinat*, 69;

Turkmen SSR, 402; Yaroslavl' Oblast, 116
Teykovo, 105 (*map*), 119
Theodosia, *see* Feodosiya
Tien Shan, mountain system, 23, 336, 365, 366, 367, 371, 377, 388; formation, 20; summer grazing land in, 65
Tiflis, *see* Tbilisi
Tighina, see Bendery
Tigrovoy, 327 (*map*), 329
Tikhaya Bay, 155 (*map*), 169
Tikhon'kaya, *see* Birobidzhan
Tikhoretsk, 211 (*map*), 219
Tikhvin, 145 (*map*), 153
Tikshozero, lake, 495 (*map*)
Tiksi, 283 (*map*), 307
Tilichiki, 311 (*map*), 325
Tilsit, *see* Sovetsk
Tim, 127 (*map*)
Timan ridge, 155 (*map*), 156
Timashevo, 183 (*map*), 192
Timashevskaya, 211 (*map*)
Timiryazevo, 491 (*map*)
Timiryazevskiy, 279 (*map*)
Tin, 38, 303
Tiraspol', 465 (*map*), 468
Tirlyanskiy, 235 (*map*), 256
Tisul', 279 (*map*)
Tisza River, 436 (*map*), 438, 463
Titanium-vanadium deposits, 246
Tit-Ary, 283 (*map*), 306
Tkibuli, 412, 425, 426, 427 (*map*)
Tkvarcheli, 412, 425, 426, 427 (*map*), 431, 432
Tkvibuli, *see* Tkibuli
Tobacco, 55, 61, 431
Tobol River, 263, 338 (*map*), 340, 352, 353; valley: wheat and dairy region, 267
Tobol'sk, 261 (*map*), 268, 269
Toguchin, 273, 279 (*map*)
Togul, 279 (*map*)
Tokarevka, 339 (*map*)
Tokmak, 373 (*map*), 376
Tolba River, 306
Tolmachevo, 145 (*map*)
Tomari, 330, 331 (*map*)
Tommot, 283 (*map*)
Tom' River, 261 (*map*), 273, 277, 279 (*map*)
Tomsk, 261 (*map*), 273, 279 (*map*)
Tomsk Oblast, 261 (*map*), 265; agriculture: area: population, 273
Topchikha, 279 (*map*), 359 (*map*)
Topki, 279 (*map*)
Topolev Mys, 359 (*map*)

Toponymy, 49-53; abrogation of names, 50 ff.; changes in suffixes, 49; disappearance of all German names, 46, 51; non-Russian names, 50
Topozero, lake, 495 (*map*)
Torkovichi, 145 (*map*)
Toro, *see* Shakhtersk
Toropets, 135 (*map*)
Torzhok, 135 (*map*), 142
Toskovo, 153 (*map*)
Tosno, 145 (*map*), 153 (*map*)
Tot'ma, 155 (*map*)
Tourist resorts, *see* Resorts
Toyohara, *see* Yuzhno-Sakhalinsk
Toy-Tyube, 395 (*map*)
Tractor works, 79, 80, 200
Trading posts, 307, 326
Trakay, 481 (*map*)
Trans-Alay range, 365, 378
Transbaykalia, 283, 286; mountain system, 20
Transcarpathian Oblast, 53, 434, 436 (*map*), 438; acquisition of, 459; area and population, 463
Trans-Caspian Railroad, development, 85; importance in Central Asia, 369; main artery of Turkmen SSR, 403; of Uzbek SSR, 392; new line projected to ease load, 404, 407
Transcaucasia, automobile plant, 428; chemical industry, 412, 416, 422, 423, 426, 430; climate, 26, 409, 410; coal, 425, 431; cotton, 413; economy, 412; ethnic groups, 422, 425; fishing industry, 417; hydroelectric projects, 420, 422, 425, 426; industries, 412; petroleum, 412, 416, 425, 426; population, 411, 414; railroads, 413, 418; soils, 33; steel industry, 430; topography, 409; vegetation, 32, 411; wild life, 411; *see further under names of oblasts as listed on p. 502-3*
Transcaucasian Soviet Federated Socialist Republic, 44, 412
Trans-Ili Ala-Tau, 337, 360, 361, 374
Trans-Kazakhstan Railroad, 355
Transportation and commerce, 82-92
Trans-Siberian Railroad, 237, 298, 353; branches, 267, 271, 301, 303; completion of trunk line, 289; electrification, 84 f.; large towns along route, 291
Trans-Ural railroad, project, 246
Trees, 30-31
Tree shelter belts, 58, 173
Trofimovsk, 283 (*map*), 306
Troitsk, 235 (*map*), 250, 251
Troitsko-Pechorsk, 155 (*map*)

Troitskoye (Altay Kray), 279 (*map*), 359 (*map*)
Troitskoye (Khabarovsk Kray), 321 (*map*)
Trotsk (Kuybyshev Oblast), *see* Chapayevsk
Trotsk (Leningrad Oblast), *see* Gatchina
Trubchevsk, 135 (*map*)
Truck- and dairy-farming areas, 67
Trudarmeysk, 279 (*map*)
Trudfront, 195 (*map*), 202
Trudovaya, 450, 451 (*map*)
Trudovoye, 327 (*map*), 329
Truskavets, 436 (*map*), 461
Trusovo, 195 (*map*)
Tsagveri, 427 (*map*)
Tsalka, 427 (*map*)
Tsarevokokshaysk, *see* Yoshkar-Ola
Tsaritsyn, *see* Stalingrad
Tsarskoye Selo, *see* Pushkin
Tsementnyy (Bryansk Oblast), 135 (*map*), 138
Tsementnyy (Sverdlovsk Oblast), 240, 241 (*map*)
Tsentral'nyy, 278, 279 (*map*)
Tsesis, 481 (*map*)
Tsimlyanskaya, 205 (*map*), 216
Tsinondali, 427 (*map*)
Tsipikan, 297 (*map*), 300
Tsiteli-Tskaro, 427 (*map*)
Tsivil'sk, 183 (*map*)
Tskhaltubo, 425, 427 (*map*), 429
Tskhinvali, *see* Stalinir
Tsulukidze, 427 (*map*)
Tsyp-Navolok, 161 (*map*)
Tsyurupinsk, 437 (*map*)
Tsyurupy, Imeni, 115 (*map*)
Tuapse, 211 (*map*), 220
Tuar-Kyr, 405
Tubinskiy, 235 (*map*), 253, 256
Tuchkovo, 115 (*map*)
Tugur, 321 (*map*)
Tukan, 235 (*map*), 253
Tula, 37, 105 (*map*), 124
Tula Oblast, 105 (*map*); area, 123; industries, 124; natural resources: population: topography, 123
Tuloma River, 161 (*map*)
Tulun, 283 (*map*), 297 (*map*), 298
Tuma, 115 (*map*)
Tumanyan, 423
Tumus, 306
Tundra belt, frozen, 27 f.; wooded, 30-31
Tungir River, 303
Tungokochen, 297 (*map*)

Tungsten mines, Eastern Siberia, 300-303 *passim;* Kazakh SSR, 355; Kirghiz SSR, 374, 377, 396; Soviet Far East, 320; Urals, 38; Uzbek SS, 391

Tungus, ethnic group, *see* Evenki

Tunguska Basin, coal, 12, 36

Tungus-Manchurian group in Eastern Siberia, 288; in Russian SFSR, 98; in Soviet Far East, 314, 318, 319

Tura, 283 (*map*), 293

Turan, 295, 297 (*map*)

Turan lowland, 20, 334, 335, 364; climate, 26; desert zone, 32

Tura River, 234, 235 (*map*), 241 (*map*)

Turgay (Akmolinsk Oblast), 339 (*map*), 354

Turgay (Kustanay Oblast), 338 (*map*)

Turgay Gates, 20, 335, 353

Turgay River, 338 (*map*), 340, 353

Türi, *see* Tyuri

Turinsk, 235 (*map*)

Turinskaya Kul'tbaza, *see* Tura

Tur'inskiy, *see* Krasnotur'insk

Turiy Rog, 321 (*map*), 327 (*map*)

Turkestan, 339 (*map*), 362

Turkestan Autonomous SSR, 368, 372, 382, 390

Turkestan range, 378, 383, 388

Turkic ethnic group, in Central Asia, 368; Eastern Siberia, 98, 288; Kazakh SSR, 345 (*see also* Kazakhs); Transcaucasia, 411; units included in groups, 40; Uzbek SSR, 390; Western Siberia, 276

Turkmen-Kala, 401 (*map*)

Turkmen, ethnic group, 368, 402

Turkmen Soviet Socialist Republic, 368, 401 (*map*) 400-408, agriculture, 203; area: climate, 400; chemical industry, 405; cities over 50,000, 509; coal, 405, 406; desert areas, 400; fishing industries, 405; food industry, 403; general survey, 400-404; manufacturing industries, 402; mineral resources, 402; oases, 400; oblasts in, 47; oblast survey, 404-408; petroleum, 402; population, 400-402; *see further under names of oblasts as listed on p. 505*

Turksib Railroad, 274, 275; construction: function, 85; extensions, 375; importance, 266, 349

Turkyany, 415 (*map*)

Turochak, 261 (*map*), 359 (*map*)

Turtkul', 389 (*map*), 399

Turukhansk, 283 (*map*)

Tushino, 115 (*map*)

Tutayev, 105 (*map*)

Tuva Autonomous Oblast, 283 (*map*), 297 (*map*); area and population: history, 294; industries: mineral resources, 295

Tuva People's Republic, 46, 294

Tuvinians in Siberia, 41, 98, 288, 289, 294, 296, 300, 302

Tuya-Muyun, *see* Tyuya-Muyun

Tuymazy, 183 (*map*), 235 (*map*); oil fields, 36, 254, 256

Tuyuk, 374

Tuzly, 465 (*map*)

Tver', *see* Kalinin

Tyan'-Shan' Oblast, 373 (*map*); area and population: economy, 377

Tygda, 317 (*map*)

Tym' River, 332

Tyndinskiy, 316, 317 (*map*)

Tyrny-Auz, 211 (*map*), 226

Tyrva, 481 (*map*)

Tyukalinsk, 261 (*map*), 271

Tyumen', 235 (*map*), 250, 261 (*map*), 268

Tyumen' Oblast, 261 (*map*), 265; area and population: industries, 268, 269

Tyup, 373 (*map*)

Tyuri, 481 (*map*), 488

Tyurya-Kurgan, 395 (*map*)

Tyuya-Muyun, 374, 378, 395 (*map*)

Ubagan River, 353

Ubaredmet, 358, 359 (*map*)

Uba River, 341, 359 (*map*)

Uch-Adzhi, 401 (*map*)

Uchimchak, 374, 379

Uchkulan, *see* Madniskhevi

Uch-Kurgan, 395 (*map*)

Uch-Kzyl, 397

Uchterek, 373 (*map*)

Uda River, 297 (*map*)

Udarnyy, 331 (*map*)

Ude, ethnic group, 314, 318, 332

Udmurt (Votyaks), ethnic group, 41, 53; Urals, 98, 237, 243, 252; Volga Region, 181, 188

Udmurt Autonomous Soviet Socialist Republic, 235 (*map*), 237, 251-52; agriculture, 252; area, 251; heavy industry, 252; population, 251; railways, 252

Udzhary, 415 (*map*), 417

Ufa, 235 (*map*), 241 (*map*), 255

Ufa plateau, 18, 235

Ufa River, 234, 235 (*map*), 241 (*map*)

Ufra, 401 (*map*)

Uglegorsk, 52, 330, 331 (*map*), 332

Uglich, 105 (*map*), 118

Uglovka, 145 (*map*), 147

Uglovoye, 327 (*map*), 329

Ugol'nyy (Chukchi National Okrug), 311 (*map*), 326

Ugol'nyy (Maritime Kray), 331 (*map*)

Ugol'nyy (Sverdlovsk Oblast), *see* Karpinsk

Ugra River, 135 (*map*)

Ugro-Finnic group, 41, 163

Uil, 338 (*map*)

Ukhta (Karelo-Finnish SSR), 495 (*map*)

Ukhta (Komi ASSR), 84, 155 (*map*), 165

Ukmerge, 481 (*map*)

Ukrainians, area of original settlement, 445; in Belorussian SSR, 472; European South, 207, 213, 216, 218, 220, 225, 226, 229; Kazakh SSR, 345, 348, 352, 360, 361; Kirghiz SSR, 372, 376, 379; Moldavian SSR, 466; Soviet Far East, 314, 318, 319; Transcaucasia, 425; Ukrainian SSR, 440, 456; Urals, 237, 254; USSR, 40; Volga Region, 172, 194; Western Siberia, 265, 267, 274

Ukrainian Soviet Socialist Republic, 434-63, 436-37 (*map*), 466; administrative-territorial system, 441; agriculture, 441, 443; area, 434; basic grain-exporting region, 441; Black Sea lowland, 454-57; chemical industry, 442 f., 449, 450, 452, 454, 458, 459, 460, 461; chief petroleum region of Western, 460; cities over 50,000, 510; climate, 438; coal, 439, 441, 450, 452, 460; Dnieper Bend, 452-54; Donets Basin, 449-52; exports and imports, 445; fishing industries, 457; general survey, 434-45; geographic regions, 445; industrial enterprises, 68; lumber industries, 461; manganese deposits, 14; mineral resources, 439; mining and metallurgical industry, 441; natural-gas industry, 443; oblasts in, 47; oblast survey, 445-63; petroleum, 439, 443, 449, 460, 461; Poles'ye, 457-58; population, 434, 439 f.; textile industry, 443; topography, 434 ff.; transportation network, 444; vegetation, 439; Western, 459-63; *see further under names of oblasts as listed on p. 501-2*

Ulala, *see* Gorno-Altaysk

Ulan-Bator, 297 (*map*), 301*n*

Ulan-Erg, 51

Ulan-Ude, 50, 283 (*map*), 297 (*map*), 300, 301, 302

Ul'ba, 358, 359 (*map*)

Ul'ba River, 341, 347

Ulla River, 471 (*map*)

Ullubiyevo, 211 (*map*), 232

Ulukhe River, 327 (*map*)

Ulu-Tau, range, 336, 345, 355

Ul'yanovka, 153 (*map*)

Ul'yanovsk, 183 (*map*), 191

Ul'yanovsk Oblast, 183 (*map*); area and economic development, 190; industries, 191; population, 190, 492

Ul'yanovskoye, 331 (*map*)

Umal'tinskiy, 320, 321 (*map*)

Uman', 436 (*map*), 446

Unangany (Aleuts), in Soviet Far East, 314, 325

Undory, 183 (*map*)

Unecha, 135 (*map*), 138

Ungeny, 465 (*map*)

Ungvár, see Uzhgorod

Union of Soviet Socialist Republics (USSR), administrative process, typical, 255*n*; administrative territorial divisions, 41-48, 500-505; agriculture, 54-67; cities: capitals of administrative territorial divisions, 500-505; cities with over 50,000 inhabitants, 506-11; climate, 24-27; coasts, 5-10; commerce, 82-92; cotton region, 391; economic criteria dictate changes in administrative geography, 319; economic pattern, 54-92; economy in state of constant flux, 47; ethnic groups and their autonomous political divisions, 512-14; formation of, 47; geologic history, 10-15; industry, 68-81; location and boundaries, 3-5; mineral resources, 35-38; oil region, principal, 416; physical setting, 3-38; political framework, 39-53; population, 39-41, 499-514; regional survey, 93-497; seas, 5-10; soils, 27-33; structure and relief, 15-20; toponymy, 49-53; transportation, 82-92; vegetation, 27-33

—— in Asia, area, 505; hydroelectric resources, 75; rivers 89; population, 505; *see also* Central Asia; Kazakh SSR; Kirghiz SSR; Russian SFSR; Siberia, Eastern; Siberia, Western; Soviet Far East; Tadzhik SSR; Turkmen SSR; Uzbek SSR

—— in Europe, area, 503; hydroelectric resources, 75; peat, 75; population, 503; *see also* Belorussian SSR; Central Black Earth Region; Central Industrial Region; Crimea, European North; European Northwest; European West; Lower Don and Northern Caucasus; Russian SFSR; Transcaucasia; Ukrainian SSR; Urals; Volga Region

Unterval'den (Unterwalden), 51

Unzha River, 105 (*map*), 118

Upper Volga Region (forest section), 173
(*map*), 172-75; exports and imports,
175; mineral resources: population:
topography: transportation, 172; *see
further under names of oblasts as listed
on p. 500*
Ural-Emba petroleum fields, 345, 346
Uralets, 239, 241 (*map*)
Ural-Kuzbas *kombinat,* 68, 74, 77, 99, 249,
265, 277
Ural Mountains, 6, 12; continuous rail
link, 84; northern, 156; topography,
233; *see also* Urals, region
Ural Oblast, former, 47
Ural River, 22, 234, 235 (*map*), 257, 337,
338 (*map*), 340, 350
Urals, region, 102, 235 (*map*), 241 (*map*),
233-59; agriculture, 237; arsenal of the
USSR, 233; chemical industry, 99, 237,
245, 246, 247, 250, 251, 255, 258; cities
over 50,000, 508; climate: forests, 236;
formation, 20; exports, 249; heavy industry, 237; high-voltage power lines,
99; intensive industrialization, 233, 242,
246; industrial and mining region, one
of largest of world, 99; industrial cities,
99, 246 f.; industrial enterprises, 68; industrial output, 69; metallurgical establishments, 99; minerals, 234; most important mining district, 233; population, 236; production of steels and ferroalloys, 77; rivers, 234; transportation,
237; *see also* Ural Mountains; *further
under names of oblasts as listed on p.
501*
Ural'sk, 338 (*map*), 349, 350, 351
Uranium, 374, 379, 385
Ura-Tyube, 381 (*map*), 383, 385, 395
(*map*)
Ura-Tyube Oblast, former, 383
Urban centers, 48
Urda, 338 (*map*)
Urdzhar, 339 (*map*), 359 (*map*)
Urgal River, 320, 321 (*map*)
Urgench, 389 (*map*), 398
Urgut, 389 (*map*)
Uritsk, 153 (*map*)
Urmary, 183 (*map*)
Ursat'yevskaya, 395 (*map*)
Urshel'skiy, 115 (*map*)
Ursk, 278, 279 (*map*)
Urta-Tokoy reservoir, 395
Urup River, 211 (*map*)
Urussu, 183 (*map*), 235 (*map*), 256
Uryankhay, *see* Tuva Autonomous Oblast
Uryupinsk, 195 (*map*), 199

Urzhum, 173 (*map*)
Usa (Kemerovo Oblast), 261 (*map*); coal
field, 278
Usa River (Komi ASSR), 155 (*map*)
Ush-Tobe, 339 (*map*), 360
Ushumun, 317 (*map*)
Usman' (Voronezh Oblast), 127 (*map*)
Usman (Yakut ASSR), 305
Usol'ye (Molotov Oblast), 241 (*map*), 247
Usol'ye or Usol'ye-Sibirskoye, 283 (*map*),
296, 297 (*map*), 298, 299
Uspenskiy, 339 (*map*), 355
Ussuri River, 309, 311, 321 (*map*), 327
(*map*); Khanka lowland, 326; agricul-
ture, 315; climate, 309, 312, 313, 328
Ussurka, 327 (*map*)
Ust'-Apuka, 325
Ust'-Bol'sheretsk, 311 (*map*)
Ust'-Dzhegutinskaya, 211 (*map*)
Ust'-Ishim, 261 (*map*)
Ust'-Izhora, 153 (*map*)
Ust'-Kamchatsk, 311 (*map*)
Ust'-Kamenogorsk, 339 (*map*), 347, 358,
359 (*map*)
Ust'-Kan, 359 (*map*)
Ust'-Karsk, 297 (*map*)
Ust'-Katav, 241 (*map*), 249
Ust'-Kut, 297 (*map*), 298
Ust'-Nlman, 320, 321 (*map*)
Ust'-Orda Buryat-Mongol National Ok-
rug, agriculture, 297 (*map*), 300; area
and population, 296, 299
Ust'-Ordynskiy, 297 (*map*), 299, 300
Ust'-Port, 283 (*map*), 294
Ust'-Sysol'sk, *see* Syktyvkar
Ust'-Tsil'ma, 155 (*map*), 165
Ust'-Urt, plateau, 18, 335, 336, 338 (*map*),
350, 351, 364, 399
Ust'-Usa, 155 (*map*), 165
Ust'-Voya, 155 (*map*)
Ust'-Yeniseyskiy Port, *see* Ust'-Port
Ustyuzhna, 155 (*map*), 166
Us'va, 241 (*map*), 244
Utorgosh, 145 (*map*)
Utyana, 481 (*map*)
Uuras, *see* Vysotsk
Uva, 235 (*map*), 252
Uvals, Northern, *see* Northern Uvals
Uyar, 291, 297 (*map*)
Uygurs (Chinese Uzbeks), in Kazakh
SSR, 345, 348, 360, 361
Uygur-Say, 395 (*map*)
Uzbek, ethnic group, 40; in Central Asia,
368; Kara-Kalpak Autonomous SSR,
390; Kazakh SSR, 345, 348, 360, 361;
Kirghiz SSR, 372, 378, 379; Tadzhik

SSR, 382; Turkmen SSR, 402; Uzbek SSR, 390, 393, 399

"Uzbek Sea," storage reservoir, 62, 397

Uzbek Soviet Socialist Republic, 346, 368, 380, 388-99, 389 (*map*); agriculture, 392; area, 388; chemical industry, 390, 391, 393, 396; cities over 50,000, 509; climate, 390; coal, 390, 391, 394, 396; cotton, 391; general survey, 388-92; impetus given to industry by enterprises evacuated by Germans, 391; industrial development, 390; mineral deposits, 390; oblasts in, 47; oblast survey, 393-99; orchard and vineyard regions, 392; petroleum, 390, 391, 393, 397; population, 388, 390, 399; steel mill, 391, 394; transportation, 392; *see further under names of oblasts as listed on p. 505*

Uzboy, dry river valley, 364

Uzgen, 373 (*map*), 378, 395 (*map*)

Uzhgorod, 436 (*map*), 463

Užhorod, see Uzhgorod

Uzh River, 436 (*map*)

Uzhur, 297 (*map*)

Uzlovaya, 105 (*map*), 111

Uzlovoye, 491 (*map*)

Vacha, 173 (*map*), 179

Vagonoremont, 52

Vaivara, *see* Vayvara

Vakhan, 381 (*map*)

Vakhan Darya, river, 381 (*map*)

Vakh River, 261 (*map*)

Vakhrushev, 331 (*map*)

Vakhrushi, 173 (*map*), 178

Vakhsh, 381 (*map*)

Vakhsh River, 365, 380, 381 (*map*); cotton, 369, 383, 386; irrigation system, 62, 384

Vakhshstroy, 381 (*map*)

Vakhtan, 173 (*map*), 179

Valamaz, 252

Valday, 145 (*map*)

Valday upland, 19, 22, 134

Valdemarpils, 481 (*map*)

Vale, 427 (*map*)

Valentin, 328

Valerianovsk, 239, 241 (*map*)

Valga, 481 (*map*)

Valka, 481 (*map*)

Valki, 436 (*map*)

Valmiera, 481 (*map*)

Valuyki, 127 (*map*)

Vanadium, 38, 385

Vanavara, 283 (*map*), 293, 297 (*map*)

Vanch, 381 (*map*)

Vankarem, 311 (*map*)

Vannovskiy, 393

Vapnyarka, 436 (*map*)

Varena, 481 (*map*)

Varfolomeyevka, 321 (*map*), 327 (*map*)

Varnek, 155 (*map*)

Varzob River, power plant, 386

Varzuga River, 161 (*map*)

Vasil'yevskiy Mokh, 135 (*map*)

Vasyugan'ye, 261 (*map*), 262, 263, 273

Vayenga, 161 (*map*)

Vaygach Island, 6, 155 (*map*), 157, 167, 169

Vaytolakhti, 161 (*map*)

Vayvara, 489

Vazhgort, 155 (*map*)

Vedi, 421 (*map*)

Vedlozero, 495 (*map*)

Vegetation, 27-33; Alpine meadow belt, 33; desert zone, 32; forest zone, 30, 31; steppe zone, 31; subtropical forest zone, 32; tundra belt, 27; wooded tundra, 30

Vel'giya, 145 (*map*), 147

Velikaya Guba, 495 (*map*)

Velikiy Bychkov, 463

Velikiye Luki, 135 (*map*), 140

Velikiye Luki Oblast, 135 (*map*), 140

Velikiy Ustyug, 155 (*map*), 167

Veliko-Alekseyevskiy, 395 (*map*)

Velikodvorskiy, 115 (*map*)

Velizh, 135 (*map*)

Vel'sk, 155 (*map*)

Venev, 105 (*map*)

Venta River, 481 (*map*), 485

Ventspils, 8, 481 (*map*), 487

Venyukovskiy, 115 (*map*)

Vereshchagino, 235 (*map*), 245

Vereya, 115 (*map*)

Verkhne-Bakanskiy, 211 (*map*), 220

Verkhne-Chebula, 279 (*map*)

Verkhne-Chusovskiye Gorodki, 36, 241 (*map*), 244

Verkhne-Stalinsk, 305

Verkhneudinsk, *see* Ulan-Ude

Verkhne-Usinskoye, 297 (*map*)

Verkhne-Vilyuysk, 306

Verkhneye, 451 (*map*)

Verkhniy Avzyan, 235 (*map*), 254

Verkhniy Baskunchak, 195 (*map*)

Verkhniy Ufaley, 241 (*map*), 249, 251

Verkhnyaya (Upper) Angara River, 300

Verkhnyaya Pyshma, 240, 241 (*map*), 242

Verkhnyaya Salda, 240, 241 (*map*), 242

Verkhnyaya Sinyachikha, 241 (*map*)

Verkhnyaya Toyma, 155 (*map*)
Verkhnyaya Tunguska River, *see* Angara River
Verkhotur'ye, 240, 241 (*map*)
Verkhov'ye, 127 (*map*)
Verkhoyansk, 24, 27, 283 (*map*), 307, 311 (*map*)
Verkhoyansk Range, 20, 282, 304, 306
Verkhozim, 183 (*map*), 190
Vernyy, *see* Alma-Ata
Vershino-Shakhtaminskiy, 303
Veselyy, 205 (*map*)
Veshenskaya, 205 (*map*)
Ves'yegonsk, 135 (*map*)
Vetluga, 173 (*map*)
Vetluga River, 173 (*map*), 182
Viborg, *see* Vyborg
Vichuga, 105 (*map*), 120
Vidlitsa, 495 (*map*)
Viipuri, see Vyborg
Viivikond, *see* Vivikond
Vileyka, 471 (*map*), 478
Vileyka Oblast, now Molodechno Oblast, 471 (*map*), 472, 478
Vileyka River, 484
Viliya River, 471 (*map*), 483, 484
Vilkavishkis, 481 (*map*)
Vilkovo, 436 (*map*), 465 (*map*)
Vil'na, see Vil'nyus
Vil'nyus, 471 (*map*), 472, 481 (*map*), 482; history, 483 f.; industries: population, 484
Vilyaka, 481 (*map*)
Vil'yandi, 481 (*map*)
Vilyany, 481 (*map*)
Vilyuy River, 22, 283 (*map*), 304; gold placers: platinum, 306
Vilyuysk, 283 (*map*), 307
Vindava, see Ventspils
Vindrey, 183 (*map*), 187
Vinnitsa, 436 (*map*), 447
Vinnitsa Oblast, 436 (*map*), 443, 445; area: economy: population, 447
Vinogradnoye, 211 (*map*), 226
Virbalis, 481 (*map*)
Virtsu, 481 (*map*)
Vishera River, 235 (*map*), 241 (*map*); paper milling at Krasnovishersk, 245, 246
Visim, 239, 241 (*map*)
Vistula Lagoon, 490, 492
Vitebsk, 471 (*map*), 475
Vitebsk Oblast, 471 (*map*); area: economy: population, 475
Viticulture, 232, 403, 404, 413, 417, 444, 457, 466; research station, 232

Vitim River, 283, 296, 297 (*map*), 302; gold-mining area, 282, 300
Vivikond, 489
Viyakhtu, 331 (*map*)
Vladikavkaz, *see* Dzaudzhikau
Vladimir, 105 (*map*), 115 (*map*), 122
Vladimiro-Aleksandrovskoye, 327 (*map*)
Vladimir Oblast, 105 (*map*); area, 121; exports and imports, 121 f.; history, 122; industries, 121-22; population, 121
Vladimirovka, 195 (*map*)
Vladimir-Volynskiy, 436 (*map*), 461
Vladivostok, 311 (*map*), 312, 321 (*map*), 327 (*map*), 328, 329
Vodla River, 496
Vodnyy, 155 (*map*), 165
Voguls, ethnic group, *see* Mansi
Volcanoes, 212, 309, 310; highest active on Kamchatka, 21; in Tertiary ranges, 14
Volchanka, 241 (*map*), 242
Volchansk, 437 (*map*)
Volga, town, 105 (*map*)
Volga-Don Canal project, 112, 171, 200
Volga German Autonomous SSR, abrogated, 44, 46, 51, 172, 194, 195 (*map*), 200
Volga Region, 102, 170-203; chemical industry, 179, 180, 185, 188, 189, 198; cities over 50,000, 507; forests, 181; industrial output, 69; industries: natural resources: population, 172, 174, 175, 176; railroad construction, 85; shale, 75; topography, 170, 172; *see also* Lower Volga Region; Middle Volga Region; Upper Volga Region
Volga River, 9, 19, 22, 105 (*map*), 134, 135 (*map*), 170, 173 (*map*), 183 (*map*), 195 (*map*), 337; Akhtuba flood plain, 201; irrigation projects, 63; lakes, 134; northern waters diverted to, 63, 246; reservoir, 141; waterway, 89
Volga upland, 15, 19, 182
Volkhov, 76, 144, 145 (*map*), 150, 152
Volkhov River, 143, 145 (*map*), 146, 148
Volkovysk, 471 (*map*)
Volnovakha, 437 (*map*), 451 (*map*)
Volochanka, 283 (*map*)
Volochayevka, 321 (*map*), 322
Volodarskiy, 153 (*map*)
Volodary, 173 (*map*)
Vologda, 155 (*map*), 166
Vologda Oblast, 155 (*map*), 165-67; area: population, 165; economic activities: transportation routes, 166
Volokolamsk, 105 (*map*), 115 (*map*)

Volosovo, 145 (*map*)

Volot, 145 (*map*)

Volozhin, 471 (*map*)

Vol'sk, 195 (*map*), 198

Volyn' Oblast, 436 (*map*), 441, 459, 461

Volyn'-Podolian upland, 19, 434, 446, 447, 456, 458, 459, 461, 462

Volzhsk, 173 (*map*), 181

Vorkuta, 84, 155 (*map*), 164, 165

Vormsi, 487

Vorona River, 127 (*map*)

Voronezh, 127 (*map*), 132

Voronezh Oblast, 127 (*map*); agriculture: area, 131; industries, 132; natural resources: population, 131

Voronezh River, 127 (*map*)

Voroshilov, 321 (*map*), 327 (*map*), 328, 329

Voroshilovgrad, 437 (*map*), 442, 451 (*map*), 452

Voroshilovgrad Oblast, 437 (*map*), 449, 451 (*map*); area: industries: population, 452

Voroshilovsk (Stavropol Kray), *see* Stavropol

Voroshilovsk (Ukrainian SSR), 451 (*map*), 452

Voroshilovskiy, 244

Vorskla River, 437 (*map*), 448, 449

Vorsma, 173 (*map*)

Võrts Järv, *see* Vyrts-Yarv, lake

Vorzel', 436 (*map*)

Voskresensk, 105 (*map*), 111, 115 (*map*)

Vostochnyy, 330, 331 (*map*)

Votkinsk, 235 (*map*), 252, 253

Votyak or Vot, ethnic group, *see* Udmurt

Voyampolka, 325

Voyevodskoye, 279 (*map*)

Voy-Vozh, 155 (*map*)

Vozhd' Proletariata, 115 (*map*)

Vozhega, 155 (*map*)

Voznesensk, 437 (*map*)

Voznesen'ye, 145 (*map*)

Vrangel' (Wrangel) Island, 6, 311 (*map*), 326

Vsevolodo-Vil'va, 241 (*map*), 245

Vsevolozhskiy, 153 (*map*)

Vtoroy-Orochen, 305

Vulkaneshty, 465 (*map*), 467

Vuoksi River, 145 (*map*), 149, 494

Vurnary, 183 (*map*), 185

Vvedenka, 436 (*map*)

Vyartsilya, 495 (*map*), 497

Vyatka, *see* Kirov

Vyatka River, 173 (*map*)

Vyatka Uval, 173 (*map*), 176

Vyatskiye Polyany, 173 (*map*), 177

Vyazemskiy, 321 (*map*)

Vyaz'ma, 135 (*map*), 140

Vyazniki, 105 (*map*), 121

Vyborg, 8, 144, 145 (*map*), 149, 152

Vychegda River, 155 (*map*), 156

Vygozero, lake, 493, 495 (*map*), 496

Vyg River, 495 (*map*)

Vyksa, 77, 173 (*map*), 178

Vyrts-Yarv, lake, 488

Vyru, 481 (*map*)

Vysha, 183 (*map*), 187

Vyshgorod, 436 (*map*)

Vyshka, 401 (*map*), 404

Vyshne-Volotsk canal system, 141

Vyshniy Volochek, 135 (*map*), 142

Vysokaya, Mount, 234, 238, 241 (*map*), 242

Vysokovsk, 115 (*map*)

Vysotsk, 145 (*map*), 152

Vytegra, 155 (*map*)

Vzmor'ye (Kaliningrad Oblast), 491 (*map*)

Vzmor'ye (Latvian SSR), *see* Rigas Yurmala

Vzmor'ye (Sakhalin Oblast), 330, 331 (*map*)

Water power, Baltic Region, 480; Eastern Siberia, 296; largest producer of Europe, 454 (*see also* Dnieper dam); Transcaucasia, 425; Western Siberia, 265; *see also* Hydroelectric power

Waterways, 21-23; interconnecting, 21; transportation routes, 82, 88

Wesenberg, *see* Rakvere

Western Bug River, 436 (*map*), 461, 462

Western Dvina River, 19, 22, 134, 135 (*map*), 469, 470, 471 (*map*), 475, 480, 481 (*map*), 485

Western Ukraine, 441, 459-63

West-Kazakhstan Oblast, 338 (*map*), 350

West Siberian Kray, former, 265

Whaling, 325, 326

Wheat, 59, 188, 452, 456; hard-grained spring, 100; introduced into flax and dairy zone, 66

White Russians, *see* Belorussians

White Sea, 5, 15, 155 (*map*), 496

White Sea-Baltic Canal, 89, 146, 493, 497

Wilejka, *see* Vileyka

Wilno, *see* Vil'nyus

Windau, *see* Ventspils

Wine-making industry, 219, 226, 417, 428, 468

Witherite deposits, 405

Włodzimierz, see Vladimir-Volynskiy
Wood, 73; *see also* Lumber
Wood distilleries, 165, 168
Wood pulp, *see* Pulp
Woodworking, 179, 181, 185
Woolen mills, 81, 191
Workers' settlements, 48
Wrangel Island, *see* Vrangel Island

Yablochnyy, 331 (*map*)
Yablonovyy (formerly Yablonoy) range, 282, 302
Yadrin, 183 (*map*)
Yagman, 405
Yagodnyy, 324
Yakhroma, 105 (*map*), 111, 115 (*map*); valley drainage, 63
Yakovlevka, 327 (*map*)
Yakut Autonomous Societ Socialist Republic, 44, 283 (*map*), 304-307; agriculture, 306; air bases, 307; area, 304; climate, 305; industries, 306; islands, 307; mineral resources, 305, 306; oil fields, 306; polar stations and trading posts, 307; population, 287, 304; transportation routes, 306
Yakuts, in Eastern Siberia, 41, 288, 289, 293, 304, 306; in Russian SFSR, 98; in Soviet Far East, 314, 324, 326
Yakutsk, 283 (*map*), 307, 311 (*map*)
Yalta, 205 (*map*), 206, 209
Yalutorovsk, 261 (*map*), 268
Yama, 451 (*map*)
Yamal-Nenets National Okrug, 261 (*map*), 265, 270
Yamal Peninsula, 6, 261 (*map*), 270
Yaman-Tau, 234
Yamarovka, 303
Yaminskoye, 279 (*map*)
Yampol', 436 (*map*)
Yana River, 283 (*map*), 285, 304; lowlands, 20, 282
Yanaul, 235 (*map*)
Yangi-Bazar, 373 (*map*), 395 (*map*)
Yangi-Yul', 389 (*map*), 395 (*map*), 396
Yaniskoski (Jäniskoski), acquired by USSR, 160
Yanis'yarvi, lake, 495 (*map*)
Yanskiy, 283 (*map*)
Yantarnyy, 491 (*map*), 492
Yar, 176, 178, 235 (*map*)
Yaransk, 173 (*map*)
Yarega, 155 (*map*), 165
Yarensk, 155 (*map*)
Yaroslavl', 105 (*map*), 108
Yaroslavl' Oblast, 105 (*map*); agriculture, 117; area, 116; industries, 116 ff.; population, 116; topography, 116
Yartsevo (Krasnoyarsk Kray), 283 (*map*), 297 (*map*)
Yartsevo (Smolensk Oblast), 135 (*map*), 140
Yasel'da River, 470
Yashkino, 279 (*map*)
Yashkul', 51
Yasinovataya, 451 (*map*)
Yasnomorskiy, 331 (*map*)
Yasnoye, 491 (*map*)
Yasnyy, 316, 317 (*map*)
Yaya, 279 (*map*)
Yayla, 206, 207
Yazykovo, 183 (*map*)
Yedintsy, 465 (*map*)
Yefimovskaya, 145 (*map*)
Yefremov, 105 (*map*), 124
Yegorlyk River, 211 (*map*), 222
Yegorshino, 234, 241 (*map*)
Yegor'yevsk, 105 (*map*), 111, 115 (*map*)
Yekabpils, 481 (*map*)
Yekaterinburg, *see* Sverdlovsk
Yekaterinodar, *see* Krasnodar
Yekaterinoslav, *see* Dnepropetrovsk
Yekaterinoslavka, 317 (*map*)
Yelabuga, 183 (*map*), 189
Yelenovskiye Kar'yery, 451 (*map*)
Yelenskiy, 135 (*map*)
Yelets, 127 (*map*), 129
Yelgava, 481 (*map*), 487
Yelizavetgrad, *see* Kirovograd
Yelizavetpol', *see* Kirovabad
Yel'nya, 135 (*map*)
Yel'tsovka, 279 (*map*)
Yemanzhelinka, 241 (*map*), 248, 250
Yemtsa, 155 (*map*)
Yena, 160, 161 (*map*)
Yenakiyevo, 442, 450, 451 (*map*)
Yenisey Bay, 6
Yenisey Ridge, gold, 290
Yenisey River, 21, 22, 262, 283 (*map*), 284, 291, 297 (*map*), 372
Yeniseysk, 283 (*map*), 297 (*map*)
Yenotayevka, 195 (*map*)
Yerbent, 401 (*map*)
Yerbogachen, 297 (*map*)
Yerevan, 50, 410, 420, 421 (*map*), 423, 424
Yergeni Hills, 193, 195 (*map*)
Yermolayevo, 235 (*map*), 255
Yermolino, 115 (*map*)
Yerofeyevka, 359 (*map*)
Yerofey Pavlovich, 317 (*map*)
Yershov, 195 (*map*)
Yessentuki, 211 (*map*), 223

Yessey, 283 (*map*)
Yevkandzhinskiy, 305
Yevlakh, 415 (*map*), 417
Yevpatoriya (or Eupatoria), 205 (*map*), 209
Yevstratovskiy, 127 (*map*)
Yeya River, 211 (*map*)
Yeysk, 211 (*map*), 220
Yezhovo-Cherkessk, *see* Cherkessk
Ynykchanskiy, 305
Yoshkar-Ola, 51, 173 (*map*), 181
Yugo-Kamskiy, 241 (*map*), 245
Yugorskiy Shar, 6, 155 (*map*), 157
Yug River, 155 (*map*)
Yukhnov, 135 (*map*)
Yuodkrante, 481 (*map*), 484
Yurbarkas, 481 (*map*)
Yurga, 279 (*map*)
Yurgamysh, 261 (*map*)
Yurino, 173 (*map*)
Yurkovka, 446
Yur'yev, see Tartu
Yur'yevets, 105 (*map*)
Yur'yev-Pol'skiy, 105 (*map*), 115 (*map*)
Yuryuzan', 241 (*map*), 249
Yuzha, 105 (*map*), 120
Yuzhno-Kuril'sk, 311 (*map*), 330
Yuzhno-Sakhalinsk, 52, 311 (*map*), 330, 331 (*map*), 333
Yuzhno-Yeniseyskiy, 283 (*map*), 290, 297 (*map*)
Yuzhnyy Alamyshik, 393, 395 (*map*)
Yuzovo, or Yuzovka, *see* Stalino
Yygeva, 481 (*map*)
Ykhvi, 481 (*map*), 489

Zabaykal'ye, see Transbaykalia
Zabolotov, 460
Zabrat, 415 (*map*)
Zadon'ye, 127 (*map*)
Zages, see Zemo-Avchala
Zaglik, 414, 416
Zagorsk, 105 (*map*), 109, 115 (*map*)
Zakarpatskaya, *see* Transcarpathian Oblast
Zakataly, 415 (*map*), 417
Zakhmatabad, 381 (*map*)
Zalesovo, 279 (*map*)
Zales'ye, 491 (*map*)
Zaluch'ye, 145 (*map*)
Zamost'ye, 436 (*map*)
Zanga River, 420, 421 (*map*), 422; industries, 423
Zangezur range, copper, 422
Zangibasar, 421 (*map*)

Zaozernyy, 297 (*map*)
Zapadnaya Dvina, 135 (*map*)
Zapokrovskiy, 302
Zaporozh'ye, 437 (*map*), 442, 443, 454
Zaporozh'ye Oblast, 437 (*map*); agriculture: area and population, 453; industrial centers, 454
Zapovednoye, 491 (*map*)
Zarasay, 481 (*map*)
Zaraysk, 105 (*map*), 115 (*map*)
Zarubino (Maritime Kray), 327 (*map*), 328
Zarubino (Novgorod Oblast), 145 (*map*), 146
Zashchita, 358
Zasheyek, 161 (*map*), 162
Zavetnoye, 205 (*map*)
Zavitaya, 317 (*map*)
Zavod imeni Stalina (ZIS), 113
Zavodo-Petrovskiy, 268
Zavodoukovskiy, 268
Zav'yalovo, 261 (*map*), 275, 359 (*map*)
Zayarsk, 297 (*map*)
Zaysan, 339 (*máp*), 359 (*map*)
Zaysan, Lake, 336, 339 (*map*), 341, 358, 359 (*map*)
Zdolbunov, 436 (*map*)
Zelenodol'sk, 183 (*map*), 188, 189
Zelenogorsk, 145 (*map*), 151, 153 (*map*)
Zelenogradsk, 491 (*map*), 492
Zel'man, *see* Rovnoye
Zemetchino, 183 (*map*), 190
Zemo-Avchala, hydroelectric station, 76, 430
Zeravshan range, mineral deposits, 383
Zeravshan River, 381 (*map*), 388, 389 (*map*), 396, 397; valley, 62, 366, 396, 397
Zernovoy, 205 (*map*)
Zestafoni, 426, 427 (*map*), 428, 430
Zeya, 317 (*map*)
Zeya-Bureya plateau, 309, 316; agriculture, 315
Zeya River, 310, 316, 317 (*map*); gold, 313
Zhagare, 481 (*map*)
Zhangiz-Tobe, 339 (*map*), 357, 359 (*map*)
Zharma, 339 (*map*), 357, 359 (*map*)
Zhashkov, 436 (*map*)
Zhatay, 307
Zhdanov, 9, 49, 437 (*map*), 442, 445, 452
Zhdanovsk, 415 (*map*), 417
Zheleznodorozhnyy (Kaliningrad Oblast), 52, 491 (*map*)
Zheleznodorozhnyy (Komi ASSR), 155 (*map*)

Zheleznovodsk, 210, 211 (map), 223
Zhelyabova, Imeni, 155 (map), 166
Zhigalovo, 296, 297 (map)
Zhigansk, 283 (map)
Zhigulevsk, 183 (map), 192
Zhiguli Mountains, 18, 37, 170, 182
Zhilaya Kosa, 338 (map)
Zhilevo, 115 (map)
Zhilkino, 299
Zhitomir, 436 (map), 458
Zhitomir Oblast, 436 (map), area: econ-
    omy: population, 458
Zhizdra, 135 (map)
Zhlobin, 471 (map)
Zhmerinka, 436 (map)
Zholymbet, 339 (map)
Zhukovka, 135 (map)
Zhukovskiy, 115 (map)
Ziddy, 381 (map), 383, 386
Zigazinskiy, 235 (map), 253
Zima, 297 (map), 298
Zimovniki, 205 (map)
Zinc, 38, 238, 265, 302, 391, 443; see also
    Lead-zinc
Zinov'yevsk, see Kirovograd
ZIS, automobiles, 113
Zlatoust, 235 (map), 237, 241 (map), 249,
    251
Zlatoustovsk, 316, 317 (map)
Złoczów, see Zolochev

Zlynka, 135 (map)
Zmeinogorsk, 274, 359 (map)
Zmiyev, 436 (map)
Znamenka, 437 (map), 456
Znamensk, 491 (map)
Zol'noye, 183 (map), 192
Zolochev (Khar'kov Oblast, Ukrainian
    SSR), 437 (map)
Zolochev (L'vov Oblast, Ukrainian SSR),
    436 (map), 463
Zolotarevka, 183 (map), 190
Zolotoye (Saratov Oblast), 195 (map)
Zolotoye (Ukrainian SSR), 451 (map)
Zor-Kul', 366, 387
Zubtsov, 135 (map)
Zugdidi, 427 (map)
Zugres, 451 (map)
Zuyevka, 173 (map)
Zvenigorod, 115 (map)
Zvenigorodka, 436 (map), 446
Zvenigovo, 173 (map)
Zverevo, 451 (map)
Zvezda, 183 (map)
Z"yezdki, 436 (map)
Zykh, 415 (map)
Zyrya, 415 (map)
Zyryan, see Komi
Zyryanka, 283 (map), 306
Zyryanovsk, 339 (map), 358, 359 (map)
Zyryanovskiy, 238, 241 (map)